AMERICAN EDUCATION

Its Men

Ideas

and

Institutions

Advisory Editor

Lawrence A. Cremin
Frederick A. P. Barnard Professor of Education
Teachers College, Columbia University

A History of
Agricultural Education
in the United States
1785-1925

Alfred Charles True

ARNO PRESS & THE NEW YORK TIMES

*New York * 1969*

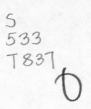
Reprint edition 1969 by Arno Press, Inc.

*

Library of Congress Catalog Card No. 76-89248

*

Manufactured in the United States of America

Editorial Note

AMERICAN EDUCATION: *Its Men, Institutions and Ideas* presents selected works of thought and scholarship that have long been out of print or otherwise unavailable. Inevitably, such works will include particular ideas and doctrines that have been outmoded or superseded by more recent research. Nevertheless, all retain their place in the literature, having influenced educational thought and practice in their own time and having provided the basis for subsequent scholarship.

Lawrence A. Cremin
Teachers College

A History of
Agricultural Education
in the United States
1785-1925

ALFRED CHARLES TRUE
1853–1929

After more than 40 years of distinguished service in the United States Department of Agriculture, Doctor True died in Washington, D. C., on April 23. As director of the Office of Experiment Stations, in the period 1893-1915, and as director of the States Relations Service, in the period 1915–1923, Doctor True made notable contributions to the development of agricultural education and research in the United States. During the period from 1923 to the time of his death Doctor True devoted much of his time to the preparation of histories of agricultural education, agricultural extension work, and agricultural research.

UNITED STATES DEPARTMENT OF AGRICULTURE

MISCELLANEOUS PUBLICATION No. 36

WASHINGTON, D. C.   ISSUED JULY, 1929

A HISTORY OF AGRICULTURAL EDUCATION IN THE UNITED STATES

1785–1925

BY

ALFRED CHARLES TRUE

Specialist in States Relations Work, United States
Department of Agriculture

UNITED STATES
GOVERNMENT PRINTING OFFICE
WASHINGTON : 1929

PREFACE

To understand the movement which has resulted in the broad development of agricultural education in this country it is necessary that its relation be shown to the general development and progress of science and education and to the background of economic conditions and of organizations of various kinds for the promotion of agriculture and country life. Considerable attention has therefore been given to these matters, particularly as related to the earlier stages of agricultural education. Such a brief outline of collateral material as is included in this work may appear trite and superficial to the experts in these subjects, but it is hoped that it will be useful to students in colleges and schools and to the general readers who may consult this publication. It has not been practicable to give accounts of the development of agricultural education in all the several States and .Territories. It has rather been the effort to use details regarding individuals, organizations, and institutions to bring out the various phases of the movement.

Our agricultural colleges have often been unfairly criticized because there has not been a good understanding of the actual organization of agricultural instruction as only a part of the much broader work of the institutions with which it is connected. Failure to recognize the widespread influence which these institutions have had on agricultural progress through their experiment stations and extension work, as well as the promotion of agricultural instruction in secondary and elementary schools, has also led many people to minimize their educational importance. The breadth of the American system of agricultural education therefore has been emphasized.

To give ample space to the history of agricultural research and extension work, however, would have expanded the discussion beyond reasonable limits. It is proposed therefore to prepare separate monographs on these very important features of agricultural education.

Credit for the inception of this publication should be given to the Association of Land-Grant Colleges, through its executive committee, which urged the preparation of such a work, and likewise to Henry C. Wallace, former Secretary of Agriculture, whose approval and encouragement were of the highest value.

The materials for this history have been drawn from a great variety of sources, and often these have been freely used. In many cases it has not been feasible to indicate the source of particular statements, but care has been taken to make the bibliography of works used fairly complete. Special acknowledgment is made of the assistance of F. A. Merrill, specialist in agricultural education, and Miss J. L. Weston, of the Department of Agriculture, in the preparation of this publication, and of Miss C. R. Barnett and Miss E. B. Hawks, of the department library, in the collection of material for this work. Miss C. L. Feldkamp, of the library of the Office of Experiment Stations, put the bibliography in proper form. D. J. Crosby, late of the faculty of the New York College of Agriculture at Cornell University, but also associated for many years with the author in the educational work of the Office of Experiment Stations and States Relations Service, carefully read the manuscript and made many helpful suggestions for its improvement.

CONTENTS

ILLUSTRATIONS

Part 1. THE FOUNDATIONS OF THE AMERICAN SYSTEM OF AGRICULTURAL EDUCATION

INTRODUCTION

With the close of the Revolutionary War and the assured independence of the United States of America the leaders of enterprise and public opinion in this country began more definitely to make plans for the promotion of the agricultural, industrial, commercial, political, and social interests of the new Nation. This was chiefly a country of agricultural and rural communities. Farming included not only the production and sale of crops and livestock, but also cutting of wood for fuel and lumber, weaving and making of clothes, tanning of leather, and the manufacture of household furniture and farm implements. Such artisans as were needed to construct and repair buildings and vehicles, shoe horses, and grind grain were often partly engaged in farming. This was also true of the storekeepers who distributed the few articles brought in from the cities and the men who had small mills and factories, many of which depended on the water power from the small streams adjacent to the farms. Even the commercial and professional people of the comparatively few cities of that period invested their surplus funds largely in land speculation and agricultural enterprises.

Many of the soldiers of the Revolution, when relieved of their military duties, together with other adventurous spirits, took advantage of the grants of land or even without this incentive pushed out into the unoccupied regions of the original Colonies and even beyond the Alleghenies to clear the land and make homes on virgin soils. Thus was begun a vast expansion of American agriculture and the building up of rural communities largely unhampered by traditions and willing to undertake experiments in agriculture, education, and social organization. Meanwhile the older settlements along the Atlantic coast had followed a crude and exhausting practice of agriculture and were seeking means of increasing the fertility of their lands. The movement of population called strongly for improved methods of communication, and there was great activity in building roads, bridges, and canals, as well as ships and boats for inland and coastwise navigation. The dispersion of farm laborers and the increasing size of farm operations made the necessity for improved farm implements more and more apparent.

Under such circumstances it was natural for political and social leaders to take a deep interest in the promotion of agriculture and to connect this closely with the promotion of commerce, manufactures, and the arts.

To understand the movement in the United States which has resulted in our nation-wide system of agricultural research and education it is necessary to know how its beginnings were related to the

1

history and progress of science and education in both Europe and North America.

While the States had withdrawn from their colonial and political relations with Great Britain, their people renewed in large measure after the war the varied intercourse with individuals and institutions in the mother country and were very largely influenced by the movements in thought and action there with reference to agricultural, industrial, and social affairs. They also took great interest in similar movements on the Continent of Europe, particularly those in France, whose timely and effective assistance had done so much to make their political independence possible, and to a less extent in those of Germany and Switzerland. These private foreign relations were stimulated and enlarged by increased correspondence, interchange of publications, travel, and residence abroad for education, business, health, or pleasure. The public embassies and consular offices established after the Revolution, as well as the visits of naval officers on official business, resulted in increase of information regarding European affairs, and this was disseminated widely in this country through the press and otherwise.

All this happened at a time when there were already in western Europe a considerable literature on agriculture and quite a number of organizations and institutions devoted to the promotion of agriculture. The natural sciences were also taking more definite shape, their relations to agriculture were becoming more apparent, and there was a growing hope that their future developments would greatly promote agricultural advancement.

The peoples and their governments were beginning to realize that the diversification and strengthening of agriculture to meet the needs of increasing populations and a more complex civilization were very important objects to be promoted. There was therefore a search for new crops, better livestock, and improved farm implements and cultural methods.

The eighteenth century in Europe had been marked by the establishment of a number of agricultural societies and schools, in connection with which agriculture was taught and practiced. Books and pamphlets on agricultural subjects were quite numerous. Knowledge of these things was available in North America and greatly influenced the origin and progress of the movement for agricultural advancement in the United States. To understand this movement it is necessary to keep in mind the similar movement in the old world.

DEVELOPMENT OF EDUCATION IN EUROPE

From the time of the Renaissance there was a tendency to relate education to the actual needs of human life and to give attention to nature and its relation to practical affairs. With the beginnings of modern science in the sixteenth and seventeenth centuries, a desire to use the new knowledge in education soon appeared. Among those who influenced this movement was Rabelais (1483–1553), who would have pupils study nature as well as books and use their knowledge in their daily occupations.

John Amos Comenius (1592–1670) aspired to have " the complete reorganization of human knowledge along Baconian lines." His teaching and textbooks were based on "presenting the object or idea directly to the child" and making whatever was taught "of practical application in everyday life" (*48*).

Samuel Hartlib (c. 1600–c. 1670) introduced the writings of Comenius to England and in 1651 published a little book entitled "An Essay for Advancement of Husbandry-Learning; or Propositions for the Erecting Colledge of Husbandry; and, in order thereunto, for the taking in of Pupills or Apprentices. And also Friends or Fellowes of the Same Colledge or Society" (*70*). This contains a detailed statement of the subject to be taught and the means to be used in securing financial support for the institution.

In the Tractate of Education, published in 1644 and addressed to Hartlib, Milton followed very largely the plan of education suggested by Rabelais, which involved a very broad study of classical literature, including agriculture, as described by Cato, Columella, and Varro. Here is found also the definition of "a complete and generous education" as "that which fits a man to perform justly, skillfully, and magnanimously all the offices both private and public of peace and war."

Out of this came the academies in England, which often included in their curriculum studies having a practical bearing. Jean Jacques Rousseau (1712–1770) held "that the educational material should be the facts and phenomena of nature" and dwelt much on the importance of manual and industrial activities in education.

Heinrich Pestalozzi (1746–1826), being influenced by Rousseau, entered on an agricultural life, and from his experience with his own children developed a more positive and practical scheme of education. From 1775 for several years he conducted a school for poor children in which part of their time was spent in raising farm products, spinning and weaving of cotton, etc.

Philip Emanuel von Fellenberg (1771–1844) conducted very successfully from 1806 to 1844, at Hofwyl, Switzerland, two manual-labor schools, which had considerable influence in the United States. (See p. 34.) These schools were for the upper classes and peasants, respectively. They were located on an estate of 600 acres, and the boys in both schools had gardens and were expected to do farm work. There was also instruction in science related to agriculture, a printing press, and workshops for making clothing and agricultural and scientific instruments. Subsequently there was a school for girls and a normal school.

EARLY AGRICULTURAL SCHOOLS

Ferdinand Kindermann (1740–1801), a Bohemian, sometimes called "father of industrial education," under the patronage of Maria Theresa, founded an elementary school in which agriculture, music, and religion were taught along with the three R's. This plan was also followed in other schools. In Bohemia an agricultural school was opened at Tirnova in 1791.

In Hungary agricultural schools were established at Zarvas in 1779; at Nagy-Micklós in 1786; the Georgicon Academy at Kezthely, founded in 1797, was for 50 years "the model agricultural college of Europe" (*3*).

Near the end of the eighteenth century Frederick the Great undertook the development of agricultural schools as a part of a broad plan for improving the agricultural condition of Prussia, and his example was followed by his successors.

Albrecht Thaer (1752–1828) successfully engaged in practical and scientific farming, and when visitors to his farm at Celle, in Hanover, became numerous he began in 1802 to give them instruction, and this led to the establishment of the agricultural institute in that town. "In 1806 he founded the agricultural school at Moeglin, near Berlin, which became famous, and which was raised to the Royal Academy of Agriculture, 1824." Through his school and his writings Thaer has had a broad influence on the progress of agriculture and agricultural education.

In 1811 the academy at Tharandt, in Saxony, was founded and a little later the agricultural college of the University of Leipzig. In Wurtemburg, the agricultural college of Hohenheim was founded in 1818, which had a large model farm. This institution was very successful and attracted much attention in other countries.

About 1820 Matthieu de Dombasle founded at Roville, near Nancy, the first school of agriculture worthy of that name in France and almost entirely with private means maintained it for some time. In 1829 the school at Grignon and the following year the school at Grand-Jouan were founded by pupils of Dombasle and later became State schools.

DEVELOPMENT OF NATURAL SCIENCES RELATED TO AGRICULTURE

The movement for agricultural schools and colleges in the United States was intimately associated with the growth of the natural sciences and their applications in Europe.

Lavoisier (1743–1794), who laid the foundations of modern chemistry, made experiments on one of his farms. Taking advantage of Lavoisier's work Sir Humphry Davy (1778–1839) began researches in agriculture in 1803 and 10 years later published his Elements of Agricultural Chemistry, a book well known in America. Fredrick Accum (1769–1833) established in London a school of chemistry with a laboratory, to which some students from the United States went, including Prof. Benjamin Silliman, sr., of Yale, and Prof. William Peck, of Harvard (15). Boussingault (1802–1887), professor of agriculture in the Conservatoire des Arts et Metiers in Paris from 1839, made and published many experimental investigations in general and agricultural chemistry, which had much influence in the United States. Students who became leaders in agricultural science in America were trained in Liebig's (1803–1873) laboratory in Germany. His Chemistry in Its Application to Agriculture and Physiology (1840) and Animal Chemistry (1842) became well known here. The works of Buffon (1707–1788) and Cuvier (1769–1832) in natural history, and of Linnaeus (1707–1778), the Jussieu family, Saussure (1767–1845), and Duhamel (1700–1781) in botany early found their way to this country. Among the early geologists was William Smith (1766–1839), who published the first geological maps of England and wrote on irrigation, and William Maclure, a Scotchman and merchant, who lived many years in the United States and made the first geological map of this country. The relation of mineralogy and geology to the study of soils and to agricultural chemistry was early recognized by those who were interested in agricultural education and research, and these subjects were generally included in the programs proposed for the higher agricultural schools.

EARLY SCIENTISTS IN NORTH AMERICA

North America was a very attractive field for students of science, particularly natural history, and during the eighteenth century and the early part of the nineteenth a considerable number of men, either residents or travelers in this country, devoted themselves to scientific work. In many cases they attracted the attention of the leaders in efforts for the improvement of education and agriculture and in person or through their writings had contacts with these leaders.

Among these early scientists, who were more or less associated with the agricultural movements, were the following: Benjamin Smith Barton (1766–1815), professor of natural history, botany, and materia medica at the Philadelphia College, who wrote much on scientific subjects and published Elements of Botany (1803); John Bartram (1699–1777) and his son William Bartram (1732–1823), who, by extensive travels and collections from New York to Florida, made important contributions to knowledge of native American plants, established a botanic garden near Philadelphia, imported many varieties of cultivated plants and disseminated many species to scientists and growers at home and abroad; Mark Catesby (c. 1679–1749), an English naturalist who visited America (1712–1719) and published a Natural History of Carolina, Florida, and the Bahama Islands; John Clayton (1686–1773), who came to Virginia from England in 1705, was clerk of Gloucester County for 51 years, made extensive botanical studies and collections and published papers in the Philosophical Transactions of the London Royal Society; Cadwallader Colden (1688–1776), a Scotch physician, who came to Philadelphia in 1708, afterwards was surveyor-general and lieutenant governor of New York State, studied the sciences, particularly botany, and introduced the classification of Linnaeus in this country; David Hosack (1769–1835), professor of Botany at Columbia College from 1795, who established a botanic garden in New York City; Peter Kalm (1716–1779), a Swedish botanist and author of Travels into North America (1770–1772); Humphrey Marshall (1732–1801), who established a botanic garden at Marshalltown, Pa., and published a catalogue of native trees and shrubs; André Michaux (1746–1802), a French botanist, who established large nurseries near Charleston, S. C., and in Bergen County, N. J., and his son, François André Michaux (1770–1855), who studied and wrote on trees east of the Rocky Mountains; John Mitchill (died 1768), who came from England in 1700 and lived at Urbana, Va., studied botany, medicine, and other sciences, wrote much on the conditions in the British colonies and was the reputed author of a book on American husbandry (1775); Gerard Troost (1776–1850), a Dutch physician, chemist, and geologist, who came to America in 1810, was founder and first president of the Philadelphia Academy of Natural Sciences, and contributed papers to the Philadelphia Society for Promoting Agriculture, being much interested in the relations of chemistry and geology to soils.

EARLY AGRICULTURAL PUBLICATIONS IN EUROPE

During the seventeenth and eighteenth centuries a considerable literature on agricultural subjects was developed in a number of European countries. The writings of certain ancient authors on such subjects were also available during this period, particularly those of Virgil, Columella, and Varro. In France the publication of works on agriculture was much stimulated by the great series of volumes commonly called the Encyclopedia (1751–1780), which contained articles on this subject. In Great Britain there were agricultural works by about 200 authors before 1800. Among English publications which had an important influence in the United States was Jethro Tull's Horse Hoing Husbandry, or a Treatise on the Principles of Tillage and Vegetation, three editions of which were published between 1733 and 1751. The Annals of Agriculture and Other Useful Arts, a periodical begun in London in 1784 by Arthur Young (1741–1820), widely promoted the advancement of agriculture in Europe and America.

AGRICULTURAL SOCIETIES IN EUROPE

The first agricultural society in Germany was established in 1764. In France there was an early Society of Agriculturists. This was succeeded by the Academy of Agriculture of France, which began the publication of proceedings as early as 1761. In Russia the Free Economical Society was established by the Empress Catherine in 1765, with a large experiment farm near St. Petersburg.

The Society for the Encouragement of Arts, Manufactures, and Commerce, organized in London in 1754, included agriculture in its program. This was followed by an organization formed at Bath, September 8, 1777, which was first called the Society of Bath for the Encouragement of Agriculture, Art, Manufactures, and Commerce. In 1790 its name was changed to the Bath and West of England Society for the purposes above stated. Its first volume of Letters and Papers on Agriculture, etc., was published in 1780.

In Scotland the first organization was the Society of Improvers in the Knowledge of Agriculture in Scotland, begun in 1723, and continued for more than 20 years. Its published record is contained in a volume of Select Transactions issued in 1743.

The Highland Society of Scotland, organized at Edinburgh in January, 1785, became a society for all Scotland. A royal charter for this society was obtained in 1787, together with its first parliamentary grant of £3,000, the interest on which was to be spent for essays, inventions, and improvements in agricultural crops, etc. Its first volume of " prize essays and transactions " was published in 1799. The Transactions issued in 1824 record the institution by the society of itinerant lectures on veterinary medicine, illustrated with demonstrations, and of experiments with salt as a fertilizer and in feeding.

In Ireland the Dublin Society for Improving Husbandry, Manufactures, and other Useful Arts was founded in 1731 and began in 1737 to publish Weekly Observations. In 1746 it received a grant of £500 a year from the Government, and was incorporated in 1750 as the Royal Dublin Society.

In their organization and work the early American agricultural societies were greatly influenced by the examples set by the societies in Great Britain.

BRITISH BOARD OF AGRICULTURE

The British Board of Agriculture was established under an act of Parliament in 1793. Its first president was Sir John Sinclair (1754–1835), who held this office for 13 years. He was a Scotch publicist and lawyer, educated at Edinburgh, Glasgow, and Oxford, and a member of Parliament most of the time from 1780 to 1811. He was very active in the promotion of the agricultural interests of Great Britain, and under his guidance the board of agriculture did much useful work.

The functions of the board, as stated by its president in a formal address to it in 1797, were as follows:

1. Collecting, printing, and circulating information on agricultural and other important subjects connected with the internal improvement of the country.
2. Making, under the inspection of the board itself or a committee of its members, useful experiments in agriculture.
3. Submitting to the consideration of Parliament such regulations as may tend to promote the general improvement of the country and recommending to its attention such useful discoveries of an agricultural nature as may be entitled to public reward (63).

As one of the first pieces of work the board undertook the preparation of a somewhat elaborate report on "the present agricultural state of the country and the means of its improvement," which involved in part what would now be called an agricultural survey of the different counties of the kingdom. Within four years the reports for some counties were completed and printed. Much interesting material in the form of communications to the board from a variety of sources had been collected and a first volume of these had been printed.

EARLY AGRICULTURAL SOCIETIES IN NORTH AMERICA

THE PHILADELPHIA SOCIETY FOR PROMOTING AGRICULTURE

The American Philosophical Society, founded in 1744 under the leadership of Franklin, in its earlier years published many articles on agricultural subjects but was developed chiefly as a scientific society. This led to the organization of the Philadelphia Society for Promoting Agriculture, in March, 1785, on the initiative of Judge J. B. Bordley, a Maryland planter, by 23 distinguished citizens of that city (356). Its object was to promote "a greater increase of the products of land within the American States," and for this purpose the society would print memoirs, offer prizes for experiments, improvements, and agricultural essays, and encourage the establishment of other societies throughout the country. Its first president was Samuel Powel, a graduate of the College of Philadelphia, and twice mayor of that city. He was succeeded in 1805 by Judge Richard Peters, who had been a member of the Continental Congress and whose estate of 200 acres was in what is now Fairmount Park. By 1789 the society had honorary members in 13 States (including George Washington, Robert L. Livingston, of New York, and Noah

Webster, of Connecticut). Among its resident members were Benjamin Franklin and Timothy Pickering.

In 1794 the society endeavored without success to have the Pennsylvania Legislature incorporate " a State society for the promotion of agriculture; connecting with it the education of youth in the knowledge of that most important art, while they are acquiring other useful knowledge suitable for the agricultural citizens of the State " (*355*). This might be done by endowing professorships in " seminaries of learning, for the purpose of teaching the chymical, philosophical, and elementary parts of the theory of agriculture."

The formation of county societies was recommended, with county schoolmasters as secretaries, who might have agricultural textbooks and combine teaching of agriculture with other subjects. As soon as funds became available the State society should establish " pattern farms " in different localities, where foreign and domestic plants and seeds should be grown and, when found useful, disseminated through the State.

SOUTH CAROLINA AGRICULTURAL SOCIETIES

A group of planters interested in the cultivation of indigo began about 1740 to hold meetings which were largely convivial but at which they talked about the indigo industry and means for improving it. In 1755 this club, known as the Winyaw Indigo Society (*373*), founded a charity school and was incorporated to maintain it. The school flourished for more than a hundred years, was revived after the Civil War, and finally was merged with the Georgetown High School.

The South Carolina Society for Promoting and Improving Agriculture and Other Rural Concerns was organized in Charleston August 24, 1785, and 10 years later was incorporated under its present name as the Agricultural Society of South Carolina (*372*). Among its 12 first officers were a Chief Justice of the United States, a Senator and 4 Members of Congress, 4 governors of South Carolina, and a signer of the Declaration of Independence. The society prospered and had many members scattered throughout the State. In 1796 Dr. John de le Howe, of the Abbeville district, devised the bulk of his property to the society for an agricultural school on his estate for poor boys and girls, at which manual labor was to be combined with instruction in science related to agriculture. The society resigned this trust to the State, which appointed a board of trustees under whom the school has since been maintained.

The Pendleton Farmers' Society was organized in 1815, chartered in 1817, and has its headquarters in Pendleton, Anderson County, S. C., about 3 miles from the Calhoun estate, on which Clemson College is now located (*369*). John C. Calhoun was a member of the society and when at home attended its meetings. Many other men prominent in the affairs of this region have also been members. The society flourished and about 1828 constructed the brick building in which its meetings have been held ever since.

THE KENNEBEC (ME.) AGRICULTURAL SOCIETY

An agricultural society was formed at Hallowell, Me. (then Massachusetts), in 1787, probably through the efforts of Charles Vaughan (*147*). Whether the original agricultural society continued for any considerable time is not known, but in 1807 there was an association called the Kennebec Agricultural Society. This was largely maintained for many years through the influence of Charles Vaughan and his brother, Benjamin Vaughan, who inherited and managed a large estate at Hallowell, carrying on agriculture and other enterprises on a large scale (*183*). They had gardens, nurseries, orchards, and farms, distributed stock, seeds, and plants, and conducted correspondence with farmers.

The Kennebec Agricultural Society was "a social organization which held no exhibitions for many years after its establishment, but had frequent meetings for the reading of papers contributed by its members and for consultation and discussion" (*147*). In 1818, through the efforts of the Vaughans and others, the Maine Agricultural Society was formed, and held one or two exhibitions at Hallowell, but, not being able to get sufficient funds for premiums, it ceased operations.

Winthrop Agricultural Society was chartered by the Massachusetts Legislature February 21, 1818, and held meetings and exhibitions until 1825, when it became inactive. In 1829 an organization under this name was incorporated by the Maine Legislature, and this in turn was merged into the Kennebec Agricultural Society in 1832.

EARLY SOCIETIES IN NEW JERSEY

An organization entitled "the New Jersey Society for Promoting Agriculture, Commerce, and Arts" was established as early as 1781, but nothing is known about its work (*230*). The Burlington Society for the Promotion of Agriculture and Domestic Manufactures was permanently organized February 6, 1790, and was active for at least 10 years. It gave prizes in contests in agricultural production and published numerous essays on agricultural subjects in newspapers. The Morris County Society for Promoting Agriculture and Domestic Manufactures was formed in 1792, but its principal activity was the establishment of a library. The second attempt to establish a State society was made in 1818, but this was not permanently organized until 1855.

COLUMBIA COLLEGE AND THE NEW YORK SOCIETY FOR THE PROMOTION OF AGRICULTURE, ARTS, AND MANUFACTURES

The original prospectus of King's College (afterwards Columbia College), issued May 31, 1754, included husbandry and commerce among the subjects to be taught there (*246*). Laws and orders adopted by the governors of the college June 3, 1755, include "agriculture and merchandise" in the course of study. It is not known that any further action was taken at this time.

About this time the New York Society for Promoting Arts was organized and in 1766 offered premiums for reports on matters which the society deemed of interest to farmers.

The New York Society for the Promotion of Agriculture, Arts, and Manufactures was organized February 26, 1791, with Robert L. Livingston as president, and was incorporated March 12, 1792 (*321*).

When the New York Legislature on April 12, 1792, granted funds to the trustees of Columbia College for additional professorships, a professorship of natural history, chemistry, and agriculture was established, and Samuel Latham Mitchill (1764–1831), a distinguished physician and from 1807 professor in the New York College of Physicians and Surgeons, was appointed to fill this position (*268*). (Fig. 1.) That year he published an Outline of the Doctrines in Natural History, Chemistry, and Economics included in the courses he was giving. The following topics related to agriculture (*270*):

Under mineralogy: Lime and gypsum as manure.
Under botany:
    1. Life of plants and vegetation.
        Farinaceous matter of plants—Wheat, rye, maize, oats, peas, potatoes, etc.
        Fibrous parts of plants—Hemp, flax, cotton, hops.
        Saccharine substance of plants—Sugar cane, apples, beets, maple, etc.
           Manufacture of sugar—Honey.
        Products of vegetables by fermentation—Wines, vinegars.
        Astringent parts of plants—Art of tanning.
Under agriculture or cultivation of plants:
    I. Soils—Sand, clay, loam, mixtures, calcarious, mould, etc.
    II. Manures—Lime, gypsum, dung, straw, sand, mud, fish, etc.
    III. Food—Water, earth, phlogiston, hydrogen, salt, oil, etc.
    IV. Diseases—Vermin, blast, smut, mildew, rust, coalgrain, drought, winter kill—Ginnani delle malattie del grano in Erba.
Under zoology:
    I. Functions of animals.
    II. Vis motrix in the vital solid.
    III. Arrangement and classification of animals.
    IV. Chemical history of different animal substances.
        1. Blood.
        2. Milk—(*a*) Whey, (*b*) cream, (*c*) cheese, (*d*) butter.
        3. Fat—(*a*) Hog's lard, (*b*) beef tallow, (*c*) mutton tallow, etc.

Under economics chemistry was taught, including its relation to medicine, agriculture, and other useful arts.

In the Transactions of the Society for 1794 the secretary stated that "lectures had been given upon the different parts of the course," which was chiefly attended by students of medicine.

Doctor Mitchill was active in promoting the agricultural interests of New York for many years. He contributed articles on grasses, cankerworms, and other subjects to the publications of the State agricultural society and delivered addresses on agricultural subjects in different parts of the State. As Representative and Senator in Congress at different times between 1800 and 1813 he acquired a wide acquaintance with leaders in agricultural affairs and became a member of many agricultural societies.

In 1804 the name of the society was changed to the Society for the Promotion of Useful Arts (*320*). Besides issuing publications, it encouraged the formation of county societies and greatly influenced the establishment of a State board of agriculture in 1819. In 1824 it united with the Albany Lyceum of Natural History and formed the Albany Institute, which continued for many years as a scientific society. It was not until 1832 that the New York State Agricultural Society was organized by the combined effort of the county societies.

THE MASSACHUSETTS SOCIETY FOR PROMOTING AGRICULTURE

The Massachusetts Society for Promoting Agriculture was organized May 31, 1792, under a State charter resulting from a petition to the legislature signed by 28 men prominent in the agricultural, business, and political life of the State (*186*). Its object was to promote "useful improvements in agriculture," and it immediately began to raise money for premiums to stimulate such work. During the first

FIG. 1.—Samuel Latham Mitchill

eight years many articles were published in newspapers and pamphlets. In 1801 the publication of a series of papers was begun and from 1813 these were incorporated in the Massachusetts Agricultural Journal, which for a considerable period was issued semiannually.

In 1814 the legislature appropriated to the society $1,000 annually for printing and circulating the publications on agriculture, the raising of seeds and plants, and agricultural experiments, and in 1816 gave an additional $500 for premiums at cattle shows.

In 1801 the society undertook the establishment of a professorship of natural history and a botanic garden at Harvard College. This was done in 1804–5. The plan for this garden " provided for scientific observation of the growth of vegetation and of the habits of noxious insects, that methods might be devised for their destruction, and a cultivation, for sale and distribution, of the seeds and roots of useful plants." The cooperation of the society and college continued for 25 years, when the annual grant which had been made by the State, in aid of this part of the society's work, ceased (186).

The following estimate of the success of this society during its first quarter of a century is made in its centennial volume, page 41:

Beginning with conditions of general apathy, of more or less prevalent distrust as to its intentions, and of incredulity that anything important could be gained to the farming interest, it had created a feeling of confidence as to the future of the agricultural industry and excited a spirit of inquiry. It had widely distributed thousands of pages of printed matter, supplying the best information then obtainable relating to the art; given impetus to the formation of numerous coworking societies, and printed the essays and contributed to the premiums of some of the more important among them; it had introduced new seeds and plants and choice breeds of farm animals from foreign lands; brought new modes of farming into acceptance among leading farmers in different parts of the State, thereby exerting an exemplary influence upon others who gave to books and pamphlets no welcome; it had set fairly at work the inventive faculty of the land in devising better farming apparatus; enlisted science to search and experiment in the behest of agriculture; and, by its successful cattle show, had reached the popular heart (which is always responsive in beholding the novel and the extraordinary), thereby entering upon a radically different but most effective method of diffusing agricultural knowledge, the method of " object teaching" (183).

ELKANAH WATSON AND THE CATTLE SHOW

The idea of the "cattle show" as a distinctively American institution with an educational purpose was suggested to Elkanah Watson (1758–1842) (fig. 2) in 1807 after he had exhibited two Merino sheep "under the great elm tree in the public square in Pittsfield," Mass. (325). He had been a prominent citizen of Albany, N. Y., where he was greatly interested in the promotion of the development of our country to the west by the building of canals, the establishment of stage routes, and the advancement of agriculture (326). In 1807 he had settled on a farm near Pittsfield. He became convinced that agricultural societies should be organized in the several counties on a more democratic basis to include "all the respectable farmers," and that means should be taken to popularize such a movement through cattle shows. On August 1, 1810, he issued "an appeal to the public," signed by himself and 28 other farmers, announcing the Berkshire cattle show, which was successfully held at Pittsfield, October 1, 1810.

BERKSHIRE AGRICULTURAL SOCIETY

The following winter the Berkshire Agricultural Society was formed under the presidency of Watson, "with ample powers—but no funds," and on September 24, 1811, a more elaborate cattle show was held, which was attended by three or four thousand people, and included a picturesque procession of members of the society (*325*). It then occurred to Watson that women ought to be included in this movement, and he therefore arranged for an exhibit of their handiwork, with premiums, on January 12, 1813. This was successful and the meeting was terminated with a ball at which "many farmers' daughters graced the floor." Returning to live at Albany in 1816,

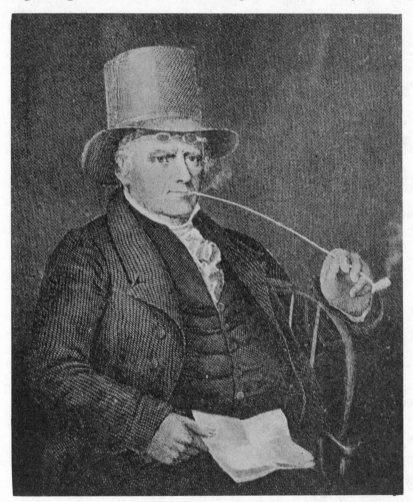

FIG. 2.—Elkanah Watson

Watson immediately promoted cattle shows in Otsego and Jefferson Counties, N. Y., which excited so much public attention that Governor Clinton recommended the establishment of a State board of agriculture to promote the organization of county agricultural societies. An act for this purpose was passed in 1819 and by the end of that year societies had been formed in all but six of the counties, with the aid of a pamphlet by Watson on the history of the Berkshire Agricultural

Society. He also carried on an extensive correspondence with societies which were being formed in other States, including New England, Illinois, Kentucky, Maryland, North Carolina, Ohio, and Virginia.

AGRICULTURAL SOCIETIES IN CONNECTICUT

The Society for Promoting Agriculture in the State of Connecticut was organized August 12, 1794, at Wallingford by "a number of citizens from different towns in the State" (103). Its constitution stated that "the object of investigations for the society shall be agriculture, with such subjects of inquiry as may tend to explain its principles." Provision was made for reports from members on the state of agriculture in their localities, including experiments and discoveries; and for publications. A considerable list of queries on a variety of agricultural subjects was compiled and disseminated. Brief reports of experiments and observations on a number of these subjects were printed in the transactions. "Many experiments have been made by the members themselves, and their observation has extended to the improvements of their neighbors."

The records of the New Haven County Agricultural Society "show that in 1803, 'A Society for promoting Agriculture' was formed at New Haven, of which Gen. James Wadsworth was president until 1813." Later, President Dwight, of Yale College, David Humphreys, and Eli Whitney held this office.

In 1817 the Hartford County Agricultural Society was formed with Henry L. Ellsworth, afterwards United States Commissioner of Patents, as secretary. Societies in the other counties were organized later and in 1852 the Connecticut State Agricultural Society was formed under an act of the legislature passed that year.

EARLY SOCIETIES IN NEW HAMPSHIRE

The legislature of New Hampshire in 1814 granted a charter to an agricultural society in Rockingham County, with headquarters at Chester or Exeter. In 1817 there were county agricultural societies in Rockingham and Cheshire Counties, each of which received a State appropriation of $100. Similar societies were organized and chartered that year in Hillsborough (221) and Strafford Counties and soon thereafter in Grafton and Coos Counties. In 1819 and 1820 all the counties had societies which held fairs and received State aid. Up to 1820 the annual appropriation to each society ranged from $100 to $300 and in all $3,000 had been expended by the State.

VIRGINIA'S GREAT AGRICULTURAL LEADERS AND EARLY AGRICULTURAL SOCIETIES

George Washington (1732–1799) as a farmer was not content to follow the ordinary farm routine which his neighbors practiced (384). He early determined to study and experiment with a view to improving agricultural conditions for himself and farmers generally. While he began with tobacco as his money crop, he changed to wheat and flour with special reference to trade with the West Indies and afterwards became largely engaged in growing forage crops and livestock.

He became a "book farmer," not only reading carefully such agricultural books as he could get, principally from abroad, but making detailed notes of some of them. This was particularly true of Tull's Horse Hoing Husbandry; Duhamel's A Practical Treatise of Husbandry; the Farmer's Compleat Guide; Home's The Gentleman Farmer; and Young's Annals of Agriculture (after 1784).

He carried on an extensive correspondence with men in England acquainted with improved farm practices and particularly with Arthur Young and Sir John Sinclair.

Beginning as early as 1760, he made many experiments on his Mount Vernon estate before and after the Revolutionary War. Among these were experiments in growing alfalfa, wheat, clover, timothy, and various other grasses and vegetables, and in the use of marl, gypsum, and salt as fertilizers. He was much interested in trying improved implements and himself devised a "barrel plough" or drill. He grew many kinds of fruits, trees, and ornamental plants collected from various countries, maintained a conservatory and a small botanic garden, and had many experimental plats on various plantations.

His experience as a farmer and experimenter convinced him that improvement of agriculture was of such fundamental importance to the growth and prosperity of the United States that the public ought to share in the maintenance of agencies for this purpose. He therefore gladly associated with the Philadelphia Society for Promoting Agriculture as a beginning of effort in this direction.

The Society of Virginia for Promoting Agriculture.—As early as 1811 an organization called The Society of Virginia for Promoting Agriculture was formed at Richmond and in 1818 published a volume of memoirs (*389*). Its membership included many of the most eminent men of the State.

Among its presidents were John Marshall, Chief Justice of the United States Supreme Court, and John Taylor, author of the collection of agricultural essays entitled "Arator."

The Albemarle Society.—The Albemarle Agricultural Society was organized May 5, 1817, under the leadership of Thomas Jefferson, by 30 men from five counties (*397*). Ultimately Fairfax County and the Great Valley were also included in its membership. Its rules and regulations were based on a plan for agricultural societies drafted by Jefferson in 1811 (*396*). James Madison was its president from 1817 to 1824.

The society prospered, published many papers in the Richmond Enquirer, its official organ, conducted fairs and exhibitions with prizes for agricultural implements, livestock, and domestic manufactures, interested itself in the development of the University of Virginia, and endeavored to obtain funds for a professorship of agriculture in that institution. Its existence covered a period of over 30 years and until its place was taken by other organizations.

Virginia State Agricultural Society.—In the decade beginning with 1826 a number of agricultural societies were formed in Virginia, and between 1836 and 1850 efforts were made to establish a State agricultural society (*400*). Though this was authorized by the legislature in 1845, its creation was not effected until 1852, and then only through the strenuous activity of Edmund Ruffin (1794–1864) (fig. 3), widely known for his Essay on Calcareous Manures and his editorship of the Farmers' Register (1833–1842) (*390*). This organization promptly got into active operation and held its first fair in 1853. At that time Ruffin wrote an essay on agricultural education for which the society gave him a prize (*388*).

FIG. 3.—Edmund Ruffin

EARLY AGRICULTURAL SOCIETIES IN THE DISTRICT OF COLUMBIA

The Society for Promoting Public Economy.—A temporary organization known as the Society for Promoting Public Economy was described by Ben: Perley Poore in the Report of the Department of Agriculture for 1866, as follows:

About 1806 an institution had been organized by "Members of Congress, officers of the Federal Government, and others, devoted to objects connected with public economy." Meetings were held at Mr. Harvey's, on Pennsylvania Avenue, every Saturday evening from 5 until 8 o'clock, and among the subjects considered were:

Our mechanical economy, or the means of abridging labor by useful inventions, implements, and apparatus.

Our agricultural economy, or the means of producing the most abundant and most reciprocal crops, under any given circumstances, without doing things by guess.

The economy of our forests, or the best management of our latent resources there (438).

The Columbian Agricultural Society.—The Columbian Agricultural Society was organized in 1809 by men interested in agriculture in the District of Columbia and vicinity (107). Its first exhibition was held in Georgetown May 10, 1809, and was attended by President Madison and members of his Cabinet, as well as many members of the society and other people. It consisted of breeds of sheep, horses, and domestic fabrics of cotton and wool.

Five other semiannual exhibitions were held, but when the War of 1812 came on it " overshadowed everything else, and as the time had expired for which the society had been organized it was dissolved."

The Columbian society also undertook the publication of a periodical entitled " The Agricultural Museum " (107), the first number of which was published at Georgetown, July 4, 1810. Among other things this publication contains the constitution and proceedings of the society.

The Columbian Institute for the Promotion of Arts and Sciences.— On June 15, 1816, an association called the Metropolitan Society was formed by 89 residents of Washington, D. C., under the leadership of Edward Cutbush and John Law. When a constitution for this society was adopted August 8, 1816, its name was changed to Columbian Institute for the Promotion of Arts and Sciences. Among its objects was the collection, cultivation, and distribution of plants and the securing of papers on agricultural subjects, including the management of livestock and their diseases. In 1838 distribution of seeds, including wheat and barley, was begun and continued for several years. (See United States National Museum Bulletin 101.)

Congress gave the society a charter April 20, 1818, the use of 5 acres of land for a botanic garden in 1820, and four years later a room in the Capitol for its meetings and collections. Its first president was Doctor Cutbush, and later that office was held by John Quincy Adams and John C. Calhoun. The society was quite active for about 10 years and hoped to secure public or private funds to establish a museum and library, but it did not acquire any substantial means and went out of existence on the expiration of its charter in 1838. A botanic garden was begun on land located at the east end of the Mall near the Capitol and its area was extended in 1824 to include the present site of the United States Botanic Garden.

EARLY AGRICULTURAL FAIRS IN NORTH AMERICA

Fairs for the sale of agricultural products, especially livestock, were early held in the American Colonies, following an English custom. Examples of such fairs were those in New Haven, Conn., in 1644; Burlington, N. J., in 1681; Rye, N. H., about 1726; and Baltimore, Md., in 1747. In South Carolina, at Strawberry in St. Johns Parish, in Berkeley County, a fair was established by an act of 1723, to be held "at least twice in every year for exposing for sale horses, cattle, and merchandise." Semiannual fairs were authorized by statute at Alexandria, Va., in 1742 and in Georgetown, Md., when that town was laid out in 1751. Horse racing and other competitions and the giving of prizes for superior animals were sometimes features of these fairs.

The first fair at Washington, D. C., was held in 1804 at the suggestion of William Thornton, the first Commissioner of Patents, and was so successful that the city government contributed $50 toward premiums at the fair held the next year (*438*).

Following the importation of Merino sheep into this country a kind of rural festival called "sheep shearing" was created and became quite popular. These affairs were in imitation of meetings of farmers held in Norfolk, England, beginning in 1778. The interest of George Washington Parke Custis in such festivals is described as follows:

> Prominent among these "sheep shearings" were those established [in 1802], and continued for a dozen years, by George Washington Parke Custis, at "Arlington," his estate opposite Washington, on the Virginia side of the Potomac. * * * Large collections of prominent men used to accept his hospitable invitation to be present at these gatherings, where he entertained his guests beneath the marquee used throughout the revolution by his illustrious guardian, George Washington (*438*).

GOVERNMENTAL RELATIONS TO EDUCATION IN THE AMERICAN COLONIES AND EARLY STATES

The granting of Federal and State lands and funds for agricultural education was the result of public policies relating to education which passed through a long period of evolution. It has, therefore, seemed desirable to trace this in outline in connection with the discussion of the foundations of our present system of agricultural education.

BEGINNINGS OF THE AMERICAN PUBLIC-SCHOOL SYSTEM

The use of public lands and funds for the encouragement and support of educational institutions began early in the American Colonies. At times and in certain places it encountered much opposition. The doctrine that the parent was responsible for the education of the child and therefore should pay for his schooling was long used to hinder the public support of education, especially as applied to primary and secondary schools. For many centuries in the Old World the church, rather than the state, was looked upon as the proper authority under which public education should be conducted as far as this was at all desirable, and the support of education was classed among works of charity. Higher education, in particular, was primarily for the training of ecclesiastical leaders, and hence colleges and universities came naturally under the control of the church. This idea of the union of church and state, so generally prevalent in European countries, was adopted by the American Colonies. As a result, it was comparatively easy at first to use public lands and funds in this country for the support of the higher educational institutions. As the separation of the state from the church developed, and particularly after the revolution when this separation was defined in State and National constitutions, a strong sentiment was created against public control of higher education. On the other hand, it became more difficult to use public funds for the maintenance, even in part, of institutions controlled by particular denominations. There was considerable ebb and flow in this sentiment, and in the different States it was modified from time to time by the racial and denominational make-up of the population.

In general, the English system of schools was adopted in this country by the early colonists from Great Britain. This included the elementary or " dame school," the grammar or secondary school, and the college. The elementary schools were at first privately maintained by tuition or in part by voluntary contributions, but in New England soon began to receive public money through the action of the town meetings. The first school in North America to receive public funds by vote of the town was established in Dorchester, Mass., in 1639. In this case the money was obtained from rental charges imposed on people occupying land belonging to the town. On January 1, 1645, the town meeting at Dedham, Mass., voted unanimously to raise £20 for the maintenance of a free school. In his textbook of the History of Education, Monroe says:

Many of the New England schools received their support from a variety of sources, such as the sale or rental of public lands, rental from fish weirs, from ferries, from bequest and private gift, from subscription, from local rates, and in nearly all cases from tuition of students (48).

In 1647 the Massachusetts Bay Colony passed a general law requiring that an elementary school should be established in every town of 50 families, and a Latin school in every town of 100 families. A similar law was passed by the Connecticut Colony in 1650. On this basis many schools were established in the New England Colonies during the next 100 years.

About 1700, when community centers of population had become established in many towns, while means of transportation remained very inadequate, a demand arose for the equalization of school privileges. To satisfy this demand the elementary school was sometimes moved about and held for a short period in from two to six places in the town during the year. This " moving school " led to the creation of permanent school districts.

Outside of New England support of education with public funds was chiefly confined to the higher institutions and the establishment of general systems of public schools was long delayed.

PUBLIC SUPPORT OF EARLY AMERICAN COLLEGES

The colleges in the American Colonies and some of the States formed early in the history of the United States in many cases received public aid through grants of land or money. A number of these institutions became land-grant colleges after the passage of the Morrill Act of 1862.

In Franklin's proposals for an academy in Philadelphia in 1749, he recommended a liberal course of study and even suggested that " a little gardening, planting, grafting, and inoculating be taught and practiced, and now and then excursions made to the neighboring plantations of the best farmers." Out of the academy grew the college which later became the University of Pennsylvania. The curriculum framed by the first provost of the college, William Smith, in 1754, included the chemistry of agriculture.

State funds were loaned to the University of Pennsylvania and $3,000 was granted in 1807 for a botanical garden and experiments to ascertain the best and cheapest food for plants and their medicinal properties and virtues. In Massachusetts when Harvard College was founded in 1636 the colonial legislature agreed to give £400, which was the first time "the people by their representatives ever gave their own money to found a place of learning." For some reason this money was not paid to the college but later it received the income of a ferry and direct grants of money. A bank tax, created in 1814, was divided for 10 years among Harvard, Bowdoin, and Williams Colleges, all of which also received grants of land. Dartmouth College in New Hampshire, King's College in New York, and William and Mary College in Virginia, received grants of land before the Revolution, and the University of Georgia soon after that war. St. John's College and Washington College in Maryland, the University of Virginia, and South Carolina College regularly received State appropriations from the time of their establishment.

SUMMARY OF METHODS OF STATE AID TO EDUCATION

In his History of Federal and State Aid to Higher Education, Doctor Blackmar thus summarized the methods of State aid:

The principal ways in which the several States have aided higher education may be enumerated as follows: (1) By granting charters with privileges; (2) by freeing officers and students of colleges and universities from military duty; (3) by exempting the persons and property of the officers and students from taxation; (4) by granting land endowments; (5) by granting permanent money and endowments by statute law; (6) by making special appropriations from funds raised by taxation; (7) by granting the benefits of lotteries; and (8) by special gifts of buildings and sites. Nearly all of these methods originated among the colonies and were adopted by the States.

*   *   *   *   *   *   *

An historical retrospect of the relation of the State to education may be presented in a few propositions, as follows: (1) In colonial times State, private. and church benevolence worked together; (2) subsequently private and church schools were prominent, still being aided by State appropriations; (3) the gradual cessation of State aid to private and church schools, and the growth of State universities (*9*).

BEGINNING OF FEDERAL AID TO EDUCATION

The disposition of the vast areas of land west of the Allegheny Mountains engaged the attention of Washington and other statesmen even before the close of the Revolutionary War. On October 10, 1780, Congress passed a resolution that the western territory ceded by the States should be disposed of for the common benefit of all the States and that the manner and conditions of the sale of these lands should be exclusively regulated by Congress. This was followed by the ordinance of 1785, which contained a clause reserving from sale "lot No. 16 of every township for the maintenance of public schools within the said township." The importance of this provision was not recognized at the time of its passage, but it established a precedent of far-reaching influence in later years and marks the beginning of a policy of using public lands for public education. The ordinance of 1787 for the government of the Northwest Territory contained the declaration that "religion, morality, and knowledge being necessary to good government and the happiness of mankind, schools and the means of education shall forever be encouraged."

Without doubt the great significance of the educational provision in the ordinance of July 13, 1787, was not appreciated by Congress or the public. The Constitutional Convention was in session in Philadelphia at that time, and the proceedings of the old Confederation Congress in New York received scant attention in the press. This ordinance made no grants of land for education, but laid the foundation for a general development of free public education throughout the United States.

It was immediately followed by the ordinance of July 23, 1787, for the sale of public lands in Ohio, under which section 16 in each township was to be reserved for the maintenance of public schools and " not more than two complete townships to be given perpetually for the purpose of a university."

Congress granted lands for schools to Ohio when it became a State in 1802 and for a university in 1803. Similar grants of land for educational purposes were made by Congress from time to time to the Territories and States formed in the Northwest Territory and beginning with 1803 in Tennessee to the new States in the South and West.

About 1820 was begun the practice of granting to each State on admission two townships of saline lands and from 3 to 5 per cent of the net proceeds of the sale of all public lands within its borders. These grants of land and money were in many cases used at least in part for education. By the internal improvement act of 1841, 500,000 acres of public lands were given to each State admitted after 1800 and these grants were devoted to education after 1845. In 1850 the swamp land grant act was passed under which 15 States received over 60,000,000 acres. In 12 States a part or all of the proceeds from the sale of these lands was given to education.

WASHINGTON'S PROPOSALS FOR A NATIONAL UNIVERSITY

In the Constitutional Convention of 1787, over which Washington presided, Charles Pinckney, of South Carolina, offered a plan for a Federal Constitution which contained a clause authorizing Congress " to establish and provide for a national university at the seat of government of the United States," and in the discussion of the Randolph constitution Pinckney and Madison moved to give Congress power " to establish an university," but this was not adopted.

In that year and the next somewhat detailed plans for a national university were published by Dr. Benjamin Rush, of Philadelphia. Among the subjects of instruction were to be " agriculture in all the numerous and extensive branches," and "those parts of natural philosophy and chemistry which admit of an application to agriculture."

In his first message to Congress in 1790 Washington suggested that science and literature might be promoted by " the institution of a national university," and in 1796 he definitely recommended the establishment of such an institution. The Commissioners of the District of Columbia thereupon asked Congress to provide for the acceptance of donations for this purpose, and on December 21, 1796, Mr.

Madison, from the committee to which this matter had been referred, reported in favor of such action.

The project for a national university was revived in 1806 when Jefferson was President. Madison was in his Cabinet, and Samuel Latham Mitchill was " one of his strongest supporters in Congress." Interest in this subject was brought about by Joel Barlow, a graduate of Yale in 1778, who had considered this matter during a long residence in Paris. On his return to the United States in 1805 he prepared a prospectus of a national institution, which was first published January 24, 1806, in an anonymous pamphlet and later in that year in the National Intelligencer at Washington (*106*). This institution, supported by public and private funds, was to have for its objects " the advancement of knowledge by associations of scientific men, and the dissemination of its rudiments by the instruction of youth." It might well be the " depository of the results of scientific research; of experiments in arts, manufactures, and husbandry, and of discoveries by voyages and travels." " No rudiment of knowledge should be below its attention."

The chancellor and trustees of the institution " shall establish a central university, at or near the seat of government, and such other universities, colleges, and schools of education as the funds of the institution will enable them to do, whether in the city of Washington or in other parts of the United States." Included in the equipment of the institution were to be " gardens for botany and agricultural experiments."

Barlow's prospectus was widely circulated and attracted so much favorable attention that he drafted a bill for the incorporation of the institution. This was introduced in the Senate by Mr. Logan, of Philadelphia, but was buried in the committee to which it was referred.

Part 2. DEVELOPMENT OF A DEFINITE MOVEMENT FOR AGRICULTURAL EDUCATION IN THE UNITED STATES, AND SOME OF THE AGENCIES CONTRIBUTING TO THIS MOVEMENT, 1820 TO 1860

In the period from about 1820 to 1860 great changes occurred in the political, social, and economic life of the people of the United States. There was a wide movement of population to the fertile lands beyond the eastern mountains and 20 new States were created. In this great region of virgin soil there was little difficulty in obtaining bountiful crops with the ordinary methods of agriculture. The settlers were therefore chiefly engrossed in solving the other problems of pioneer life and developing means of transportation. The building of roads, bridges, and canals, and then of railroads and telegraph lines, involving the work of great numbers of administrators, engineers, mechanics, and laborers, was done on a large scale during this period.

In both the old and new communities of the South agriculture, carried on largely with slave labor, was the predominant industry. After the invention of the cotton gin, cotton growing developed rapidly and became much more extensive as the use of cotton fabrics at home and abroad was vastly increased through the development of water and steam power, invention of improved machinery, and organization of the factory system.

Writing of the change of sentiment regarding agriculture at the beginning of this period Professor Babson, of the Massachusetts Agricultural College, says:

Just as the country was well started toward helpful discussions and improvements along agricultural lines the second war with England placed many hindrances in the way of further progress in this direction, and those hindrances were subsequently strengthened by the varied growth of manufacturing facilities and wealth-seeking industries. The tendencies of the times were cityward, and the era of good feeling naturally became an era unfavorable to great agricultural advancement. Nevertheless, the farmers and their friends, clearly understanding the unsatisfactory state of affairs, did what they could in spite of the indifference of the general public regarding their efforts.

GROWTH OF AGRICULTURAL SOCIETIES

Local and county agricultural societies continued to be organized and spread over the country with the progress of settlement westward. In 1852 it was estimated that there were about 300 active organizations in the 31 States and 5 Territories, and in 1860 there were 941 agricultural organizations recorded in the books of the United States Agricultural Society. The movement to establish State societies proceeded slowly, but such societies were established during this period in Connecticut, Kentucky, Michigan, New Hampshire, Pennsylvania, and Wisconsin.

The first State horticultural society was formed in New York in 1818. Pennsylvania followed in 1828, Massachusetts in 1829, Kentucky in 1840, and Delaware in 1847. Indiana undertook the organization of such a society in 1842, but it was short-lived. The Ohio Pomological Society began in 1847 and the Northwestern Fruit Growers' Association was organized in Illinois in 1851.

In 1852, at a convention called by 12 State agricultural associations, the United States Agricultural Society was organized (71).

The agricultural societies became more democratic and brought a considerable and growing body of the most intelligent and progressive farmers into active relations with a nation-wide movement for the advancement of agriculture. Through meetings, fairs, correspondence, publications, and articles in the agricultural and other papers they sought to make the public feel that the interests of agriculture and farming population were entitled to more consideration by Congress and the State legislatures. They were increasingly active and influential in the efforts to establish State boards of agriculture, a national Department of Agriculture, the teaching of agriculture in schools and colleges, the carrying on of experiments and scientific investigations for the improvement of agriculture, and the building up of agricultural journals and books.

EARLY STATE BOARDS OF AGRICULTURE

NEW YORK

The first State board of agriculture was established in New York under a law passed April 7, 1819, but was not actually organized until January 10, 1820 (306). This law was largely due to the efforts of men connected with the New York Society for the Promotion of Useful Arts, whose active leader was Governor De Witt Clinton (1769–1828). He advocated the establishment of such a board in his messages in January, 1818, and 1819. The measure finally passed was " an act to improve the agriculture of this State " and appropriated $10,000 per year for two years, " to be distributed among the several counties " as offset for money raised by the county agricultural societies to be used for premiums and reports. At the organization of the board 26 counties were represented and Stephen Van Rensselaer was elected president. (Fig. 4.) The board ceased to exist by expiration of the law in April, 1825.

The functions of a board of agriculture were performed to a considerable extent for many years by the New York State Agricultural Society organized in 1832, as the result of an agricultural State convention, and reorganized in 1841, with State funds for the premiums of the county societies and for an " annual cattle show and fair " (305).

In 1893 a State department of agriculture was organized out of a former dairy commission and took over the distribution of the county fair money. The State society published reports and held fairs up to 1900 when a State fair commission was established.

NEW HAMPSHIRE

The example of New York was very soon followed in New Hampshire by the passage of an act December 19, 1820, largely through the persistent efforts of Humphrey Moore, of Milford. This provided that the presidents and one delegate from each agricultural society should form the board of agriculture, which was to receive and examine reports from the county societies and publish these and other essays " relative to improvements in agriculture " at the expense of the State in a pamphlet with an edition not exceeding 1,000 copies, to be distributed through the societies. It should also examine the work of the societies and recommend alterations and improvements. An amendatory act of June 27, 1821, limited the board to one delegate from each county society. The legislature appropriated $800 for the board and the societies. The money for the board was principally for the preparation and printing of the annual report. The board was organized June 19, 1821, and held but few meetings before going

FIG. 4.—Stephen Van Rensselaer

out of existence. Its only report was issued in 1822, as the New Hampshire Agricultural Repository No. 1 (*223*).

OHIO

In Ohio an act was passed March 12, 1839, to encourage the establishment of agricultural societies by permitting the county auditors to grant them funds derived from the license fees paid for holding public shows under an act of February 28, 1831. On February 27, 1846, a broader " act for the encouragement of agriculture " was passed. This repealed the act of 1839 but provided for a board of agriculture, as well as for aid to agricultural societies. Fifty-three persons from the several counties were named in the act to constitute a body corporate, with perpetual succession, to be known as the Ohio State Board of Agriculture (*336*).

An amendatory act passed February 8, 1847, reduced the board of agriculture to 10 members and appropriated $200 for its use. On the same day an "Act to create a permanent agricultural fund for the State of Ohio" was passed, under which half of the proceeds from permits for shows in the counties and the proceeds of sales of escheated lands were to be devoted to this purpose.

The board was organized April 1, 1846, at Columbus, and Allen Trimble was elected president. At one of its early meetings it urged the formation of township and neighborhood farmers' clubs with libraries and discussions and lectures on agriculture. It was planned to hold the first State fair in 1849, but owing to an epidemic of cholera it was not held until 1850.

MASSACHUSETTS

In Massachusetts an act of 1819 appropriated $200 annually to each agricultural society raising $1,000 and in like proportion up to $3,000. Between 1803 and 1844, 10 societies were formed. Through their influence in 1837 an agricultural survey act was passed under which a person was to be appointed "to collect accurate information of the State and condition of its agriculture and every subject connected with it, point out means of improvement, and make a detailed report thereof," and $2,500 was appropriated for this purpose. Henry Colman was appointed commissioner and made four reports containing a large amount of information (*160*). These reports were widely circulated. The act was repealed in 1841, but the following year an act was passed which required the agricultural societies to make returns to the secretary of the Commonwealth in order to receive their State allowance, and this was amended in 1845 to make their returns include "all reports of committees and all statements of experiments and cultivation" deemed worthy of publication, marking those passages most worthy of public notice. Under this law the secretary of state annually published abstracts of these returns (*181*). In 1851 the societies were exempted from taxation and in 1852 their funds invested in real estate were to be counted in determining their State allowance (*182*). Meanwhile an active propaganda in favor of an agricultural college was carried on. Largely to promote this movement, in which he was deeply interested, Marshall P. Wilder (fig. 5) at a meeting of the trustees of the Norfolk Agricultural Society, of which he was president, held January 28, 1851, brought about the passage of a resolution that the president and secretaries of this society be a committee "to mature and adopt a plan for a convention of delegates from the various agricultural societies of the Commonwealth * * * to concert measures for their mutual advantage, and for the promotion of the cause of agricultural education." This convention was held at Boston March 20, 1851, with Wilder as president.

The convention voted for a central board consisting of three delegates from each incorporated agricultural society (*182*). This body met September 3, 1851, and Wilder was elected president. At a second meeting, January 14, 1852, it adopted a constitution and by-laws. Its objects were stated to be "the encouragement of agricultural education and the improvement of agriculture in all its departments" in this State.

As the result of the activities of this voluntary board an act was passed April 21, 1852, to establish a State board of agriculture, to consist of the governor, lieutenant governor, and secretary of state, ex officio; one member from each agricultural society receiving State

Fig. 5.—Marshall P. Wilder

funds and three members appointed by the governor and council for a term of three years. The duties of this board, as described by the act, were "to investigate all such subjects relating to improvement of agriculture in this Commonwealth as they may think proper, and they are hereby empowered to take, hold in trust, and exercise control over any donations or bequests that may be made to them for promoting agricultural education or the general interests of husbandry" (182).

The board held its first meeting July 22, 1852. The members appointed by the governor were Edward Hitchcock, president of

Amherst College; Marshall P. Wilder, of Dorchester; and Nathaniel Wood, of Fitchburg.

At the third meeting, September 7, 1852, a committee was appointed to consider the expediency of preparing a manual on agriculture for the use of common schools, and another on the best means of promoting the interests of agriculture by public lectures. At the next meeting the second committee reported in favor of calling public attention to the importance of having lectures on agriculture in courses by lyceums and similar associations in rural districts. At the fifth meeting, January 12, 1853, the first committee reported with reference to agricultural education "that studies of this description might be attended to with much benefit under competent teachers" and commended the manual entitled "The Progressive Farmer," by J. A. Nash, of Amherst College. At this meeting President Hitchcock read a paper in which he advocated the organization of " farmers' institutes " after the manner of teachers' institutes.

AMERICAN AGRICULTURAL PERIODICALS

Before the beginning of the nineteenth century agricultural subjects were often treated in newspapers or other journals of a general character. The first issue of the New Jersey Gazette, established in 1776, stated that "Proposals for improvements in agriculture, and particularly in the culture of hemp and flax, will be inserted with pleasure and alacrity." This resulted in the publication of agricultural articles from time to time. The Rural Magazine, published weekly in Newark in 1796, was devoted to the publication of "a judicious selection of essays on religion, morality, agriculture, and miscellaneous subjects." The Newton Farmers' Journal, begun in 1797 at Newton, N. J., was probably a newspaper giving special attention to agricultural matters.

The Agricultural Museum, first published July 4, 1810, at Georgetown, D. C., was issued in the interest of the Columbian Agricultural Society but was essentially an agricultural journal since it was "designed to be a repository of valuable information to the farmer and manufacturer and the means of a free communication of sentiment, and general interchange of ideas on the important subjects of their occupations" (107). Each number was to contain 16 pages and the price of the 24 numbers to be issued annually was $2.50. The first volume is complete but only 11 numbers of the second volume were issued and publication ceased in May, 1812.

The American Farmer, established at Baltimore, Md., by John S. Skinner, April 2, 1819, was a much more substantial and successful journal. It was a weekly of eight quarto pages. This paper continued until about 1862. Another journal by the same name was begun in 1866. The original American Farmer largely served as a model for the agricultural papers which succeeded it in different parts of the country. It covered a wide range of subjects through original articles and others compiled from a variety of sources, including agricultural papers in this country and abroad, proceedings of agricultural societies, etc. It was interested in agricultural experimentation and the education of the farming people through better common schools, manual labor schools, and the teaching of the natural sciences and agriculture in seminaries and colleges.

On June 15, 1819, the first issue of The Plough Boy appeared at Albany, N. Y. The first New England Farmer began at Boston, Mass., in 1822; the first New York Farmer at New York City about 1827; and the Southern Agriculturist at Charleston, S. C., in 1828. The Genesee Farmer was established at Rochester, N. Y., January 1, 1831, and was united in 1839 with the Cultivator begun at Albany, N. Y., in 1834. This in turn was merged in 1866 with the Country Gentleman, which had begun as an independent paper in 1853. In an address delivered by him in 1838 Jesse Buel, editor of the Cultivator, stated that there were then nearly 20 agricultural papers, read probably by 100,000 farmers. The partial list compiled by Gilbert M. Tucker in 1909 shows 36 papers established up to the end of 1850. These papers had headquarters in 16 States, but 11 of them were published in the State of New York. In January, 1837, the edition of the Cultivator had reached 18,000 and a list of the number of subscribers in the several States published by this paper that year showed that it was distributed in 27 States and the District of Columbia.

The first horticultural journal was the Horticultural Register, begun January 1, 1835, at Boston, Mass. This continued for four years and was succeeded by Hovey's Magazine of Horticulture. In 1846 the Horticulturist was established at Albany, N. Y. These covered the whole field of horticulture, including pomology, floriculture, and landscape gardening. Further specialization is seen in the Orchardist's Companion begun at Philadelphia in 1841.

By 1850 the agricultural press had already become quite important and made its influence felt throughout the United States. The agricultural papers of that day were not only diffusing a large amount of practical and useful information on a great variety of agricultural subjects but they were also setting before the farming people the advantages of the application of science to agriculture and the desirability of establishing institutions in which these sciences should be taught, along with the theory and practice of agriculture.

AGRICULTURAL BOOKS

The first distinctively American book on agriculture is commonly said to have been Essays Upon Field Husbandry, by Jared Eliot (1685–1763), of Connecticut, which contained six essays originally printed separately and first brought together in an enlarged edition issued in Boston in 1760.

Samuel Deane, of Massachusetts, in 1790 published an encyclopedic work entitled "New England Farmer," or Georgical Dictionary.

John Beale Bordley, of Maryland, published Essays and Notes on Husbandry and Rural Affairs in 1799 and with additions in 1801.

A Treatise on Practical Farming by John A. Binns, of Virginia, published at Frederick Town, Md., in 1803, contained accounts of his experiments with gypsum.

The Pennsylvania Farmer, by Job Roberts, published in Philadelphia in 1804, was "a selection from the most approved treatises on husbandry interspersed with observations and experiments." It contained reference to The Practical Farmer, by John Spurries, of Brandywine Hundred, New Castle County, Del., published in 1793, and Gleanings on Husbandry, by James Humphreys, published in Philadelphia in 1803.

The earliest literature on horticulture was in the form of calendars which were inserted in almanacs and then sometimes published separately. An example was the Gardener's Kalender first published in an almanac at Charleston, S. C., in 1752. An American edition of Marshall's Introduction to the Knowledge and Practice of Gardening was published at Boston in 1799. The American Gardener, by John Gardiner and Daniel Hepburn, appeared at Washington, D. C., in 1804. A View of the Cultivation of Fruit Trees and the Management of Orchards and Cider, by William Coxe, published at Philadelphia in 1817, was the first comprehensive American book on pomology (*230*).

Arator, by John Taylor, was a collection of agricultural essays, originally published separately, but brought together first in 1813 and published anonymously "by a citizen of Virginia." A revised and enlarged edition with the author's name appeared in 1814, and was followed by several more editions, the sixth in 1818.

The Farmer's Assistant, by John Nicholson, was published at Albany, N. Y., in 1814, "embracing every article relating to agriculture, arranged in alphabetical order."

Nugae Georgicae (Agricultural Trifles), by William Johnson, senior vice president of the Literary and Philosophical Society of Charleston, S. C., published in 1815, is an "endeavor to sketch the outlines of a picture of the cares and amusements, the duties and employments, of the Carolina farmer."

In 1835 in an article on agricultural books in the New England Farmer (v. 13, p. 402), it is stated that American books on this subject are few. Those listed are Deane's New England Farmer, Bordley's Husbandry, Taylor's Arator, Armstrong's Treatise on Agriculture, Nicholson's Farmer's Assistant, Lorrain's Husbandry, Ruffin's Essay on Calcareous Manures, and Fessenden's The Complete Farmer.

Andrew Jackson Downing, of New York, in 1841 published a Treatise on the Theory and Practice of Landscape Gardening and Cottage Residences, and in 1845 Fruits and Fruit Trees in America.

In 1846 the first edition of a translation of Albrecht D. Thaer's Principles of Agriculture, by William Shaw and Cuthbert W. Johnson, was published in New York. A limited number of other agricultural books were published in this country during this period, and foreign agricultural books, particularly those issued in England, were increasingly available in the United States.

AGRICULTURAL TEXTBOOKS

As soon as agriculture began to be taught in schools in the United States, it was apparent that books adapted to school use in this country were required and efforts were made to supply this need. What was accomplished in this direction during the period now under consideration is very well brought out in Bailey's article, Development of the Textbook of Agriculture in North America, published in the Annual Report of the Office of Experiment Stations of the United States Department of Agriculture for 1903 and in revised form in the Cyclopedia of American Agriculture (*3*).

The following textbooks were issued between 1824 and 1860:

The Agricultural Reader, by Daniel Adams, Boston, Mass., 1824; The Farmer's School Book, by J. Orville Taylor, Albany, N. Y., 1837; A Treatise on Agriculture, by John Armstrong, New York, 1839; Elements of Scientific and Practical Agriculture, by Alonzo Gray, Andover, Mass., 1842; A Textbook on Agriculture, by N. S. Davis, illustrated, New York, 1848; Scientific Agriculture, by M. M. Rodgers, illustrated, Rochester, N. Y., 1848; Elements of Agriculture, for the use of Primary and Secondary Schools, by L. Bentz (translated and adapted to the use of primary schools in the United States by F. G. Skinner), New York, 1848; Elements of Scientific Agriculture, by John P. Norton, professor of scientific agriculture in Yale College, New York, 1850; Lessons in Modern Farming, by John L. Blake, New York, 1851; The Progressive Farmer, by J. A. Nash, instructor of agriculture in Amherst College, New York, 1854; The Elements of Agriculture, by George E. Waring, jr., New York, 1854; The American Textbook of Practical and Scientific Agriculture, by Charles Fox, lecturer on agriculture in the University of Michigan, Detroit, Mich., 1854; A Manual of Scientific and Practical Agriculture for the School and the Farm, by J. L. Campbell, professor of physical science, Washington College, Va., illustrated, Philadelphia, 1859.

GENERAL EDUCATIONAL PROGRESS

With the growth of population in the United States and its rapid spread westward during this period the number of elementary and secondary schools and colleges greatly increased. There were, however, no fixed standards for these institutions, and consequently there was great variety in the work which they actually undertook.

Above the common schools were two types of secondary schools, (1) those confined to preparing students for colleges, often called grammar or Latin schools, and (2) the academies or seminaries.

The high schools as a part of a city system of public education began in Boston in 1821 with the establishment of the English Classical School, which from 1824 was called the English High School. They existed in 80 cities by 1851, and in 1852 there were 64 in Massachusetts alone.

The academies gave particular, though often superficial, attention to the rapidly developing natural sciences. In English and mathematics some of the academies gave more liberal courses than most of the colleges. They often had classes for teacher training and paved the way for the normal schools. Some of them were coeducational or they led to the establishment of separate schools for girls. In general, they were the popular schools of their time, and the colleges themselves began to feel their liberalizing influence.

THE LYCEUMS

Among the factors which broadened the educational outlook of the people and laid the foundation for vocational education was the lyceum movement. This was originated in 1826 by Josiah Holbrook (1788–1854), brought up on a farm at Derby, Conn., graduated at Yale in 1810, and later on an attendant at lectures there by Professor Silliman. In 1819 he began an industrial school on Fellenberg's plan and in 1824 undertook an agricultural school at Derby. When this failed through lack of sufficient financial support he began a propaganda for the more general diffusion of education among adults and children. This was to be done through the organization of associations of adults (1) " to procure for youths an economical and practical education and to diffuse rational and useful information through the community generally, and (2) to apply the sciences and the various branches of education to the domestic and useful arts and to all the common purposes of life" (*93*).

The societies were to have meetings, institute regular courses by lectures or otherwise, procure books, apparatus, and collections, and aid in establishing institutions for a thorough education and " in application of the sciences to agriculture and the other useful arts and for qualifying teachers."

In November, 1826, he organized the Millbury (Mass.) Lyceum as No. 1 Branch of the American Lyceum. Other branches were soon formed and combined into the Worcester County Lyceum. The same thing was next done in Windham County, Conn. A State association was formed in 1830 in Massachusetts, and the American Lyceum Association was organized in 1831 at a meeting in New York City at which Stephen Van Rensselaer presided and seven States were represented.

In 1831 about 900 towns had lyceums, and for the next 20 years most public lectures were delivered before such organizations. These covered a wide range of subjects, and the lecturers were often very distinguished men in literature, science, and political affairs. For example, Professor Silliman, Wendell Phillips, and Henry Ward Beecher often appeared on lyceum platforms. The movement also led to the establishment of many local libraries.

HORACE MANN AND THE EDUCATIONAL REVIVAL

In 1837 Horace Mann (1796–1859) in Massachusetts began what has often been called the great educational revival. Alarmed by the generally weak condition of the district schools, owing largely to the ignorance and prejudices of the local boards controlling them, he undertook to arouse public sentiment for a more efficient system of public education, with special reference to the common schools. As a member of the legislature he secured the passage of an act creating a State board of education and became its first secretary. He enlisted the aid of popular speakers, and through the lyceums held hundreds of public meetings throughout the State. This led to further important legislation for the betterment of the school system. He organized teachers' institutes, using the best available instructors and beginning in 1838 brought about the establishment of three normal schools for which the State soon assumed full responsibility. For 12 years he published elaborate reports on the educational situation at home and abroad and measures for the improvement of the schools. In 1838 he established the Common School Journal, and later used Barnard's American Journal of Education as a medium for his discussion of educational subjects.

In these and other ways he aroused great interest in popular education far beyond the borders of Massachusetts. His efforts and those of his followers produced considerable improvement in the public schools, though he was not able to break down local control of the schools in small districts or to secure trained superintendence, particularly for the rural schools.

THE BROADENING OF THE COLLEGE CURRICULUM

During the eighteenth century and the early years of the nineteenth century instruction in the natural sciences had been gradually introduced in a number of North American colleges. Reference has already been made to the beginnings of such instruction at the University of Pennsylvania and Columbia College. A department of mathematics and natural philosophy was established at Harvard College in 1727 and a professorship of natural history in 1804. A chair of chemistry was provided at Princeton in 1795. Instruction in physics and chemistry was given at Dartmouth College and in physics at Union College before 1800. At Yale College Benjamin Silliman was elected professor of chemistry, geology, and mineralogy in 1801. Williams, Bowdoin, William and Mary, Dickinson, and Hobart Colleges, and the universities of Georgia, North Carolina, and South Carolina were among the institutions giving instruction in some branches of natural science prior to 1820. The early instruction was mainly by lectures, supplemented to a limited extent by the exhibition of specimens or by demonstrations conducted by the teachers. Princeton had a chemical laboratory about 1800, Williams College fitted one up in 1812, and Harvard provided one a little later. The Rensselaer Institute established at Troy, N. Y., in 1824, had wide influence on the teaching of natural sciences by observational and experimental methods. On account of its early relations to agricultural education further reference to this school is made in a subsequent discussion. (See p. 39.)

The constant growth of the natural sciences, the development of the literature in the various modern languages, and the accumulation of knowledge in other branches, as well as the contact of American students in larger numbers with foreign institutions of higher learning, particularly in Germany, led to the widening of the curriculum in leading American colleges, introduction of a number of elective studies, and an increase in the number of professorships in the newer subjects.

Amherst College in 1826 announced a science course in which French and Spanish were substituted for Latin and Greek. There was also to be a department devoted to the science and art of teaching and a department of theoretical and practical " mechanism."

Yale College under the presidency of Timothy Dwight began in 1802 the development of instruction in the natural sciences, which led to the establishment of the scientific school as a separate branch of the university. (See p. 62.)

In 1842 Francis Wayland, president of Brown University, criticized the American system of collegiate education and proposed material changes in his book entitled " Thoughts on the Present Collegiate System in the United States " (*364*). At Brown University he introduced an elective system, established a 3-year course for the bachelor's degree, encouraged graduate study and research, and made the sciences prominent in the curriculum.

As the teaching of the natural sciences in colleges and schools developed, the need of textbooks, apparatus, and illustrative material became apparent. Teaching by lectures was common but as textbooks became more numerous they were more largely used in both colleges and secondary schools. Science instruction then became more and more a mere matter of memorizing and recitation. A few teachers, however, introduced so-called experiments; that is, demonstrations performed in the presence of the students. Botanical studies, including examination of plants and student collection of small herbaria, was greatly stimulated by the teaching and publications of Asa Gray, whose Manual of Botany appeared in 1848.

The Sillimans, father and son, at Yale College, were very influential in extending and improving the teaching of chemistry and geology and, as will be seen later, laid the foundation for the teaching of agricultural chemistry and agriculture at that institution.

An event of very great importance in the history of science teaching in this country was the coming of Louis Agassiz to Boston in 1846 to deliver a course of popular lectures at the Lowell Institute. This led to the establishment of the Lawrence Scientific School in 1847, in which Agassiz became professor of zoology and geology. He traveled and lectured extensively in this country. In this way and through his writings, including textbooks on physiology and natural history and on methods of teaching natural history, he gave a great impetus to the movement for incorporating science more broadly in the curricula of colleges and secondary schools. He also helped greatly to infuse life into science teaching by his insistence on actual participation of the students in the examination and handling of the objects of scientific study.

Agassiz was for several years a member of the Massachusetts State Board of Agriculture and had a direct connection with the movement for agricultural education, particularly in his relation to the establishment of the Massachusetts Agricultural College.

MANUAL-LABOR SCHOOLS

A movement which had a more direct relation to the early efforts to establish agricultural schools in this country grew out of the influence of the teachings and work of Fellenberg in his schools at Hofwyl, Switzerland (25). Information regarding the considerable success of his enterprises was brought to our people by American visitors to Hofwyl, in publications issued at home and abroad, and in other ways. Certain features of Fellenberg's theories and activities fitted into educational and financial conditions here in the first half of the nineteenth century and excited so much interest that widespread efforts were made to conduct schools based at least in part on his ideas.

It was hoped that the labor of both teachers and students on school farms and in workshops would make the institutions and the students partly or wholly self-supporting. Students of that day were very often dyspeptic from lack of physical exercise, which the Fellenberg system would supply. It was also believed that manual labor associated with intellectual pursuits had a definite educational value.

Between 1819 and 1830 manual-labor schools were in operation in Connecticut, Florida, Maine, Massachusetts, New Jersey, New York, North Carolina, Ohio, Pennsylvania, and South Carolina. In 1831 a department of manual labor was established at the college at Waterville, Me., with a shop and superintendent. The students put up buildings and made doors, bedsteads, tables, etc. There were similar departments at Oberlin College in Ohio and some other colleges.

The Manual Labor School Society, organized in 1831 with Theodore F. Weld as field agent, attempted to promote this movement on a broader scale. Its only permanent impress on educational progress was in promoting gymnastics in schools.

The school at Whitesboro, N. Y., which was in operation between 1827 and 1834, may serve as a good example of the manual-labor school of this period. The students worked three hours a day at farming, horticulture, and mechanic arts, and the rest of the day was given to classroom work in the English branches.

AGRICULTURAL SCHOOLS AND ACADEMIES

Along with the manual-labor schools in which agricultural operations were conducted simply as a means of physical exercise and a source of income to the school or the students, there were developed institutions in which instruction in the application of the natural sciences to agriculture or in the theory and practice of agriculture itself was combined with practical work in fields and shops and instruction in various academic branches usually taught in secondary schools. These institutions, which are conveniently classed as agricultural schools, varied greatly in the quantity and character of the instruction relating to agriculture, farm equipment, the ages and previous training of their students, and general educational grade. In general their agricultural instruction was superficial and temporary. They are, therefore, chiefly interesting as showing a more or less earnest purpose to give agriculture a pedagogical status by uniting theory with practice in the school curriculum and to satisfy the demand of a considerable number of the more intelligent farming people of that day that in some way agriculture should reap the benefit of advancing knowledge regarding the phenomena and laws of nature. They were premature developments, because there was not yet a body of knowledge relating to agriculture which could be successfully used in secondary schools. As experimental ventures in education they served, however, to stimulate the movement which was to result in the establishment of agricultural colleges and experiment stations.

GARDINER LYCEUM (MAINE)

The Gardiner Lyceum was established at Gardiner, Me., in 1821 and incorporated the following year (3). Its founder was Robert Hallowell Gardiner (1782–1864), a graduate of Harvard College in 1801, who inherited a tract of land "six miles on the Kennebec River and running 11 miles back." He resided on this estate more than 60 years and was prominent in the business, political, educational, and religious life of the State. "Though not himself a practical farmer, he took a deep interest in promoting agriculture, fostering agricultural societies and seeking to make the farm which he reserved for his home a model, by introducing superior breeds of animals, improved machinery, and valuable fruits and grains." Under his leadership the school was organized and a petition for its incorporation was addressed to the Maine Legislature, stating "that a donation had been offered of land lying on the Kennebec River, in the town of Gardiner, estimated at $4,000, for the purpose of establishing within said town a school for teaching mathematics, mechanics, navigation, and those branches of natural philosophy and chemistry which are calculated to make scientific farmers and skillful mechanics." To give the institution more than a local status the board of visitors appointed under an act of February, 1823, were the governor, the president of the senate, the speaker of the house of representatives, the presidents of Bowdoin and Waterville Colleges, and nine other men from different parts of the State, including Benjamin Vaughan, of Hallowell (*148*). A substantial stone building was erected and the school was opened January 1, 1823. The first principal was Benjamin Hale, afterwards a professor in Dartmouth College and then president of what is now Hobart College. His immediate successor was John H. Lathrop, later a professor in Hamilton College and subsequently president of the State universities of Missouri, Maryland, and Wisconsin, respectively, who was followed by E. L. Cushing, afterwards supreme judge in New Hampshire, and Ezekiel Holmes. Doctor Holmes (1801–1865), a native of Massachusetts and graduate of Brown University and the medical department of Bowdoin College, was widely versed in the natural sciences of his time and their application to agriculture (*3*). "He gave lectures on agriculture before what was called a special class in agriculture, had charge of the farm which was operated by him, and on which the records show he agreed to employ 12 students during one summer; he was also steward." In 1826 he became professor of agriculture and natural history. After leaving this school in 1832 he was editor of the Maine Farmer from 1833 to 1865, and secretary of the State board of agriculture and of the State Agricultural Society. Just before his death he persuaded the legislature to establish the State College of Agriculture and Mechanic Arts under the land grant act of 1862, as a separate institution and one of the principal buildings of that institution, now the University of Maine, bears his name.

It will thus be seen that the men who shaped the policies and work of the Gardiner Lyceum were strong and well-trained men. In 1823 the legislature gave the school $2,000 and from 1825 for six years $1,000 annually. The school began with 20 students. In 1824 it had 53 and in 1825 there were 120, but in 1826 the number fell to 55, of whom only 2 were natives of Gardiner. It continued thereafter with varying success until 1832, when it was closed, owing to the financial embarrassment of Mr. Gardiner and to other causes.

When the professorship of agriculture was established in 1824 its objects, as stated by the trustees, were (1) "to give the future agriculturist the knowledge of those principles of science upon which his future success depends and to let him see them reduced to practice" and (2) "to furnish a beneficial employment as recreation and to try a series of agricultural experiments adapted to the soil of Maine."

AGRICULTURAL SEMINARY AT DERBY, CONN.

The Agricultural Seminary at Derby, Conn., founded by Josiah Holbrook on his own farm with the assistance of Trueman Coe, a teacher, in the spring of 1824, continued only about a year. Mr. Coe says that they did what they could to train the students in the analysis of soils, in the application of the mechanical powers to all farming operations, and took out the young men often into the field and country for practical surveying, geological excursions, road making, and the labors of the farm (*3*).

Eight hours a day were given to school exercises, including recitations and " experimental lectures," and two hours to work in the garden or field. About 50 boys and girls attended this school.

One prominent object of the school is to qualify teachers. The most approved methods of instruction will be introduced, and lectures will be given on most of the physical sciences, attended with demonstrations and illustrations sufficiently plain and familiar to admit of their being introduced into common education. Courses on natural philosophy, chemistry, mineralogy, and botany will commence at the opening of the seminary. Ladies will be admitted to the lectures, and there will be a department connected with the institution where females can pursue any branch of education they may desire (*3*).

BOSTON ASYLUM AND FARM SCHOOL

A successful school in which elementary instruction in agriculture is given and which illustrates the charity feature of this movement is the Boston Asylum and Farm School on Thompson's Island, in Boston Harbor (*163*). This school resulted from a meeting in Boston, January 27, 1832, to consider what might be done to aid children needing special attention because of poverty and other disadvantages. The conclusion was "that the establishment of a farm school in the country, where idle and morally exposed children of the city may be rescued from vice and danger, and may enjoy the advantages of a good physical and moral education, would be not only a great benefit to such children, but would greatly conduce to the peace and good order of this community." To carry out this purpose a " Boston Farm School Society " was formed and chartered. This society purchased a farm of about 140 acres on Thompson's Island, on which it erected buildings. Becoming cramped by lack of funds it united in 1835 with the more opulent Boston Asylum for Indigent Boys, founded in 1814, which had a school in Boston.

A report of the farm school in 1833 states that—

A school is kept both morning and evening for about six hours daily in which are taught the elements of useful knowledge, reading, writing, arithmetic, geography, and grammar. During the evening, especially in the winter months, instruction is also given in the first principles of agriculture, horticulture, and botany; the different kinds of soils, the most important processes of cultivation, and the names, uses, and distinctive qualities of seeds, plants, and trees are explained and illustrated. * * * And they are required to perform as much of the manual labor done on the farm as their various ages and capacities will permit (*163*).

The New England Farmer (vol. 16) contains an account of a visit to this school August 25, 1837, at which time 104 boys were in attendance. In 1901 a more definite course in agriculture was introduced for the elementary grades. In 1907 the name of the school was changed to The Farm and Trades School. Boys may enter from 10 to 14 years of age if they have reached the sixth grade, and remain until ready for the high school.

CREAM HILL AGRICULTURAL SCHOOL (CONN.)

The Cream Hill Agricultural School (later called Cream Hill Academic School, with an agricultural department), at West Cornwall, Conn., was established in 1845 and continued with considerable success until 1869 (*90*). The prospectus is as follows:

The plan of this institution is to receive a select and limited number of pupils, under the superintendence of well-qualified teachers, to be fitted for college, or any of the useful pursuits of life.

This school embraces two important departments of instruction. First, thorough attention to the various elementary and scientific branches taught at the best academic institutions. Second, both scientific and practical instructions in agriculture and horticulture, embracing the most approved method of tillage, rearing of stock, cultivation of trees, the laying out of grounds, ornamental gardening, chemical analysis of soils, composts, etc. A portion of each day will be allotted to these subjects, so that the pupil may become a scientific and practical farmer.

The farm, containing 200 acres, with convenient buildings, situated on Cream Hill, surrounded by a picturesque country scenery, furnishes a location unrivaled for healthfulness and freedom from immoral tendencies, and peculiarly fitted for such an institution.

The Housatonic Railroad furnishes daily access to New York. The students will become members of the family of the instructors. A parental supervision will at all times be exercised over each individual. All will be treated with kindness, and every attention rendered, with affectionate regard to health, deportment, and morals.

The institution will be conducted by Samuel W. Gold, Theodore S. Gold, and Thomas R. Dutton [who, however, did not actually take part in the school].

There will be two terms in each year; the first commencing the first Wednesday in May, and terminating the first Wednesday in November; the second from the first Wednesday in December to the first Wednesday in April.

Terms: The pupils will be furnished with tuition, board, fuel, lights, washing, privileges of the library, and riding, at $200 a year, one-half to be paid at the beginning of each term. West Cornwall, Conn., March 31, 1845 (*90*).

In the catalogue of 1849 it is stated that—

Each pupil cultivates a garden of about 130 square yards; is instructed in laying out, planting, and application of manures. Small premiums are awarded for the best gardens. Ample opportunity is afforded each to acquire a knowledge of general farming, tending and rearing the various kinds of stock, etc.

In a letter to the director of the Office of Experiment Stations November 8, 1894, T. S. Gold states that he " taught botany, mineralogy, agriculture, etc., in the classroom and in the garden and field. Some pupils were taught all the operations of the farm."

Samuel W. Gold had been for years the principal physician in Goshen, Conn., but had removed to his farm in West Cornwall shortly before the opening of the school. His son, Theodore Sedgwick Gold (1818–1906) had graduated at Yale College in 1838 and had been principal of Goshen Academy for three years (*92*). For many years he was very influential in agricultural affairs in Connecticut. He was active in organizing the Connecticut Agricultural Society in 1853 and for years was one of its directors. He also helped to organize the Connecticut Board of Agriculture in 1866 and was its secretary for 34 years. He strongly supported the movement which resulted in the establishment of the Connecticut Agricultural Experiment Station in 1875 and was a member of its board of control until his death. He was also active in connection with the founding in 1881 of the agricultural school at Storrs, which is now the Connecticut Agricultural College, and was for 20 years a trustee of this institution. " He was always a student, an extensive reader on subjects relating to natural science, a man having wide acquaintance with men of learning and prominence and withal an excellent, practical farmer." At one time an editor, he was for more than 60 years a frequent contributor to the agricultural press.

Other schools in which agriculture was taught during this period were the Teachers' Seminary at Andover, Mass.; Eden Hill Farm Institute near Philadelphia; Franklin College near Nashville, Tenn.; the school founded by Daniel Lee, editor of the second Genesee Farmer, in cooperation with Rawson Harmon, at Wheatland, N. Y.; Mount Airy Agricultural Institute near Philadelphia; New York Central College at McGrawville, N. Y.; Oakwood Agricultural Institute at Lancaster, N. Y.; Union Academy at Shiloh, N. J.; and the Mapes School, near Newark, N. J.

The widespread interest in the introduction of instruction relating to agriculture into schools privately maintained during this period, as well as the difficulty of actually accomplishing this in a way which would be attractive or useful to students, is shown in the frequent discussion of this matter in the agricultural and other press, and the number and variety of institutions which made the attempt with little or no success. In many cases apparently the effort got no further than an announcement in the catalogue or an advertisement in some paper. In other cases it resulted only in a few lectures on agricultural subjects in connection with instruction in natural sciences, or references to the applications of such sciences to agriculture.

The widespread development of secondary education through public high schools and private preparatory schools led to considerable standardization of courses of study in such schools and the requirement of college training for their teachers. The influence of the colleges very generally permeated the secondary schools and brought about the restriction of their field to general education. Sentiment in favor of vocational education in any line in the secondary schools was little in evidence. There were practically no trained teachers of agriculture to be had and the limited literature of this subject was ill adapted for use in schools. Public attention was more and more directed toward efforts to establish agricultural colleges. It seemed to be dimly understood that these higher institutions would be needed before agriculture could be successfully taught in the lower schools and many people thought that such colleges could supply all the agricultural instruction which it was worth while to give.

The movement for the teaching of agriculture in secondary schools therefore waned, and by the time of the outbreak of the Civil War such instruction had almost entirely disappeared in this country.

AGRICULTURAL INSTRUCTION IN PRIVATE COLLEGES

RENSSELAER INSTITUTE

The Rensselaer Institute at Troy, N. Y. (242, 314), occupied a unique position in the early movement for scientific education related to agriculture and the mechanic arts. This school was founded in

1824 by Stephen Van Rensselaer (1764–1839). (Fig. 4.) He had become by inheritance patroon of a district originally 24 by 48 miles in extent, comprising what are now Albany, Columbia, and Rensselaer Counties. This great tract, as developed up to his death in 1839, contained over 3,000 farms, which were leased on moderate terms. Van Rensselaer was greatly interested in the improvement of agriculture, became a leading member and officer of the State Society for the Promotion of Useful Arts, and in 1820 was president of the newly created State board of agriculture. He graduated at Harvard College in 1782 and, through his interest in education, was made a regent of the University of the State of New York and became its chancellor in 1835. He was also active in politics, being a member of both houses of the State legislature, lieutenant governor for six years, and a Member of Congress, where he served as chairman of the Committee on Agriculture. He was on the first State commission to explore a route for a canal between the Hudson River and the Lakes and later on the Erie Canal Commission.

About 1820 Van Rensselaer came in contact with Amos Eaton, who had already attracted considerable attention as an itinerant lecturer on natural science. Eaton (1776–1842) (fig. 6) was the son of a farmer at Chatham, N. Y., graduated at Williams College in 1799, studied law and practiced this profession at Catskill, N. Y., but became enamored of the field study of botany and mineralogy. In 1810 he began to give popular lectures on botany and compiled an elementary treatise on this subject. Then he went to Yale College and studied chemistry, geology, and mineralogy under Silliman and botany under Ives. Going back to Williamstown, Mass., in 1817 he lectured outside the college on botany, mineralogy, and geology, and so interested the students that they published his Manual of Botany, which was gradually enlarged and in its eighth edition in 1840 contained descriptions of 5,267 species. He also gave lectures in a number of the large towns in New England and New York and in 1818 on invitation of Governor Clinton spoke to the New York Legislature on geology and its application to agriculture through surveys. Two years later he was called to the professorship of natural history in the somewhat famous Medical College at Castleton, Vt. What attracted the greatest attention in connection with Eaton's lectures was that he not only illustrated them with specimens and demonstrations but led his students to make collections in the field and to construct simple apparatus for various purposes. This had come about from his experience as a boy on the farm. Impressed by the unusual ability of Eaton, Van Rensselaer then employed him—

in the summer of 1824, to traverse the state on or near the line of the Erie Canal, provided with sufficient apparatus and specimens to deliver, in all the principal towns where an audience of business men or others could be collected, a series of lectures, accompanied with experiments and illustrations, on " chemistry, natural philosophy, and some or all of the branches of natural history." This undertaking was entirely successful.

To perpetuate and broaden such work Van Rensselaer established in the fall of 1824 a school to instruct persons "in the application of science to the common purposes of life." (In the language of this purpose is seen the influence of Count Rumford, who in 1799 used the same words to describe the aim of the Royal Institution of London, which he was founding.)

Referring to the success of Eaton's summer lectures in western New York Van Rensselaer declares that his principal object in establishing a school is—

to qualify teachers for instructing the sons and daughters of farmers and mechanics in the application of experimental chemistry, philosophy, and natural history to agriculture, domestic economy, the arts and manufactures. * * * Apparatus for the necessary experiments has been so much simplified, and speci-

Fig. 6.—Amos Eaton.   [From Pioneers of Science in America, p. 475; courtesy of Appleton & Co.]

mens in natural history have become subjects of such easy attainment that but a small sum is now required as an outfit for an instructor in the proposed branch of science; consequently every school district may have the benefit of such a course of instruction about once in two or three years as soon as we can furnish a sufficient number of teachers.

He appointed a board of nine trustees, among whom was Simeon De Witt, and chose Eaton as senior "professor of chemistry and experimental philosophy, and lecturer on geology, land surveying, and the laws regulating town officers and jurors," and Lewis C. Beck as junior " professor of mineralogy, botany, and zoology, and lecturer on the social duties peculiar to farmers and mechanics." Eaton's influence is seen in the " order " regarding the course in chemistry.

The students are to be divided into sections, not exceeding five in each section. These are not to be taught by seeing experiments and hearing lectures, according to the usual method. But they are to lecture and experiment by turns, under the immediate direction of a professor or a competent assistant. Thus, by a term of labor, like apprentices to a trade, they are to become operative chemists.

Professor Eaton was much opposed to athletics as commonly practiced in colleges and substituted as " amusements " exercises in land surveying, general engineering, collecting and preserving specimens in botany, mineralogy and zoology, examining workshops and factories, watching the progress of agricultural operations, making experiments on fertilizing materials for vegetables in the experimental gardens, etc. Beginning with 1827 he began taking students on tours on the Hudson River and Erie Canal to observe and to make collections. Unsuccessful attempts were made to carry out the original purpose by establishing branches in the State and by showing academies and common schools how to teach science and its applications with cheap apparatus.

At one time it was proposed to give a student from each county free tuition if he would agree to teach by the experimental method for one year. During the first 10 years the institution was for the most part a school of science, placing emphasis on the practical applications of science. Its requirements were relatively severe and comparatively few students were able to meet them. It did not have more than 25 students at any one time, but a considerable number of these were graduates or members of colleges.

Courses relating to surveying and other branches of engineering were gradually developed, and in 1835, after the name of the school had been changed to Rensselaer Institute, it was divided into departments of natural science and engineering. The latter gained the ascendancy and about 1850 it became a great school of engineering under the name of Rensselaer Polytechnic Institute.

This institution undoubtedly had considerable general influence on the movement for scientific education relating to agriculture and mechanic arts which culminated in the land-grant act of 1862. It was well known to those leaders in New York and other States who were promoting the establishment of colleges and other public agencies for the promotion of agriculture. Some of its students had direct relations with this movement.

Ebenezer Emmons, of the class of 1826, became chief of the agricultural section of the New York State Geological Survey and between 1846 and 1854 issued important reports on soils, crops, fruits, and noxious organisms. Asa Fitch, jr., graduated in 1827, specialized in entomology, and became State entomologist. James Hall, of the class of 1832, became eminent as a geologist and extended his influence as far west as Iowa, where during a brief connection with the Iowa State University in its early days he helped in starting the movement which resulted in the establishment of the Iowa State College of Agriculture and Mechanic Arts. Ezra Slocum Carr, graduated in 1838, became the first professor of chemistry as applied to agriculture in the universities of Wisconsin and California. In the latter State he laid the foundations for the experiment station at the university and was active in the affairs of the Grange, whose history he published.

George Hammell Cook, of the class of 1839, specialized in geology, but had a broad interest in other sciences and their practical applications and became professor of chemistry and natural sciences in Rutgers College in New Jersey, and of geology and agriculture in 1880. He was State geologist for many years and influential in the establishment of the New Jersey State Board of Agriculture. He was also the first director of the New Jersey Agricultural Experiment Stations.

WASHINGTON (NOW TRINITY) COLLEGE

In 1824 the first catalogue of Washington (now Trinity) College at Hartford, Conn., announced that—

An agricultural establishment will be connected with the institution, and the students will have an opportunity of becoming acquainted with this primary art of living, by the courses of lectures, illustrated by the practical operations of farming and gardening. Military exercises will also be embraced in the system as a healthful occupation for some of the hours usually devoted to recreation (3).

A botanic garden was also maintained at the college for a considerable period and courses in "practical applications of chemistry and botany" were listed in a number of early catalogues.

BUSSEY INSTITUTION

In a will dated July 30, 1835, Benjamin Bussey, of Roxbury, Mass., gave to Harvard College half the income of about $300,000 and his farm of over 200 acres on condition that there be established on this farm—

a course of instruction in practical agriculture, in useful and ornamental gardening, in botany, and in such other branches of natural science as may tend to promote a knowledge of practical agriculture and the various arts subservient thereto and connected therewith, and cause such courses of lectures to be delivered there at such seasons of the year and under such regulations as they may think best adapted to promote the ends designed ; and also to furnish gratuitous aid, if they shall think it expedient, to such meritorious persons as may resort there for instruction ; the institution so established shall be called the "Bussey Institution" (163).

Though the will was probated in 1842, it was not deemed advisable to begin the establishment of the Bussey Institution until 1870. It has since been conducted mainly as a research institution. (See p. 127.)

AMHERST COLLEGE

In 1843 Amherst College in Massachusetts listed in its catalogue a "lecturer on agricultural chemistry and mineralogy," and in 1852, under the presidency of Edward Hitchcock, a scientific department "entirely independent of the regular course" was established (163). In this department J. A. Nash, as instructor in agriculture, and later author of the textbook entitled "The Progressive Farmer," was to "take charge of any who may wish to study the elements of agriculture, theoreticaly and practically," and William S. Clark, afterwards president of the Massachusetts Agricultural College, was to give " practical instruction in analytical and applied chemistry, with special reference to agriculture, pharmacy, and metallurgy." This department was discontinued in 1857.

The Country Gentleman contains an announcement, dated December 23, 1853, by Mr. Nash, of his course in practical and scientific agriculture for " young men not pursuing a full collegiate course. Instruction will be given, through textbooks, lectures, and free conversations * * * on the applications of science to the cultivation and improvement of soils, the preservation and use of manures, the growing and disposal of crops, the care of animals, and generally to whatever relates to the management of a farm." Students may take the whole or a part of this course and may have access to other lectures by the president and professors of Amherst College. " The teacher of agriculture will accompany his class to the lectures on geology, chemistry, philosophy, and natural history, and then at the earliest opportunity will review with them the subject of each lecture in a way to show its practical bearings and to fix it in the memory."

FARMERS' COLLEGE IN OHIO

In 1846 an institution named Farmers' College was organized at College Hill, Ohio, 6 miles from Cincinnati (*334*). This was an outgrowth of a literary school known as Pleasant Hill Academy, begun in 1833 by Freeman Grant Cary (1810–1888), a cousin of Alice and Phoebe Cary, and a graduate of Miami University, Oxford Ohio, in 1832.

In 1845 a plan was made to enlarge the school by issuing stock for " a building for an institution of learning especially suited to the wants of the agricultural and business community." The building was to be called Farmers' Collegiate Hall of Hamilton County. Over 400 persons, mostly farmers and mechanics, contributed. A charter, granted by the legislature February 23, 1846, created a corporation known as Farmers' College of Hamilton County. " The objects of this association shall be to direct and cultivate the minds of the students in a thorough and scientific course of studies, particularly adapted to agricultural pursuits."

About 7½ acres of land adjoining the site of the academy were obtained and on this tract a three-story brick building, 120 by 48 feet, with 27 rooms was erected, costing with its furniture about $13,000. In 1855 the legislature gave the college authority to grant the degrees of A. B. and A. M. John H. Scott, a native of Pennsylvania and graduate of Washington College, who had also studied science under Silliman at Yale College, was professor of chemistry and its application to agriculture and the arts until 1849. Benjamin Harrison, afterwards President of the United States, was a student in this institution in 1848–1850.

Increasing public interest in agricultural education led the board of trustees in 1853 to resolve to raise $100,000 " to secure a farm and establish an agricultural professorship and department of practical agriculture and horticulture and constitute a building fund." The committee to prepare a plan for subscription reported that " it was the original design to connect with this institution a farm for scientific and practical experiments in agriculture and horticulture, including the analysis of soils and their adaptation to the various products of the earth. * * * A college furnished with ample facilities for applying the principles of science to husbandry and the mechanic arts is indispensable in developing the resources of the country" (*334*).

President Cary resigned to take charge of the farm department and to raise funds for its support. William Cary gave $10,000 for this department and a Cary professorship of practical agriculture was established in his honor.

The course as outlined in the catalogue included field lectures, the study of textbooks and essays on agriculture and horticulture during four years, general and agricultural chemistry, entomology, mineralogy, geology, natural philosophy, physiology, English, mathematics, history, political economy, mental and moral philosophy, drawing, etc.

A monthly journal, called The Cincinnatus, was published at the college, beginning January 1, 1856 (*332*). It contained articles on a great variety of agricultural subjects, including agricultural education, accounts of experiments, agricultural production and economics, meteorology, etc. It continued through five volumes. In the first volume it is stated that 100 acres of land were purchased " for a model and experimental farm," a botanic garden of 20 acres was being laid out, with vegetables, fruits, shrubs, and forest trees of many varieties—the whole farm to constitute "a grand laboratory." Small lots for variety tests were to be made on the farm. The building, called Polytechnic Hall, was completed in the fall of 1856 and dedicated with appropriate ceremonies, including an address by Mr. Cary on industrial university education—its mission. This building contained rooms for professors of chemistry, botany, and vegetable physiology, and theoretical and practical agriculture, a chemical laboratory, a shop with forge, and other mechanical apparatus, etc. " Every student is to be an operator."

The college as a whole grew in popularity and in 1856 had 330 students. But its funds were not sufficient to maintain it on the scale on which it was being operated, and as the shadow of the Civil War approached it was difficult to secure adequate financial support. Two memorials were sent to Congress asking for grants of land for the college, but without avail. An effort to have this college made the beneficiary of the land grant act of 1862 also failed. The professorship of agriculture was nominally maintained until 1880, but long before that the farm department had disappeared and the farm itself had been sold. In 1884 the institution became Belmont College and this was merged into the Ohio Military Institute in 1890.

THE MOVEMENT TOWARD PUBLIC SUPPORT OF AGRICULTURAL COLLEGES

While the teaching of agriculture in purely private institutions was being attempted with small success, friends of agricultural education began to look forward to State aid for such instruction, and in a few States movements were begun which were to lead up to the establishment of State agricultural colleges and their endowment under the national land grant act of 1862.

NEW YORK

There is little doubt that after the attempt of Doctor Mitchill to teach science in its relations to agriculture at Columbia College in 1792 the group of influential men who were prominent in the early agricultural societies in New York discussed from time to time the possibility of doing something for agriculture in colleges or through professorships connected with the societies or other institutions. This came to the surface as already stated in Governor Clinton's message of 1818 favoring a State board of agriculture, wherein he also suggested that a professorship of agriculture might well be " connected with the board or attached to the university."

DE WITT'S PLAN FOR AN AGRICULTURAL COLLEGE

The following year his cousin, Simeon De Witt, published anonymously at Albany a pamphlet of 42 pages, entitled " Considerations on the Necessity of Establishing an Agricultural College and Having More of the Children of Wealthy Citizens Educated for the Profession of Farming " (*258*). He had in 1799 publicly advocated " a school of practical instruction in the business of husbandry," with which there should be experiments and instruction in the science of agriculture (*230*).

He now attempted to show that farming is not only honorable, but may be and often is profitable, and that even its difficulties and hardships are much better for men to contend with than a life of idleness; that in foreign countries gentlemen are in many cases owners of large estates, in the management of which they often endeavor to improve agriculture by experiments, the results of which they disseminate to their tenants and through societies or boards of agriculture.

The absence of such a class in this country has led the small, but independent, farmers to follow traditional methods and thus to prevent improvements in agriculture. The agricultural societies are doing something to remedy this situation. " The institution now proposed will not be their rival but rather a cooperator. * * * It is intended not so much to give instruction to farmers as to make farmers from other classes of society."

It may be called an agricultural school, academy, or college, no matter which; but if any importance is to be attached to names, I would give it the most respectable, and call it the Agricultural College of the State of New York.

Its primary object should be to teach the theory and practice of agriculture, with such branches of other sciences as may be serviceable to them, its secondary, to make improvements (*258*).

On the faculty should be a " professor of practical agriculture acquainted with both theory and practice and capable of making experiments. He will have direction of the labor of the students in the field."

Instead of giving formal lectures, this professor, who must constantly attend his classes while thus engaged, will, during the progress of their work, explain to them the best manner in which everything is to be done, the reason of it, and the errors that are or may be committed in it; on all which the students will be required to make notes and comments at their hours of relaxation and undergo examinations at stated times (*258*).

There should be a farm of considerable extent and variety of soil and it should " be made not only instructive, but, if possible, profitable." A workshop for the repair of implements by the students and for a collection of " models of all the best implements of husbandry " should be provided. Account books should be kept in detail of all the farm transactions and the professors should lecture on this subject.

De Witt's plan for an agricultural college was given considerable publicity in various ways in New York and other States and undoubtedly laid a somewhat definite basis for consideration of this subject in legislatures and elsewhere. It had, however, one unfortunate result in giving credence to the idea, often urged by opponents of public aid to agricultural colleges, that they were to be institutions for the rich and therefore not worthy of support from public funds.

ELKANAH WATSON'S PLAN FOR A PATTERN FARM

In 1819 Elkanah Watson (see p. 12) issued a plan for a pattern farm of from 100 to 200 acres under the board of agriculture with a professor of agriculture to carry on experiments on crops, trees, implements, architectural plans, animals, manures, " and all that relates to chemistry, horticulture, botany, and mineralogy." Provision was to be made for the education there annually of 20 young men at the expense of the agricultural fund. These students were to be selected by the presidents of the agricultural societies. There were to be classes on the theory and practice of agriculture and student labor at least three hours a day. The next year these students should teach in academies or schools under direction of the county societies and be provided with cheap books on the first elements of agriculture and chemistry. Watson, however, states that he did not expect this plan to be adopted for some time to come.

JESSE BUEL'S PLAN FOR AN AGRICULTURAL SCHOOL

In 1823 there appeared in the New York Assembly an agricultural leader who was to keep up for about 15 years a persistent campaign for the establishment of an agricultural college. This was Jesse Buel (1778–1839), a native of Coventry, Conn., who had learned the printer's trade at Rutland, Vt., and thereafter published papers in Troy, Poughkeepsie, and Kingston, N. Y. (*244*). In 1813 he established the Argus at Albany, which for many years was an influential journal, and was its editor until 1821. During this period he was also State printer. While a resident of Kingston he was judge of the court of common pleas. After retiring from the Argus he settled on a small farm near Albany, which he greatly improved through experiments in agriculture and horticulture.

As a member of the committee on agriculture of the New York Assembly in 1823 Buel brought in a report favoring an agricultural school (*304*).

The curriculum should cover every branch of science relating to agriculture and every department of practical husbandry. Tuition should be low. Appropriations should be loans rather than donations. It is stated that Hon. Stephen

Van Rensselaer has offered land. The school will supersede the board of agriculture and might have the $10,000 now annually given to the county agricultural societies. For its support a tax on bank stock is suggested. On the State appropriations to colleges and schools an agricultural school should be included. A bill to establish the school accompanies the report.

In a letter to W. M. Barton, vice president of the Agricultural Society of the Valley of Virginia, December 6, 1823, Buel referred to this report and stated that he considered the plan of the Albemarle Society for a professorship of agriculture at the University of Virginia defective because "it makes agriculture an auxiliary study," whereas "it ought to be the principal, and botany, chemistry, literature, etc., should be subservient to this great study." "The pupil should go to it with the express view of learning to be a farmer."

In 1825 the New York Committee on Agriculture reported that "it is in some measure indispensable to establish an experimental farm in connection with an agricultural seminary" but "while the committee indulge a belief that such a system will eventually be established to its full extent, yet they apprehend that public sentiment is not yet sufficiently mature to embrace the plan."

In 1826 James Tallmadge, then lieutenant governor of New York, in the report of a committee to inquire into the condition of the College of Physicians and Surgeons in New York City, "urged that it was not sufficient that the sciences connected with agriculture and the mechanic arts should be diligently studied and correctly understood by a few votaries in our literary institutions." He therefore advocated lectures on these subjects in public schools and colleges.

NEW YORK STATE AGRICULTURAL SCHOOL

In 1832 at the first meeting of the new State agricultural society a committee was appointed to report on a plan for an agricultural school. Pending this report the Albany Argus began a series of articles, undoubtedly by Jesse Buel, to call public attention to this matter.

On February 14, 1833, the committee reported a plan for a school, with an estimate of expense on the basis of an attendance of 200 students (*3*). A farm of 400 acres, with buildings and equipment, would cost $57,550 and the annual expense for instruction and board would be $23,400, of which only $5,100 was for salaries of officers and teachers. With board and tuition at $150 and proceeds of sale of farm produce the annual receipts would be $34,000.

The committee proposed a bill to be introduced in the legislature asking for authorization to issue stock certificates to the amount of $100,000, with interest at 5 per cent, to be sold at auction. Three commissioners were to purchase the farm and erect buildings to accommodate 200 students, who at entrance must be at least 14 years old.

The society presented this plan and bill to both houses of the legislature, through a committee of which Buel was a member. Favorable reports on the project were made, but the legislature took no action. Then in March, 1834, Buel established the monthly journal called The Cultivator, very largely as a medium of propaganda for the school. For a considerable period this paper was issued in the name of the State agricultural society. It circulated widely throughout the country, and undoubtedly had much influence in molding public opinion on agricultural education. In general it advocated schools "in which the theory and practice of agriculture shall constitute the paramount study," as distinguished from manual-labor schools. It was also favorable to the teaching of agriculture as far as possible in the common schools and hoped that the agricultural schools would be able to prepare teachers for the lower schools. It favored but did not insist on the use of public funds for the maintenance of agricultural schools.

In 1835 the legislature was again asked to charter an agricultural school without State aid. The bill passed the house with only three opposing votes, but the senate committee held it until near the end of the session and then reported it with amendments, which changed its character and prevented its passage. The friends of the measure renewed their efforts and a State agricultural convention was held at Albany February 8, 1836, at which Buel presided. This convention sent a memorial to the legislature asking for the establishment of a " school of scientific and practical agriculture." There was now evidently more favorable public opinion behind this movement, with the result that on May 6, 1836, an act to incorporate the New York State Agricultural School was passed. This provided a corporation with capital stock of $100,000 which might be increased to $200,000, to be used for the equipment and maintenance of a school " for the purposes of instruction in literature and science and improvement in scientific and practical agriculture and the mechanic arts."

Seven commissioners, named in the act, were to receive subscriptions for the stock, interest on which was limited to 5 per cent. No subscription was to be for more than $1,000. The corporation was to be managed by 32 trustees of whom the governor and lieutenant governor were to be members ex officio, the remaining members to be stockholders and citizens of the State, elected annually by the stockholders. The trustees were to purchase a farm of about 500 acres of land near the Hudson River and the city of Albany, and erect buildings thereon, and appoint the faculty and other employees of the school. "An indispensable requirement" for the faculty and students was that they should occupy half their time during school sessions between March and December, " either in the practical agricultural business of the farm, or in the laboratories or mechanic shops " connected with the school. The governor was required "to appoint annually a committee of three persons " to visit the school and report on its condition to the legislature.

The commissioners named in this act, of whom Buel was the chairman, made an active effort to secure subscriptions to the stock of the school, but with disheartening results.

However, the State agricultural society continued its efforts to promote agricultural education. In the New York Assembly in 1839 a committee had before it 80 petitions for aid to agriculture, with nearly 6,000 signatures. The committee in its report expressed surprise " that there is no school, no seminary, no subdivision of any school, in which the science of agriculture is taught," though this is " a business which occupies eight-tenths of our population," and recommended that an agricultural school be established.

In 1840 the assembly committee on agriculture urged that the legislature should promote the science of agriculture with as much liberality as it does with reference to literary institutions.

The act of May 5, 1841, under which the State agricultural society was reorganized, greatly strengthened it and through its series of publications enabled it to give more prominence to its efforts for agricultural education (*305*). In 1842 the society published an article on agricultural education by A. S. Wynkoop and that year the legislature considered a proposition to establish agricultural schools in each county. In 1843 many petitions to the legislature were again prepared, and at its ensuing session the assembly committee reported that if the State was to give further funds to benefit agriculture " it should be to endow a college for the purpose of disseminating scientific knowledge of agriculture throughout the State." There was also in 1844 another report which recommended an appropriation for public lectures on practical and scientific agriculture in different parts of the State. The chairman of this committee was Daniel Lee, editor of the Genesee Farmer, who for years went about the State delivering lectures on agricultural chemistry and advocating an agricultural college. In the sessions of the legislature in 1844 and 1845 he secured the passage in the assembly of a bill to establish an agricultural college and in 1845 this bill came within one vote of passing the Senate.

In 1846 the American Institute of New York City asked the legislature to establish under their auspices an agricultural college near New York City (*272*). The institute had been organized in 1828 to promote the interests of agriculture, commerce, manufactures, and arts through fairs and exhibitions. It had a farmers' club which was quite active. In their petition to the legislature they stated that they had professors in various departments and wanted State aid to organize an agricultural department. The institute's proposition was before the legislature for several years but did not secure favorable action.

Meanwhile the State agricultural society was discussing what it should do further for agricultural education, and there was some difference of opinion as to whether a separate institution or departments of agriculture in existing colleges was the better plan. By 1849 the society had decided to ask the legislature to establish an agricultural college and this was advocated by Gov. Hamilton Fish in his message that year. By concurrent resolution adopted April 6, 1849, a commission was appointed to consider the propositions for agricultural education. The commission made a detailed report and submitted a bill for the establishment of the Agricultural College of the State of New York. The legislature that year also had before it memorials for an agricultural department at the Genesee Seminary and for agricultural schools in each of several districts in the State (*278*).

In 1851 the assembly committee on agriculture again reported in favor of an agricultural college (*280*). It also agreed that a mechanical school or college would be a good thing but did not favor its attachment to an agricultural college. The mechanical college should be in a large city or village.

The committee stated its belief that since this matter had been so long under consideration and the petitions relating to it were so numerous, "the great mass of the agricultural community throughout the State demands the establishment" of an agricultural college, and therefore it should be "endowed by the State and be considered a State institution." The recommendation was for a—

college and farm of 60 acres cultivated by students working four hours a day, and instructed in the raising of plants and animals; the proper time to sell produce and how to put it in market; the manner of keeping farm accounts and farm management; chemistry, natural philosophy, geography, mineralogy, botany, horticulture, veterinary medicine, land measurement, drainage, irrigation, farm implements and buildings, and rural laws, together with higher departments of English education.

For admission: English, grammar, geography, arithmetic.

Age of entrants: 16 years.

Faculty: President, six professors, farm superintendent, gardener, carpenter, mason, blacksmith.

It was thought an annual appropriation of $10,000 would provide for the current expenses of the school, when taken together with money obtained from students and sales of farm products.

A minority report (281) stated that both farmers and laboring men are opposed to such institutions which would involve large expenditures without corresponding benefit and lead to favoritism and corruption. The bill that year failed by a narrow margin. The matter came up again in the legislature in 1852 with the same result.

Meanwhile the State agricultural society had been actively supporting this measure and had given publicity to addresses and other material favoring an agricultural college. A new leader had arisen in the person of John Delafield (1786–1853), who was made president of the society in 1851 and in his annual address in January, 1852, discussed "the need of an agricultural college" (3).

With the backing of the State agricultural society and other friends of agricultural education Delafield secured an act of incorporation for the New York State Agricultural College April 15, 1853. Three days earlier the friends of a college which should include mechanic arts together with agriculture and other subjects, had secured a charter for the People's College for the purpose of promoting literature, science, arts, and agriculture. From this time until the establishment of Cornell University the streams of influence relating to higher education in agriculture and other industries under State patronage were distinctly divided, as will be noted by following the history of the New York State Agricultural College and the People's College.

THE NEW YORK STATE AGRICULTURAL COLLEGE

The act of April 15, 1853, incorporating the New York State Agricultural College, reads as follows:

The people of the State of New York, represented in senate and assembly, do enact as follows:

1. John Delafield, Henry Wager, B. P. Johnson, William Kelly, John A King, N. B. Kidder, Joel W. Bacon, William Buel, Tallmadge Delafield, Robert J. Swan. and such other persons as shall or may be associated with them for that purpose, are hereby constituted and created a body politic and corporate by the name, style, and description of the "New York State Agricultural College," and the said corporation shall have and enjoy all the corporate rights and privileges enjoyed by an incorporated college in the State of New York, and shall

be subject to the provisions and exercise the powers and duties contained and set forth in the second article of the fifteenth chapter, title 1, of the revised statutes.

2. The farm and grounds belonging and attached to the said college shall consist of not less than 300 acres.

3. The plan of instruction shall embrace the following branches of knowledge: Practical and scientific agriculture, chemistry and its manipulations so far as it may be usefully connected with agriculture, mathematics and mechanics, surveying and engineering, geology and botany, the practical management of the farm, of the dairy, and of the various kinds of livestock; also such other branches of knowledge as may be deemed useful and proper.

4. The persons named in the first section of this act shall be and form the first board of trustees.

5. This act shall take effect immediately.

The trustees named in the act incorporating the New York State Agricultural College very soon organized the college, elected John Delafield president, and appointed a committee on its location. This committee reported in favor of Mr. Delafield's farm known as Oaklands. Arrangements were made to obtain subscriptions to the capital stock of the institution. Little had been accomplished when the sudden death of Mr. Delafield, October 22, 1853, put an end to this enterprise.

The next move was made by the academy at Ovid under the leadership of Amos Brown (1804–1874). He was born at Kensington, N. H., and spent his early boyhood on a farm. He graduated at Dartmouth College in 1832 and then studied at the Andover (Mass.) Theological Seminary. As principal of academies at Fryeburg and Gorham, Me., he showed marked success as a teacher and organizer. Afterwards he was for a time pastor in a Congregational church at Machias, Me. In 1852 he went to Ovid, N. Y., and became principal of the academy there. This school had been chartered in 1826 and when Brown came to it had very few students. He persuaded the trustees

to provide by subscription the salary of one teacher, who was to give instruction in the school in chemistry, agricultural chemistry, and botany, and was to deliver lectures on these and kindred subjects, to which the subscribers with their families were to be admitted free of further charge.

William H. Brewer, who had spent two years in the Yale Scientific School, studying chemistry, agriculture, and other sciences under Professors Silliman and Norton, was appointed under this agreement.

Six teachers were employed and the school prospered greatly. Within the next six years a considerable number of students were prepared for college. Among these students who afterwards achieved notable success as educators were Professors Morris, of Cornell University; Doolittle, of Rutgers College; and Lounsbury, of Yale College; and President Folwell, of the University of Minnesota.

Mr. Brewer gave the winter lectures, which were open to the public. Regarding these he says in a letter to W. T. Hewett, of Cornell University, March 11, 1894 (copy in Office of Experiment Stations):

Until we had suitable rooms in the academy itself they were given in the courthouse, and that large hall was generally filled and often crowded. These lectures were an important factor in bringing the matter of scientific instruction for practical ends prominently before the people roundabout and was a sowing of seed for the growth of the future agricultural college.

The old academy building was soon too small to accommodate the students and Mr. Brown raised money for a larger additional building, dedicated August 1, 1855, with elaborate exercises, including an address on the agricultural college, which for some time Mr. Brown had desired to connect with the academy. Immediately after this Mr. Brewer went to Europe, where he studied chemistry, geology, and botany at several universities, under such men as Bunsen, Liebig, and Wagner, with the understanding that on his return he would be professor of agricultural chemistry at the agricultural college if it came to Ovid. This plan was not carried out.

Brown and his friends secured from the legislature March 31, 1856, a loan of $40,000 of State funds for 21 years, on condition that an equal amount be raised by subscription. It was stipulated that the college should be located in Seneca County and should include a farm of 300 acres. Largely through Brown's efforts $47,000 was subscribed and the trustees purchased 686 acres at Ovid. Brown's opponents prevented his election to the presidency of the new college and he became president of the People's College. For a short time Samuel Cheever served as president of the agricultural college and was succeeded September 23, 1859, by M. R. Patrick, a graduate of West Point Academy.

Provision was made for professors of chemistry, mathematics, philosophy, and astronomy. A course was planned covering three years, divided into two terms from April 15 to November 1 and from December 1 to March 1. It included intellectual and moral philosophy, English language and literature, Constitution of the United States and New York, laws relating to contracts, highways, fences, etc.; natural sciences, mathematics, surveying, drawing, bookkeeping, and construction of roads, bridges, and fences, besides the application of these subjects to agriculture, instruction in veterinary medicine, farm implements, machinery and buildings, and practical exercises in agronomy, horticulture, animal husbandry, and farm engineering.

A college building had been partially erected when the college opened December 5, 1860. Twenty-seven men were in attendance during the winter. The Civil War broke out before the end of the school year and Major Patrick went into the Army. The school was closed and efforts to reopen it in later years did not succeed. Ultimately the State was forced to take over the farm and buildings and they were used as an asylum for the insane.

THE PEOPLE'S COLLEGE

The plan which ultimately resulted in the organization of the People's College was originated by Harrison Howard, a mechanic residing at Lockport, N. Y. He was a member of the organization commonly called the Mechanics' Mutual Protection. In his account of this organization (266) Howard says that after the panic of 1837 there was much discussion regarding measures for solving the labor problem. One result of this condition was the holding of a convention of mechanics at Buffalo, N. Y., July 13, 1843, at which was organized the Right Worthy Mechanics' Grand Mutual Protection, having as its object " to raise the mechanics of America to their true position in society." This was to be attained by (1) " a more general diffusion of the principles and sciences governing mechanics and the arts, to elevate our brethren in their varied capacities and thereby give them the greatest proficiency in their several callings "; (2) by extending to apprentices a good education; (3) by mutual help in sickness and to families and by furnishing employment; and (4) by cultivating a proper understanding between employees and employed. This organization soon established numerous branches in different parts of New York and in several other States.

Previous to this Howard had become interested in education for mechanics and had studied the manual-labor schools through such works as Weld's Report as agent of the Manual Labor School Society in 1832, the Manual Labor Journal, Henry Colman's reports on agriculture and technical schools in Europe, and Woodbridge's Annals of Education. He became convinced that the manual-labor schools were failing because they made labor drudgery. Gradually he formed a plan to "establish mechanical schools for the promulgation of the economic arts similar to those of other professions, with the exception of supporting the institution with the labor of its students " (*265*). To accomplish this it was suggested that there should be a "mechanical society " with branches in each county, with one or more traveling agents to form societies, get subscriptions, etc. As soon as possible a charter should be obtained for a school in which "there should be taught natural philosophy, chemistry, geometry, architecture, drawing, etc., not neglecting any other branches taught in our best colleges and universities." A fund of $100,000 was to be raised by dollar subscriptions from mechanics, of whom there were thought to be about 125,000 in New York.

This plan was submitted first to the local organization of the Mechanics Mutual Protection at Lockport, and afterwards to the State organization in December, 1849.

The plan proposed to combine labor with study and improvement in manual skill with intellectual culture—to have in time a mechanics' institute or seminary in every county or senate district, but in the first effort to establish one central or State college of practical science, wherein our youth, aspiring to efficiency and eminence in life as architects, engineers, or artisans of any sort, might receive a thorough physical and mental training, laboring a part of the day and thus paying at first a part and afterward for a whole of subsistence and teaching (*265*).

This plan attracted the attention of Horace Greeley, who in an editorial in the New York Tribune of May 9, 1850, approved it but said that—

this university should embrace agricultural as well as mechanical instruction and the farmers should be invited to cooperate in founding it. It should have a square mile of land—a part of it very good, or capable of being made so—and this should be made in time the model farm of the State and its nursery and seeds should hold the first rank in the public estimation.

Howard and his followers gladly assented to this proposition, whereupon Greeley actively supported the movement, became a member of the association formed to promote it, and later a trustee of the college which grew out of the movement.

Before his election in 1850 Gov. Washington Hunt was led to indorse this project and in his first message to the legislature he said, " the beneficial effects of an agricultural and mechanical school will not be limited to the individuals who may participate in its privileges." The graduates will become teachers "imparting to those around them the light of their own intelligence."

An organization called the People's College Association was formed at Lockport, August 12, 1851, and after several meetings adopted a prospectus of People's College. This institution was " to minister to the educational wants of the youth of the whole people " by " the dissemination of practical science, including chemistry, geology, mineralogy, and those sciences most immediately and vitally essential to agriculture and the useful arts, though instruction in the classics shall be amply provided." " Every pupil and every teacher shall be required to devote some hours in each of five days in each week to bona fide useful labor in some branch of productive industry." "Agriculture with the various branches of manufactures and the mechanic arts shall be systematically presented, and no student allowed to graduate without examination in agriculture or mechanic arts" (*307*). Women were to be admitted and instruction provided for them in housekeeping, dressmaking, fine needlework, etc.

This prospectus had been drawn up by Greeley and sent to Howard and T. C. Peters for revision. Peters, an influential member of the State agricultural society (its president in 1865) and editor of the Wool Grower, had previously approved the project and later as a member of the legislature did much to secure a charter for the college. A meeting of the association to discuss the prospectus was called at Buffalo, January 15, 1852, when a severe snowstorm prevented the attendance of the members, except Howard. He appointed Greeley and Peters to memorialize the legislature for a charter. At a meeting at Rochester resolutions reported by Greeley and adopted set forth that " it is eminently desirable that a People's College be established in this State subject to the control of no sect or party, wherein productive labor shall be practically honored and inflexibly required of all " (*265*) and that an agent be appointed to get members of the association and subscriptions for the endowment of the college. A promotion committee consisting of persons from every county was appointed.

Ladies, including Lucy Stone, attended at least one meeting of the association in order to make sure that women were to have equal privileges with men in the college. The admission of negroes was also favored. In the charter obtained there is no reference to either of these matters.

Howard was appointed field agent of the association and many meetings were held in different parts of the State. These were attended by many prominent persons, including Henry Ward Beecher and Professor Youmans, at a meeting in Brooklyn. Influential politicians, including W. H. Seward and Martin Van Buren, became members of the association.

A meeting of the association was held at Albany January 12, 1853, and on February 18 of that year the bill for a charter for the college was reported favorably in the assembly by the committee on agriculture of which Mr. Peters was a member (*285*).

The bill as passed April 12, 1853, incorporated " the People's College for the purpose of promoting literature, science, arts, and agriculture." The capital stock was to be $250,000, which might be increased to $500,000. When $50,000 was subscribed and paid the trustees were to locate the college. The faculty was to be chosen as soon as accommodations for at least 100 students were provided.

The courses of instruction were to include the sciences "vitally essential to agriculture and the useful arts," but there was also to be "ample provision for instruction in the classics." "Every student shall be allowed (with the advice and consent of his parents and guardians, and the faculty) to pursue such branches of learning as he may select" (*3*).

On April 20, 1853, trustees of the college were selected and a committee of which Greeley was chairman was appointed to outline a plan of studies and labor, which was discussed at great length. At a later meeting Greeley was appointed to draft an address to the public for circulation throughout the State.

Propaganda in the interest of the college became extremely active. Howard, as field agent, reported November 24, 1853, that during that year he had visited 20 counties, addresses had been delivered by different men in more than 200 places, 25,000 copies of a pamphlet describing the project had been distributed, and the press had been aroused to a lively interest.

Subscriptions to the stock, however, went on slowly and it was not until 1856 that Charles Cook, of Havana (now Montour Falls), Schuyler County, made a proposition to make up the remainder of the $50,000 required for the location of the college. He offered a farm and indicated that he would also make a liberal contribution of money. As a result the college was located at Havana.

In August, 1857, Amos Brown was elected president of the college and Mr. Cook was made chairman of the executive committee and of the building committee. "The financial crisis of 1857 destroyed all hope of raising the necessary funds by popular subscription." For a time the hope of the passage of the land-grant bill introduced in Congress by Mr. Morrill in 1857 and strenuously worked for by Mr. Brown, who went to Washington for that purpose, encouraged the friends of the college, but in this they were disappointed by President Buchanan's veto of this measure. Meanwhile the erection of the college building went on and on September 22, 1858, the corner stone was laid in the presence of an audience variously estimated as including 8,000 to 15,000 people (*309*). Mr. Cook presided and President Brown made "a brief exposition of the plans and purposes of the college." There were also addresses by President Mark Hopkins, of Williams College, and Horace Greeley.

President Brown began making arrangements for a faculty, and building proceeded until about $70,000 had been spent, of which Mr. Cook gave about $56,000. Mr. Cook became a member of the State senate and in April, 1862, the legislature appropriated to the college $10,000 a year for two years, "but on technical grounds the controller refused to pay this sum."

Largely through the efforts of Mr. Cook and President Brown an act giving the Federal land grant to this college was passed by the legislature May 14, 1863. It contained conditions, however, which the college could not meet and this enterprise came to an end. (See p. 173.)

The buildings were used for a time for a masonic school and orphan asylum. In 1872, Elbert W. Cook, a younger brother of Charles Cook, turned over to the Baptist State Convention the main building and 40 acres of land of People's College, together with over $40,000 endowment to establish Cook Academy. The school was chartered with a board of trustees and opened for students September 17, 1873. It has prospered and in 1925 was maintained as a standard secondary school, serving also as a high school for the village of Montour Falls.

VIRGINIA

PLAN FOR PROFESSORSHIP OF AGRICULTURE IN THE UNIVERSITY OF VIRGINIA

As early as 1800 Jefferson had included agriculture in the list of sciences to be taught in the university which he hoped would soon be established in Virginia, and in 1814 his plan for a university included a school of rural economy. When the act for a university was passed in 1818 it was for an institution "wherein all branches of useful science were to be taught." Then Jefferson, as president of the board established under this act to locate the university and provide for its operation, in a report to the legislature, stated that among the objects of higher education is the function "to harmonize and promote the interests of agriculture, manufactures, and commerce."

At a meeting of the Albemarle Agricultural Society, October 7, 1822, on motion of John H. Cocke, resolutions were adopted favoring the establishment of a fund, the income of which would be used to support a professorship of agriculture in the University of Virginia (*397*). The society pledged $1,000 for this purpose and invited the cooperation of the other agricultural societies in the State. Madison, as president of the Albemarle Society, was requested to prepare an address to them, and a committee to solicit donations from individuals was appointed (*386*). This appeal met with very little response, and the professorship of agriculture was not provided for when the university opened in 1825.

MICHIGAN

UNIVERSITY OF MICHIGAN

Article 10 of a constitution framed to create the State of Michigan and ratified by the people November 2, 1835, provided for the appointment of a superintendent of public instruction, directed the legislature to "encourage by all suitable means, the promotion of intellectual, scientific, and agricultural improvements," including a system of common schools and township libraries, and created a perpetual fund for the support of schools and a university from the proceeds of land grants from the United States.

John Davis Pierce was appointed by Governor Mason as the first State superintendent of public instruction and directed to prepare a plan for a system of common schools and a State university. Under his guidance the legislature passed the act of March 18, 1837, establishing the University of Michigan as an integral part of the public-school system of the State. The university was to be divided into

three departments: (1) Literature, science, and arts, including instruction in "practical farming and agriculture"; (2) law; and (3)
medicine. The board of regents was to establish branch schools in
different parts of the State whenever the legislature authorized their
creation. In these branches, in addition to other studies in preparation for the university, there was to be "a department of agriculture
with competent instructors in the theory of the subject, including
vegetable physiology and agricultural chemistry and experimental
farming and agriculture." Eight branches were established between
1838 and 1849, but for lack of funds were short lived. "None of these
attempted to teach agriculture" (*193*).

The university was opened in 1841 with 2 teachers and 6 students.
The number of students speedily increased, and the first graduating class, in 1845, contained 11 members. But it was only after
considerable agitation that the teaching of agriculture was attempted
in the university.

THE STATE AGRICULTURAL SOCIETY AND AGRICULTURAL EDUCATION

"As early as 1844 Jonathan Shearer ably advocated the more thorough education of farmers in the Michigan Farmer" (*193*). In
1849 the State agricultural society was organized (*198*), and that
year State and county agricultural societies listened with interest to
addresses on the need of provision for education directly relating to
the theory and practice of agriculture and began to appeal to the
legislature for funds for this purpose.

The memorial to the legislature explains that "a labor school"
was contemplated, which "should be attached to, or form a branch of,
the State university." The studies should include agriculture, mathematics, accounts, mechanics, natural philosophy, natural sciences
(with applications to agriculture), anatomy and diseases of animals,
entomology, and to some extent engineering, architecture, landscape
gardening, literature, and fine arts. As a result of this memorial the
legislature passed a resolution April 2, 1850, asking Congress to give
Michigan 350,000 acres of land for agricultural schools. The constitutional convention of 1850 put in the revised State constitution
a provision (art. 13, sec. 11) that "The legislature shall encourage
the promotion of intellectual, scientific, and agricultural improvement, and shall as soon as practicable provide for the establishment
of an agricultural school."

> The legislature may appropriate the twenty-two sections of Salt Spring lands
> now unappropriated, or the money arising from the sale of the same, where
> such lands have already been sold, and any land which may hereafter be
> granted or appropriated for such purpose for the support and maintenance of
> such school, and may make the same a branch of the University, for instruction
> in agriculture and the natural sciences connected therewith, and place the same
> under the supervision of the regents of the University.

In 1852 the State agricultural society again appealed to the legislature to establish "a State agricultural college." At the same time
Francis W. Shearman, as State superintendent of public instruction,
declared in favor of an agricultural college which should be "a labor
school" and connected with the State university for the sake of economical management. It should have a botanic garden and "the

studies taught at this college should be of an eminently practical kind."

In the act of March 25, 1850, relative to the normal school at Ypsilanti it was provided that this institution should " give instruction in the mechanic arts and in the arts of husbandry and agricultural chemistry." When this school was established in 1852 it made an effort to give instruction in agriculture.

The question as to how higher education in agriculture should be organized was actively discussed from various angles by the State agricultural society and particularly by its executive committee. John Clough Holmes, a native of Salem, Mass., was secretary of the society and a very influential member. For many years he was active in the agricultural affairs of the State, giving special attention to horticulture. In 1852 he established the Horticultural Gazette, afterward united with the Michigan Farmer. Ira H. Butterfield, grandfather of Kenyon L. Butterfield, president of the Michigan Agricultural College, 1924 to 1928, was a member of the executive committee of the State agricultural society.

The State superintendent of public instruction urged the society to approve the teaching of agriculture at the normal school on the ground that " a concentration of the means afforded by the State for the advancement of agriculture must be considered an object of importance, at all events, for years to come " (*198*). Henry P. Tappan, chancellor of the State university, informed the society that an agricultural school had been organized in the university.

On March 14, 1853, a circular was issued by the regents of the University of Michigan, announcing that a free course of lectures on agricultural science would be given at the University from April 27 to June 28 of that year. The Rev. Charles Fox was announced as the lecturer on " Theoretical and Practical Agriculture." Mr. Fox was an Englishman, educated at Rugby, and rector of the Episcopal church at Grosse Isle, near Detroit. Other lectures were given by Professor Douglass, of the geological department, and by Professor Sager. Mr. Fox published his lectures in 1854 in the form of a text-book. Fox soon thereafter removed to Ann Arbor; he lectured during the winter, and was soon thereafter appointed " Professor of Theoretical and Practical Agriculture." He died after filling the university position less than two years. He worked in harmony with the State Agricultural Society, and was its delegate to a meeting in Washington of the United States Agricultural Society (*198*).

In December, 1852, a resolution was adopted by the State agricultural society favoring an agricultural school as a branch of the university, with a model and experimental farm of not less than 640 acres, but the school and farm "should not be established in immediate proximity to any existing educational institution." This, however, was not wholly satisfactory to Mr. Holmes and other members of the society and the debate went on. January 25, 1854, the executive committee of the society visited the university and called on President Tappan (*198*). He informed them that a course of lectures by Professor Fox (p. 92) was then in progress, "embracing all subjects connected with practical and scientific agriculture," and also that Doctor Douglass in chemistry " dwelt fully upon the application of this science to the mechanic arts and to practical and scientific agriculture." In company with Professor Fox and others the committee visited the museum and listened to a lecture by Professor Douglass on " burning gasses." Then they attended a lecture by

Professor Fox on rotation of crops, drainage, etc. " He also gave a synopsis of his preceding lectures, with all of which we were highly pleased." The committee reported in favor of continuation of these lectures " until our legislature shall provide more liberal and extended facilities for agricultural education." The next day the committee was at the Ypsilanti Normal School, where they listened to a lecture by Professor Fiske on the " organic and inorganic nature of soils and the production of vegetable matter by the mechanical operations of agriculture, including manuring, draining, plowing, and the proper pulverization of the soil. * * * The lecture was delivered in a happy style and comprehensive manner."

On the work at this school the committee reported that " the teaching of agricultural science at this institution will be felt to a greater or less degree in almost every school district throughout our State, but we do not think the information to be derived from these sources is sufficient to constitute the education of a professional and practical farmer." At a meeting of the committee December 12, 1854, the matter of an agricultural school was brought up by Mr. Holmes, as secretary. After full discussion, on motion of S. M. Bartlett, of Monroe, it was resolved " that an agricultural college should be separate from any other institution." This was followed by a memorial to the legislature

praying for an appropriation sufficient to purchase a body of land suitable for an experimental farm and for the erection of suitable buildings for an agricultural school, placing it upon a basis of its own, separate from any other institution of learning, and for the endowment of the same in such manner as shall place it upon an equality with the best colleges of the State (*198*).

A petition to the legislature to take action without delay was widely circulated.

MICHIGAN AGRICULTURAL COLLEGE

Mr. Bartlett was appointed to draft a bill establishing the college and secured the assistance of Isaac P. Christiancy, of Monroe, afterwards chief justice of the State supreme court and United States Senator. The message of Governor Bingham to the legislature January 4, 1855, recommended the establishment of an agricultural school. The bill was passed substantially as drawn by Mr. Christiancy and was approved by the governor February 12, 1855 (*193*). This act established the Agricultural College of the State of Michigan as a separate institution under the supervision of the State board of education, on a large farm near Lansing, and directed that "the chief purpose and design" of the college "shall be to improve and teach the science and practice of agriculture."

The course of instruction in said college shall include the following branches of education, viz: An English and scientific course, natural philosophy, chemistry, botany, animal and vegetable anatomy and physiology, geology, mineralogy, meteorology, entomology, veterinary art, mensuration, leveling and political economy, with bookkeeping and the mechanic arts, which are directly connected with agriculture, and such others as the board of education may from time to time see fit to prescribe.

There shall be two scholastic terms in each year, the first term commencing on the first Wednesday in April and ending on the last Wednesday in October, the second term commencing the first Wednesday in December and ending on the last Wednesday in February.

All students must perform manual labor, which in the period between April and October must occupy at least three hours daily.

Even after the passage of the law establishing and locating the agricultural college the opponents of a separate institution, and particularly the friends and authorities of the State university, did not cease their efforts to prevent the carrying out of this plan. The most comprehensive and ablest statement of the case for the university was made in a paper presented to the executive committee of the State agricultural society, March 10, 1855, by Alexander Winchell (1824–1891), professor of geology, zoology, and botany in the university, and later author of important works on geology (*193*). He stated first his understanding of the reasons for establishing a separate agricultural college, including (1) jealousy of centralization—a bugbear and unwise desire to distribute public institutions to different towns; (2) " fear that a sufficiently technical education would not be furnished by the university"; (3) fear that the State agricultural society would not sufficiently control an agricultural college in the university. His reasons for advocating the connection of the agricultural college with the university may be briefly summarized as follows: The effecting of a great saving in the first outlay and subsequent support for site, buildings, library, museums, and apparatus; a separate college will " necessarily afford instruction somewhat inferior to that offered by the university," because of difficulty in getting equally good professors and equipment; "the particular principles of scientific agriculture constitute properly an inseparable part of university instruction," as is illustrated in the case of medicine and civil engineering; union " would tend to the centralization and reproduction, instead of the dispersion and dissipation, of our educational resources"; time may be saved by attaching the college to the university; and this union " is even now a feasible project."

Mr. Holmes was the leader in presenting the argument in favor of a separate agricultural college. He called attention to what was being done in other States, particularly New York, Massachusetts, Pennsylvania, and Ohio, and laid great stress on the experience of European schools giving instruction in agriculture. He quoted largely from the report of the Massachusetts commission (*175*) appointed in 1850 to consider what was best to do regarding the establishment of agencies for agricultural education in that State. (See p. 78.)

Summing up his argument, Mr. Holmes said:

> So far, then, as we are able to judge from the past experience of others, I think we may safely say that if we expect to meet with success in establishment, continuance, and practical utility of an agricultural school it must stand separate and apart from all other institutions of learning and upon a basis of its own. To teach thoroughly the science and practice of agriculture must be the main object of the institution, for our agricultural interest is paramount to all other interests in this State; therefore these teachings must not be made secondary or subservient to any other object (*193*).

The president and executive committee of the State agricultural society, who under the act establishing the college constituted a committee to select and purchase a farm for the college, secured the farm on which the college is now located. The board of education then undertook the construction of a college hall, boarding hall, and small brick stable, and with the exception of the barn these buildings were completed by May, 1857. Joseph R. Williams was appointed president and director of the farm, together with professors of mathematics, chemistry, English literature, farm economy, horticulture, and an assistant in chemistry. In an announcement of the college issued December 10, 1856, it was stated that "the course of study has been arranged with direct reference to the wants and interests of the agricultural class in our State. * * * Special attention will be given to the theory and practice of agriculture in all its departments and minutiæ." May 11 to 13, 1857, entrance examinations were held and 73 students were admitted. The exercises of dedication took place May 13, 1857, and were recorded in a pamphlet entitled "The Agricultural College of the State of Michigan," Lansing, 1857. They took place "in the presence of the governor, several officers of the State government, and a large concourse of citizens from various parts of the State." Addresses were delivered by H. L. Miller, president of the board of education; Gov. K. S. Bingham, and President Williams. In discussing the course of instruction proposed for this college President Williams said that the farmer should be taught the sciences and their applications to agriculture, including chemistry, veterinary art, entomology, and natural philosophy. On the college farm the student should "test various modes of cultivation, the effect of rotation of crops, the economy of labor-saving implements, the relative qualities of manures, the results of judicious draining, the relative productiveness of seeds, vegetables, and fruits, and the characteristics, uses, and value of various breeds of livestock."

An ode composed for this occasion by I. M. Cravath contains these lines:

> Tiller of the earth!
> Thy day of triumph's come!
> Science now owns thy worth
> And builds with thee her home.

Progress up to this point had been made amid much opposition.

And even after the college was opened efforts were made from time to time to change its status. In 1859, and finally in 1869, bills were introduced in the legislature to connect this college with the university and transfer it to Ann Arbor. In 1859 the board of education recommended the creation of a State board of agriculture, among whose duties would be the general control of the agricultural college. Under the act of 1861 establishing this board it was given power "to confer, for similar or equal attainments, similar degrees or testimonials to those conferred by the University of Michigan."

(For additional statement regarding Michigan Agricultural College see p. 130.)

CONNECTICUT

YALE SCIENTIFIC SCHOOL

In Connecticut the movement for college education relating to agriculture came from the interest of certain scientists at Yale College in the applications of the sciences, particularly chemistry, to the useful arts. Yale College, under the presidency of Timothy Dwight from 1795 to 1817, became active in the teaching of the natural sciences. Dwight, as we have seen, was a member and for some time

president of the New Haven County Agricultural Society and doubt-
less was interested in the application of the sciences to agriculture.
It was under his influence that Benjamin Silliman (1779–1864), a
native of Connecticut and a graduate of Yale in 1796, gave up the
profession of law and was made professor of chemistry and natural
history in 1802.

His son, Benjamin Silliman, jr. (1816–1885), graduated at Yale in
1837 and took much interest in the applications of science to the arts.
As early as 1842 he had private pupils in the sciences, including John
P. Norton. In 1845, when the philosophical department of Yale
College was established, he was made professor of chemistry and
kindred sciences as applied to the arts.

A benefactor proposed to give $5,000 for the endowment of a professorship of
agricultural chemistry and of vegetable and animal physiology, provided that
$20,000 be raised for that purpose. Three professorships were at once estab-
lished, and in 1847 the name of the new department was changed to the department of philosophy and the arts.

That year sufficient interest in agricultural education was aroused
in the Connecticut Legislature to induce the joint standing committee
on education to urge " the importance of scientific instruction in its
relation to agriculture and the useful arts " and to recommend the
establishment of a professorship of agriculture and the arts at Yale
College.

Before this, according to Professor Brewer—

almost as soon as chemistry was taught in the college its applications to agriculture formed a part of the general course of lectures upon chemistry, and
after a time specific lectures on agricultural chemistry are said to have been
delivered. They certainly were delivered by professors outside of the college
course. Prof. B. Silliman, jr., delivered, by invitation, a course of lectures on
agricultural chemistry in the winter of 1845–46 in the city of New Orleans.
Students came for private instruction in chemistry, for its agricultural applications, before the scientific school was founded, even in its rudimentary form.

In 1846 John Pitkin Norton (1822–1852) (fig. 7) was appointed
professor of agricultural chemistry and vegetable and animal physiology. He was born at Albany, N. Y., but moved to Farmington,
Conn., in 1835. As a boy he was not interested in the studies usually
taught in schools, but fortunately one of his teachers took advantage
of his interest in making a collection of minerals to direct his studies
to mineralogy and chemistry. He determined to become a farmer
and his father assented to this on condition that he would be educated
for that business.

From 1838 to 1843 he worked at farming, principally on his
father's farm, finally taking entire charge of a part of this farm.
His winters were spent in studying the sciences and other subjects
at Albany, New York City, Boston, and Yale College. Then he went
abroad to fit himself to give instruction in agricultural chemistry and
studied at Edinburgh in the laboratory of the Agricultural Chemical
Association under James F. W. Johnston, and again in 1846 at
Utrecht, Holland, under Mulder. Meanwhile he was a contributor
to agricultural journals in this country, prepared two papers for the
British Association for the Advancement of Science, and won a prize
offered by the Highland and Agricultural Society of Scotland for the
best analysis of the oat plant. With Doctor Johnston he made many
excursions to the best farming districts of England and Scotland.

Norton preferred to confine his professional work to agricultural chemistry and took up his duties under that title in the fall of 1847. At that time the catalogue of Yale College announced that " Professor Norton will instruct in the applications of science to agriculture and in analytical chemistry." Under the subheading " School of Applied Chemistry " it continued:

Professors Silliman and Norton have opened a laboratory on the college grounds, in connection with their departments, for the purpose of practical instruction in the application of science to the arts and agriculture. Every

FIG. 7.—John Pitkin Norton

facility will be afforded to those who desire to obtain special instruction in general and analytical chemistry and in mineralogy. A course of lectures on the connections of science with agriculture by Professor Norton will commence in January and continue about two months, at the rate of about four lectures in each week. Professor Silliman, jr., will deliver during the summer a course of lectures upon some other department of applied chemistry (99).

Regarding Norton's lectures the memorial to him published in 1853 states:

The deep interest he felt in his subject led him to communicate all the knowledge possible in the lecture hour and by perspicuity of style and skill of arrangement to make it most available to the student. We have the testimony of the best scholars that they attended no lectures where they got more information. The number of scholars the first year was small but it each year increased, till at last the experiment of the school was decided, a new department of professional study in the university was created, and a liberal and scientific pursuit opened to the young men of our country (97).

Norton delivered many addresses before agricultural societies and elsewhere and contributed to scientific and agricultural journals. In 1850 he published the Elements of Scientific Agriculture, originally written as an essay for a prize offered by the New York State Agricultural Society. He also edited Stephen's Farmers' Guide, to which he added notes and an appendix.

His friends at Albany, N. Y., secured his interest in the movement to establish a university there, which it was hoped the State would patronize, especially as an agency for the promotion of agriculture and the sciences related thereto. In the winter of 1851–52 he repeated there the course of lectures given that year at Yale, and this additional work is thought to have contributed to his early death, which occurred the following October.

Norton was succeeded by John Addison Porter, who came from Brown University. In 1856 Professor Porter was transferred to the professorship of organic chemistry in Yale College and his place in the scientific school was taken by Samuel William Johnson, who had studied under Norton and had been assistant in the analytical laboratory, giving special attention to analyses of fertilizers.

Johnson's primary interest was in agricultural research, but through his dealings with his students and through his outside lectures and writings he exerted a broad influence on the movement for agricultural education in this country. His textbooks entitled " How Crops Grow " (1868) and "How Crops Feed" (1870) were very important in the early days of the land-grant colleges and have a considerable permanent value.

The Yale Scientific School was in a difficult financial condition until 1860, when Joseph E. Sheffield, one of whose daughters was the wife of Professor Porter, bought the old medical school building, remodeled and enlarged it for the use of the scientific school, and gave funds which put the school on a permanent foundation.

MARYLAND

THE STATE AGRICULTURAL CHEMIST

As early as 1830 a joint resolution was passed by the Maryland Legislature, proposing an agricultural school for the State. A State geologist made his first report December 29, 1834, and at the session of the legislature in 1847–48 "An act to provide for the appointment of an agricultural chemist for the State" was passed (151). It was made his duty to examine the soils in each county, as well as marl or other vegetable or mineral deposits. He was also to deliver one public lecture in each elective district in each county and a course of lectures at each county town and at some central place in Baltimore County, and to give a copy of his lectures to the clerk of the levy court or tax commissioners for publication if they thought this expedient. This act was amended in 1852 to provide for an assistant chemist and to reduce the number of lectures required in each county to three. James Higgins was the first State agricultural chemist and made reports for several years which contained considerable information on agricultural subjects. It did not prove practicable to fully carry out the law regarding lectures, and there was considerable disappointment because this educational requirement was not adequately fulfilled.

MARYLAND AGRICULTURAL COLLEGE

In 1848 the organization commonly known as the Maryland State Agricultural Society, which had developed out of the Maryland Agricultural Society formed in 1818 "for the Eastern Shore," appointed a committee "to inquire into the propriety of establishing an agricultural school." In 1852 a committee on agricultural education of the society reported in favor of the establishment of a professorship of agricultural chemistry at St. John's College at Annapolis. The next year this recommendation was modified to include professorships of natural history and chemistry and a practical farmer at some existing college. The society needed to own land on which to hold its exhibitions, and it was proposed to secure a farm for this purpose and as the site of an agricultural school and model farm and to do this by getting subscriptions of private funds.

In October, 1854, the society issued an address relative to the proposed college and farm to the citizens of Maryland and contiguous States, in which it was stated that it was proposed to locate the institution within 10 miles of Baltimore.

In December, 1855, Governor Ligon commended the project in his message to the legislature, and January 14, 1856, a committee of the society conferred with the agricultural committees of both houses and asked for an appropriation of $6,000 annually on condition that $50,000 be raised for the college.

March 6, 1856, the legislature passed "An act to establish and endow an agricultural college in the State of Maryland." Funds for the college were to be raised by stock subscriptions and the stockholders were to constitute the corporation, which would elect 22 trustees representing the several counties and the city of Baltimore.

If within two years 2,000 shares were subscribed for, trustees elected, a farm of not less than 50 acres purchased, and the necessary buildings erected thereon, the State was to make an annual grant of $6,000 to the college.

This act was amended in 1858 by reducing the par value of shares of stock to $5 and providing for the election of a trustee from the District of Columbia, and the Eastern and Western Shores of Maryland, and honorary trustees without a vote from other States. Nearly 500 persons made subscriptions within a short time and the institution was organized. A farm of 428 acres in Prince Georges County, within 10 miles of Washington, D. C., the present site of the University of Maryland at College Park, was purchased and the corner stone of the main building was laid August 24, 1858. To carry out the provision of the act of 1856 with reference to the college farm, experiments were begun in 1858 to test the relative value of the different manures offered for sale in Baltimore and Washington as applied to corn, oats, and potatoes. The college building was 120 feet long, 55 feet wide, and 5 stories high, and provided accommodations for 200 students.

The college was opened for students in September, 1859, and within a year 105 students matriculated. Boys were admitted to a preparatory course at 12 years of age and the regular course occupied four years. The subjects in this course in 1861 were Latin, Greek, French, German, English, history, geography, mental and moral philosophy, political economy, mathematics, botany, entomology, and pomology. Daily work in the farm and garden was a part of the course. The first professor of the science of agriculture, including chemistry and its application to the arts, geology, and mineralogy, was George C. Schaffer. He was soon succeeded by Montgomery Johns. In 1861 Townend Glover, who was professor of natural history, botany, and pomology, used his models of fruits and his insect collection in connection with his instruction.

The Civil War prevented the development of the college as had been expected but it continued in operation. The first class of two students, receiving the degree of B. S. and A. B., respectively, was graduated in 1862. In 1865 there were 75 students. The regular course continued to be chiefly classical, but there was a partial or agricultural course, which included English, mathematics, and agricultural science, modern languages being optional.

In 1865 the college was given the income from the Federal land grant, and in 1866 the legislature granted it $45,000, in three annual installments, for the payment of its debts and the purchase of furniture and apparatus but on condition that the State of Maryland be made equal joint owner of all the property of the college. The board of trustees was reduced to 11 members, of whom 4 must be members of the State board of education, 6 residents of Maryland, and 1 of the District of Columbia. The annual State appropriation from 1859 to 1881 was usually $6,000, but it was then withdrawn and that year the college had only 36 students.

Thereafter the institution had a slow growth and it was difficult to get the State to take any large interest in it as long as it remained partly on a private foundation. The annual appropriation of $6,000 was resumed in 1891 and increased to $9,000 in 1895. Moderate appropriations for buildings were occasionally made. In 1914 the legislature passed an act to foreclose the mortgage on the college property held by the State. By this action the State, which already owned a half interest, took over the balance, with the consent of the private stockholders, and thus the college became wholly a public institution. In 1916 its title was changed to Maryland State College of Agriculture, and in 1920 it was combined with other schools in the University of Maryland. Since then it has had a large development and its agricultural work has been greatly strengthened.

PENNSYLVANIA

FARMERS' HIGH SCHOOL (NOW THE PENNSYLVANIA STATE COLLEGE)

As early as 1837 a committee of the Pennsylvania Legislature reported that agriculture "must in some way be interwoven with our system of education" and suggested the establishment of an agricul-

tural school and a pattern farm (*360*). Under the leadership of the
Philadelphia Society for Promoting Agriculture a convention held
at Harrisburg, January 21, 1851, organized the State agricultural
society. During that year a letter from W. D. Brinckle drew the
attention of the society to the desirability of establishing an agricultural school, and on January 18, 1853, the society indorsed the
proposition of Gov. William Bigler for the establishment of such an
institution. A committee appointed to consider the expediency of
creating a school to be called "The Farmers' High School of the
State of Pennsylvania" reported in favor of holding a convention
of delegates from agricultural societies and other friends of agricultural education. This convention met at Harrisburg, March 8, 1853,
unanimously favored the establishment of a school for the education
of farmers, and appointed a committee to appeal to the legislature.
A plan for the school was presented to the State society January
20, 1854, by Frederick Watts, and the matter was put before the
legislature with the result that an act was passed April 13, 1854,
incorporating an institution with that name. This was to be "an
institution for the education of youth in various branches of science,
learning, and practical agriculture as they are connected with each
other." The act provided that the president and vice president of
the Pennsylvania State Agricultural Society and the presidents of
the several county agricultural societies were to be ex-officio members
of and constitute the board of trustees. The principal shall be a good
practical farmer with whatever scientific attainments the board shall
deem necessary. The school was to have a farm of at least 200 acres,
but the income from its property was not to exceed $25,000. The
State Agricultural Society might make an initial appropriation of
$10,000 to the school and other sums annually. This act was found
defective in some respects, particularly because the board of trustees
was too large and unwieldy to function properly.

A few of the trustees met June 13, 1854, and through a committee
decided that the charter should be amended and an appropriation
asked for from the legislature. An address to the people to support
the school and suggest places where it might be located was issued
July 21, 1854.

A substitute act of February 23, 1855, was therefore passed at the
request of the State society, in which the number of trustees was
limited to 13, including the governor, secretary of state, the president of the Pennsylvania State Agricultural Society and the principal
of the school, ex officio, and nine other persons named in the act,
among whom was Frederick Watts. He was chosen to be the first
president of the board. He was a graduate of Dickinson College, had
been the first president of the State agricultural society, and in later
years was United States Commissioner of Agriculture. (See p. 194.)

In 1855 the legislature gave the school $10,000 and the State agri-
cultural society undertook to raise an equal amount. The trustees
considered various propositions for the location of the school and
accepted General Irvin's donation of 200 acres of land in Centre
County at the present site of the Pennsylvania State College, together with $10,000 from the people of that county. They also leased

an adjoining 200 acres with privilege of purchase at $60 an acre, which was afterwards done.

The farm was laid out and orchards planted by William G. Waring. A considerable number of field experiments were also begun. A barn and farmhouse were erected and a school building to cost $55,000 was begun. This building was to be 230 feet long and five stories high, with a wing at each end.

On May 20, 1857, the legislature gave the school $25,000 to be offset by an equal amount already secured by subscription, and an additional $25,000 which might be paid in installments of $1,000 whenever a like sum had been subscribed.

This act also provided that an office should be established at the school for the analysis of soils and manures sent in by citizens and that reports of experiments with plants, soils, and livestock should be sent to at least one paper in each county monthly, or as soon as results were available.

Mr. Waring was appointed general superintendent of the school and professor of horticulture, and professors of mathematics, English literature, and natural science were selected. On February 16, 1859, the school was opened. Doctor Pugh thus describes that event:

Over 100 pupils had engaged places, and 69 were present on the first day of opening; during the session 119 students were entered, though there were never more than about 100 at any one time, owing to the dismission and expulsion of some and the withdrawal of others. The school was opened under innumerable difficulties and disadvantages. The buildings were only partially finished, and in the absence of the intended dining-room and kitchen a board shantee, which could neither be kept warm in cold nor dry in wet and stormy weather, was used to cook and eat in. Proper apartments for museums, laboratories, and recitation rooms were wanting. The farm was yet rough, and the lumber and materials for mason and brick work for the completion of the building, were piled around in shapeless masses on all sides of the latter, rendering it almost impossible to get about it, and presenting a most forlorn aspect to the students, who first entered the college, through the well-tramped mud of the breaking up of the winter frosts (3).

On December 7, 1859, the trustees formally elected Evan Pugh (1828–1864) president of the school (358). He was born at Jordan Bank, Chester County, Pa. At the age of 19 when he was a blacksmith's apprentice, "he bought the residue of his time, supported himself, and studied for a year at a manual labor school at Whitestown [in which was the village of Whitesboro, see p. 35], N. Y., then having fallen heir to a small estate in Oxford, Pa., which included the rather unusual adjunct of an academy, he taught this school for two years. In 1853 he sold his school which had prospered under his management and went abroad for study." At Leipzig, Germany, he met S. W. Johnson, of Connecticut, who became his lifelong friend and correspondent. In 1855 they considered returning to America to jointly establish an agricultural school in Pennsylvania, and when Johnson returned to this country that year he suggested to the trustees of the Pennsylvania State Agricultural Society that Pugh was the best man to place at the head of the school they were fostering. He studied at the universities of Leipzig, Göttingen, and Heidelberg, and in Paris, and received his doctor's degree at Göttingen in 1856.

In 1857 he proposed to J. B. Lawes that he should make at Rothamsted an investigation on the accumulation of free nitrogen by plants.

This proposition was accepted after he had gone to Rothamsted and convinced Lawes of his ability to conduct such an investigation. He worked there for two years and reported his findings, which seemed at that time to settle the question in the negative by confirming the work of Boussingault. Returning home in the fall of 1859 he assumed the duties of the presidency of the Pennsylvania Farmers' High School, and continued to work with great zeal in that office until his untimely death in the midst of a struggle with reference to the retention by this institution of the land-grant fund, a share in which was claimed by a number of other colleges in the State.

In the first catalogue (*343*), issued in 1859, it is stated that—

the object of the Farmers' High School of Pennsylvania is to afford a system of instruction as extensive and thorough as that of the usual course in our best colleges, but to differ from the latter in devoting no time to the study of the ancient languages, and in devoting a correspondingly longer time to scientific instruction; most particularly is it desirable to develop and adopt a system of instruction which shall embrace to the fullest extent possible those departments of all sciences which have a practical or theoretical bearing upon agriculture and agricultural interests.

Labor to the extent of three hours a day was to be combined with study during the college course. The curriculum included in the first year general chemistry, botany, anatomy and physiology, practical agriculture, and the details of management on the college farm; in the second year agricultural chemistry, vegetable anatomy and physiology, zoology and veterinary, geology and practical agriculture, and horticulture; in the third year surveying, veterinary surgery, entomology, agricultural botany, and practical agriculture and pomology; in the fourth year veterinary pharmacy, gardening, agricultural accounts, and farm management. Along with these studies were English language and literature, arithmetic, algebra, geometry, analytical geometry, calculus, and qualitative and quantitative chemical analysis.

In a separate document that year a nursery catalogue was published by the school, containing a list of varieties of orchard and small fruits, decorative plants, shrubs, and flowering plants which the school was prepared to sell (*344*). "One of the objects of the institution is that of disseminating well-tried and valuable subjects of farm and garden culture."

Financial trouble growing out of the advent of the Civil War made it very difficult to secure the means necessary to the continuance of the school, but on April 18, 1861, an act was passed by the legislature granting $49,900 to complete the buildings.

That year the first class of 11 persons was graduated with the degree of bachelor of scientific agriculture. The terms of the charter of the school made it possible under State law to change its name by court order, and May 1, 1862, it became the Agricultural College of Pennsylvania. It continued to have this name until January 26, 1874, when by a similar process it became the Pennsylvania State College.

The changes of the name of this institution represent the growth of the ideas of its managers and the public regarding what its status in the educational system of the State ought to be. Even during Doctor Pugh's life the breadth of its opportunities grew in his mind and he came to see that it should become much more than an agricultural institution. One step in this development is shown in the pamphlet which he prepared for a committee of the board of trustees in 1862, wherein it is set forth that the college should be not only an educational institution in which a wide range of natural sciences and their applications to agriculture, together with agricultural practice, should be taught, but also "an experimental institution" in which the principles of agricultural science should be developed, as well as a "means of protecting the industrial interests of the State, particularly by defending the farmers against frauds in the sale of manures, seeds, plants, and implements" (*337*). The undergraduate course is made more elaborate, particularly as regards the sciences and mathematics, provision is made for graduate courses, while at the same time a "partial scientific and practical course" is arranged for those students "who are incapable of making progress in mathematical studies" and a short "practical course" for those students of limited education who desired to get some benefit from the study of agriculture at the college. (For further account of this college see p. 165.)

GEORGIA

PROFESSORSHIP OF AGRICULTURE IN UNIVERSITY OF GEORGIA

Agricultural instruction at Franklin College of the University of Georgia was provided for in 1854 by the gift of $20,000 from William Terrell, of Hancock County. In a letter to the board of trustees, of July 27, 1854, he praises the form of government of the United States and declares that every patriot should do what he can "to give perpetuity to the compact of these confederated States. Education is doing much for this great object in every department of knowledge except in agriculture," in which "the United States are far behind most of the States of Europe."

The best form of government for a country where a system of agriculture prevails that is constantly tending to impoverish the soil can not long sustain a thrifty population or be able to defend itself. To avoid such a calamity, which there is reason to fear will be our condition at no very distant day, the people of the Southern States must find the means of preserving their lands from destruction by bad tillage, which is so strikingly observable in every part of the country.

To aid in this great enterprise, if you will allow me to call it such, I propose to your honorable body to give to Franklin College bonds of the State to the amount of $20,000, the annual interest of which shall be applied permanently as compensation for a professor whose duty it shall be to deliver in the college a course of lectures during its term on "Agriculture as a science; the practice and improvement of different people; on chemistry and geology, so far as they may be useful in agriculture; on manures, analysis of soils, and on domestic economy, particularly referring to the Southern States"; the lectures to be free.

If this proposition is acceptable to you, I shall ask the privilege of recommending to your consideration for the appointment of the first professor, Dr. Daniel Lee, who has spent 20 years of his life in the study and practice of agriculture, and who will bring to its duties all his skill and a zeal that ought to ensure success (*113*).

The board of trustees gladly accepted Doctor Terrell's gift, established the Terrell professorship of agriculture, and at his suggestion appointed Dr. Daniel Lee, of the State of New York, to fill the first professorship in agriculture, beginning January 15, 1855. It was made his duty "to deliver every year within the college grounds to the students of the college and such other persons as may choose to attend a course of lectures upon the subjects enumerated by the donor."

A committee of the trustees issued an address to the people of Georgia setting forth the need and value of education in the sciences related to agriculture and expressing the hope that Doctor Terrell's example would " induce the State to add to the endowment, until on the foundation of the Terrell professorship a great school of agriculture shall have been erected in which everything that can conduce to its prosperity or elevation, shall be taught both by principle and practice."

Doctor Lee accepted this appointment and held this professorship for about eight years (1854–1862). He was not unknown to the agricultural people of the State (*111*), since he had been editor of the Southern Cultivator since August, 1847, and continued in that position until April, 1859. His home was in western New York and he had received a degree of doctor of medicine. For a time he was associate editor of the Commercial Advertiser at Buffalo and from 1844 was on the staff of the New Genesee Farmer, at Rochester, becoming editor of that journal in February, 1845. He was for many years an active member and for a time corresponding secretary of the New York State Agricultural Society. He was much interested in the sciences related to agriculture, particularly chemistry and geology, and delivered lectures on these subjects in different parts of New York. In 1845 he was a member of the legislature and in 1846 he cooperated with General Harmon in the attempt to establish an agricultural school at Wheatland, Monroe County, N. Y. That summer, in company with 12 students, he made a geological excursion in western New York, and in October gave at the school lectures on agricultural chemistry and geology to which teachers were especially invited. From 1851 to 1853 he was in Washington as collector of agricultural statistics for the agricultural section of the Patent Office, and in 1852 was among the delegates who organized the United States Agricultural Society. He also prepared for publication the first volume of its proceedings.

OHIO

NORTON S. TOWNSHEND AND OHIO AGRICULTURAL COLLEGE

In Ohio the agricultural leader who finally brought about the establishment of a permanent agricultural college was Norton S. Townshend (1815–1895) (*3*). He was born in England but came with his parents to a farm in Avon, Lorain County, Ohio, in 1830. Seven years later he began the study of medicine with R. L. Howard, at Elyria, Ohio, and in 1839 attended the college of Physicians and Surgeons of the University of New York where he received the degree of M. D. in 1840. For a time he was a voluntary assistant in the chemical laboratory of John Torrey of that institution. He then went to Europe to visit hospitals, and returning home in 1841 practiced medicine first at Avon and afterward at Elyria. In 1848 he was a member of the Ohio Legislature and in 1850 of the Ohio Constitutional Convention and then a Member of Congress for one term.

In 1853 he was a senator in the Ohio Legislature where he secured the passage of the act establishing the Ohio Institution for the Education of Feeble Minded Youth, of which he was a trustee for 21 years.

He became deeply impressed with the importance of providing scientific training for young farmers, and in 1854 united with Professors Fairchild and Dascomb of Oberlin College, and John S. Newberry of Cleveland, Ohio, in attempting to establish courses of lectures on agricultural science. For this purpose the Ohio Agricultural College was organized and was in operation one year at Oberlin and two years at Cleveland.

The original announcement of this enterprise stated that its object was " to place within the reach of farmers, both old and young, the means of acquiring a thorough and practical acquaintance with all those branches of science which have direct relations to agriculture " (*3*).

Courses of lectures on the several branches of agricultural science and their applications to soils, manures, field crops, vegetables, fruits, domestic animals, farm implements, rural engineering and architecture, and landscape gardening were to be given during the winter months.

This institution attracted few students, the largest attendance being about 40. When it became evident that it could not be maintained with private funds Doctor Townshend made an unsuccessful appeal to the State board of agriculture to ask the legislature to grant an appropriation of $3,000. The school was therefore abandoned.

For six years from 1858, and again in 1868 and 1869, Doctor Townshend was a member of the State board of agriculture, meantime serving as a medical inspector in the Union Army. He took an active interest in the passage of the land grant act of 1862 and in securing the acceptance of that act by Ohio in 1864. He was elected professor of agriculture in the Iowa Agricultural College in 1869. The next year the Ohio Agricultural and Mechanical College was established at Columbus as the land-grant institution of that State, but was not opened for students until September 17, 1873. Doctor Townshend was a member of the board of trustees of the college at that time, but at the request of the other members he resigned to become professor of agriculture. In this capacity he served until January, 1892, when he was retired as professor emeritus. He continued, however, to lecture on agriculture to students as long as he lived. The institution became Ohio State University in 1878 (*333*). One of the important buildings of its college of agriculture is called Townshend Hall.

WISCONSIN

UNIVERSITY OF WISCONSIN

The University of Wisconsin was foreshadowed when Gov. Henry Dodge of that Territory on October 26, 1836, in his message to the legislature recommended application to Congress for a township of land as a basis of support for one academy. The legislature took no action on this matter, but during this session passed an act to establish at Belmont an institution under the name of Wisconsin University. Nothing was done under this act. In 1837 another act provided for the University of the Territory of Wisconsin, with a board of 21 visitors, including the governor, secretary of the Territory, the judges of the supreme court, and the president of the university as ex officio members.

Congress was asked for $20,000 for buildings and two townships of land. An act of Congress of June 12, 1838, gave the land, which might be located in 72 parcels. But the powers of the board of visitors were merely nominal and they did practically nothing.

Part of this Territory became the State of Wisconsin in 1848, under the enabling act of Congress of August 6, 1846. The State constitution of 1848 contained the following provision:

Provision shall be made by law for the establishment of a State university, at or near the seat of State government, and for connecting with the same from time to time such colleges in different parts of the State as the interests of education may require. The proceeds of all lands that have been or may hereafter be granted by the United States to the State for the support of a university shall be and remain a perpetual fund, to be called the "university fund," the interest of which shall be appropriated to the support of the State university, and no sectarian instruction shall be allowed in such university.

The constitution also made the secretary of state, the treasurer, and the attorney general a board of commissioners for the sale of the school and university lands of the State and for the investment of the proceeds, and they were authorized to accept mortgages, with 7 per cent interest, in lieu of the purchase money. The system of investments pursued was unsatisfactory, and in the end the university obtained from this source a fund of only $150,000. To meet its necessities money was loaned to it by the State, but the interest on the loans reduced the income available for educational purposes, so that by 1866 the university had less than $6,000 for its maintenance.

The State act of incorporation of the University of Wisconsin was passed in 1848. This act put the control of the university in a board of regents, consisting of a president and 12 members. The members were to be chosen by the legislature. They were to elect a chancellor, who should be ex-officio president of the board. The first meeting of the board was held October 7, 1848, but nothing was done toward the organization of the university until January 16, 1849. Madison was selected as the site of the university and 50 acres of land were purchased there. John H. Lathrop, then president of the University of Missouri, was elected chancellor, and he was installed January 16, 1850. There were then few academies in the State where students could be prepared for college, and the regents therefore first established a preparatory school, which was opened in February, 1850. The first college class was formed August 4, 1850, and was instructed by the chancellor and one professor.

The act of incorporation provided for departments or schools of (1) science, literature, and the arts; (2) law; (3) medicine; and (4) "theory and practice of elementary instruction."

In November, 1849, steps were taken to establish the first and fourth departments, the former with six professorships and the latter with a normal professorship. But insufficient funds prevented the carrying out of this plan until 1855–56, and even then the normal instruction consisted of only short courses for two years, after which they were suspended for several years. The first college class of two students was graduated in 1854.

On March 8, 1851, the Wisconsin State Agricultural Society was organized at Madison " to promote and improve the condition of agriculture, horticulture, and the mechanical, manufacturing, and household arts," and held its first fair at Janesville October 1 and 2, 1851 (405). At this fair the chancellor of the university made an address in which he urged farmers to learn the theory as well as the practice of agriculture, and stated that the regents intended to establish a department of the " applications of science to agriculture and the useful arts."

In a conference of the executive committee of the society with a committee of the regents of the university " it was mutually determined that an attempt be made at once to procure the establishment and organization of an agricultural department in our university."

In 1854 a professor of chemistry and natural science was added to the university faculty, and in 1855 Ezra Carr (see p. 42) gave a course of lectures on agricultural chemistry and the application of science to the useful arts. In 1855 the executive committee of the State agricultural society suggested that preliminary steps be taken to establish and endow an agricultural school and in 1857 asked the governor to recommend to the legislature " to make suitable provision for the founding of an agricultural college in connection with an ample experimental farm " and " endow the college with State lands or ask Congress for a special grant of land," such as had been made to railroads. One argument used was that if Wisconsin does not act in this matter agricultural students will go from this State to the Michigan college.

A bill to reorganize the university was introduced in the legislature in 1858, but failed to pass. This proposed eight departments, including agriculture. Financial difficulties and the Civil War crippled the university. After the passage of the Federal land grant act of 1862 there was a struggle in Wisconsin over the disposal of the grant. Finally an act for the reorganization of the university was passed in 1866 and the land grant was given to this institution. This act provided for as broad development of the university as circumstances permitted. Colleges of arts and letters were named in the act and a college of law was soon established by the regents.

Sec. 2. The college of arts shall embrace courses of instruction in the mathematical, physical, and natural sciences, with their applications to the industrial arts, such as agriculture, mechanics, and engineering, mining, and metallurgy, manufactures, architecture, and commerce; in such branches included in the college of letters as shall be necessary to a proper fitness of the pupils for their chosen pursuits, and in military tactics; and as soon as the income of the university will allow, in such order as the wants of the public shall seem to require, the said courses in the sciences and their application to the practical arts shall be expanded into distinct colleges of the university, each with its own faculty and appropriate title.

A professor of agriculture was added to the faculty in 1868, but little was done in this department until after 1881 when W. A. Henry came as professor of botany and agriculture. H. P. Armsby was made professor of agricultural chemistry in 1884, S. M. Babcock succeeding him in 1887. Then Professor Henry organized the short course in agriculture and the dairy school. (See p. 212.) The college of agriculture in the university was not established until 1893.

MASSACHUSETTS

PROPOSAL FOR AGRICULTURAL COLLEGE IN 1825

On September 9, 1825, there appeared in the New England Farmer (vol. 4, p. 54) an article entitled "Massachusetts Agricultural College." This contained an argument and plan for such an institution with a 4-year course for boys over 14 years of age, who had had a common-school education. Professors of agriculture, mechanics, domestic economy, moral philosophy, and books "seem indispensable requisites," this article asserted.

Connected with the college will be a farm, with soil "best adapted to agricultural experiments." The buildings will include "mechanic workshops." The students will have "exercise at agricultural experiments, or at the mechanic arts in workshops two hours each day," together with military tactics and gymnastics. "A regular journal of the results of agricultural experiments * * * will be kept by the students and published semiannually."

An article in the same journal on October 21, 1825, favored "an agricultural professorship with each of the existing colleges," supported by State funds, which should also provide "a farm with suitable buildings and stock." The students would thus not only receive instruction in agriculture but in other branches taught at these colleges, and would form acquaintances among literary men which would promote harmony among people of different occupations. All the students and visitors at the colleges would learn about improvements in agriculture and widely disseminate information about them. Farmers thus educated would in after life "intermingle literary pursuits with manual labor" and be "able to exert a controlling influence in legislative assemblies and other public meetings."

This paper also records a meeting, held in Boston November 8, 1825, "of the friends of the proposed Massachusetts Agricultural College," at which a committee was appointed to solicit funds for the college. This meeting favored a location near Boston, but it became necessary to combat the views of those who, like the writer in the Franklin Post of Greenfield, argued for its location further west, perhaps in connection with an established institution, such as the Deerfield Academy. No practical result came from this effort to establish an agricultural college, but the record of it shows that it aroused some of the important questions which in later times were much debated in connection with the establishment of an agricultural college in Massachusetts.

That year the town of Stockbridge asked the legislature to endow "an institution best calculated to afford instruction to laborious classes in practical arts and sciences." On this matter two committee reports were made in 1826 and a third report in 1827, and a bill was drawn up "to establish the Massachusetts Seminary of Arts and Sciences."[1]

The later movement, which resulted in the establishment of the State agricultural college, centers in two men, Marshall Pinckney

---

[1] See Massachusetts Resolves VI, pp. 379, 381; also House Doc. 5 and Senate Doc. 23 of second session, 1826-27.

Wilder and Edward Hitchcock, under whose leadership the movement took shape and made definite progress.

Mr. Wilder (1798–1886) was born at Rindge, N. H., but soon moved to Sterling, Mass. He was brought up on the farm and at the age of 16 was offered by his father a choice of a college course, a business career, or a farming career. He chose farming, but soon his father's store needed him and he entered on a business career. In 1825 he became a West Indies merchant in Boston and from 1837 was partner in a commission house. For many years he was director in an insurance company and in a bank. In 1839 he was a member of the lower house in the State legislature and in 1850 was president of the State senate. He also served as a member of the governor's council. In 1830 he became a member of the Massachusetts Horticultural Society, which had been organized the year before, and was its president from 1840 for eight years. His activity in horticulture was greatly increased after the purchase of an estate at Dorchester in 1832. At one time he had there 2,500 pear trees of 800 varieties. He made many experiments with fruits and flowers, in connection with which he imported many varieties. He was also a member of the Massachusetts Agricultural Society and for eight years its president.

In 1848 he was one of the signers of a call for a national convention of fruit growers which resulted in the organization of the American Pomological Society, of which he was the first president. He was largely instrumental in the creation of the Massachusetts State board of agriculture and as president of the board issued the call for a convention which formed the United States Agricultural Society, of which he was president from 1852 to 1858.

In 1845 he was one of the incorporators named in the act authorizing the establishment of the Massachusetts Academy of Agriculture to be located in Westborough, Worcester County, but this institution did not come into existence.

In October, 1847, the Hampshire, Franklin, and Hampden Agricultural Society at Northampton voted to "make application to the next legislature for the endowment of an institution in the Connecticut Valley for instruction in the various departments of agricultural science." At the fairs of the agricultural societies in these counties that year Charles Upham Shepard, Massachusetts professor of chemistry and natural history in Amherst College, had made an address which contained a plea for an agricultural school in that region (*187*).

In 1848 Mr. Hubbard, of Sunderland, raised in the legislature the question of the establishment of a State agricultural school or of an agricultural department in one or more existing colleges. That year the legislature also received petitions for an agricultural school in the interior of the State. This resulted in the incorporation of the Massachusetts Agricultural Institute, authorized to hold $50,000 of real and personal estate, for establishing in some town on the banks of the Connecticut River, or in a town immediately adjoining such towns, an agricultural school and experimental farm, the object of which shall be instruction in agricultural science and improvements in all the arts connected with the practice of farming.

EDWARD HITCHCOCK

Edward Hitchcock (1793–1864) was named first in the list of incorporators. He was born in Deerfield, spent his boyhood on a farm, and afterwards worked at carpentry and surveying. He early became a student of nature and theology and a writer. Ill health prevented him from taking a regular college course, though he pursued studies in chemistry and geology under Silliman and in theology at Yale College. He was principal of Deerfield Academy (1815–1818), professor of chemistry and natural history in Amherst College (1821–1844), president and professor of natural theology and geology in that college (1845–1854), and thereafter lecturer in his department until his death. He was State geologist in Massachusetts beginning with 1830, and from 1857 to 1861 in Vermont. He was pastor of a church at Conway (1821–1825), and at that time made a scientific survey of the western counties of the State. He was an original and forceful preacher, and while president of Amherst once preached on the text "Selah," which he interpreted to mean "stop and think." Miss Mary Lyon was for a time a member of his family, and he assisted her in the foundation of Mount Holyoke Seminary (now College) at South Hadley. His breadth of interest in science is shown by the fact that at some time he taught chemistry, botany, mineralogy, geology, zoology, anatomy, physiology, astronomy, natural philosophy, and natural theology. His interest in agriculture was shown in his institution of instruction in that subject at Amherst College and in his connection with the agricultural societies, State board of agriculture, and the movement for agricultural education.

COMMISSION ON AGRICULTURAL EDUCATION

In 1849 Mr. Wilder, in an important address on agricultural education before the Norfolk County Agricultural Society, called attention to the need of an agricultural college in Massachusetts. This address aroused much interest in this subject throughout the State, and on January 8, 1850, Governor Briggs asked the legislature to give favorable consideration to this matter.

This portion of the governor's address was referred to the joint committee on agriculture, together with petitions from the Massachusetts Society for Promoting Agriculture and the Norfolk, Hampden, Middlesex, Worcester, and Essex agricultural societies. This committee reported five resolutions regarding agricultural education which were adopted by the legislature and approved by the governor, May 3, 1850. These resolutions provided for a board of five commissioners to consider broadly the subject of agricultural education in its relation to the State (175).

HITCHCOCK'S REPORT ON EUROPEAN AGRICULTURAL SCHOOLS

Wilder and Hitchcock were among the commissioners appointed under this act. The latter went to Europe, where he made a thorough study of agricultural institutions and prepared an elaborate report on them, with his conclusions regarding their usefulness and suggestions for a system of agricultural education in Massachusetts. This report was widely circulated and had considerable influence on the movement for agricultural education throughout the country. It is, therefore, worth while to consider at least its more important features. It contains brief accounts of 352 schools in different European countries.

The lessons Doctor Hitchcock derived from the European schools were that (1) they usually failed unless they received sufficient aid from the government; (2) agricultural societies are not sufficient agencies for agricultural education; (3) theory must be tested by practice; (4) these schools are doing very much to promote the progress of agriculture; (5) to teach agriculture in primary schools and academies does some good, but is not sufficient; (6) agricultural professorships in colleges and universities are not sufficient because (a) only a few students are attracted by lectures, (b) professional and agricultural students have little sympathy with each other, (c) without such sympathy students would have no pride in the institution and therefore it would not prosper, (d) such professorships, unless numerous, would be insufficient to accomplish the objects desired; (7) agricultural institutions succeed best when started and sustained by joint efforts and contributions of individuals or societies and the government; (8) independent agricultural institutions are essential because (a) scientific and practical agriculture requires broad education in science and knowledge of literature (b) extensive collections, (c) a large number of instructors, and (d) the interests of agriculture are large enough to demand an institution devoted to their promotion; (9) agricultural schools constitute " the most ready and effectual mode of making farmers understand the principles on which good husbandry is founded, and will furnish the most effectual means of introducing among farmers improvements in husbandry "; (10) " agriculture, more than any other art, needs special help "; (11) agriculture in this country is crude compared with that of Europe.

Hitchcock advocated an agricultural school or college of superior class with a 2-year course to give education in the principles and practice of agriculture, including instruction in chemistry, zoology, botany, mineralogy, geology, anatomy and physiology, and veterinary medicine and surgery, with a variety of collections and a " model and experimental farm " of from 100 to 200 acres. Optional courses in ancient and modern languages and higher mathematics should also be given.

The lower schools should prepare for the college.

A State board of agriculture, with a secretary, should be established to look after agricultural interests, including agricultural schools.

On the basis of Doctor Hitchcock's report the commissioners made the following recommendations (175): (1) An appropriation of $20,000, if offset by an equal amount of private funds, to establish a central agricultural college; (2) an incorporated academy having $2,000 for an agricultural department, with lands suitable for experiments, and at least 10 students in agriculture may annually draw $200 from the

State treasury; (3) the establishment of a State department of agriculture, with a board of commissioners and a secretary; (4) increased State aid to agricultural societies; (5) a premium for the best elementary treatise on agriculture suitable for common schools; (6) the formation of a fund for agricultural schools, for charitable purposes, and for education.

In the legislature in 1851 his report was referred to the committee on agriculture, which reported a bill to establish a State board of agriculture, among whose functions might be " to receive, hold in trust, and exercise control over any donations or bequests from private sources made to advance agricultural education." This bill did not pass.

STATE BOARD OF AGRICULTURE

Meanwhile Mr. Wilder had brought about the convention of delegates from the agricultural societies in the State, which resulted in the organization of the voluntary board of agriculture. (See p. 26.) Among the resolutions adopted by that convention March 20, 1851, were those favoring agricultural schools and the use of the proceeds from State public lands for education and charity, with a view to extending aid and encouragement to agricultural education (*163*).

When the board met September 3, 1851, a committee on agricultural education was appointed, of which Mr. Wilder was chairman, and at the meeting held January 14, 1852, the board in defining its objects in its constitution put first " the encouragement of agricultural education." The committee on agricultural education reported that Massachusetts should add to her educational system "institutions for the scientific education of the farmer." The executive committee was then instructed to take this matter to the legislature.

The State board of agriculture was established April 21, 1852, and from time to time considered propositions relating to agricultural education, but did nothing definite with reference to a school until January 16, 1856, when a committee reported in favor of an experimental farm with an agricultural school.

A special committee of which Wilder was a member was appointed to apply to the legislature then in session " for an act authorizing the formation of a board of trustees, capable of holding funds to be applied in establishing an experimental farm and agricultural school connected with it, designed to furnish instruction in every branch of rural economy, theoretical and practical."

MASSACHUSETTS SCHOOL OF AGRICULTURE

As a result the legislature that year passed an act under which Wilder and six other men were made a corporation known as the " Trustees of the Massachusetts School of Agriculture," for the purpose of " holding, maintaining, and conducting an experimental farm and school thereupon, with all needful buildings, library, apparatus, and appurtenances, for the promotion of agricultural and horticultural art within this Commonwealth."

In 1860 the charter of this school was transferred to citizens of Springfield, who undertook to raise $75,000 as a fund for its opening, but the coming of the Civil War prevented consummation of this project. In 1861, however, as the result of petitions in favor of agricultural schools at Springfield, Northampton, and Bernardston the legislature authorized the appointment of three commissioners "to prepare a plan for the establishment of an agricultural school or college" and this commission was continued in 1862, but took no action pending the passage of the Federal land grant act.

The State board of agriculture on April 7, 1858, expressed its approval of Mr. Morrill's Federal land grant bill and in January, 1861, passed resolutions favoring the immediate establishment of "an agricultural school of high grade" and made Mr. Wilder chairman of a committee to cooperate "with any men or body of men who may have any plan for an agricultural school," and bring in a report to the board at its next meeting.

MASSACHUSETTS INSTITUTE OF TECHNOLOGY

Meanwhile, the Massachusetts Institute of Technology had been incorporated as the result of a meeting in Boston, February 18, 1859, at which were present about 40 persons " representing associations of agriculture, horticulture, art, science, and various industrial, educational, and moral interests of the State." Mr. Wilder presided and Louis Agassiz was among the speakers. A committee appointed at this meeting memorialized the legislature on March 1, 1859, with the result that an act was passed in 1861 by which certain persons were made a—

body corporate by the name of the Massachusetts Institute of Technology, for the purpose of instituting and maintaining a society of arts, a museum of arts, and a school of industrial science, and aiding generally, by suitable means, the advancement, development, and practical application of science in connection with arts, agriculture, manufactures, and commerce (163).

MASSACHUSETTS AGRICULTURAL COLLEGE

On February 27, 1863, as the result of a statement by Mr. Wilder regarding the work of the committee appointed in 1861 the board of agriculture decided to appeal to the legislature to devote the land-grant fund principally "to the establishment of an educational institution for the practice and scientific study of agriculture, and for the instruction of youths who intend to follow industrial pursuits, and that the institution should not be immediately connected with any institutions established for other purposes."

The legislature accepted the land grant April 18, 1863, and after much discussion passed the act of April 29, 1863, to establish the Massachusetts Agricultural College, which was to receive the proceeds of the sale of one-tenth of the land scrip for the purchase of a farm and two-thirds of the income of the fund obtained from the sale of the remaining nine-tenths. The other third of the income was granted to the Massachusetts Institute of Technology. There was much discussion regarding the location of the college and persistent efforts to connect it with Amherst, Williams, or Harvard College. Harvard had the strongest argument for this connection in the fact that it already had the Bussey estate, on which it was obligated to establish an agricultural institution. Governor Andrew and Professor Agassiz were much in favor of the union with Harvard. But the legislature held out against such influence and the college was established as a separate and strictly agricultural college. It was located at Amherst but was not opened to students until 1867. (See p. 143.)

VERMONT

ALDEN PARTRIDGE AND NORWICH UNIVERSITY

Alden Partridge (1785–1854) was born at Norwich, Vt., brought up on a farm, studied at Dartmouth College, and graduated at the United States Military Academy in 1806, where he served as professor of mathematics and engineering for 10 years, and then was superintendent (1815–1817). In 1810 he was commissioned captain of engineers and resigned from the Army in 1818. In the early part of 1819 he was the engineer in charge of surveying the northeastern boundary of the United States under the treaty of Ghent, and in 1822 became surveyor general of Vermont. Meanwhile he had become interested in general educational problems and undertook writing and lecturing on these subjects. A volume of his lectures was published in 1825. To carry out his ideas in a practical way he founded in his native town in 1819 the American Literary, Scientific and Military Academy, which was opened for students September 4, 1820. This institution was intended to show how certain defects in the ordinary system of education might be remedied by making it more practical, providing physical training, keeping the students busy, restricting their spending money, providing optional courses, and not prescribing the length of time for completing the course (*375*).

Much stress was laid on mathematics and the sciences relating to engineering, and there was also practical field work in engineering. Chemistry, botany, geology, and mineralogy were taught in the academy, and very likely some of their applications to agriculture were pointed out. Captain Partridge also gave some lectures on agriculture, but probably these were mainly with regard to the relations of this art to commerce and manufactures in a course under the general head of political economy.

In 1825 the academy was transferred to Middletown, Conn., but was brought back to Norwich two years later, and in 1834 was chartered as Norwich University, with Captain Partridge as president. He resigned in 1843 and in 1866 the university was moved to Northfield, Vt.

The history of Captain Partridge and the Norwich University is chiefly interesting to the student of agricultural education because of the views which he held so early regarding a broader and more practical education and the connecting links between him and Senator Morrill. Mr. Morrill's home was at Strafford, about 12 miles from Norwich. His partner in mercantile business from 1831 to 1855, when he went to Congress, was Jedekiah Hyde Harris (1784–1855), who was one of the incorporators of Norwich University in 1834 and a trustee until his death. This makes it quite probable that Mr. Morrill was intimately acquainted with the affairs of Norwich University and Captain Partridge's views on education. It may be that importance should be attached to the statement of Charles A. Plumley, president of the university, that "Alden Partridge used to visit Justin

Morrill when on his tramps and hiking expeditions and discussed with him his educational theories. There are many people now living who believe that the land-grant colleges have Alden Partridge to thank for having inspired Justin S. Morrill."

PARTRIDGE'S MEMORIAL TO CONGRESS FOR FUNDS FOR EDUCATIONAL INSTITUTIONS

Captain Partridge brought his views on education to the attention of Congress in a memorial " praying Congress to adopt measures with a view to the establishment of a general system of education for the benefit of the youth of this Nation." This memorial was read in the House of Representatives January 21, 1841, and laid on the table, but was published as a public document. (H. R. Doc. 69, 26th Cong, 2d sess.) The essential features of his plan are shown in the following summary from this memorial:

Your memorialist will next proceed to propose a plan, which, if carried into practical effect, would establish a national system of education in the United States which would be in perfect accordance with the principles of our republican institutions, and which would supersede the present *anti republic and monastic* system. It is as follows: Let Congress pass a general law, appropriating $40,000,000, to be paid by annual installments, out of the proceeds of the sales of the public lands, for the purposes of education; this money to be distributed among the States, in proportion to their representation on the floor of Congress, in such manner that the smallest States shall have at least one institution, and the largest five. The terms on which the States shall be entitled to receive money to be as follows, viz: That the legislature of each State shall establish (either by establishing new or remodeling old institutions) such number of seminaries as it shall be entitled to, on the following course of instruction.

These institutions should be strictly nonpartisan and nonsectarian.

The course of study should include mathematics, physics, chemistry, natural history, science of government, history, moral and mental philosophy, ancient and modern languages and literature, logic, civil engineering, military science and practice, architecture, and political economy, including agriculture, manufactures, and commerce. There should be physical education, with regular military exercises, including fencing, etc., as a substitute for idleness or useless amusements.

Each student should be allowed to progress as rapidly as possible in his studies, consistent with the thorough understanding of the same, and not be retarded, to be kept in college with such as might have less capacity, or be less studious than himself.

It is believed that this was the first definite proposition made to Congress for the use of the proceeds of the sale of public lands on a large scale for distribution to the States in proportion to their representation in Congress for the endowment of new or old institutions in which there should be a broad curriculum, including the natural and economic sciences with their applications to agriculture, engineering, manufactures, and commerce, as well as military science and practice, in order that American youths might have an education which would make them more efficient farmers, engineers, mechanics, or business men.

ILLINOIS

JONATHAN BALDWIN TURNER'S PLAN FOR INDUSTRIAL UNIVERSITY

In Illinois the movement which ultimately led to the establishment of the University of Illinois, with its college of agriculture, centers in Jonathan Baldwin Turner (1805–1898). He was born at Templeton, Mass., brought up on a farm, studied at Salem Academy, and graduated at Yale College in 1833. He was a professor in Illinois College at Jacksonville from 1833 to 1848, when on account of failing health he returned to the farm, where he gave special attention to horticulture.

Eugene Davenport has made the following interesting statements regarding him (*115*):

As early as 1833 he became interested in the education of the masses. He literally campaigned the State in the interest of the common schools, traversing on horseback hundreds of miles of the then unbroken prairie, to awaken interest in education. It was he who sought industriously for some material to fence the prairies, in order that the people would be able to restrain their animals, live more in communities, and establish schools. [For this purpose he brought to Illinois the Osage orange tree from the Ozark Mountains.]

Professor Turner found time in these days to write upon such subjects as microscopic insects, rotation of crops, and analysis of soils. He was the first man to plant corn by machinery. Almost a giant in stature, as he was in intellect, he toiled tirelessly with his hands by day and used his brain at night to write upon both philosophical and industrial subjects. He was at home with both, but his great interest lay with the masses of people and their activities. He was in touch with the greatest men of his day, both educators and statesmen, a fact well attested by his voluminous correspondence in which, as well as in his public addresses, high ground was taken regarding public questions.

He endeavored to awaken the popular mind to the need of proper books and magazines devoted to the conditions of the working classes. In this connection, he remarked, " It is said that farmers and mechanics do not, and will not, read ; but I say give them the literature and the education suited to their wants and see if it does not reform and improve them as it has reformed and improved their professional brethren. The agricultural classes have no practical congenial literature."

He was a personal friend of Lincoln. They were boys together, and he told me personally, a few years before his death, that he and Lincoln, as young men, had discussed these very matters at intervals between lessons, when he was teaching our great President the elements of mathematics (*115*).

Agricultural societies had been formed in 19 counties in Illinois when, in 1841, the Union Agricultural Society, covering nine counties in the northeastern part of the State, was organized. This society established the Union Agriculturist and Western Prairie Farmer, which in 1843 became the Prairie Farmer. The discussion of plans for agricultural education and information about what was being done in this direction in other States had a place in this journal from its beginning.

In 1848 Turner, in a letter to President Blanchard, of Knox College, proposed that agricultural instruction should be connected with a classical school by adding professors of chemistry and botany and " a professor of what—the green earth," who should purchase and conduct an experimental farm at his own expense. After two years' further consideration of this matter he was ready to propose a much broader and radically different plan. This was apparently first promoted by him at a Pike County teachers' institute and probably also at a public meeting at Griggsville some time in 1850. But its most important and complete promulgation was at a farmers' convention at Granville, November 18, 1851.

This convention had resulted from the action of a group of Illinois farmers, who for some time had been interested in agricultural education. On February 23, 1846, these farmers, who had already been associated in an educational way for two years, met at Lowell,

La Salle County, and formed the Buel Institute and Agricultural Society. A principal feature of this organization was the holding of an annual fair. At the fair in 1851 it was decided to hold a farmers' convention at Granville, Putnam County, in November of that year, "to take into consideration such measures as might be deemed expedient to further the interests of the agricultural community, and particularly to take steps toward the establishment of an agricultural university."

The immediate cause for this meeting was the agitation in the State regarding the disposal of the college and seminary fund of about $150,000 and 72 sections of land, which had accumulated from the sale of the State's public lands and the Federal land grant in accordance with the enabling act of 1818. A considerable number of private colleges thought they ought to share in this fund, but there was strong opposition to its use for this purpose.

This meeting was attended by farmers, mechanics, professional men, and members of both houses of the legislature from various parts of the State. Professor Turner was one of the vice presidents and chairman of the committee on business. This committee brought in resolutions which commended existing institutions "for the education of our brethren engaged in professional, scientific, and literary pursuits," but held that such institutions can not meet the needs of "the industrial classes, including all cultivators of the soil, artisans, mechanics, and merchants," and therefore we should—

take immediate measures for the establishment of a university, in the State of Illinois, expressly to meet those felt wants of each and all the industrial classes of our State; that we recommend the foundation of high schools, lyceums, institutes, etc., in each of our counties, on similar principles, so soon as they may find it practicable so to do (*122*).

After reading these resolutions Professor Turner gave his plan for an industrial university. The next day the convention approved this plan, and voted to seek its publication in the Prairie Farmer and other papers and to distribute 1,000 copies in pamphlet form to State officers, members of the legislature, and others, to secure speakers on this subject in each county, and to have a committee of which Turner was chairman call a convention at Springfield to lay this matter before the legislature at its next session and solicit the governor to bring the matter to the attention of the legislature. An appeal to the people of the State was also provided for.

Turner's plan for an industrial university was based on the presumption that society is made up of two classes, professional and industrial.

All civilized society is, necessarily, divided into two distinct cooperative, not antagonistic, classes: a small class, whose proper business it is to teach the true principles of religion, law, medicine, science, art, and literature; and a much larger class, who are engaged in some form of labor in agriculture, commerce, and the arts (*122*).

The professional class have ample educational institutions and facilities while the industrial class have practically none. The latter, he contended, want and ought to have like facilities "for understanding the true philosophy, the science and the art of their several pursuits (their life business), and of efficiently applying existing knowledge thereto and widening its domain." This want can not be supplied by any of the existing institutions for the professional classes, nor by any incidental appendage attached to them as a mere secondary department.

The industrial class "need a similar system of *liberal education* for their own class, and adapted to their own pursuits; to create for them an INDUSTRIAL LITERATURE, adapted to their professional wants, to raise up for them *teachers* and *lecturers*, for subordinate institutes, and to elevate them, their pursuits, and their posterity to that relative position in human society for which God designed them (*122*).

Since the history of education shows, Turner maintained, that it is necessary to begin with the higher institutions as foundations of knowledge from which supplies of teachers, etc., can be drawn, therefore the first thing needed is a "National institute of science" which it is hoped will be supplied by the Smithsonian Institution at Washington, D. C.

To cooperate with this noble institute, and enable the industrial classes to realize its benefits in practical life, we need a university for the industrial classes in each of the States, with their consequent subordinate institutes, lyceums, and high schools, in each of the counties and towns.

Plan for the State University

There should be connected with such an institution, in this State, a sufficient quantity of land of variable soil and aspect, for all its needful annual experiments and processes in the great interests of agriculture and horticulture.

Buildings of appropriate size and construction for all ordinary and special uses; a complete philosophical, chemical, anatomical, and industrial apparatus; a general cabinet, embracing everything that relates to, illustrates, or facilitates any one of the industrial arts; especially all sorts of animals, birds, reptiles, insects, trees, shrubs, and plants found in this State and adjacent States.

Instruction should be constantly given * * * in all those studies and sciences, of whatever sort, which tend to throw light upon any art or employment, which any student may desire to master, or upon any duty he may be called upon to perform; or which may tend to secure his moral, civil, social, and industrial perfection, as a man (*122*).

Whether a distinct classical department should be added or not would depend on expediency.

To facilitate the increase and practical application and diffusion of knowledge, the professors should conduct, each in his own department, a continued series of *annual experiments* (*122*).

Connected with this institution should be "a botanical and common garden, orchards, and fruit gardens," grounds illustrating landscape gardening, and an experimental farm, with all varieties of domestic animals and useful plants appropriate to the State; suitable buildings, including a repository in which useful implements and machines would be kept and tested; and an industrial library to which the professors should contribute works of their own creation.

The professors should be "men of the most eminent practical ability in their several departments" and should have a fixed tenure of office.

Instruction, by lectures and otherwise, should be given mostly in the colder months of the year, leaving the professors to prosecute their investigations, and the students their necessary labor, either at home or on the premises, during the warmer months.

The institution should be open to all classes of students above a fixed age, and for any length of time, whether three months or seven years, and each taught in those particular branches of art which he wishes to pursue, and to any extent, more or less. And all should pay their tuition and board bills, in whole or in part, either in money or necessary work on the premises—regard being had to the ability of each.

At some convenient season of the year, the commencement, or annual fair of the university, should be holden through a succession of days. On this occasion the doors of the institution, with all its treasures of art and resources of knowledge, should be thrown open to all classes, and as many other objects of agricultural or mechanical skill, gathered from the whole State, as possible, and presented by the people for inspection and premium on the best of each kind; judgment being rendered, in all cases, by a committee wholly disconnected with the institution. On this occasion, all the professors, and as many of the pupils as are sufficiently advanced, should be constantly engaged in lecturing and explaining the divers objects and interests of their departments. In short, this occasion should be made the great annual gala day of the institution, and of all the industrial classes, and all other classes in the State, for the exhibition of their products and their skill and for the vigorous and powerful diffusion of practical knowledge in their ranks, and a more intense enthusiasm in the extension and pursuit (122).

The financial support of this university should come from " the fund given to this State by the General Government " and this fund should be under the control of agents representing the people of the State. A board of trustees of five persons from different parts of the State should be nominated by the governor and confirmed by the senate. They should have authority to add 12 members, and the board thus constituted should have perpetual power to fill vacancies by a two-thirds vote. Members should be subject to impeachment by court proceedings.

This plan for an industrial university was reprinted in whole or in part in the Prairie Farmer for January, 1852, and in many other papers in different parts of the country (including the New York Tribune and Philadelphia North American), as well as in the Report of the Illinois State Board of Agriculture and the United States Patent Office Report for 1851. Gov. Augustus C. French in his message to the legislature in 1852 referred to this matter as worthy of its consideration.

In the Prairie Farmer for March, 1852, Turner proposed a grant of public lands by Congress to each State for the establishment of industrial universities in the following words:

And I am satisfied that if the farmers and their friends will now but exert themselves they can speedily secure for this State and for each State in the Union, an appropriation of public lands adequate to create and endow in the most liberal manner, a general system of industrial education, more glorious in its design and more beneficent in its results than the world has ever seen before.

During the next two years three other conventions were held to promote the adoption of Turner's plan for a university. The Industrial League of the State of Illinois, with Turner as director, was formed to raise funds for disseminating information on this subject. Memorials were presented to the Illinois Legislature asking that the seminary fund be devoted to a single institution maintained by the State and suggesting an appeal to Congress " for an appropriation of public lands for each State in the Union for the appropriate endowment of universities for the liberal education of the industrial classes in their several pursuits."

In 1853 a memorial of this character was also addressed directly to Congress.

At the session of the legislature in 1853 a bill to incorporate the Industrial University of the State of Illinois was tabled, but a bill for the Northern Illinois Agricultural College became a law February 12, 1853. The Illinois State Teachers' Association, organized in December, 1853, was much interested in getting State funds for a normal school. Turner and his associates in the Industrial League endeavored to make this a part of the plan for a university. In 1855 a bill was favorably considered in the legislature, which was to grant funds to Illinois University with the understanding that it would begin with a teachers' seminary and agricultural and mechanical departments. When this bill failed to pass Turner agreed not to oppose the separate organization of a normal school, hoping that later it would become a part of a State university. An act of February 18, 1857, established the Illinois State Normal University. The continuance of the movement which culminated in the establishment of the Illinois Industrial University is described later. (See p. 181.)

THE NATIONAL MOVEMENT FOR EDUCATION RELATING TO AGRICULTURE AND OTHER INDUSTRIES

Attention has already been called to the policy of the National Government with reference to grants of public lands for educational purposes as inaugurated in the ordinance of 1787 relating to the Northwest Territory, and in subsequent legislation relating to various new States. Washington's efforts to get Congress to establish a national university and a board of agriculture have also been mentioned, as well as Elkanah Watson's plan for such a board presented to Congress and discussed there in 1816.

On January 11, 1797, a committee of the House of Representatives, to which Washington's proposal for a board of agriculture had been submitted, reported in favor of establishing at the seat of government a society under Government patronage whose membership would include Congress, judges, the Secretaries of State, Treasury, and War, the Attorney General, and such other persons as might choose to become members under regulations prescribed by the society. This organization was to elect officers and choose a board of agriculture of not more than 30 members. Congress took no action on this proposition.

The Columbian Agricultural Society, formed in the District of Columbia, functioned in some respects as a national society from 1809 to 1812. (See p. 17.)

In 1838, Charles L. Fleischman, a naturalized citizen from Bavaria, and a graduate of the Royal Agricultural School of that country, presented a memorial to Congress in which he described the progress of agricultural education in Europe and urged the establishment in the United States of schools in which instruction would be given in mathematics, surveying, mechanics, natural philosophy, chemistry, zoology, botany, mineralogy, geology, drawing, "the veterinary art and agriculture in all its branches." This memorial was again presented in 1839 with the suggestion that the Smithson fund be used for agricultural schools, which should have experiment farms and workshops. Soon after this Joseph L. Smith and others presented two memorials and a petition, which included a recommendation that the teaching of agriculture and horticulture should be introduced into the elementary and other schools.

Congress made the first appropriation for the promotion of agriculture in 1839 on the recommendation of Henry L. Ellsworth, Commissioner of Patents, who was an active member of the agricultural society in Hartford County, Conn. The Patent Office soon began the publication of articles relating to agricultural education, as well as the diffusion of practical and scientific information on agricultural subjects and the distribution of seeds.

Captain Partridge's memorial to Congress in 1841 for the endowment of institutions for military, scientific, and vocational education in all the States with the proceeds of sales of public lands, has already been mentioned (p. 83).

In 1840 Solon Robinson, agricultural editor of the New York Tribune, and others called a convention which met in Washington in 1841 and organized the Agricultural Society of the United States, which held only one other meeting, May 4–5, 1842. A concrete object of this organization was to secure Smithson's fund " with which to establish a great school and library of agricultural science and experiment, with a garden, that should bear and be worthy of the name of Smithson." H. L. Ellsworth, as chairman of a committee, presented a petition for this purpose to Congress, which was laid on the table. The establishment of the Smithsonian Institution in 1846 turned that fund in other directions.

The Patent Office report for 1845 contains the address to the people of the United States prepared by a committee, of which Mr. Robinson was chairman, at the third national " convention of farmers and silk culturists " held under the auspices of the American Institute of New York. The interest of the convention in agricultural education is shown in the following paragraph from this address:

It is one of the objects of this convention to seek out a way by which the condition and character of the cultivators of the American soil can be elevated and improved. For this purpose we recommend the extensive formations of farmers' clubs, and largely increased reading of agricultural papers and other valuable publications, which have, of late years, been so extensively multiplied for the farmer's use. We also recommend most earnestly to all our common as well as higher schools to adopt, as an unvarying branch of education, subjects calculated to impress upon the minds of the young the necessity of applying science to the cultivation of the earth, and that is the original and most honorable, as well as the most happy and healthy of all employments. We also recommend that an earnest appeal be made to Congress to adopt at once the recommendation of our father, Washington, and establish a "home department" for the encouragement and support of the agricultural interests of our country. In aid of these views we offer the following resolutions:

Resolved, That the American Institute, by whose cooperation this convention was called, be requested to continue their noble efforts in the cause of agricultural movement, by adopting measures to have this matter brought before the next meeting of Congress.

In 1848 a memorial was presented to the United States Senate by John S. Skinner, asking for—

an appropriation, to be applied, under the direction of the State governments * * * to the establishment of institutions for instruction in geology, mineralogy, and vegetable and animal physiology; in civil engineering, as applied to road making, bridge building, and other rural architecture; and also to instruction in the mechanical principles on which depend the labor-saving properties and efficiency of agricultural implements and machinery.

Daniel Lee in the Patent Office report for 1850 advocated that Congress

establish an institution of the scientific grade of West Point Academy and procure such gentlemen as Liebig and Boussingault to serve as teachers until a reasonable number of talented Americans could be prepared to fill professorships in State agricultural colleges.

The report for 1851 contained an article by Harvey Dodge recommending the establishment by Congress of a large agricultural institution, with smaller schools in each State.

THE UNITED STATES AGRICULTURAL SOCIETY

On January 14, 1851, the Massachusetts Board of Agriculture under the influence of Marshall P. Wilder, its president, asked him to correspond with State and other agricultural associations on the expediency of calling a national agricultural convention. In responding to this call the Pennsylvania and Maryland societies declared in favor of making the convention a means for the establishment of a national agricultural society. A call for the convention was issued May 20, 1852, by Wilder, representing the Massachusetts society, and the presidents of associations in Pennsylvania, Maryland, New York, Ohio, Indiana, New Hampshire, Vermont, and Rhode Island. One hundred and fifty-two delegates from 23 States and Territories met at the Smithsonian Institution, Washington, D. C., June 24, 1852. Daniel Webster, "The Marshfield farmer," attracted much attention as a delegate. Mr. Wilder presided, and on motion of Daniel Lee, editor of the Genesee Farmer in New York, but then connected with the Patent Office in Washington, it was voted to form a national agricultural society. A constitution was adopted in which the organization was named the United States Agricultural Society. Going back to the suggestion of the congressional committee in 1797, the society incorporated in its constitution a proposal to form within itself a board of agriculture of three members from each State, Territory, and the District of Columbia.

It shall be the duty of this board to watch the interests of agriculture as they are or may be affected by the legislation of the country; to make such reports, memorials, and recommendations as may advance the cause of agriculture, promote and diffuse agricultural knowledge; to examine, and when necessary, report upon the practicability of establishing agricultural schools, colleges, and model farms; to set for the advantages of agricultural and geological surveys, and to show the importance of the application of science to agriculture; to represent through their reports the relation of American agriculture to that of foreign countries, and endeavor to obtain information from such countries; to point out the advantage of introducing any new staples, seeds, and plants, and obtain, so far as practicable, annual statistical returns of the conditions of agriculture throughout the different States; all which information shall be published by the society, and form part of its transactions (71).

This board never actually came into existence but the society itself acted to a considerable extent in that capacity. Wilder was elected president of the society. He continued in this office six years and actively promoted the work of the society.

The influence of the society was widely extended by the publication of a journal and by the exhibitions held in succeeding years in different States.

At the meeting in 1852 there was a long discussion on a proposal to ask Congress to establish an agricultural department in the Federal Government. Among other objections to this plan was the thought that this new society through its board of agriculture could function sufficiently for the national promotion of agriculture, and this was further brought out in 1853 when the society asked Congress to give it part of the money before appropriated to the Patent Office. A compromise resolution was finally adopted in which Congress was simply asked "to take action upon the subject of agriculture and afford such efficient aid" as they deemed best. This, however, was not altogether satisfactory and after a few months' reflection the society at its meeting February 2, 1853, adopted a resolution favoring a department of agriculture with a cabinet officer at its head and this action was reaffirmed at later meetings.

ILLINOIS MEMORIAL TO CONGRESS FOR LAND GRANT FOR INDUSTRIAL UNIVERSITIES

Turner's plan for industrial universities was brought to the attention of the society by Richard Yates, then a Congressman from Illinois, who had been one of his students. Yates was also interested in the establishment of a Federal department of agriculture and wanted to make Turner its head.

In 1851 and 1852 Turner's plan for an industrial university in each State attracted wide attention throughout the country and this interest was intensified by the adoption of the second Illinois farmers' convention in 1852 of a resolution that Congress be asked to use the proceeds of the sale of public lands to endow educational institutions.

On February 8, 1853, the Governor of Illinois approved resolutions unanimously passed by both houses of the State legislature, asking the support of Congress in the public land educational fund project.

Resolved, by the House of Representatives, the Senate concurring herein, That our Senators in Congress be instructed, and our Representatives be requested, to use their best exertions to procure the passage of a law of Congress donating to each State in the Union an amount of public lands not less in value than five hundred thousand dollars, for the liberal endowment of a system of industrial universities, one in each State in the Union, to cooperate with each other, and with the Smithsonian Institution at Washington, for the more liberal and practical education of our industrial classes and their teachers; a liberal and varied education adapted to the manifold want of a practical and enterprising people, and a provision for such educational facilities being in manifest concurrence with the intimations of the popular will, it urgently demands the united efforts of our national strength.

Resolved, That the governor is hereby authorized to forward a copy of the foregoing resolutions to our Senators and Representatives in Congress, and to the executive and legislature of each of our sister States, inviting them to cooperate with us in this meritorious enterprise.

Horace Greeley, who as already stated (p. 54) was vitally interested in the People's College in New York, commented editorially on these resolutions in the New York Tribune of February 26, 1853:

Here is the principle contended for by the friends of practical education abundantly confirmed, with a plan for its immediate realization. And it is worthy of note that one of the most extensive of the public land (or new)

States proposes a magnificent donation of public lands to each of the States, old as well as new, in furtherance of this idea. Whether that precise form of aid to the project is most judicious and likely to be effective, we will not here consider. Suffice it that the Legislature of Illinois has taken a noble step forward in a most liberal and patriotic spirit, for which its members will be heartily thanked by thousands throughout the Union. We feel that this step has materially hastened the coming of scientific and practical education for all who desire and are willing to work for it. It can not come too soon.

The memorial to Congress from the Illinois Legislature was presented in the House of Representatives at Washington, March 20, 1854, by Elihu B. Washburne and in the Senate by James Shields, where it was referred to the Committee on Public Lands. The breadth of interest in this matter is indicated by a letter from San Francisco, May 11, 1854, to Mr. Washburne, which was written " at the instance of a large assembly of farmers, machinists, and artificers now operating on the Pacific coast " and which commended him for his " vigilant attention " to the Illinois resolutions. Congress, however, took no action on these resolutions.

On April 14, 1854, Richard Yates asked Turner to prepare a bill embodying his plan, which he did, but it was not deemed wise to introduce it at that session. Yates was not reelected and nothing further was done in Congress with this matter during the Presidency of Mr. Pierce. He had shown his opposition to land grants by vetoing in 1854 a bill carrying such a grant for the support of the indigent insane, and it was not probable that he would be favorable to grants for education.

The United States Agricultural Society took no immediate action with reference to the proposal of the Illinois farmers regarding industrial universities. At its meeting in February, 1854, a committee of the Maryland State Agricultural Society called attention to their plan for a national agricultural department, with instructors, library, cabinet, and apparatus, to be attached to the Smithsonian Institution for the study of the science of agriculture. This also involved a proposal for the purchase of the Mount Vernon estate for a national experimental farm. This latter proposal was favored by the United States Society, which appointed a committee to present it to Congress.

This project is probably referred to in the Congressional Globe where it is stated that on December 7, 1853, Mr. Lyon, of New York, gave notice that " he would ask leave to introduce a bill for the establishment of a national agricultural college and experiment farm." No practical result came from this movement.

At the meeting in 1854 the society's interest in agricultural education was further stimulated through an address by Professor Fox, who was then teaching agriculture in the University of Michigan. In 1856 Turner's Illinois organization, which was still seeking a land grant act from Congress, asked the aid of the society for this measure. A difficult situation was thus created in the society, illustrating how such a proposition excited sectional animosities growing out of the existing political situation, whch was finally to result in the Civil War. This was one of the things with which Mr. Morrill had to contend in connection with his first land grant bill and which probably led to the course he pursued in avoiding extended discussion of his bill on the floor of Congress. The South was so predominantly agricultural that on many accounts it would have seemed easy and natural for public sentiment and political leaders there to favor a measure likely to result in Federal grants for agricultural education. But at that time the South felt very strongly that anything was inimical to its interests which even to a slight extent imperiled the doctrine of State rights, considered as a thing absolutely necessary to the maintenance of its social and industrial life.

The committee appointed by the United States Agricultural Society to consider the Illinois proposition brought in majority and minority reports. Professor Henry, of the Smithsonian Institution, and Mr. Byington, of Connecticut, who signed the majority report, favored the proposition, but Mr. DeBow, of Louisiana, in the minority report strongly opposed it. When it became evident that harmony could not be brought about on this proposition the matter was laid over to the next annual meeting, when a favorable resolution was passed with a majority of only three members.

Meanwhile Turner and his associates were active in disseminating information and arousing interest regarding the proposal for Federal endowment of industrial universities. President Cary, of the Farmers College, near Cincinnati, Ohio, brought about the Northwest industrial convention September 13 to 15, 1854, at which a number of States were represented. Turner was unable to go, but the Illinois league was represented by Bronson Murray. A paper by Turner was furnished for the proceedings, an account of which was published in the Prairie Farmer for October, 1854. President Tappan, of the University of Michigan, approved Federal aid for education and on his invitation Turner addressed an educational meeting at Detroit in August, 1856.

Turner, Kennicott, and Murray also had correspondence with influential individuals and societies in Iowa, Minnesota, Oregon, and other States between 1854 and 1857.

When the Presidency of the United States passed to Buchanan in 1857, the friends of Federal land grants for industrial universities decided to bring this matter again to the attention of Congress. On October 7, 1857, Turner wrote Senator Lyman Trumbull, of Illinois, that " in conversation with Senator Douglas on the cars the other day he expressed his opinion that such a grant could be obtained at the next session." Turner followed this up by sending Douglas a copy of the pamphlet on industrial universities, the receipt of which was favorably acknowledged October 12, 1857. Senator Trumbull wrote Turner October 19, 1857, as follows:

Since the receipt of your letter I have reread the pamphlet in regard to industrial universities. The idea is a grand one, if it could be carried out and made practical. I thought I saw in the last Congress an opposition springing up against any further grants of land in the States, but perhaps it was confined to those made to new States, and your project contemplating a grant to all the States might meet with more favor. Several large grants were made last year, but it was done grudgingly. For my own part I have been favorable to an early disposition of the public lands by the General Government, and if they could only be secured to actual settlers, I would be glad to see it divested at once of this great source of patronage and corruption. If some of the old States would take hold of the matter, I think it not unlikely that a grant of lands might be obtained from Congress; but coming from the new States, which have already obtained such large grants for schools and other purposes it would be likely to meet with less favor (114).

Justin S. Morrill, of Vermont, entered the Federal House of Representatives December 4, 1855, and was a delegate to the meeting of the United States Agricultural Society in February, 1856, at which the Illinois plan for a Federal land grant for universities was discussed. On February 28, 1856, Mr. Morrill showed his interest in agricultural education by an unsuccessful attempt to introduce in Congress a resolution that the "Committee on Agriculture be requested to inquire into the expediency of establishing one or more national agricultural schools." Just what happened between this action on his part and the introduction of his land grant bill December 14, 1857, is not positively known.

Mrs. Mary Carriel, Turner's daughter, in her biography of her father, has stated that after his receipt of the letter of October 19, 1857, from Senator Trumbull, " it was decided to send all documents, papers, and pamphlets to Mr. Morrill with the request that he introduce a bill. This at first he was reluctant to do, but after much persuasion he consented."

This is substantially confirmed in a statement which Burt E. Powell, in his Semicentennial History of the University of Illinois, claims was made to him by J. R. Reasoner, of Urbana, Ill., "that at one time he had a long conversation on the subject of the land grant act with Jonathan Turner, who told him that he had taken the matter of having the bill introduced in Congress to Mr. Morrill " (*124*). No evidence has yet been produced to show whether Turner himself corresponded with Mr. Morrill or sent the papers in this case to some Illinois representative for transmission to Morrill.

On the other hand, Mr. Morrill never admitted that he had received such papers, but on the contrary several times publicly stated regarding his college land grant bill that he did not know where he received "the first hint of such a measure." This matter is more fully discussed in a later section dealing with the history of the land grant act of 1862. (See p. 97.)

Part 3. THE MORRILL LAND GRANT ACT OF 1862 AND THE EARLY WORK OF THE LAND-GRANT COLLEGES, 1860–1887

The author and successful promoter of the land grant act of July 2, 1862, was Justin Smith Morrill (fig. 8), then Representative in Congress from Vermont. He was born at Strafford, Vt., April 14, 1810, the eldest son of Nathaniel and Mary (Hunt) Morrill. His father was a blacksmith. His shop was equipped with a trip hammer, grindstone, and blower, and he made axes, hoes, and scythes. Like many mechanics in his time he owned and operated a farm. There Justin, among other things, helped his mother by churning and afterwards acknowledged that he thus learned that perseverance which enabled him to secure the passage of his land grant bill. For when the butter did not come easily his mother made him stick to his task until the desired result was accomplished.

Strafford was a village of about 20 houses and it had only a small red schoolhouse. When he had completed the elementary course there Justin went one term to Thetford Academy and another term to Randolph Academy. At the age of 15 years, after considering further preparation for college, he took the advice of the leading citizen of Strafford, Jedekiah H. Harris, and entered on the career of a merchant because he was told that thus he might be "more sure of an independence." He worked first for six weeks in the store of Royal Hatch at Strafford and then in that of Judge Harris, who paid him $45 for the first year and $75 for the second. When 18 years old he went with a cousin to Portland, Me., where his uncle, Jacob Hunt, resided. After two years in business there he returned to Strafford where he was engaged to sell out the stock of a mercantile firm. In 1834 he accepted a proposition made by Judge Harris and became his partner. Their business expanded until they had four stores, one of them 80 miles away at Derby Line, near Canada. Six years later the firm of Morrill, Young & Co. was formed and by 1848 this and other business undertakings of Morrill had proved so successful that he retired and settled down to manage a small farm.

Meanwhile he was beginning to take another cue from his friend Harris, who was much interested in politics and whose store was long a forum for political discussions. As early as 1844 Morrill was chairman of the Orange County Whig committee; then he became a member of the State committee of that party in 1848 and delegate to its national convention at Baltimore in 1852. Two years later he was elected a Congressman from Vermont by a plurality of only 59 votes, the closeness of the contest being due to a split in the Whig Party caused by the free-soil movement. This led in 1855 to the formation of the Republican Party, which in Vermont was aided by Morrill. It is not within the purpose of this work to follow in detail Mr. Morrill's legislative career, but a brief statement regarding some of his most important services in Congress may serve to show its character.

In the House of Representatives he was first a member of the Committee on Territories and then on agriculture. In 1858 he was

FIG. 8.—Justin S. Morrill

honored with appointment to the great Committee on Ways and Means. In that capacity he became the author of the tariff bill of March 2, 1861, and though he had previously declined the chairmanship of the committee in favor of Thaddeus Stevens, he was raised to that position in 1865. The next year he was elected Senator and served in that body until his death on December 28, 1898.

As chairman of the Committee on Finance he was the author of the tariff bill of 1883. As a member and afterwards chairman of the Committee on Buildings and Grounds he was greatly interested in securing the erection at Washington of suitable public buildings. His greatest achievement in this matter was the passage of his bill for the magnificent building in which the Library of Congress is housed. On this measure Morrill worked for 14 years.

He was distinguished for his great industry as a Member of Congress. He made over 100 formal speeches and through these and by resolutions, petitions, motions, or suggestions he appears in the Congressional Record 2,477 times. His spirit of friendliness and his conciliatory attitude toward his opponents contributed much to his success in both private and public life.

When as a youth he gave up an engagement to teach a district school at $11 a month to enter on a mercantile career he did not lose his interest in education. In 1827 he started a subscription for a town library and thereafter read Blackstone's Commentaries, Milton, Addison, Sam Johnson, Goldsmith, and other standard literature. On his return from Maine to Strafford he formed a debating society. He also wrote anonymously for the papers. He was asked to be a trustee of Norwich University in 1848, but declined because he did not like certain policies of the institution. His marriage in 1851 to Ruth Barrell Swan, daughter of Dr. Caleb Swan, of Easton, Mass., undoubtedly promoted his interest in education since she had been a teacher and was familiar with the educational movements of that time.

Through his life in his early home where mechanic arts was combined with agriculture, through his efforts to increase his own education, through his association with Judge Harris who was vitally interested in Norwich University, and through the intelligent interest of his wife in educational matters Mr. Morrill was prepared to undertake the great educational tasks involved in the formulation and passage of the land grant act of 1862 and the supplementary act of 1890.

THE ORIGIN OF THE MORRILL LAND GRANT BILL

During the first session of the thirty-fourth Congress, on February 28, 1856, Mr. Morrill introduced the following resolution:

That the Committee on Agriculture be requested to inquire into the expediency of establishing one or more national agricultural schools upon the basis of the naval and military schools, in order that one scholar from each congressional district and two from each State at large may receive a scientific and practical education at the public expense.

This resolution was objected to by Mr. Keitt, of South Carolina, and was not received.

Meanwhile Turner's plan for industrial universities was being kept alive. Attention has already been called (p. 92) to the meetings in Washington in 1856 and 1857 when the United States Agricultural Society had this plan under consideration and finally indorsed it by a small majority. Mr. Morrill was a delegate from Vermont to both of these meetings. The published transactions of the society do not show that he took any part in the discussion of Turner's plan.

Marshall P. Wilder presided at both of these meetings. Horace Greeley, trustee of the People's College in New York, was a delegate to the 1856 meeting. It seems probable that Mr. Morrill knew about Turner's proposition even if he took no part in discussing it. Something must have happened which led Mr. Morrill to bring forward a bill differing materially in its purpose from that indicated in his resolution above cited.

MORRILL'S ACCOUNT OF THE CONGRESSIONAL PROCEEDINGS RELATING TO HIS LAND GRANT BILL

In the biography entitled "The Life and Services of Justin Smith Morrill," by William Belmont Parker (*379*), published in 1924, is a copy of a paper prepared by Mr. Morrill, "apparently in 1874," which contains the following statement of his purpose in preparing and introducing the land grant bill:

The idea of obtaining a land grant for the foundation of colleges I think I had formed as early as 1856. I remember to have broached the subject to Hon. William Hebard, the former Member of Congress from the second district, and he observed that such a measure would be all very well, but that of course I could not expect it to pass. Where I obtained the first hint of such a measure, I am wholly unable to say. Such institutions had already been established in other countries and were supported by their governments, but they were confined exclusively to agriculture, and this for our people, with all their industrial aptitudes and ingenious inventions, appeared to me unnecessarily limited. If the purpose was not suggested by the well-known fact of the existence of agricultural schools in Europe it was supported by this fact and especially by constant reflections upon the following points, viz:

First, that the public lands of most value were being rapidly dissipated by donations to merely local and private objects, where one State alone might be benefited at the expense of the property of the Union.

Second, that the very cheapness of our public lands, and the facility of purchase and transfer, tended to a system of bad-farming or strip and waste of the soil, by encouraging short occupancy and a speedy search for new homes, entailing upon the first and older settlements a rapid deterioration of the soil, which would not be likely to be arrested except by more thorough and scientific knowledge of agriculture and by a higher education of those who were devoted to its pursuit.

Third, being myself the son of a hard-handed blacksmith, the most truly honest man I ever knew, who felt his own deprivation of schools (never having spent but six weeks inside of a schoolhouse), I could not overlook mechanics in any measure intended to aid the industrial classes in the procurement of an education that might exalt their usefulness.

Fourth, that most of the existing collegiate institutions and their feeders were based upon the classic plan of teaching those only destined to pursue the so-called learned professions, leaving farmers and mechanics and all those who must win their bread by labor, to the haphazard of being self-taught or not scientifically taught at all, and restricting the number of those who might be supposed to be qualified to fill places of higher consideration in private or public employments to the limited number of the graduates of the literary institutions. The thoroughly educated, being most sure to educate their sons, appeared to be perpetuating a monopoly of education inconsistent with the welfare and complete prosperity of American institutions.

Fifth, that it was apparent, while some localities were possessed of abundant instrumentalities for education, both common and higher, many of the States were deficient and likely so to remain unless aided by the common fund of the proceeds of the public lands, which were held for this purpose more than any other.

Upon these points and some others I had meditated long and had delved in more or less statistical information, convincing to myself but not the most attractive for a public speech, as I have often found such data, indispensable as it is to the basis of most of our legislative measures, less welcome than even very cheap rhetoric interesting to few and entertaining to none. Discreet legislators can not get on without reliable facts.

Certainly I was not clear that I could succeed in carrying through Congress the college land bill, but I had nearly determined to attempt it, and, like a young lover after the engagement, I sought the advice of some of the old members of the House and Senate, who almost uniformly said: "You can try, but of course it is of no use." This would have killed the project if they had not in many instances immediately added, "It would be a grand measure, however, and so far as my vote is concerned you shall have it."

Mr. Morrill also claimed complete authorship of this bill in various statements made in later years. It is hard to believe that Mr. Morrill knew nothing about what was going on in this country with reference to agricultural and technical colleges. Leaving out of account Turner's special efforts to get before Congress his plan for industrial universities, the plans for the People's College and the State Agricultural College in New York, the Michigan Agricultural College, the Farmer's High School in Pennsylvania, Mr. Wilder's efforts to get an agricultural college in Massachusetts, etc., were being published in the agricultural press and in other ways. Petitions were constantly coming to Congress for land grants for agricultural colleges in different States.

Mr. Morrill must have known about Captain Partridge's memorial to Congress in 1841, and he knew about Norwich University. The mere fact that his father was a blacksmith would hardly have been sufficient to have led him to formulate a plan which so closely resembled the People's College and Turner's Industrial University.

Why he did not refer to American sources of information about agricultural and technical schools as having had anything to do with the formulation of his bill is not known. But it would not be creditable to Morrill to suppose that he did not know about them. His statement of his reasons for making the bill is peculiarly personal. It may be true that he personally did draft his bill and he deserves very great credit for its form and for the masterly way in which he brought about its passage. That Morrill's bill was not a copy of a bill given to him by Turner or his friends is indicated by the statement of Turner after the Morrill bill was introduced that it needed amendment (124). Morrill's measure was in fact the culmination of the long movement for agricultural and technical schools, as shown in a previous chapter of this history, and it is altogether likely that Morrill derived the ideas incorporated in the bill from various sources connected with that movement.

THE FIRST COLLEGE LAND GRANT BILL

The first land grant bill was introduced in the House of Representatives by Mr. Morrill, December 14, 1857.

H. R. 2

A bill donating public lands to the several States and Territories which may provide colleges for the benefit of agriculture and the mechanic arts.

Be it enacted by the Senate and House of Representatives of the United State of America in Congress assembled, That there be granted to the several States and Territories, for the purpose hereinafter mentioned 6,340,000 acres of land, to be apportioned to each State a quantity equal to 20,000 acres for each Senator and Representative in Congress to which the States are now respectively entitled, and to each Territory 60,000 acres.

SEC. 2. And be it further enacted, that the land aforesaid, after being surveyed, shall be apportioned to the several States and Territories in sections or subdivisions of sections, not less than one-quarter of a section; and whenever there are public lands in a State of Territory worth $1.25 per acre (the value of said lands to be determined by the Governor of said State or Territory), the quantity to which the State or Territory shall be entitled shall be selected from such lands, and the Secretary of the Interior is hereby directed to issue to those States in which there are no public lands of the value of $1.25 per acre, land scrip to the amount of their distributive shares in acres under the provisions of this act, said scrip to be sold by said States and the proceeds thereof applied to the uses and purposes prescribed in this act, and for no other uses or purposes whatsoever: *Provided*, That in no case shall any State or Territory to which land scrip may thus be issued be allowed to locate the same within the limits of any other State, or of any organized Territory of the United States, but their assignees may thus locate said land scrip upon any of the unappropriated lands of the United States subject to private entry.

SEC. 3. And be it further enacted, that all the expenses of management and superintendence of said lands, previous to their sales, and all expenses incurred in the management and disbursement of the moneys which may be received therefrom, shall be paid by the States to which they may belong out of the treasury of said States, so that the entire proceeds of the sale of said lands shall be applied without any diminution whatever to the purposes hereinafter mentioned.

SEC. 4. And be it further enacted, that all the moneys derived from the sale of the lands aforesaid by the States or Territories to which the lands were apportioned, and from the sale of land scrip hereinbefore provided for, shall be invested in stocks of the United States, or of the States, or some other safe stocks, yielding not less than 5 per cent upon the par value of said stocks; and that the moneys so invested shall constitute a perpetual fund, the capital of which shall remain forever undiminished (except so far as may be provided in section 5 of this act) and the interest of which shall be inviolably appropriated by each State or Territory which may take and claim the benefits of this act, to the endowment, support, and maintenance of at least one college where the leading object shall be, without excluding other scientific or classical studies, to teach such branches of learning as are related to agriculture and the mechanic arts, in such manner as the legislatures of the States and Territories may respectively prescribe, in order to promote the liberal and practical education of the industrial classes in the several pursuits and professions in life.

SEC. 5. And be it further enacted that the grant of land and land scrip hereby authorized shall be made on the following conditions, to which, as well as to the provisions hereinbefore contained, the previous assent of the several States and Territories shall be signified by legislative acts:

First. If any portion of the fund invested, as provided by the foregoing section, or any portion of the interest thereon, shall, by any action or contingency, be diminished or lost, it shall be replaced by the State or Territory to which it belongs, so that the capital of the fund shall remain forever undiminished; and the annual interest shall be regularly applied without diminution to the purposes mentioned in the fourth section of this act, except that a sum, not exceeding 10 per cent upon the amount received by any State or Territory under the provisions of this act, may be expended for the purchase of lands for sites or experimental farms, whenever authorized by the respective legislatures of said States or Territories.

Second. No portion of said fund, nor the interest thereon, shall be applied. directly or indirectly, under any pretense whatever, to the purchase, erection, preservation, or repair of any building or buildings.

Third. Any State or Territory which may take and claim the benefit of the provisions of this act, shall provide, within five years, at least not less than one college, as described in the fourth section of this act, or the grant to such State or Territory shall cease; and said State or Territory shall be bound to pay the United States the amount received of any lands previously sold, and that the title to purchasers under the State or Territory shall be valid.

Fourth. An annual report shall be made regarding the progress of each college, recording any improvements and experiments made, with their cost and results, and such other matters as may be supposed useful—one copy of which shall be transmitted by mail free, by each, to all the other colleges which may be endowed under the provisions of this act, and to the Smithsonian Institution, and the agricultural department of the Patent Office, at Washington.

Under the rules of the House this bill would go to the Committee on Public Lands, but Mr. Morrill made an unsuccessful effort to have it referred to the Committee on Agriculture, of which he was a member.

The bill was received by the Committee on Public Lands December 15 and was printed December 16. It remained in the custody of the committee four months and was then adversely reported April 15, 1858, by Mr. Cobb, of Alabama, the chairman. Mr. Walbridge, of Michigan, presented a minority report of those in favor of the bill.

On April 20, a pending motion to postpone consideration of the bill permitted Mr. Morrill to deliver a speech submitting a substitute bill to be recommitted to the Committee on Public Lands. He recognized that the chief argument against the bill would be that it was unconstitutional. To offset this he pointed out that under the Constitution a way had been found to protect and promote commerce, to educate officers for the Army and Navy, to open up fields for internal trade by immense grants to railroads, to protect literary labor by copyright, and to encourage inventors by patents. But direct encouragement to agriculture had been withheld. This had prevented the improvement of agriculture, with the result that our soils had been widely exhausted through lack of proper treatment and fertilizers, and livestock had suffered greatly from diseases which might have been prevented or cured if trained veterinarians had been available. Farmers had in recent years been aroused to their need of more knowledge relating to their art. The fairs of the agricultural societies are thronged and farm papers have great influence. There is a great demand for field and laboratory experiments. " Let us have such colleges as may rightfully claim the authority of teachers to announce facts and fix laws, and to scatter broadcast that knowledge which will prove useful in building up a great nation." Miners and mechanics should also have the means to acquire culture, skill, and efficiency.

Our present literary colleges need not fear the competition of agricultural colleges, which will move in a different sphere, for the farmers and the mechanics need special schools and appropriate literature as much as those in the so-called learned professions. There should be " a careful, exact, and systematized registration of experiments—such as can only be made at thoroughly scientific institutions." In Germany, Belgium, France, Great Britain, and Russia, agricultural schools, colleges, and experiment stations have been established, very largely with Government aid. Already in our own country some agricultural schools and colleges have been established. In Michigan, for example, such a college is supported by the State. But in general neither the States nor private individuals have been able to maintain such institutions. This bill is needed to give them life and success. Four-fifths of our population are in agricultural and mechanical employments and it is believed that if they could be consulted they would overwhelmingly favor this measure.

The original States have given up their claims to the ownership of the public lands with the understanding that the Federal Government would use them as "a common fund for the use and benefit of all." Many millions of acres have been granted to soldiers, to railroads, and to new States and Territories for schools and universities. These grants, as well as those made in the bill, increase the value of the public lands which the Government has for sale.

Washington and Jefferson favored Government support for a national university and Jackson was liberal in his attitude toward grants of public lands. The act of January 29, 1827, donating lands in Kentucky for an asylum for the deaf and dumb, passed both Senate and House by large majorities, and had the affirmative vote of James Buchanan and James K. Polk, then Members of the House.

Other acts show that "the power of Congress to dispose of the public lands at its discretion is plain, absolute, and unlimited."

The persuasive arguments of precedents; the example of our worthiest rivals in Europe; the rejuvenation of wornout lands; the petitions of farmers everywhere yearning for "a more excellent way"; philanthropy supported by our own highest interests—all these considerations impel us for once to do something for agriculture worthy of its national importance.

The substitute bill offered by Mr. Morrill differed from the original bill by the omission of all reference to the Territories and by the addition of a provision that—

When lands shall be selected from those which have been raised to double the minimum price, in consequence of railroad grants, they shall be computed to the State so selecting at double the quantity.

On April 22, Mr. Morrill's demand for the previous question was granted in the House and this insured a definite vote on the bill. Mr. Cobb was allowed to be heard in opposition to the bill. He cited the adverse report on this bill which he had made as chairman of the Committee on Public Lands. If lands or money can properly be granted for the purpose designated in this bill a principle will be established which may lead to grants for a great variety of purposes. The committee sees no difference between an appropriation in lands or in money. "If the revenue from public lands is destroyed, the deficiency must be met by tax on the people." Congress may properly make grants of land for improvements which will enhance the value of adjacent public lands. It is on this theory that grants for township schools in the new States or Territories have been made. In a few instances Congress has acted contrary to this principle but such precedents should not be followed. To support local institutions does not come within the province of the Federal Government. If this bill passed, the lands thus granted would be put on the market so rapidly that their value would be destroyed.

Mr. Morrill's substitute bill was agreed to as an amendment to the original bill and was passed in the House by a vote of 105 yeas and 100 nays.

In the Senate the bill was referred to the Committee on Public Lands and reported back without recommendation. It then went over to the following session, when under the leadership of Senator Benjamin Wade, of Ohio, it was discussed at great length on February 7, 1859, and finally passed by a vote of 25 to 22.

Among the active opponents of the measure were Senators Clay, of Alabama; Green, of Missouri; Mason, of Virginia; and Jefferson Davis, of Mississippi. Their chief arguments were based on its alleged unconstitutionality. Senator Clay summed these up when he called attention to the fact that only a few Democrats favored the bill, and reproached them because they were going contrary to their professions—

to be advocates of State rights; of a strict construction of the Federal Constitution; opposed to enlarging Federal powers by construction; in favor of the largest liberty of the States consistent with the prohibitions of the Constitution; opposed to the distribution of the proceeds of the public lands; in favor of the principles and sentiments enunciated by General Jackson in his veto of the land-distribution bill; opposed to any intervention by Congress with the domestic affairs of the States; and in suffering them to manage their own internal and local affairs in their own way, subject only to the Constitution.

President Williams, of the Michigan Agricultural College; Cary, of Ohio; Kennicott, of Illinois; Amos Brown, of New York; M. P. Wilder, of Massachusetts; L. C. Byington, of Iowa; D. P. Holloway, of Indiana; W. F. M. Arny, of Kansas; representatives of the Pennsylvania College; and others were in Washington and did much to aid Morrill in securing the passage of the bill by furnishing material for its defense and by soliciting the support of Members of Congress. Evidently the personal canvass was efficient and there were a sufficient number of definitely pledged Congressmen to insure the passage of the bill by a small majority. Turner and his associates in Illinois and elsewhere were active by correspondence. Influence was also brought to bear on President Buchanan in the hope of preventing a veto. Resolutions and petitions from State legislatures, agricultural societies, and other sources came in great numbers from all parts of the United States. It has not been practicable to get a complete list of these but at least 45 have been noted. Mr. Morrill stated in February, 1859, that such papers had come from at least 13 State legislatures.

The greatest hope that President Buchanan would sign the bill lay in his vote in Congress in 1827 in favor of a bill to grant public lands for a deaf and dumb asylum in Kentucky. Such a vote was also an embarrassment to other opponents of Morrill's bill and one of them said frankly that this vote was an error which ought not to be repeated. The President evidently accepted this view of that matter. On February 26, 1859, he returned the Morrill land-grant bill to the House of Representatives with a veto message. His reasons for refusing to sign the bill have been well summarized by Doctor Powell, of the University of Illinois, as follows:

It was extravagant as its effect would be to deprive the almost depleted Treasury of the $5,000,000 which the sale of public lands was expected to produce during the next fiscal year; it was impolitic because it would encourage the States to rely upon the Federal Government for aid to which they were not entitled; it was injurious to the new States since it would force down the value of land scrip and make it possible for speculators to obtain large tracts within their borders; it was insufficient to assure the promotion of industrial education because, although the State legislatures were required to stipulate that they would apply the land to the purpose for which it had been granted, there was no power in the Federal Government to compel them to execute their trust; it was unjust since it would interfere with and probably injure colleges already established and sustained by their own effort; it was unconstitutional since there was no grant of power to the Federal Government to expend public money or public lands for the benefit of the people in the various States (124).

After the President's message had been delivered, Mr. Morrill in a brief but forceful speech asked the reconsideration of the bill.

When the final vote was taken, 105 Representatives voted for and 94 against this measure, and thus the veto was not overruled. The bill received, however, the same number of favorable votes as in its first test in the House.

THE SECOND COLLEGE LAND GRANT BILL

Though greatly disappointed at the unsuccessful outcome of the great and widespread efforts in behalf of the first college land grant bill, the friends of this measure did not lose all hope of the final passage of a similar measure.

A presidential election was approaching and its result might turn the scale in favor of such a Federal grant for education. The United States Agricultural Society discussed the matter at its meeting in Washington in January, 1860, but an attack by one of its members on President Buchanan prevented favorable action. In Illinois the State agricultural and horticultural societies joined in calling a meeting at Bloomington, June 27, 1860, to which representatives of all agricultural, horticultural, and mechanical associations in the State and all individuals interested in agricultural education were invited. The following resolution prepared by a committee of which Turner was chairman was adopted:

Resolved, That this convention hereby request the executive committees of our State agricultural and horticultural societies to appoint a committee, whose duty it shall be, First, to memorialize Congress to grant to each of the States of the Union such aid as was contemplated in the bill called the "Morrill bill," which passed the House and Senate at a recent session; Second, to memorialize and urge upon our State legislature, to renew their petition to Congress, for the same substantial aid; Third, to urge the establishment by the State legislature of a school or department of agriculture, under the general direction of a board appointed conjointly by the same State agricultural and horticultural societies for this purpose; Fourth, to provide courses of lectures on agriculture and horticulture, similar to the course at the last session in Yale College, to be delivered at such times and places as they shall deem most fit, and to take measures needful to secure these results (*124*).

Believing that Abraham Lincoln would be nominated for President of the United States, Turner asked him to support the college land grant bill. Lincoln is said to have replied: "If I am elected I will sign your bill for State universities." Stephen A. Douglas also assured him: "If I am elected, I will sign your bill." He followed this up after his defeat by writing Turner in June, 1861, for his plan for an industrial university and its history in order that he might introduce a land grant bill at the next session of Congress. His death prevented even a reply to this friendly message.

When Congress met in December, 1861, Mr. Morrill gave notice that he would again introduce a college land grant bill and this was done December 16. The bill was referred to the Committee on Public Lands, of which Mr. Potter, of Wisconsin, was chairman. This was a very different committee from the one which had considered the previous bill. Two elections had changed its complexion completely and its personnel had been materially reduced by the withdrawal of one of the national parties from Congress. A new party had also come into power. This committee nevertheless was adverse to Federal grants for vocational education, especially since this proposition had not been received favorably by most of the State legislatures. Mr. Potter was instructed to report the bill adversely, but in so doing on May 29, 1862, gave no reasons for this action. Mr. Morrill did not attempt to have the bill considered in the House at this time because a similar bill introduced in the Senate had been favorably reported there. He asked leave on June 5 to print a substitute bill, but this was refused on objection by Mr. Holman, of Indiana.

Meanwhile Senator Wade, of Ohio, probably by arrangement with Mr. Morrill, had introduced a similar bill in the Senate on May 2, 1862. This was referred to the Committee on Public Lands of which Senator Harlan, of Iowa, a friend of this measure, was chairman. It was favorably reported May 16, with two amendments. Opposition then centered in Senators Lane, of Kansas, and Wilkinson, of Minnesota.

Senator Lane on May 21 offered an amendment which would have prevented purchasers of the land scrip granted to the States under this bill from locating any lands within the States, though they could locate it in the Territories. He supported this amendment in a long speech in which he claimed that the language used in the original bill would throw into the hands of nonresidents every foot of valuable public lands in Kansas before the State could select her school lands or get her share of railroad lands.

Mr. Pomeroy, of Kansas, also favored this amendment because Kansas had not received the usual amount of public lands.

The effect of the land grants in this bill on the new Western States was further discussed on May 22, 24, 28, and 30, and on June 10. In a statement made May 24, Mr. Harlan showed that Congress had been very liberal in making large grants of lands for various public purposes to the " land States."

Nevertheless the feeling among Senators from the new States that too much land granted under this bill might be located in single States led to the introduction by Senator Lane of an amendment that not more than 1,000,000 acres should be located in any one of the States; that no such locations should be made before one year from the passage of this act.

This amendment was supported by Mr. Wilkinson, who expressed his belief that without it the bill would interfere with the operation of the homestead act which had just passed Congress, and that speculators would get the scrip and locate the best lands, against the interests of soldiers serving at this time in the Union Army.

So much sentiment in favor of this amendment was aroused in the Senate that Mr. Wade, who was in charge of the bill, said on May 30 that he would not oppose it. There was also considerable reluctance to bring this measure to a vote, and it was not until June 10 that Senator Wade was able to secure its final consideration. The amendment above cited was adopted, together with another offered by Senator Collamer, of Vermont, that—

No State shall be entitled to the benefits of this act unless it shall express its acceptance thereof by its legislature within two years from the date of its approval by the President.

An amendment offered by Senator Pomeroy, of Kansas, that all scrip issued should bear upon its face a statement that it was issued under this law, that no assignment of the scrip should be valid unless it was annexed to the face of the scrip, and furthermore that no one person should receive an assignment of more than 640 acres, was adopted by a vote of 20 to 19 and then reconsidered. Discussion having died down Senator Wade forced a vote, which was 32 to 7 in favor of the amended bill.

Mr. Morrill, now one of the leaders in the House, called up the Senate bill June 17, when Messrs. Potter and Holman tried to have it referred to the Committee on Public Lands or to postpone the vote. But Morrill would not consent and finally secured a vote. It was passed by a vote of 90 to 25 and the long struggle to obtain this land grant for colleges was over. President Lincoln signed the bill July 2, 1862, having already on May 15 approved the bill creating the United States Department of Agriculture. This was also the day when the Army of the Potomac began its retreat after the disastrous battle of Malvern Hill, and the fortune of war seemed to be against the preservation of the Union. The act of 1862 was practically the same measure as the bill of 1857. The important differences were the omission of the Territories, the increase of the land grant for each member of Congress from 20,000 to 30,000 acres, the exclusion of the benefits to States while in the act of rebellion, and the requirement to teach military tactics.

Amendments to the act of July 2, 1862, were made by Congress in the act of March 3, 1883, which permitted States having no State stocks to invest the proceeds of the sale of the land scrip "in any other manner after the legislatures of such States shall have assented thereto," and engaged that this land-grant fund shall yield not less than 5 per cent and that the principal shall forever remain unimpaired, and in the act of July 23, 1866, extending the limit of the time of acceptance of land grant to three years from the passage of this act, and the establishment of the colleges to five years after the filing of the acceptance in the General Land Office, and providing that when any Territory shall become a State, it shall be entitled to the benefits of this act by expressing acceptance within three years after its admission to the Union, and providing a college or colleges within five years after such acceptance, and providing further that any State which has heretofore accepted the act shall have five years to provide at least one college after the time for doing this named in the act of July 2, 1862, shall have expired.

THE INTENT OF THE COLLEGE LAND GRANT ACT

Questions as to the real intent of the Morrill Land Grant Act arose as soon as it was passed and these questions continued to arise from time to time. William H. Brewer, who in 1864 became professor of agriculture in the Sheffield Scientific School, made the following statement regarding these problems (*12*):

In Connecticut many questions arose immediately as to the details of th intent of the act. The same (or similar) questions arose in other States both those with colleges already formed, and in those States building nev colleges and universities, according to the conditions existing in the severa States. Many plans were proposed both as to the disposal of the funds an the methods of instruction to be given. Suggestions, theories, and scheme were proposed by educators, enthusiasts, cranks, associations, legislators, etc as to how the grant might be used, how it could be used, how it ought to be used, what was the *intent* of the law, what was the *spirit* of the law in which it should be interpreted, and what the *letter* of the law which must be obeyed.

In nearly every State there were many propositions as to how this gift could be used to the best advantage. Some advisers would have a purely agricultural school and separate purely technical school. Others advocated that the two should be combined.

Some advocates would have manual labor schools and trade schools united, or separate. Some would use the income from the grant in one large college of high grade; others, divide the fund and make several lesser institutions of lower scholastic grade. Some would divide it still more widely and appoint special professors in several schools of the State. Some would apply it largely to lectures before mechanic associations and agricultural societies, and others would devote a considerable portion of it to itinerant lecturers.

One eminent writer on agricultural matters would have it used for the wider dissemination of the regular agricultural newspapers, and so on through schemes too numerous to enumerate.

For an interpretation of the law it is natural to turn first to its author. In the elaborate speech which Mr. Morrill made when his bill was before the House of Representatives in 1858 he frequently uses the term "colleges" to denote the institutions to receive the benefits of the bill. The grade of these institutions is indicated in the following statement from him:

Let us have such colleges as may rightfully claim the authority of teachers to announce facts and fix laws, and to scatter broadcast that knowledge which will be useful in building up a great nation.

He mentions the Michigan Agricultural College and evidently considers it in the class of institutions to be benefited by his bill. That he expects such institutions to provide distinctive instruction is clear from his statement that agricultural colleges and "literary" colleges "move in separate spheres."

He clearly expects the land-grant colleges to advance knowledge by experimental inquiries, for—

We need a careful, exact, and systematized registration of experiments, such as can be made at thoroughly scientific institutions and such as will not be made elsewhere.

This is followed by a considerable list of the agricultural experiments needed. These institutions may not be able to discover means for controlling cotton or wheat insects but " some resulting improvements may safely be predicted upon the labors of 32 or more institutions actually engaged in scientific agriculture." As regards the education of mechanics " let us furnish the means for that arm to acquire culture, skill, and efficiency."

In 1867 Mr. Morrill was invited to visit the Sheffield Scientific School in order that the faculty there might " talk with him regarding his intent in planning the bill, and his interpretation of the law." The following summary of the conference there is taken from notes made at that time by Professor Brewer (*12*). Professors Brush, Lyman, and Brewer met Mr. Morrill at the residence of Professor Gilman (afterwards president of Johns Hopkins University) and " talked over the whole matter," and the next day Professor Brewer had further conversation with him.

Mr. Morrill wished the bill to be broad enough so that the several States might use it to the best advantage. For this a wide latitude of use was necessary. The general wants and local conditions were very different in the different States and for the best use of this fund there must be much variety allowed in the *details*, although all the colleges should be the same in spirit and essentially of the same grade, that is—*colleges*, in which science and not classics should be the leading idea.

He did not intend them to be *agricultural* schools. The title of the bill was not his, and was not a happy one. A clerk was responsible for the title.

He expected the schools to be schools of science rather than classical colleges; that the schools be, in fact, *colleges* and not institutions of lower grade, not mere academies or high schools. We asked upon this matter in considerable detail because there was much talk in some of the States about dividing the sum for lower grade schools.

He said that the bill was *purposely and carefully* planned so that the *old* colleges might use this as an aid in expanding in the direction to give them more science teaching or that *new* colleges might be organized as the conditions and needs in the several States might demand. There were classical colleges enough. More science was needed in every State.

But in all he wished as a prominent feature the "useful sciences" be taught and that where the natural influences of the studies might have less tendency to draw the students into purely literary and professional pursuits and away from the business pursuits. He "thought that at least one college in every State should teach military science."

As to farms, they might or might not be attached. He did not consider them essential or he would have made it a condition as he had the condition of the teaching of the sciences. But he assumed that many, perhaps most, of the institutions would find a farm desirable. He himself thought it was a desirable aid in agricultural instruction but he would not make it imperative. He had in his mind to aid science instruction, scientific schools, education for business pursuits. He praised our plan highly (the Sheffield Scientific School), and said over and over again it was working on a line he greatly commended, a line which complied with the letter, and the spirit, and the intent of the law.

I inquired again specifically about the manual labor question then so much discussed. He thought it might be well for physical exercise, thought many schools would adopt it, but he was not sure enough of its real value as an educational factor to make it compulsory, etc., etc., etc. (*12*).

At the Massachusetts Agricultural College June 21, 1887, in connection with the celebration of the twenty-fifth anniversary of the passage of the land-grant act, Mr. Morrill spoke as follows (*170*):

The land-grant colleges were founded on the idea that a higher and broader education should be placed in every State within the reach of those whose destiny assigned them to, or may have the courage to choose industrial vocations where the wealth of nations is produced; where advanced civilization unfolds its comforts and where a much larger number of its people need wider educational advantages and impatiently await their possession.

The design was to open the door to a liberal education for this large class at a cheaper cost from being close at hand and to tempt them by offering not only sound literary instruction but something more applicable to the productive employments of life. It would be a mistake to suppose it was intended that every student should become either a farmer or a mechanic, when the design comprehended not only instruction for those who hold the plow or follow a trade, but such instruction as any person might need—with "the world all before them where to choose"—and without the exclusion of those who might prefer to adhere to the classics. Milton in his famous discourse on education gives a definition of what an education ought to be, which would seem to very completely cover all that was proposed by the land-grant colleges; and Milton lacked nothing of ancient learning, nor did he suffer his culture to hide his statement of republicanism. * * * It is a gratification to find that the largest endowment in any State has been husbanded most successfully, having fallen into very astute and worthy hands, and has served, with other large bounties, to build up the most complete and prosperous of these institutions.

Speaking in behalf of the University of Vermont and State Agricultural College before the Vermont Legislature at Montpelier in 1888, Mr. Morrill said (*377*):

Only the interest from the land-grant fund can be expended, and that must be expended, first, without excluding other scientific and classical studies, for teaching such branches of learning as are related to agriculture and the mechanic arts—the latter as absolutely as the former. Obviously not manual, but intellectual instruction was the paramount object. It was not provided that agricultural labor in the field should be practically taught, any more than that the mechanical trade of a carpenter or blacksmith should be taught. Secondly, it was a liberal education that was proposed. Classical studies were not to be excluded, and, therefore, must be included. The act of 1862 proposed a system of broad education by colleges, not limited to a superficial and dwarfed training, such as might be had at an industrial school, nor a mere manual training, such as might be supplied by a foreman of a workshop, or by a foreman of an experimental farm. If any would have only a school with equal scraps of labor and of instruction, or something other than a college, they would not obey the national law.

*   *   *   *   *   *   *

Whatever else might be done under the national law of 1862, scientific and classical studies, as already stated, were not to be excluded, were, therefore, to be preserved, and this is set forth at the very starting point, but the national bounty act brought to the front "branches of learning related to agriculture and the mechanic arts"—learning in the broad fields of the practical sciences, and none are broader than those related to agriculture. The useful was to have greater prominence in the eyes of students, as it will have in all their after-life, and not stand unequal and shamefaced even in the presence of ancient literature. Military tactics were also to be included, not merely as a healthful physical exercise, but as a valuable, incidental acquirement for all young men, with patriotic blood in their veins, and upon whom our country must rely as ever ready to stand among its future guardians and defenders.

The fundamental idea was to offer an opportunity in every State for a liberal and larger education to larger numbers, not merely to those destined to sedentary professions, but to those much needing higher instruction for the world's business, for the industrial pursuits and professions of life.

There has been much discussion even down to recent times as to whether "mechanic arts," as used in this act, meant engineering, trade education, or mechanic arts as applied to agriculture only. R. A. Pearson, president of the Iowa State College, summed up this matter very well in a paper read at the annual meeting of the Association of American Agricultural Colleges and Experiment Stations in 1915 (57). He points out that in the dictionaries in use when the land-grant bill was being considered "mechanic arts" is a broader term than engineering or trades:

The Encyclopedia Britannica of 1857 states that mechanics, applicate or applied, is a term which, strictly speaking, includes all applications of the principles of abstract mechanics to human art. The article continues "thus have theory and practice in all ages promoted each other's advance; and the greatest obstacle to the advancement of both has always been a popular and scholastic fallacy that they are inconsistent." Happily that fallacy is now disappearing and its occurrence in the writings of any author may be considered as a mark either of ignorance or of the inconsiderate use of words.

In the Federal acts of 1883, 1890, and 1907 Congress had not indicated any objection to the high-grade work in mechanic arts or engineering being done by the land-grant colleges. Immediately after the passage of the land grant act of 1862 plans were made for giving the highest grade of instruction in mechanic arts at the Massachusetts Institute of Technology, Cornell University, and other land-grant institutions.

The Bureau of Education reported that—

The first want felt in the establishment of this class of schools was the education of men of science to man them, but the first purpose for which they were established was the instruction of able, educated, trustworthy technologists, such as well-informed engineers, architects, mechanicians, manufacturers, miners, agriculturists, and the like, for which the country was at that time loudly calling (57).

It has sometimes been contended that "mechanic arts" in the land grant act was a wholly incidental matter and that only mechanic arts in their relation to agriculture was intended. This view is evidently refuted by Mr. Morrill's statement about the act. Moreover the movement which culminated in the plans for the People's College in New York and industrial universities in Illinois had included instruction in mechanic arts as well as agriculture. The agricultural societies and other friends of agricultural education had often included instruction in mechanic arts in their programs. Mr. Morrill was therefore in line with the progressive educational thought of the times when he put mechanic arts on the same plane as agriculture in his land grant bill. Many of the States immediately undertook the establishment of agricultural and mechanical colleges or introduced both branches in their universities.

It was inevitable that a measure so broadly formulated and so indefinitely discussed before its passage should be interpreted in different ways and according to the educational conditions in the several States. In Michigan it was natural to give the land grant to an agricultural college; in Massachusetts to divide the grant between institutions for agriculture and mechanic arts; in Connecticut and some other States to give it to a scientific institution in which along with other sciences the science of agriculture would be taught to a few students; in Southern and some Western States to provide for literary and scientific education, with a little agricultural instruction; and in New York, Illinois, Wisconsin, and other States to create departments of agriculture and mechanic arts in universities. In many of the States there were few secondary schools and these were not generally accessible to the farming people. The land-grant colleges were therefore compelled to establish preparatory classes and to make their entrance requirements quite liberal. Trained teachers of the natural sciences were comparatively few and in the colleges generally it was expected that they would teach more than one science. There were practically no trained teachers of agriculture. This subject must be taught by the science teachers or by farmers with sufficient general education to prepare lectures and with enough farm experience to give direction to the farm labor of the students. Most agricultural books were of foreign origin or filled with material from foreign sources. There was no body of tested knowledge derived from American experience. Agricultural instruction was largely given through lectures, which were more often very theoretical or confined to the personal experience of the author. In a large part of the country pioneer conditions prevailed in farming, land was abundant and cheap, and production outran demand. In these regions there was little incentive to study agriculture in a college. State control of higher education was a new thing. Politicians were naturally inclined to take a hand in the management of the land-grant colleges and in the absence of a civil-service system appointments of college presidents and faculties were not always based on merit. Frequent changes in boards of control and faculties made these colleges unstable in administrative policies and curricula. Under such conditions it is not surprising that after the first enthusiasm aroused by the land grant and the novel organization of these colleges had subsided they grew slowly or even declined in the number of their students.

The statistics of the first decade are very imperfect, but it appears that in 1872–73 12 of these colleges had less than 200 students in all their branches, 6 had less than 300, 4 less than 400, and 4 over 400. In their agricultural and mechanical departments 12 had less than 50 students, 6 less than 100, 6 less than 150, and only 3 over 150.

ACCEPTANCE OF THE COLLEGE LAND GRANT BY THE STATES

Under the act of July 2, 1862, the States were required to express acceptance of this provision within two years, but by the acts of April 14, 1864, and July 23, 1866, this time was extended to July 23, 1871, and as each Territory was admitted to statehood provision was made in its enabling act for a grant of land for agricultural and mechanical colleges in lieu of the original grant of 1862.

Iowa accepted the provisions of the Morrill Land Grant Act on September 11, 1862, and was followed by Vermont on October 29 and Connecticut on December 24 of that year. Fourteen States accepted it in 1863, 2 in 1864, 1 in 1865, 6 in 1866, 4 in 1867, 3 in 1868, 1 in 1869, and 2 in 1870, making 36 in 9 years. During that period 35 institutions received its benefits by action of the State legislatures; 15 were colleges and 20 were universities at that time or later developed into universities. In Connecticut, Mississippi, North Carolina, South Carolina, and Rhode Island the use of the land-grant funds was finally taken away from the university and given to a separate college. In Delaware, Florida, Maine, Maryland, New Hampshire, and Ohio colleges were first given the land grant and afterwards became universities. In 9 States the land grant was given to 2 colleges and 7 universities wholly or partly on a private foundation and in 10 States to publicly supported colleges, which had more than an agricultural curriculum and were often designated agricultural and mechanical colleges. Massachusetts divided the fund between the Massachusetts Agricultural College and the Massachusetts Institute of Technology.

Colleges for negroes in Virginia, Mississippi, and South Carolina received a portion of the land-grant fund.

USE OF THE COLLEGE LAND SCRIP BY THE STATES

Many of the States, particularly in the East and South, put the land scrip on the market so rapidly that they received much less for their land than the standard Government price of $1.25 an acre. They thus established such small funds that the annual interest was not sufficient for the maintenance of a college. The Central and Western States were more careful in locating and managing their land.

As regards the investment and use of the funds derived from these land grants it proved impracticable to carry out the exact letter of the law. In 1918 the Bureau of Education stated that there was scarcely one State which had not, in some way, at some time, been in default. On this subject the bureau stated further that—

The principal lines of default have been a delay in investing the capital, or investment at less than 5 per cent, causing loss of income to the college; use of capital for other purposes than for the college; and finally the use of income for purposes not authorized by law, such as for the administration of lands or expenses of investments. In general these defaults have been made good as soon as proper attention was directed to them.

Although defaults have been corrected, in the main immediately on being recognized, yet seldom have deficits been refunded or made up. Especially in the matter of loss of interest from lack of investment or from deficient interest return, it has been usual to replace the investment so as to obtain the required 5 per cent but to allow past losses to remain unsatisfied. There are, however, several exceptions to this practice (1).

In the States which received scrip or land under the original act several plans for obtaining the required 5 per cent have been adopted as follows:

(1) In a large number of the States, when it became evident that a continuous 5 per cent investment would be difficult to find, the fund was turned over to the State treasury and the State itself assumed the load of interest, the capital being considered as part of the irreducible State debt. This was done in Connecticut, Delaware, Georgia, Indiana, Kentucky, Louisiana, Maine, Massachusetts, New Hampshire, New Jersey, New York, and Pennsylvania.

(2) In other States the receipts from the sale of lands were turned in to the State treasury as fast as received and added either to the State sinking fund or to general State funds, no attempt at outside investment being made. In such cases the State issues certificates of indebtedness at a good rate of interest. Michigan, Missouri, and Ohio handled their funds in this way.

(3) Other States have invested the funds at the best rate obtainable in the open market, and make up the difference between the rate obtained and the required 5 per cent by direct legislative appropriation. Maryland and Rhode Island handle the funds in this way.

(4) In Florida, Minnesota, and Wisconsin the legislature has authorized the governing board of the college to transfer funds from other general college funds in order to make up the deficit in interest.

(5) In Illinois, North Carolina, and South Carolina the fund has been lost by defalcation or dishonesty and has been restored by the legislature. A State bond for the amount has been issued in each of these States.

The newer States received invariably, in their State enabling acts, grants of public lands for many different purposes and running into the millions of acres. The care of these lands has become one of the principal administrative duties of the State. In every case a State land board has been created which locates the lands under the different grants and arranges for their use either by sale to individuals who will develop them, or by rental of the lands or of the privileges, such as grazing, mining, lumbering, water power, etc. Sales of lands are usually made on a part cash basis, the State collecting a liberal rate of interest on the deferred payments.

The amount received from actual sales of lands of the agricultural college grants is turned over to the State treasurer and invested either by him or by some other authorized agency, at the best rate obtainable (1).

In 1923 the Bureau of Education reported that the total number of acres actually received by the States was 10,928,295, of which 939,-800.58 acres with an estimated value of $13,592,749.21 were not yet sold. The fund accumulated from the sale of lands aggregated $17,416,096.03. The largest fund in a State was $1,569,406.50 in North Dakota; Michigan had $1,003,495.12. Twelve other States had from $500,000 to over $700,000. Rhode Island had $50,000. Arizona had sold only a small portion of her grant for $3,855.91.

THE FIRST DECADE OF THE LAND-GRANT COLLEGES, 1862–1872

CONDITIONS AFFECTING THE PROGRESS OF THESE COLLEGES

In 1862 the United States was in the midst of civil war over secession and negro slavery. It was vitally important to control and develop the great empire west of the Mississippi River. Congress therefore passed the homestead act of May 20, 1862, under which 65,000,000 acres were settled up to 1880. Railroads received 159,000,000 acres between 1850 and 1871, in addition to 55,000,000 acres given them by the States. The war and the westward movement of population to engage in farming, the building of railroads, and the development of villages and cities caused a greatly increased demand for manufactures. From 1860 the United States increasingly became the chief source of food products and raw materials for Europe. The war greatly stimulated agricultural production. Scarcity of labor on the farms induced the use of more machinery, horses, and mules. Even before the war reapers, mowers, horserakes, cultivators, horse hoes, seed drills, and other improved machines had come into common use. Thereafter the variety and number of farm machines in actual use constantly increased. It has been estimated that in 1865 there were 250,000 reapers, each of which cut 10 acres per day of 12 hours. Within the half century ended in 1880 the average amount of grain harvested, threshed, and prepared for market per man per day increased from 4 to 50 bushels. As soon as the war was over many of the 1,000,000 men who were in the Union Army, together with large numbers of Confederate soldiers, went to swell the huge hosts of natives and immigrants who were settling on western lands. The population of the grain States increased over 42 per cent between 1860 and 1870 and with the rapid building of railroads during the next decade over 297,000 square miles, an area equal to Great Britain and France, were added to the cultivated land of the United States. From about 1870 the manufacture of new-process flour made possible a great expansion of the area devoted to spring wheat. Improvements in transporting and handling grain, general reduction of freight rates, as compared with those prior to the coming of the railroads, and the use of elevators also characterized this period.

To the South the war brought disaster and impoverishment. A blockade largely prevented the exportation of cotton and tobacco. The abolition of slavery wiped out the vast values represented by human chattels. Farm equipment was largely ruined. Great numbers of the white men who would have been owners or managers of farms lost their lives in the war. At first an attempt was made to continue the old plantation system and this was helped by the high price of cotton. But overproduction materially reduced the price, the negroes were unaccustomed to a wage system and would not work continuously or efficiently, debts incurred in reestablishing the plantations could not be paid, and excessive taxation by the carpetbag governments made the planters' condition more hopeless. Many planters were forced to go out of business and great tracts of land became idle. It is estimated that the money value of southern farms declined 48 per cent between 1860 and 1870.

Much land was then purchased in small tracts by white men and some by negroes. The latter, however, were generally content to become tenants and work little farms for a share of the crop. By 1876 about 40 per cent of the men working on southern farms were whites as compared with 11 per cent before the war. More fertilizers and somewhat better machinery were used and the yield of cotton per acre increased from 172 pounds in 1860 to 222 pounds in 1870.

There was also some diversification, but food supplies largely came once more from northern farms. A credit system was established which has ever since kept multitudes of the small farmers, especially the negroes, in financial bondage.

In the Northeast dairy farming, poultry raising, fruit growing, and market gardening were largely developed. During the war the farmers in that region who remained on their farms were generally prosperous, but many went into the army or into other industries and many joined the hosts of emigrants to the western lands. There was a general reduction in the value of farm lands in that region and much of the poorer land went into pastures or woodlands. The growing of great numbers of cattle and sheep on the vast free ranges of the West largely restricted animal husbandry on the farms to the raising of hogs, which were used as a means of disposing of a large share of the corn crop. In general American farming after the Civil War became chiefly a matter of raising a limited number of staple crops. West of the Alleghenies these were principally raised on soils which required no fertilizers.

With the rapid spread of population during the decade succeeding the passage of the land-grant college act production of crops outran demand, particularly where the means of transportation were limited.

The railroads contributed very greatly to the rapid spread of population and together with other economic and social conditions kept both the old and new communities in a constant state of flux. Great numbers of the more vigorous and adventurous native people of the East went into the new communities and their place was more than taken by the hordes of emigrants from northern Europe. Many of the more enterprising and financially able of the Eastern people settled where comparatively well-organized communities already existed and built up villages and cities with the complicated financial, industrial, and social elements of modern civilization. This caused an exodus of the poorer but active people who had occupied this territory and they renewed their efforts to establish agriculture and rural communities farther west. There they found the pioneer settlers who had already demonstrated the agricultural value of the land but had not the means to develop it fully, and being of a restless nature were willing to sell out and resume their pioneering still farther west. Thus there was constant agitation and movement from East to West, and men and women were principally engrossed in seeking new avenues for their activities and making a livelihood or fortunes by comparatively superficial means.

In agriculture, in particular, there was little incentive to thorough and painstaking work. If the farm one owned was not satisfactory the family could easily get another where with comparatively rough-and-ready methods abundant crops could be produced and where perchance there was a better opportunity for enlarged farming operations and better provision for the family's future. Or if one were a farm laborer he might at least become a homesteader and in a few years owner of 160 good acres as a result of quite simple farming.

As regards education, outside of New England the question of complete support of even elementary schools with public funds had been settled in the Northern States only a few years before the Civil War. In New York while a system of free schools was provided by law in 1849 this was much opposed and actually abolished for a time. In Pennsylvania the maintenance of free schools was optional until 1854. In Ohio, Illinois, and Iowa the schools were made wholly free between 1853 and 1858. In Kansas nearly all schools were private prior to 1859, and in Michigan free schools were not generally established until 1869. When the college land grant act was passed and in many places in the North long thereafter the term of free public schools in rural communities very often covered only a few weeks. The three R's, with perhaps a little geography and United States history, were imperfectly taught in the great majority of these rural schools.

In the South anything like a general State public school system did not exist before 1870. That year there were only about 160 public high schools in the United States.

When the Michigan Agricultural College was opened in 1857 there were about 200 colleges in the United States. In most of them the classical course leading to the degree of bachelor of arts was the only regular collegiate course. Chemistry, physics, botany, zoology, geology, and astronomy were often included in this course, but usually taught with lectures and textbooks, without laboratory practice by the student. Latin and Greek were the principal entrance requirements, to which were usually added English grammar, geography, arithmetic, algebra (through simple equations), and sometimes history. Yale was the first college to require geometry, and this was done in 1856.

According to the catalogue for 1857 the faculty of Harvard University consisted of 51 persons. In the regular undergraduate course in Harvard College chemistry and botany were required in the sophomore year, and physics in junior and senior years. Botany was an elective in junior year and geology, anatomy, and zoology in senior year. There were 398 undergraduates and 4 graduate students; in the divinity, law, and medical schools there were 231 students.

In the Lawrence Scientific School of Harvard University there were only 67 students.

Candidates for admission must have attained the age of 18 years, have received a good English education and be qualified to pursue to advantage the courses of study to which they propose to give their attention. "The degree of bachelor of science may be conferred on any student, who, having attended the instruction of the school for at least one year, and completed the prescribed course of study in one or more departments, shall have passed a satisfactory public examination." There were 17 students in chemistry, 6 in geology and zoology, 8 in comparative anatomy and physiology, 1 in botany, and 1 in mineralogy and geology. Professor Horsford gave a course in "experimental chemistry and research," including among other things analyses of soils and ashes, and manufacture of manures.

In zoology and geology, besides the lectures, Professor Agassiz "will afford students access to his laboratory during certain hours, in order to show them how to observe different formations and how to conduct a regular geological survey." Excursions in term-time and vacation are also offered.

In botany Professor Gray will give "special practical instruction" "in classes of not more than 3 each," from April 1 to the close of the term. The botanic garden is accessible to students (547).

In Yale College in 1857 the faculty numbered 41 persons. In the regular undergraduate course there were 447 students and in theology, law, and medicine 82 students. In the bachelor of arts course there were only six electives, of which mineralogy was one (for a single term—one-third year). Among the required subjects were natural philosophy and astronomy in junior and senior years, one term of chemistry, and short courses of lectures in mineralogy, geology, meteorology, and anatomy.

The Yale (Sheffield) Scientific School had only 36 students, of whom 13 were in chemistry. The course occupied two years. Previous study of chemistry was not required for admission to the school. The analytical laboratory was fully equipped for practical instruction in all branches of analytical and experimental chemistry.

The atmosphere of even Harvard, Yale, and the University of Michigan, where the study of the sciences was much more encouraged than at the other colleges, was so charged with the traditional influences of the classical learning that few students could be persuaded to take the scientific courses which had practical applications. The land-grant colleges were therefore entering on what was practically an uncultivated field of education in this country. Their subject matter, curricula, and methods of instruction had to be developed to suit new traditions. On the one hand they felt obliged to keep close to their agricultural and mechanical constituency, particularly the farmers, and therefore to make the requirements for admission comparatively low. On the other hand they felt the influence of the college standards then in vogue, particularly since their administrative officers and faculties were necessarily drawn from the ranks of men trained in the classical courses or in the pure sciences. In agriculture there was very little knowledge which had been tested scientifically. The instruction therefore necessarily dealt almost entirely with practical details of farm operations or with theories resting on shallow and often unsound basis.

To satisfy the demand for practical instruction these new colleges fell back on the manual-labor theory and practice, which fortunately for them still had some standing among educators. It is almost safe to say that it was the manual-labor feature of many of the early agricultural colleges which made it possible for them to exist and to draw considerable numbers of students from the farming people. Where this was omitted or minimized the agricultural students were very few. This manual-labor system was bound to fail because it had little educational value. It served, however, to give the agricultural colleges under the land grant act time to get organized and fairly well settled in their general educational program and to begin through experimental inquiries to collect the tested knowledge necessary to the construction of worth-while agricultural courses.

ORGANIZATION AND EARLY WORK OF THE LAND-GRANT COLLEGES

When the land grant act passed there were in operation agricultural colleges in Maryland, Michigan, and Pennsylvania, and agriculture was taught at the Yale Scientific School in Connecticut. Within the next 10 years agricultural instruction was given in agricultural and mechanical colleges in Alabama, Arkansas, Delaware, Iowa, Kansas, Maine, New Hampshire, New Jersey, Texas, Virginia, and in universities in California, Georgia, Illinois, Kentucky, Minnesota, Mississippi, Missouri, Nebraska, New York, North Carolina, South Carolina, Tennessee, Vermont, West Virginia, and Wisconsin. In Massachusetts a college devoted to agriculture only and a separate institution for the mechanic arts had been established.

The influence of the Yale Scientific School was strongly felt in the organization of the land-grant institutions in a number of States. In New Hampshire the land-grant college was attached to Dartmouth College, where the Chandler Scientific School had been organized on the basis of an endowment by Abiel Chandler for mechanic arts and civil engineering. This was supplemented by a gift from Sylvanus Thayer for architecture and civil engineering. A course in applied science was offered. Work under the land grant act was begun in September, 1868. With the aid of the land-grant fund professors of agricultural chemistry and animal and vegetable physiology were employed.

In Rhode Island the land-grant fund was given to Brown University, which organized a scientific curriculum of three years, including a brief course of lectures on agriculture.

At the University of Vermont in 1867 instruction in analytical and agricultural chemistry was offered in the scientific department, which had a three-year curriculum, including a course of lectures on agriculture in February and March. In New Jersey a scientific school was opened at Rutgers College in 1866, which had a farm of 100 acres for experimental purposes.

In 1867 agricultural and mechanical colleges were opened at Orono, Me., with 13 students; at Morgantown, W. Va., with preparatory and scientific and agricultural departments. That year the University of Wisconsin announced that a student might give three years to agriculture or join the college of letters or arts and devote as much time as he pleased to agriculture and in 1868 it appeared that the student well up in science could complete the agricultural course in one year.

The Maryland Agricultural College had a scientific course in 1867 with perhaps some instruction relating to agriculture. The Kansas Agricultural College which had opened in 1863 five years later had an academic or classical curriculum and an agricultural and scientific curriculum of three years. Many of the students were in preparatory classes. Special efforts were made to train teachers. The student body contained 97 men and 71 women.

In New York Cornell University was opened in 1868, with a college of agriculture, and professors of agricultural chemistry and veterinary medicine. Prior to 1873 it had great difficulty in securing a satisfactory teacher of agriculture, and the number of students in the strictly agricultural classes was small.

The Massachusetts Agricultural College, the only land-grant institution intended to be exclusively for students interested in agriculture and agricultural science, was opened in 1867 and the following year had 96 students.

Five years later, at the end of the first decade after the passage of the land grant act, there were reported to be in agricultural and mechanical courses in Michigan, 143 students; in Pennsylvania, 130; in Maryland, 130; in Maine, 103; in New Hampshire, 22; in Vermont, 21; in New Jersey, 67; in New York, 151; and in Rhode

Island, 25. In agriculture alone West Virginia had 29; Massachusetts, 139; Kansas, 50. In Wisconsin, 30 students in the College of Arts attended lectures on agriculture.

In the land-grant institutions opened after 1867 there were students in agriculture and mechanic arts as follows: In Alabama, 53; Georgia, 151; Kentucky, 181; Mississippi, 5; Oregon, 50; Tennessee, 37; Virginia, 122. In agricultural courses there were in Arkansas, 50; Delaware, 14; North Georgia, 25; Illinois, 87; Iowa, 243; Missouri, 138; and Ohio, 176.

In Pennsylvania the death of Doctor Pugh in 1864 was a very severe blow to the college. It had many internal difficulties and in 1868 there was an entire change of faculty. The college tended to become an institution for scientific and literary education and its name was changed in 1874 to the Pennsylvania State College.

In Connecticut the agricultural work was only a small part of the curriculum of a scientific school. There was instruction of a comparatively high order in analytical and agricultural chemistry, with laboratory practice. Beyond that there were brief courses of lectures on agricultural subjects. The institution had no farm and the course was too severely scientific to attract many students.

In 1868 the school stated its aims regarding agriculture as follows:

> We can not expect to equal the special schools of agriculture in the very desirable work of training practical farmers, though we hope by the prosecution of the science of agriculture, and by the training of scientific professors and agriculturists to contribute to the progress of agriculture.

In 1871 a meeting of representatives of the agricultural colleges was held at Chicago. In a letter to Dean Davenport, of Illinois, E. W. Hilgard, who was present at that meeting, writes about one of the principal subjects discussed there as follows:

> It followed the meeting of the American Association for the Advancement of Science, from where a number of men, includ.ng myself, went to Chicago as the result of a call issued some time before by a committee of agricultural college men, to discuss the question of agricultural education, which at that time already had begun to be sharply contested between the advocates of the "Michigan plan," also followed by Pennsylvania, and those who, with the Sheffield School, Harvard, and a few others, favored the university grade of agricultural education. I, after a few years' trial of the Michigan plan at the University of Mississippi (which I then represented), contended strongly for the second, with the corollary that in order to interest the farmers, experimental work bearing directly upon each State's practical problems, is the prime need. We had quite a lively time, Michigan battling strongly for the student-labor plan, as the only "practical" one, and which would not "educate the students away from the farm." Gilman, then librarian of Yale, and I were the chief fighters on the university side, seconded in a measure by Gregory (president of Illinois University) and the delegates from Wisconsin and Minnesota.

During the first decade after the passage of the college land grant act the States had accepted the provisions of the act and had sold their land scrip so rapidly that the price of the land had been depressed with the result that in most States relatively small land-grant funds had been acquired and it was necessary for the States to supplement these materially if State colleges of the character contemplated in the land grant act were to be maintained; and the colleges to receive the benefits of this act had been selected and put or continued in operation, but financial, economic, and educational conditions had been such that only a limited number of students had been attracted to these institutions. The Civil War, in which many men of college age were engaged as soldiers, also hindered the early development of the land-grant colleges. It had proved particularly difficult to construct good agricultural courses. The teaching of chemistry, botany, and zoology and their relations to agriculture, and of practical systems of agriculture, principally by means of lectures, had been combined with manual labor on the college farms, which for the most part had had comparatively little educational value. The development of laboratory work in the natural sciences in which the students participated and the direction of the study of the sciences toward their applications to agriculture and other useful arts had thus far been the chief educational contribution of the land-grant colleges. The need of experimental inquiries to develop a body of scientifically tested knowledge which might be used as a basis for more thorough and satisfactory instruction in agriculture was beginning to be apparent. Neither the managers and teachers in the land-grant colleges nor the farmers were satisfied with their agricultural work. Economic conditions were developing which would turn the efforts of the land-grant colleges largely in the direction of the mechanic arts and keep the number of agricultural students at a relatively low level for a number of years pending the carrying on of agricultural experimentation on a broad scale and with large practical results.

These colleges were also about to show that while their systematic courses in agriculture were weak they could broadly aid agricultural progress by their contacts with large numbers of adult farmers in their societies and farmers' institutes and through the agricultural press.

Farmers' institutes were first held at the Kansas Agricultural College in 1868, by the Illinois Industrial University in 1870, the Iowa Agricultural College in 1871–72, and the University of Nebraska in 1873–74.

THE EXPERIMENT STATION AND EXTENSION MOVEMENTS IN THE LAND-GRANT COLLEGES, 1873–1887

GENERAL ECONOMIC CONDITIONS IN THIS PERIOD

The great panic of 1873 was the culmination of a period of rapid expansion of agriculture, manufacturing, and railroad building. The capital of the country had too largely been locked up in speculative and legitimate enterprises which were giving little or no return. The efforts of the Federal Government to put money on a sound basis by contraction of the paper currency and the limitation of the coinage of silver brought about the difficulties which usually accompany deflation. The great fires in Boston and Chicago helped to make the financial situation unusually bad. The general result of the situation brought about by this panic was a great lowering of the prices of merchandise and agricultural products and of wages and salaries. There was an extensive redistribution of the wealth of the country and the reorganization of its business activities. A great contest arose regarding the use of silver and paper money as related to gold. It was decided to continue the coining of the silver dollar, giving it a weight of 412½ grains, but the amount of such coinage was definitely limited. The greenbacks were retained but not increased and on January 1, 1879, specie payment was resumed.

Protection of manufacturers through a tariff became a settled policy, under which the home market was very largely reserved for domestic goods. The growth in urban communities with greatly varied industries, the continuing expansion of agriculture, and the reconstruction of the South provided a constantly enlarging home market. Mechanic arts grew in variety and extent; the applications of science to such arts became more and more numerous. By 1880 the annual value of manufactures in the United States had risen to over $5,000,000,000. There was also a great increase in the mining of coal, iron, silver, gold, petroleum, etc. Activity in railroad building was soon resumed after the panic of 1873. Between 1870 and 1880 the railroad mileage doubled and in the next 10 years grew from 93,296 to 163,597 miles. The largest part of this development was in the Central and Western States. Communication through the postal routes and telegraph lines was greatly extended, and in 1876 the telephone came.

To meet the needs of reviving industry, immigration was strongly encouraged. In 1879 the number of immigrants rose to 789,000 as compared with 460,000 in 1873. Combinations of capital in railroading and manufacturing increased greatly in number and extent and produced profound results in the industrial world. These combinations at first took the form of agreements between competitors to fix prices, limit output, or divide territory or profit. Then came the more substantial and permanent combinations known as "trusts," beginning with the Standard Oil Co. in 1882. When these were made illegal, "holding companies" were devised. The growth of large trusts was promoted by alliances with natural monopolies, especially railroads. The giving of rebates on freight charges to large shippers became very prevalent. The railroads themselves broke down competition with each other to a considerable extent through "pooling."

The transfer of the mechanical industries to large factories or organizations like the railroads and the increase of their management through corporations vitally affected the relations of industrial workers with their employers. Labor came to be looked upon more generally merely as a commodity, and its human relationships were too often ignored. After the Civil War wages did not increase as rapidly as prices. This led to the formation of unions by the locomotive engineers, bricklayers, iron and steel workers, and other laborers. In 1866 the National Labor Union was formed, but this was soon wrecked through its political activities. Then came the Knights of Labor. Begun in 1869, it was for 10 years a secret society and open on that account to much misrepresentation and attack. Its aims were "to bring within the folds of organization every department of productive industry, making knowledge a standpoint for action, and industrial and moral worth, not wealth, the true standard of national greatness." It wished "to secure to the workers the full enjoyment of the wealth they create, sufficient leisure in which to develop their intellectual, moral, and social faculties, all of the benefits, recreation, and pleasures of association" (11). The accomplishment of many of its demands could be brought about only by legislative action, and it ultimately became entangled in politics. It was also unfavorably affected by disastrous strikes in 1877 and 1886. Its government was highly centralized and autocratic and this brought it into conflict with other labor organizations. Its greatest influence was exerted between 1880 and 1890. At one time it claimed a membership of over 700,000. When it declined its place was taken by the American Federation of Labor, distinctly a " confederation," in which each trade was organized separately and represented in the national body by its union. The federation aimed to deal only with matters of general interest to the unions.

Agriculture went on expanding after 1873 in spite of economic difficulty. Free public land and cheap private land in the West lured great multitudes of men to seek their fortunes by farming on virgin soils and under the freedom of pioneer conditions. The area of cultivated land spread beyond the region of adequate rainfall. The successful example of farming under irrigation which the Mormons had demonstrated prior to the Civil War stimulated attempts at irrigation elsewhere. Railroads and speculators widely advertised the advantages of irrigation. Between 1870 and 1880 a million acres were brought under irrigation ditches and then under the influence of the speculative boom the irrigated area was increased to 3,631,381 acres by 1889. The desert land act of 1877, under which 640 acres was offered at $1.25 an acre to the settler practicing irrigation, proved of chief benefit to the irrigation companies and to sheep and cattle ranchers, whose business was growing enormously during this period.

The rapid expansion of agriculture, while it gave employment to multitudes of men and made comparatively easy the passage from the status of farm laborer to that of farm owner, constantly tended toward overproduction of crops and livestock. The railroad building which accompanied the agricultural expansion outran the limits of safe business and led to charges for transportation which often seemed unfair to the agricultural people. The necessary sale of farm products through commission merchants, who were often far away and had few personal contacts with the farmers, created suspicions of unfair dealing which were in many cases justified. Federal taxation, which produced more revenue than the Government needed for ordinary expenses, and State and local taxation to provide for roads, schools, and other things required by new communities or in old communities by the rapidly expanding requirements of the new age, bore heavily on the agricultural people. If to these things was added a heavy burden of mortgages with high interest rates the farmer naturally felt that he did not have a fair deal in a country where wealth was tending to accumulate more and more in comparatively few hands. Though for a brief time after 1880 the farmers were somewhat more prosperous, the locking up of vast sums of money in farm lands and railroads again caused financial difficulties, culminating in the panic of 1884. At that time the price of wheat fell to 64 cents a bushel. Agriculture then remained in a depressed condition for a number of years.

THE FIRST MASS MOVEMENT OF FARMERS

American farmers had from colonial times lived comparatively isolated lives on separate farms, rather than in villages, and had prided themselves on their independence. Such societies as had arisen among them had had a small membership composed largely of the more wealthy and better educated men, many of whom united farming with other pursuits and were more or less influential in public affairs. It is an interesting fact that when the time was ripe for the first mass movement of American farmers to better their condition it was brought about through the activity of a very small number of this same type of men. And it is also noteworthy that it paralleled the attempt of the laboring men of that time to form a broad organization through a secret society, such as the Knights of Labor.

In 1866 when agricultural and other conditions in the South were giving the country much anxiety President Johnson consulted the United States Commissioner of Agriculture, Isaac Newton. The results was that Oliver Hudson Kelley (fig. 9), a native of Boston, Mass., who in 1849 had taken up farming at Ithaca, Minn., and was at this time a clerk in the Department of Agriculture, was sent South to study conditions there. He found that his membership in the masonic order made him an acceptable visitor to many southern people. This suggested to him that a secret farm organization with a ritual and different orders would be a good thing and when later he visited his niece, Miss Carrie A. Hall, in Boston, she persuaded him to include the membership of women in the plan for this organization. Returning to Washington as an employee in the Post Office Department, he formed the acquaintance of W. M. Ireland, John Trimble, and William Saunders, for many years in charge of the gardens and grounds of the Department of Agriculture. These men favored Kelley's project and he therefore elaborated his plan of organization and ritual. J. R. Thompson, A. B. Grosh, and F. M. McDowell were also " founders of the order." On December 4, 1867, the National Grange of the Patrons of Husbandry was organized, with Saunders as master and Kelley as secretary. The original objects of the grange were wholly educational and social.

In his first printed circular, November 1, 1867, Kelley stated that its main object is " to encourage and advance education in all branches of agriculture," and in the circular of February 3, 1868, " with regard to the modes of education, mention may be made of mental instruction through the reading of essays, and discussions, lectures, formation of select libraries, circulation of magazines, and other publications touching directly upon the main subject desired, namely, those inculcating the principles governing our operation in the field, orchard, and garden " (*38*). Mr. Saunders, in 1870, said that—

to increase the products of the earth by increasing the knowledge of the producer is the basis of our structure; to learn and apply the revelations of science as far as it relates to the farmer's products of the vegetable world, and to diffuse the truths and general principles of the science and art of agriculture, are the ultimate objects of our organization.

When Kelley went out in February, 1868, to organize granges and traveled across the country from Pennsylvania and New York to his home in Minnesota he had very little success. The farther west he went the more he was reminded by the farmers that what they wanted was an organization to protect them against the injustices of railroads and middlemen in the transportation and selling of agricultural products and the buying of farm supplies and ma-

FIG. 9.—Oliver H. Kelley

chinery. He yielded to this demand and in a circular of September, 1868, broadened the objects of the grange, which now are "to advance education, to elevate and dignify the occupation of the farmer, and to protect its members against the numerous combinations by which their interests are injuriously affected." This made the organization of granges in Minnesota easier and by 1869 there was a State grange in that State which wanted the order to collect and disseminate information about crops, prices, and transportation; establish depots in cities for sale of products, purchase and exchange of seeds; a labor office; and testing of farm supplies and implements. They appointed that year a State agent to buy supplies and implements and issued the first grange paper.

By 1870 there were 40 granges in Minnesota. In 1871, 130 new local granges and 2 State granges were formed. Grange agencies were established in several cities and the movement for grange stores began. That year the somewhat mythical character of the National Grange was disclosed, when, for the first time, the masters of the State granges were invited to attend its annual meeting at Washington. One thousand one hundred and five local granges were organized in 1872, of which 652 were in Iowa. All sections of the country including 25 States now had granges and there were 10 State granges. The celebrations and picnics of this order brought thousands of farming people together. The first delegate session of the National Grange was held in January, 1873, at which 24 men and 4 women represented 11 States. The order grew very rapidly and 32 State granges were represented the next year in the National Grange. A famous "declaration of purposes" was issued at this time.

We propose meeting together, talking together, working together, buying together, selling together, and, in general, acting together for our mutual protection and advancement as occasion may require. * * * For our business interests we desire to bring producers and consumers, farmers and manufacturers into the most direct and friendly relations possible. Hence we must dispense with a surplus of middlemen. Transportation companies of every kind are necessary and every State should increase facilities for transporting cheaply. We shall advance the cause of education among ourselves and for our children by all just means within our power. We especially advocate for our agricultural and industrial colleges that practical agriculture, domestic science, and all the arts which adorn the home be taught in these courses of study (2).

Conditions arising out of the panic of 1873 greatly intensified and broadened the discontent of the farmers. As a result the membership of the granges grew with marvelous rapidity and reached its maximum of about 1,000,000 men and women in 1875. Meanwhile the order had embarked on an extensive program of cooperative buying and selling, including numerous agencies and stores. Even the manufacture of implements and other articles and the management of banks and life and fire insurance companies were undertaken. The time was not ripe for such a movement in this country and most of these cooperative enterprises failed. However, through them the farmers discovered the real value of the services of middlemen, merchants, and manufacturers and the advantage of direct and large purchases. They were to a certain extent able to modify the existing credit systems. Many farmers got a training in business methods. They learned the power of organization and service and from that time have used it for business purposes in increasing measure.

The grange was also very prominent and influential in a broad agrarian movement which sought to improve the conditions of agriculture and rural life through legislation. Numerous farmers' clubs participated in this movement as well as larger organizations, such as the Farmers Alliance, which became competitors of the grange.

It is, however, generally known as the granger movement. This was most influential in the North Central States, California, and Oregon. Its greatest effort was to secure public control of railroads by the States. It secured the passage of laws for the establishment of maximum rates for transportation, the creation of State railroad commissions, prevention of pooling, prohibition of free passes to public officials, etc. There was also much agitation for Federal control, but attempts to secure legislation on this subject by Congress failed. In his work entitled "The Granger Movement," S. J. Buck, of the University of Illinois, sums up the results of this effort as follows:

On the whole it seems that the immediate economic results of the granger agitation for railroad regulation were small. * * * The indirect and political results of the movement, however, were more important; it led to decisions by the United States Supreme Court which established the right of States to control railroads; and it laid the foundation for later legislation (16).

This movement also brought about State reforms in taxation, public education, the establishment of boards of agriculture, the collection of agricultural statistics, etc., and in the local communities favorably affected many interests. In educational matters the grange stood for the improvement of the rural schools, and from 1878 favored the teaching of agriculture in these schools. While it often criticized the land-grant colleges and in some States attempted strongly to change the character of their agricultural instruction it favored liberal State and Federal support of these institutions and at times helped materially to promote their growth. It also worked efficiently toward the strengthening of the United States Department of Agriculture and the State and Federal legislation for the establishment and maintenance of the agricultural experiment stations.

The failure of its cooperative enterprises and dissatisfaction and differences of opinion regarding its legislative efforts led to a very large decline in the membership of the grange after 1875 and in 1889 it had only about 100,000 paid members. In many localities it disappeared, particularly in the South and West. In the Northeastern and a few North Central States it reverted very largely to its original status as an educational and social organization. On this basis it has done much useful work and in recent years has spread out more widely and again has become one of our largest and most influential farm organizations. As a social organization through its local, State, and national meetings, and even its business enterprises, it has brought large numbers of the farming people together for instructional, recreational, and charitable purposes. In its recognition of the activities of women and young people as essential and important elements in the social life of the farm home and rural community it has done much to better the conditions of country life. It has supported scholarships at some of the agricultural colleges. Many members of the grange have taken part in the farmers' institutes and other extension activities or have sent members of their families to the agricultural schools and colleges.

GENERAL EDUCATIONAL PROGRESS

As population spread westward between 1870 and 1890 the free public schools of elementary grade greatly increased in number. In the South public school systems were established and had considerable growth during this period. The States generally took more interest in education, organized or strengthened departments of education, and materially increased school appropriations. The public high schools greatly increased in number and attendance. By 1890 there were in the North Atlantic States 786 high schools; in the South Atlantic States, 115; in the South Central States, 158; in the North Central States, 1,376; and in the Western States, 91; making a total of 2,526. The principle of public support of higher education had been generally adopted. There were State universities in 33 States, of which 16 had been opened for students after 1865. The courses of instruction in the high schools and colleges were greatly broadened. The free elective system which had been begun by Harvard University in 1867 under the leadership of President Eliot spread rapidly throughout the country during this period. The teaching of the natural sciences was much broadened and specialized and the laboratory method was widely used. The applications of science to the mechanic arts greatly increased in variety and there was enormous development of manufacturing, railroading, mining, irrigation, and road and bridge building. Persons versed in science or engineering were therefore in great demand as experts or teachers. The land-grant institutions especially felt the influence of this demand and enlarged their departments of science, mechanic arts, and engineering to meet it. Students flocked into these departments because the prospect of profitable employment for those who pursued such courses was so bright.

AGRICULTURAL EDUCATION AND RESEARCH IN THIS PERIOD

Overproduction of agricultural products by comparatively crude methods and the depression of agricultural values during this period deterred young men from entering the agricultural courses of the colleges. Even the members of farm organizations which advocated agricultural education often advised students to keep out of the agricultural courses. Much of the agricultural instruction given in the colleges was either too theoretical or did not rise above the level of informational accounts of the farm products and operations. There was in this period little systematic effort to improve agricultural instruction pedagogically or systematically. Each teacher of agriculture very largely went his own way. Courses were often arranged to catch students or to meet the needs of young, ill-organized, and poorly equipped institutions. In many of the land-grant institutions the agricultural departments were completely overshadowed by the popular courses in engineering, general sciences, and liberal arts. Nevertheless, agricultural instruction was broadened in scope and the way was opened for the great and rapid development which was soon to follow. A beginning was made in the preparation of suitable textbooks and manuals of agricultural subjects, though less than 100 books on agriculture and related sciences were issued by agricultural college men up to 1895, as compared with nearly 300 in the next decade. It was in this period that Professor Henry of the University of Wisconsin, seeing the small demand for advanced agricultural instruction, organized the first successful short courses

in 1886, and four years later the special dairy school for the practical instruction of men to manage creameries and cheese factories.
It has been shown that from the beginning men who in the early societies advocated the establishment of agricultural schools and colleges expected to make experiments and scientific investigations a part of the work of these institutions. This was included in the consideration of the land grant act of 1862. As soon as colleges were established under this act they undertook such work. Little was accomplished during the first decade, but before the end of that period it became apparent to a number of men engaged in the work of the agricultural colleges that progress in agricultural instruction depended very largely on the accumulation of agricultural knowledge through systematic investigation and experimentation. Professor Hilgard dates the beginning of the experiment station movement in this country from the time of the meeting of the representatives of the land-grant colleges at Chicago in 1871 (p. 192), but before this Professor Johnson and his associates in the Yale Scientific School in Connecticut had inaugurated work looking toward the establishment of such stations. The experiments of Lawes and Gilbert at Rothamsted, England, the investigations of Boussingault in France, and the organized work of experiment stations in Germany, had already attracted attention in this country. From 1855 the United States Patent Office had employed men to conduct investigations in entomology, chemistry, and botany, and this work was enlarged after the Department of Agriculture was established in 1862.

In 1870 the Bussey Institution (p. 43) was established as a branch of Harvard College to give instruction in agriculture and related sciences. In the same year the trustees of the Massachusetts Society for Promoting Agriculture granted to the corporation of Harvard College a considerable sum "for the support of a laboratory and for experiments in agricultural chemistry, to be conducted on the Bussey estate." As soon as the laboratory was completed in 1871, F. H. Storer, professor of agricultural chemistry, and his assistants began field tests and chemical analyses of fertilizers. Reports of this work and of investigations on hybridizing plants, the composition of feeding stuffs, injurious fungi, etc., were soon published. The great fire in Boston in 1872 and the commercial crisis of 1873 crippled this institution financially and it did little more original work for a number of years.

DEVELOPMENT OF THE UNITED STATES DEPARTMENT OF AGRICULTURE

The United States Department of Agriculture established by the act of Congress of May 15, 1862, as an outgrowth of the agricultural division of the Patent Office, became increasingly an important factor in the promotion of agricultural education and research. It published the accounts of the progress of the land-grant institutions and in other ways aided their agricultural work. It distributed seeds and plants collected from domestic and foreign sources. For a number of years the grounds where department buildings now stand were used for field experiments. It published agricultural statistics and developed a system of crop reporting. Investigations in agricultural chemistry, economic entomology, agricultural botany, forestry, economic zoology, and animal diseases were undertaken and results of large importance in some of these lines were obtained within the first 25 years of the department's operation.

EARLY STATE EXPERIMENT STATIONS

The dearth of agricultural students in the land-grant colleges gave the teachers in the agricultural departments of these colleges time for experimental work and they turned their attention to such work with increased zeal during this period. In 1872, at a convention of representatives of agricultural colleges held in Washington in response to a call issued by the United States Commissioner of Agriculture, the question of the establishment of experiment stations was discussed and the report of a committee in favor of such institutions was adopted by the convention. (See p. 194.)

The University of California decided in 1873 to organize an experiment station and this was done by Professor Hilgard almost as soon as he went to the university in 1875. That year he equipped a laboratory for research in agricultural chemistry and began field experiments on deep and shallow plowing for cereals. Meanwhile Professor Johnson was attempting to secure the definite organization of an experiment station in Connecticut. Peculiar circumstances enabled Prof. W. O. Atwater, who had studied agricultural chemistry in Johnson's laboratory and then in Germany, actually to establish the first State agricultural experiment station in the United States, in 1875, at Wesleyan University, Middletown, Conn., but this was removed to New Haven in 1877 and put under Professor Johnson's direction. For several years its work was carried on in the laboratory of the Sheffield Scientific School. In 1877 the North Carolina Experiment Station was established by the State legislature and located at the State University, which was then a land-grant institution. In New York the Cornell University Experiment Station was organized in 1879 by the voluntary action of the faculty of agriculture of the university, and the following year the New Jersey State Experiment Station was created in connection with the Scientific School of Rutgers College. Prior to the passage of the Hatch Act in 1887, stations were also established in connection with the land-grant institutions in Alabama, Indiana, Kentucky, Louisiana, Maine, Massachusetts, Minnesota, Nebraska, New Hampshire, Ohio, Tennessee, Vermont, and Wisconsin. Experimental work in agriculture was also carried on in increasing measure at other land-grant colleges during this period. The results of the experimental work of the colleges and stations, while limited in extent and importance, were widely disseminated through their publications and the press.

As early as 1872 the need of increased funds for the land-grant colleges had been so impressed on Mr. Morrill that he introduced in Congress a bill for their further endowment by the Federal Government and repeated this effort many times within the next 18 years. When this for the time being was unavailing, the colleges took advantage of the widespread popularity of the experiment stations and began to plead for national funds for their support. In 1882

Seaman A. Knapp, then president of the Iowa State College, drafted a bill for this purpose and secured its introduction in the House of Representatives. A convention of delegates of the land-grant colleges which met in Washington in 1883 discussed and indorsed this project and through their united action, together with the active support of the United States Department of Agriculture, the grange and other friends of agricultural advancement, the experiment station act was passed four years later. The history of the movements for increased national support of agricultural education and research will be more fully treated in succeeding chapters.

During this period there was a great increase in the avenues of approach by the colleges to the farmers. The wide development of the granges, farmers' clubs, and other organizations gave the agricultural college workers very many opportunities for disseminating information through lectures, public or otherwise. The farmers' institutes grew materially in number and attendance. In a considerable number of States they were directly connected with the land-grant colleges and when otherwise organized college officers were often regularly on their staffs. Legislatures were beginning to make special appropriations for the support of the institutes. County and State fairs became more numerous and the college workers made exhibits or addresses at many of these fairs. The agricultural papers increased in number and circulation and published a great many articles by agricultural college workers.

While the farmers were very often discouraged by their difficult situations in this period and therefore were not inclined to have their sons study in the agricultural courses of these colleges, they nevertheless wanted all the helpful information these institutions could give them. The general influence of the land-grant colleges among the farming people was therefore much strengthened and widened.

The attitude of the farmers, especially as they were represented by their organizations, in many States, was for a long time strongly in favor of land-grant institutions separate from the universities, and this was intensified by the failure of the universities in most cases in the early years to attract any considerable number of agricultural students. This led to the separation of the agricultural college from the university in Mississippi in 1880, in Rhode Island in 1888, in North Carolina in 1889, in South Carolina in 1889, in Connecticut in 1893, and from Dartmouth College in New Hampshire in 1891. Between 1877 and 1893 separate colleges were established in eight of the new Western States but in Idaho, Nevada, and Wyoming, the agricultural work was connected with the State university. In Ohio an agricultural and mechanical college was broadened into a State university and in 1897 this was also done in Maine and more recently in Florida, Delaware, Maryland, New Jersey and New Hampshire.

TYPICAL LAND-GRANT INSTITUTIONS AND THEIR RELATIONS TO AGRICULTURAL EDUCATION

The conditions in the land-grant colleges, with special reference to agricultural education during the first quarter of a century after the passage of the Morrill Act of 1862, can best be shown by examples of the history of typical institutions during that period. Such examples are given in the following pages of this work.

MICHIGAN AGRICULTURAL COLLEGE

Michigan was the seventh State to accept the land grant under the act of Congress of July 2, 1862. The State act of acceptance was passed February 25, 1863, and the State received scrip for 240,000 acres of land. An agricultural land-grant board of six State officers, including the governor, was created to have charge of the selection, care, and disposal of the lands, and was directed to invest the proceeds of the sales of these lands in such manner as would establish a perpetual fund, the annual interest on which should be regularly applied under direction of the State board of agriculture to the maintenance of the State agricultural college. The lands actually located aggregated 235,663 acres and were strictly agricultural lands, timber lands being omitted. As the lands were sold, the amounts received were turned over to the State treasurer and loaned on a book account to the State at 7 per cent interest and this interest was paid to the college, beginning with 1870.

In 1862 the State appropriation for current expenses was $10,000; it rose to $20,000 in 1867 and remained at about this amount until 1874 when it dropped to $13,000; for the next 10 years it ranged from about $5,000 to $8,385 and then disappeared altogether for 15 years. The total income of the college in 1862 was $10,218, and thereafter until 1888 ranged from about that amount to about $40,000, leaving out of account the appropriations for special purposes.

When the land grant act passed the college had been in operation five years, and to comply fully with that act needed only to have authority to give military instruction, which was provided for by a State act in 1863. However, a separate mechanical and engineering division was not established until 1885, but civil engineering and subjects included in rural engineering were taught in this college even prior to the passage of the land grant act.

For 33 years the requirements for admission to the freshman class were "to pass a satisfactory examination in arithmetic, geography, grammar, reading, spelling, and penmanship. A knowledge of elementary algebra is desirable " (*193*).

Beginning with 1861 the college had authority to grant the degree of bachelor of science to students who had completed a 4-year course. Even with these low requirements for admission it was necessary to have preparatory classes for many of the students. Conditions arising out of the Civil War, combined with other circumstances, made it very difficult to secure a student body for this new type of education, or funds for the proper maintenance of the college. In 1863 the State appropriation was not made until three weeks after the beginning of the spring term and the papers gave the public the impression that the college would be closed. The total number of students that year was 60 and at one time only 48 were in attendance.

Theophilus Capen Abbot, who had been professor of history and English literature at this college, was elected president in December, 1862, and served in that capacity for 22 years. He also retained his professorship. In 1863 the other members of the faculty were: Manly Miles, M. D., professor of zoology and animal physiology; C. A. Kenaston, A. B., instructor of the preparatory class and secretary; R. C. Kedzie, A. M., M. D., professor of chemistry; Albert N.

Prentiss, B. S., instructor in botany and horticulture and superintendent of gardens; and Oscar Clute, B. S., instructor in pure and applied mathematics.

President Abbot was a graduate of Waterville College, now Colby College, at Waterville, Me., and had studied at the Bangor Theological School; Professor Miles was a graduate of the Rush Medical School at Chicago, Ill., had studied chemistry, zoology, comparative physiology, and anatomy, and had been assistant State geologist and engaged in a survey of the State with special reference to its fauna. He was also familiar with practical agriculture and deeply interested in the applications of science to this art. Professor Kedzie was a graduate of Oberlin College and of the Medical College of the University of Michigan and had been a practicing physician in Michigan for 11 years. Instructor Prentiss had been an advanced student at the college from 1857 to 1861, and taught there from 1863 to 1869, when he became professor of botany and horticulture in Cornell University. Instructor, afterwards professor, Clute was a graduate of the college in 1862, and its president from 1889 to 1893, when he became president of the Florida Agricultural College.

In 1865 George Thompson Fairchild, a graduate of Oberlin College, joined the faculty of the Michigan Agricultural College as instructor in English literature and was promoted to the professorship of this subject the following year. In 1879 he was called to the presidency of the Kansas State Agricultural College.

The personal character, fine scholarship, and strong teaching of the members of the early faculty enabled the Michigan Agricultural College to develop successfully and strongly in its new field, to exert a broad influence on the development of the land-grant colleges, and to gain the respect of educators in other types of institutions for higher learning.

Daniel Strange, of the class of 1867, thus describes the equipment of the college in 1864:

When I entered in '64, aside from the one dormitory, there was but the one College Hall devoted to instruction. This, of course, housed the library, museum, chemical laboratory and all biological laboratories, if indeed any could be said to exist. The farm buildings were but the one large cattle barn, a very small brick horse barn and a pig sty. The teams were two worn-out horse teams and two good ox teams. There were three shorthorn cows, two Devon cows, and a bull of each of these breeds. There were a few grade cattle and Suffolk and Essex swine, but I think no sheep until the following year.

There were four small brick cottages for the president and professors.

The above with the farm constituted the College's material equipment (*193*).

There was no regular professor of agriculture until 1865, when Doctor Miles was made professor of practical agriculture and superintendent of the farm. The following is a partial outline of the course in agriculture announced in the catalogue of that year (*193*):

PRACTICAL AGRICULTURE

First year.—Laying out of farms; farm fences; arrangement and planning of farm buildings; general principles of tillage; principles of drainage; laying out and construction of drains; implements for preparing the soil for crops; mechanical preparation of the soil; methods of seeding; implements for seeding—their construction and management; harvesting crops; implements and machines used in securing crops; principles of stock breeding; and breeds of domestic animals—their characteristics and adaptation to particular purposes.

Fourth year.—General principles of farm economy; manures—their management and mode of application; succession of crops; preparation of the soil for particular crops; cultivation of grain crops; cultivation of root crops; management of grasslands; stock husbandry; care of animals and principles of feeding; fattening of animals; and management of sheep.

The provision in the State act of February 12, 1855, requiring the students at this college to engage in manual labor was faithfully carried out and until about 1889 all students were compelled to work from 12 to 15 hours a week and received wages which helped toward paying their college expenses.

After that time until 1894 students who showed proficiency in farm operations were given educational labor and later educational field work or laboratory work was substituted for all compulsory labor.

The college year began late in February and continued until about the middle of November. By this arrangement students were employed on the farm during the growing season and such pay as they received aided them to meet their college expenses. It also enabled a considerable number of them to earn money as school teachers during the winter. Many colleges at that time had a long vacation in the winter for this purpose or made special arrangements for students engaged to teach school at that season. The Michigan Agricultural College continued to have the long winter vacation until 1896.

The methods of teaching employed at this college in early days have been described by C. E. Bessey, a student there from 1863 to 1869 and afterwards professor of botany and dean of the Agricultural College of the University of Nebraska, as follows:

It was emphatically the period of the textbook. Some of the professors gave lectures, but in every subject the student always had his textbook as the basis of his study, and daily recitations were the rule. We learned things from books, and were asked to repeat them orally at greater or less length to our teachers. * * *

Chemistry, even at that early day, was taught by practical work in the laboratory. We had one lecture or recitation a day, and in addition two hours daily of laboratory work. In the lecture the professor accompanied his presentation of the subject by carefully planned demonstration experiments, greatly to our edification, and occasionally to our amusement. In the laboratory we plunged at once into the qualitative analysis of unknown substances. We learned to handle chemicals and apparatus by the very simple plan of actually handling them ourselves. * * *

In marked contrast to chemistry, was the presentation of physics, which was wholly a textbook study. We used Olmstead's Natural Philosophy, reciting and demonstrating (on the blackboard) from its pages, but neither making experiments ourselves nor seeing any made by the professor.

Surveying was made a living subject for us by the addition to a stiff textbook, of a considerable amount of field work, with compass, transit, and level, and the accurate plotting of results.

Our geology was still a textbook subject only. There was no thought of the use of specimens of rocks or fossils by the class, nor was there any required field work in connection with the subject. Yet there were in the museum on the third floor many such specimens. * * *

In zoology we used a textbook, but its required use was small, indeed. The professor (Doctor Miles) loved to talk to us, and helped us in his talks far deeper into the subject than did any textbook of that period.

Even the subject of entomology was mainly a textbook study. We memorized so many pages and repeated them as nearly as possible verbatim. Here we looked at specimens brought to the class. There was also some desultory collecting of specimens, and now and then a student was seen frantically pawing the air with a "bug-net" in his efforts to capture some beetle, bug, or butterfly.

In my own science of botany the work was then mainly confined to daily recitations from a textbook, accompanied later by dissections and "analyses" of plants in the classroom, under the direction of the professor. We had a few simple dissecting microscopes which we used in these exercises. Here was no doubt the germ of the laboratory idea as applied to botany. (*193*).

Of the agricultural instruction at the college as he found it when he first came Doctor Beal says:

In 1870 it was not difficult to plan a course of study for an agricultural college. Except some points gathered from manual labor, which were not numerous nor very important, the students received, all told, eight weeks of daily instruction in horticulture and ten weeks in agriculture, and these topics were chiefly taught by the slow process of lectures. There were few books and papers to aid students in their pursuit of agriculture. The college was in the woods, so to speak, with no model to follow (*193*).

The year 1870 was an important one in the history of the college. Influenced apparently by the example of the University of Michigan, whose regents had decided that year to admit women, the agricultural college allowed 10 women to take work there that year. President Abbot advocated a course especially suited to women, including especially household economy, but this was not established until long after.

They studied chemistry, botany, horticulture, floriculture, trigonometry, surveying, entomology, bookkeeping, and other branches. Their progress in study was rapid and their improvement marked.

Work was furnished them when it could be; they prepared seed for the ground, cut potatoes, transplanted tomatoes and flowering plants, pruned shrubbery, gathered small fruit, did some work in the greenhouse and many other kinds of work (*193*).

The lack of suitable quarters for women at the college prevented the attendance of any considerable number and as late as 1886 there were only 12 women students. In 1895 the college building known as Abbot Hall was devoted to the exclusive use of women students as a dormitory and a laboratory for a course in home economics.

Up to 1870 the college had had a severe struggle for existence. Its income had been less than $40,000, but that year the State appropriation was $70,000, including $10,000 for a chemical laboratory, the first laboratory building erected on the campus. The faculty was enlarged from four to seven professors, the number of students increased, and from that time the value of the institution in the educational system of the State was increasingly appreciated by the public.

That year William James Beal, then professor of natural history in the old Chicago University, came to the college to lecture in botany, and in 1871 became professor of botany and horticulture. He was a graduate from the classical course of the University of Michigan and also had the degree of bachelor of science from Harvard University, where he had studied under Asa Gray, Jeffried Wyman, and Louis Agassiz. He brought to the college full information regarding the new methods of scientific study then being introduced in this country under the inspiring leadership of Agassiz and was able to adapt those methods to the peculiar conditions at the agricultural college. He was also largely influential in broadening and strengthening the scientific work of the college. His students were

required to make observations of living plants, as well as dried specimens, and record them in notes and drawings. The college herbarium
was greatly enlarged, particularly as regards the Michigan flora, and
the plantations of horticultural and other plants on the college
grounds were also increased in variety and extent. In 1873 plats
of different kinds of grasses and clovers were planted and in 1877
a botanic garden was begun. In this garden and other places at the
college ultimately at least 5,000 species and varieties of plants were
grown. An arboretum begun in 1875 had at one time 215 species
of trees and shrubs.

The daily program of studies in 1871 was as follows (*193*) :

First term

Class	8 a. m.	9 a. m.	10 a. m.	11 a. m.
Senior		Agriculture, zoology.	Astronomy, French.	Landscape gardening, civil engineering.
Junior	Analytical chemistry.	Analytical chemistry.	Praxis, 4 weeks, analytical chemistry.	Drawing, 6 weeks.
Sophomore		English literature	Praxis, 4 weeks, botany.	Elementary chemistry.
Freshman		Praxis, 6 weeks, history.	Algebra	Bookkeeping, 6 weeks, physical geography.

Second term

Senior		Mental philosophy.	Moral philosophy, political economy.	French.
Junior		Mechanics.	Physiology.	Chemical physics.
Sophomore	Analytical chemistry.	Analytical chemistry.	Praxis, 3 weeks, analytical chemistry.	Botany, 10 weeks, horticulture.
Freshman	Agriculture	Praxis, 4 weeks, botany.	Algebra, common geometry.	

That year there were 141 students, including 1 graduate student,
12 seniors, 9 juniors, 26 sophomores, 81 freshmen, 4 special students,
and 8 women students.

The number of students fluctuated in the following years. In
1883–84 there were 171. That year there were 10 professors, including those in practical agriculture, horticulture, and veterinary medicine, and assistants in chemistry and mathematics. In practical
agriculture the course included lectures two terms in sophomore year,
and a half term in senior year, with a term's work in agricultural
engineering that year. The students began to do a little stock
judging on the college herd. In horticulture there were lectures on
landscape gardening one term in sophomore year, and in general
horticulture two terms in junior year. In veterinary medicine there
were lectures and demonstrations three terms in senior year. On the
college farm 200 acres were still in the original forest, 110 acres in
pastures, 180 acres in crops grown in rotation, 10 acres in experiments,
and about 100 acres in lawns, building sites, gardens, and orchards.
The college buildings included three substantial brick halls for
classrooms and dormitories, a chemical laboratory, a botanical
laboratory, a library and museum, a small astronomical observatory,
a carpenter's shop, a large greenhouse, and separate barns for cattle,
horses, sheep, and grain.

Students in the regular agricultural course did not aggregate more than 209, except from 1886 to 1888, until 1910 when they numbered 313. Thereafter their numbers materially increased. The total attendance at the college was greatly increased after the establishment of the engineering division, which began with 35 students in 1886 and enrolled 414 students in 1910.

The number of graduates in the agricultural division ranged from 5 to 30 between 1870 and 1880 and from 11 to 38 between 1881 and 1910. Graduate students ranged from 1 to 7 between 1871 and 1885, and from 11 to 37 between 1886 and 1897, after which there were not more than 9 for many years.

In 1885 Edwin Willits became president of the college and undertook the establishment of a course in mechanical engineering. Thus the college passed into the class of agricultural and mechanical colleges. The faculty was increased by the addition of professors in military science and tactics, and in mechanics and French. In 1887–88 there were also three assistant professors and two instructors. The students numbered 312. The buildings had been increased by a veterinary laboratory, a mechanical laboratory and workship, and a barn for experimental feeding. The course in practical agriculture had been changed to include lectures one term in freshman year and two half terms in sophomore year with electives for seniors during two terms. The required work in agriculture was given in three series of lectures covering drainage, rotation of crops, manures, cultivation, stock breeding and feeding, " farm economy," accounts, " selling," farm law, history of agriculture and agricultural literature. "A practical familiarity with the system practiced on the college farm fixes in the student's mind the instruction received in the classroom." The scientific basis of agriculture continued to be taught in the departments of chemistry and botany. L. H. Bailey served as professor of horticulture from 1885 to 1888. His lectures were supplemented by the textbook and more definitely related field work. " The first distinctively horticultural laboratory in this country " was built at this college in 1887.

Experimental work in agriculture has been carried on at the college since its establishment. Provision for a record of experiments on the college farm was made in the act establishing the college and in the act of March 15, 1861, reorganizing it. The first account of experiments at the college appeared in the annual report of the State board of agriculture for 1863 and thereafter each year until 1885 when the legislature authorized the college to issue and distribute bulletins containing reports on its experiments. In the department of chemistry analytical studies were made of Michigan soils, muck, wheat, and sorghum, as well as of a variety of materials sent in by the farmers; field experiments were made with muck, composts, and commercial fertilizers, and meteorological records were regularly kept and published, beginning with 1863. In the department of zoology and entomology there was much work in the collection and study of injurious insects and later in their control. There were also experiments with bees. In the department of botany and horticulture, besides the extensive collection and study of the Michigan flora, field experiments were made with varieties of grasses, clovers, apples, pears, cherries, plums, grapes, small fruits, potatoes, and other vegetables; breeding by selection and crossing of wheat, corn, beans, onions, tomatoes, and other vegetables; root pruning of corn, cultivation of an apple orchard, seed testing, etc. In the department of agriculture there were field experiments with the cereals, potatoes, and root crops. In animal husbandry between 1864 and 1870 there were experiments in breeding sheep and cattle, and in the feeding of pigs and sheep, and later feeding experiments with cattle, on the influence of different rations on the quality of milk, on the creaming of milk at different temperatures, etc. With the spread of the experiment-station movement, beginning about 1875, the experimental work at this college increased in variety and extent. In 1882 the college cooperated with Professor Atwater, of Connecticut, in the extensive series of experiments with nitrogen fertilizers then being conducted under his direction in a number of States. That year the college had a special State appropriation of $1,000 for experiments in the making and use of silage, the culture of sorghum, and variety tests of grain and beets.

While the limited financial resources of the college and the pressure of other duties, especially with the increase in the number of students, prevented the development of experimental work on an extensive scale, sufficient useful experiments were made prior to the establishment of the Michigan Experiment Station to greatly strengthen the position of the college in its relation with the farmers of the State.

Farmers' institutes under the auspices of the college were begun in 1876, when two institutes were held. Thereafter until 1889 six institutes were held each year in different parts of the State and did much to bring the college to the favorable attention of the farmers. From its beginning the college had the active support of the State agricultural society, but the number of members of this organization was small. From 1875 a broader influence on the development of the college was exerted by the grange, which favored liberal appropriations for its support and otherwise aided its work. The grange was much interested in the experiments carried on by the college and in the farmers' institutes.

The general influence of this college on the movement for agricultural education and research during this period was also quite important. It so maintained its distinctive character as an institution primarily for agricultural education that it attracted much attention from the friends of such education throughout the country. Its teachers and graduates were much sought for by the land-grant colleges in other States.

During the first 30 years this college gave more or less instruction in the theory and practice of agriculture and in the related sciences to about 4,000 students, of whom about 400 completed the regular college course. About half of these students engaged in agriculture in Michigan and elsewhere and a considerable number of the graduates became teachers or investigators in agriculture or writers on agricultural subjects. Through their connection with agricultural colleges, societies, farmers' institutes, the agricultural press, and in other ways the men and women who had studied at the Michigan Agricultural College during these years exerted an important influence on the advancement of American agriculture.

KANSAS STATE AGRICULTURAL COLLEGE

The Kansas State Agricultural College had its origin in Bluemont Central College, chartered February 9, 1858, under the auspices of the Methodist Episcopal Church. As actually organized it was an institution of the ordinary classical type, but its founders desired to make it helpful to the agriculture of the State. Its charter provided for—

an agricultural department, with separate professors, to test soils, experiment in the raising of crops, the cultivation of trees, etc., upon a farm set apart for the purpose, so as to bring out to the utmost practical results, the agricultural advantages of Kansas, especially the capabilities of the high prairie lands (*141*).

In 1860 this college was offered to the State on condition that it be made the State university. After the passage of the Morrill Land Grant Act the authorities of the college again offered to donate it to the State and this offer was accepted in connection with the State's acceptance of the Federal college land grant, February 3, 1863.

On February 19, 1863, as soon as the legislative resolution could take effect, the State of Kansas took over the property in fee simple of Bluemont Central College Association located near Manhattan in the county of Riley.

Under the Morrill Act of 1862 Kansas was granted 90,000 acres of land. Three commissioners were appointed by the governor to locate the lands. Some of the sites were within railroad limits and thus counted double. The final amount of land received by the State was 82,313.52 acres. In 1866 J. M. Harvey began the appraisal of these lands and completed the work on July 27, 1867. I. T. Goodnow, one of the founders of Bluemont College, was appointed land agent, which office he held until 1873 when about $180,000 had been obtained from the sale of about 42,000 acres. Ten years later this fund had increased to about $240,000, and in 1921 to $491,746.74. This sum is invested in Kansas school and municipal bonds paying 6 per cent interest. As late as 1907 the college received an additional grant making the 90,000 acres complete. This was not attained until after a legal contest and a long-time appeal to Congress. President Cleveland vetoed the first favorable resolution passed, but President Roosevelt signed a later one.

The State appropriations from 1864 to 1873 ranged from $2,700 to $23,000 and totaled $79,634; from 1874 to 1879 they amounted to $78,287 and from 1880 to 1887 to $121,961. The township of Manhattan in 1871 donated $12,000 in bonds for the purchase of a farm. Funds loaned by the State were given to the college under an act of March 1, 1870.

Immediately after the approval of this act, the board of regents had engraved or lithographed 364 pieces of scrip, so-called "College greenbacks," of the denomination of $100 each, made payable at different times for a period of eight years, beginning July 1, 1870. These orders were used in purchasing the farm and supplies for the same, for boarding-house repairs, and for improvements of various kinds. On December 22, 1871, the issue of this depreciated paper was stopped by the board of regents, but the $33,700 already issued proved a serious burden to the institution for many years, on account of the high rate of interest which prevailed at that time in Kansas (*141*).

In 1877 the legislature required that not more than $15,000 annually should be spent to pay teachers until the debts of the college were paid in full and until " said college shall refund to the State all moneys advanced by the State to pay for instructors and running expenses."

When the agricultural college took over the equipment of Bluemont College it had only one substantial building, located on a farm of 100 acres. A boarding hall which had been erected by private parties was purchased by the college. After the purchase of a second farm of 155 acres in 1871, later increased to 219 acres, separate buildings for horticulture, chemistry, and mechanic arts, and a part of a main college building were erected during President Anderson's administration. Under President Fairchild up to 1887 the main building was completed, a residence for the president, an armory, and a greenhouse were erected and the farm buildings enlarged.

As a State college the institution was opened for students September 2, 1863. Regarding its beginnings, J. D. Walters has written as follows in his history of the college:

> It is natural that the college should have remained for a time, as it did, under the care of its founders and generous donators, and should have conformed to the ideal before their minds. The charter provided for four departments—science and literature, mechanic arts, agriculture, and military tactics. Of these, that of science and literature was put in operation. The course was laid out to cover four years, with an indefinite preparatory, and conformed closely with that of Bluemont Central College. The first catalogue gives the names of ninety-four students in the preparatory department and fourteen in the college proper. Seventy-four were from Riley County (*141*).

The president, Joseph Denison, was a farmer's son, a native of Massachusetts, and a graduate of Wesleyan University, Middletown, Conn. After serving as a teacher and minister in his native State he came to Kansas in 1855 and was one of the prime movers in the organization of Bluemont College, and its third president. He was a conservative in educational matters and apparently was especially interested in the training of teachers for the rural schools. This was a matter of prime importance in the early history of the State. Lack of schools among the rural people made it very difficult for young people on the farms to prepare for college and therefore in the early years of the Kansas college most of the students were in preparatory classes.

Apparently there was from the beginning more or less pressure upon the college to do something for the promotion of agricultural education. The first year botany, general and agricultural chemistry, zoology, and other natural sciences were included in the course of study, together with Liebig's husbandry, and in 1864 a separate agricultural course of three years was outlined in the catalogue. This included lectures and textbook work on fruits, treatise on the horse, book of the farm, diseases of domestic animals, agricultural chemistry, and soil analysis.

In 1865 the scientific work of the college was strengthened by the appointment of Benjamin F. Mudge as professor of natural science and higher mathematics. He was a native of Maine, a graduate of Wesleyan University and State geologist in Kansas. The next year John S. Hougham was made professor of agricultural science and a more elaborate course in agriculture and science was offered in the catalogue. Professor Hougham was a graduate of Wabash College, Crawfordsville, Ind., and had been a teacher in Franklin College in that State. After leaving the Kansas college in 1872 he was for a time professor of agricultural chemistry in Purdue University.

In 1868 the preparatory course covered three years; the four-year courses were designated as agricultural and scientific, college, and military; mention was also made of mechanic arts, civil engineering, commercial, and mercantile courses. That year the first farmers' meeting at the college was held.

The agricultural course, as outlined in 1869, included the following subjects: Freshmen—soils, tillage, draining, and fertilizers; sophomores—crops and farm machinery, physiology and diseases of animals, and horticulture; juniors—field crops and animal husbandry; seniors—history of agriculture and systems of agriculture. Excursions were taken for observation of farm operation.

In 1870 the catalogue gives in detail two 2-year preparatory courses, one agricultural and the other literary, and four 4-year courses, agricultural, mechanic arts, military science, and literary. That year Fred E. Miller, a graduate of the Michigan Agricultural College, became professor of practical agriculture and superintendent of the farm, and Elbridge Gale, a graduate of Brown University, who had come to Manhattan in 1864 and established a nursery there, was made professor of horticulture and botany.

In 1871 the only courses offered were a 2-year course in the preparatory department and a 4-year course in the collegiate department. The catalogue stated there would be—

from 7 to 10 hours of practical instruction in agriculture under Superintendent Miller; in horticulture under Superintendent Gale; and in mechanics under Superintendent Todd. * * * Students laboring in agricultural, horticultural, and mechanical departments are paid by the hour.

The annual report of the college for that year includes as lecturers C. V. Riley in entomology and H. J. Detmers of the Illinois Industrial University in veterinary science.

The students in 1871 numbered 111 men and 72 women. There were 4 women graduates in the literary course and 1 man in the agricultural course, who was the first student to receive the degree of bachelor of science. In collegiate courses there were 3 seniors, 3 juniors, 2 sophomores, and 7 freshmen in the literary course, and 1 junior, 4 sophomores, and 5 freshmen in the agricultural and science course. However, Professor Hougham reported 2 classes of 14 and 5 members, respectively, in agriculture, using Waring's Elements of Agriculture as a textbook. Thirty men and women attended lectures in horticulture and forestry. Thomas's American Fruit Cultures was used and there was practical instruction in root grafting, etc. The regular classes in agriculture and horticulture occupied two terms each. For practical work the classes were organized in divisions of 8 or 10 students with a leader. Four divisions of men and one of women did practical work on the farm and in the orchard, vineyard, and garden. Labor was required for one hour on Monday and Thursday. Additional labor was voluntary and was paid from 3 to 15 cents per hour.

Progress in establishing instruction directly relating to agriculture and other industries was not sufficiently rapid to satisfy the farmers of the State. The general atmosphere and influence of the college were too much on the side of classical and scientific education. The grange grew very rapidly in Kansas at this time and by 1873 had great influence in the political affairs of the State. As a result the legislature passed an act, approved March 6, 1873, reconstructing the government of the State institutions. Under this act the governor appointed a new board of regents for the agricultural college. President Denison resigned and John A. Anderson was appointed to succeed him.

The 10 years after 1863 showed very little growth in the college attendance. Up to 1873 only 15 students had graduated. The total attendance at any one term never reached 125. Professor Walters comments on this period in the history of the college as follows:

The reasons for this slow growth must be looked for in many directions: The newness of the State, the western location of Manhattan, the inadequacy of means, the founding of rival literary institutions at Lawrence, Baldwin, Topeka, etc., and the fact that industrial education was in its experimental stage. President Denison and a majority of the professors were classic students, and had no faith in the educational results of technical instruction not connected with the classics. They planned to add elective work in practical science and applied mathematics to the "old education," but it was intended to supplement, and not supplant, this. The introduction of obligatory daily manual labor as an educational factor was not attempted. Aside from occasional lectures on general topics, little was done for agriculture and the mechanic arts, and the increasingly frequent demands for an institution that would educate toward, instead of away from, farm and the workshop were met with uncertain promises. The board, largely composed of professional men, must have held similar views, though the report of the State commissioners of 1873 says that "attempts were made by members of this body at different times to change the curriculum of study, and in other respects to alter the running of the college so as to make it conform more nearly to the demands of the people" (*141*).

President Anderson was a native of Pennsylvania and a graduate of Miami University. He had been a minister in California, chaplain in the Army, and a prominent worker in the United States Sanitary Commission. He had come to Kansas in 1868 as pastor of the Presbyterian Church at Junction City. He was a man of strong and positive character, well fitted to undertake the task of putting the college on a more practical basis.

His views of education, which molded the educational future of this institution, were as follows:

Ninety-seven per cent of the people of Kansas are in the various industrial vocations, and only 3 per cent in the learned professions; yet prominence is given to the studies that are most useful to the professions instead of those that are most useful to the industrial pursuits. This state of things should be reversed, and the greatest prominence given to the subjects that are the most certain to fit the great majority for the work they should and will pursue.

Most young men and young women are unable to go "through" college. Therefore, each year's course of study should, as far as practicable, be complete in itself.

The natural effect of exclusive headwork, as contradistinguished from handwork, is to beget a dislike for the latter.

The only way to counteract this tendency is to educate the head and the hands at the same time, so that when a young man leaves college he will be prepared to earn his living in a vocation in which he fitted himself to excel.

Putting off the choice of an occupation until after the student leaves college as a graduate, instead of making it when he enters college, or as soon thereafter as possible, is a mistake.

Some agricultural colleges take as an objective point the graduation of agricultural experts, experimenters, professors of sciences, editors, etc.; the Kansas State Agricultural College should take as an objective point the graduation of capable farmers and housewives, and it should make an effort to graduate thousands of such.

Whatever else may yet need to be tried, there is no use in repeating the experiment of flying a literary kite with an agricultural tail, so often made in various quarters. It is a pleasant regental and professional amusement, and quite attractive to an immediate locality; but there is nothing in it for the industrial student, whose estate pays for the kite (*141*).

The board of regents, adopting his views, discontinued the division of literature and organized those of agriculture and the mechanic arts. Edward M. Shelton, a graduate of the Michigan Agricultural College, was made professor of practical agriculture and superintendent of the farm in 1874. The farmers' course and the women's course covered six years and the mechanics' course five years.

Workshops in iron and wood, a printing office, a telegraph office, a kitchen laboratory, and a sewing room were equipped. Fifty minutes of educational manual labor were added to the daily work of every student.

In 1876 the course of study was reduced to four years. The preparatory course was abolished and Butler's Analogy, Latin, German, and French were discontinued. Admission requirements were lowered to reach the better grades of the public schools.

Throughout President Anderson's administration the great majority of the students were in the first year's course and only 25 graduated during his term of office. The regular teaching of agriculture was for a term in both the second and fourth years. There was also instruction in horticulture and agricultural chemistry. The agricultural operations of the college were greatly enlarged. A considerable number of students participated in the farm operations, experiments with crops and livestock were conducted, and farmers' meetings were addressed.

To defend his educational policies, as well as to afford practice for the students in printing, President Anderson, in 1875, established a weekly college paper called the Industrialist. This also furnished a medium for dissemination of information regarding the work of the college. Under Anderson's vigorous editorship this paper became widely known. It has been continued ever since, but in 1897 was changed to a monthly magazine.

The number of students increased during the first years of Anderson's presidency but declined after 1876. There was much conflict both within and without the institution regarding his educational policies, which were radical and if fully carried out would have reduced the college largely to the status of a trade school. In 1878 he was elected to Congress and this led to his resignation in 1879.

His successor was George T. Fairchild, a native of Ohio and a graduate of Oberlin College, who had been professor of English literature at the Michigan Agricultural College and its acting president in 1873. He was a man of mature judgment, progressive ideas in education, and fine spirit. His ideal of education related to agriculture was set forth in an article written while he was at the Michigan college for the Chicago Farmers' Review, and afterwards published by the Michigan State Board of Agriculture.

True scientific principles are to be taught and enforced by a thorough drill in observation. The eyes must see and the hands handle the very elements of nature, in order to gain proper ideas of nature's use. There must be a definite training to think accurately and connectedly, and intensely if need be. * * * Added to this must be the formation of habits of ready action to a purpose. * * * The college must gather and impart the best of instruction in the art of tilling the soil. * * * [The course of study must be thorough and] in this there must be systematic instruction by the most approved methods in the sciences, training to logical investigation of facts and principles, history and general knowledge of civilization enough to kindle inquiry and technical training enough to give a general ability. This involves a drill in manual labor that shall make the hands ready and the eyes quick.

By careful work and avoidance of antagonisms President Fairchild greatly strengthened the Kansas college. He established weekly faculty meetings, encouraged discussion of educational problems, and created a loyal and united faculty. A single course of study with limited electives, especially to meet the requirements of men and women, was adopted. The requirements for admission were gradually raised and the industrial work of the students was extended, strengthened, and systematized. The number of students increased from 276 in 1879-80 to 481 in 1886-87. During this period there was still great difficulty in holding students beyond the freshman year. In 1886-87 there were 303 freshmen (including about 75 pursuing preparatory studies), 100 sophomore, 44 junior, 24 senior, and 10 post graduate students. The number of graduates increased from 7 in 1880 to 21 in 1886 and 1887. Agriculture continued to be taught in one term of sophomore and senior years. The number of students who gave special attention to agriculture continued to be relatively small. In 1882-83 the classes in agriculture included 7 seniors and 39 sophomores. There was also practical work in agriculture by 22 juniors and 12 sophomores. Dairying was taught to 7 women in the sophomore class. In 1886-87 there were 22 seniors and 49 sophomores in agricultural classes and 38 juniors and 38 sophomores in farm work. Horticulture was taught to 48 men and 31 women and practical work in horticulture was taken by 27 juniors and 29 sophomores. In other industrial work there were in 1885-86, 54 students in telegraphy, 70 in printing, and 240 in the mechanical department, mostly doing work in carpentering.

Experimental work was begun early in the history of the college. In 1867, 500 forest trees, 200 apple trees, and small numbers of other fruit trees were planted on the college farm. By 1873 the experimental forest contained 36,370 trees and there were many varieties of fruits being tested. Trials were being made of fertilizers, soil preparation, methods of planting, special crops, etc. In 1874 Professor Shelton introduced alfalfa and experiments were also begun with wheat, cowpeas, grasses, and other forage plants. In 1883, 1884, and 1885 special publications were issued which showed a considerable range of experiments, including those in the seeding, cultivation, and manuring of corn, feeding of pigs, steers, and milk cows, with special reference to the use in the rations of corn in different forms, alfalfa, and grasses. An annex to the college barn was built in 1884 for use in experiments with livestock.

The first farmers' institute was held at Manhattan November 14, 1868, and January 2 to 10, 1872, there was a "well-organized and widely advertised farmers' institute under the auspices of the faculty. It was well attended by representative farmers from all parts of the State." Some other more or less informal meetings of farmers were held at the college in its early days. Under President Fairchild's leadership a regularly organized system of institutes was inaugurated in 1881. At least six institutes were held each winter in as many different counties. Members of the faculty also attended meetings of granges and other farm organizations.

During the first 25 years over 2,500 students attended the Kansas Agricultural College, of whom about one-third were women. Most of these students remained at the college for only a part of the course and it has been estimated that three-fourths of these came from and returned to the farm. Up to 1890 there were 232 graduates, of whom 73 were women. Previous to 1877, with two exceptions, the 27 graduates received the bachelor of arts degree. After that the bachelor of science degree was given. Only about 30 of these graduates became farmers or horticulturists, but a number of them have occupied important positions as administrators, teachers, or investigators in Federal or State agricultural institutions. Through its instruction in the natural sciences and their applications to various useful arts, its development of systematic courses in home economics, its teaching of the theory and practice of agriculture, and its insistence on the importance of vocational training, in connection with a more liberal culture, it laid a strong foundation for its future extensive growth and exerted a wide influence on the development of our system of higher education relating to agriculture and other industries.

MASSACHUSETTS AGRICULTURAL COLLEGE

When the problem of the acceptance and disposition of the land grant of 1862 was presented to the Massachusetts Legislature by Governor Andrew in 1863 decided differences of opinion developed. This is shown in the report of the joint committee on the governor's message (*178*). The committee argued that Massachusetts should provide institutions for mechanic arts, as well as agriculture. The resolutions adopted at a meeting in Boston February 16, 1863, in favor of having the Massachusetts Institute of Technology represent mechanic arts, were cited. The committee believed that agriculture should not be neglected, though some thought "that agricultural schools are not beneficial." Others believed that the agricultural school should be elementary, but the committee was opposed to this plan.

This college of agriculture and the mechanic arts ought not to rival the primary schools, or grammar schools, or high schools, or district schools of the State. The true theory of education is that all the children and youth of the State should be educated together in the public schools of the Commonwealth, without any reference to the occupation of their parents, or to the occupation that they themselves intend to pursue, until they arrive at an age when it is proper for them to choose their own occupation. The people would not tolerate a blacksmith's high school, clergyman's high school, or sailor's high school. Why, then, a farmers' high school for the sons of farmers?

An agricultural school should be *a professional school,* or a college for young men * * * who desire to obtain a good education in the science and art of agriculture. Whatever pertains to agriculture should there be taught and whatever has no immediate connection with agriculture should not be taught. * * * Instruction should be given principally by lectures and by exhibitions of drawings, models and experiments to illustrate and confirm the truths presented. The instruction should be so systematized as to furnish aid alike to those who could afford to enjoy the advantages of the school but a short time, and to those who could complete its full course of instruction. * * * There can be but one serious impediment in the way of making a true professional agricultural school in this State prosper, and that is a want of interest in it among the agricultural population (*178*).

The governor and other leading men favored an arrangement with Harvard College, the Institute of Technology, and Zoological Museum, which in effect would create " a grand university." This would include use of the Bussey fund and farm for instruction and experiments. Objectors to these plans urged that agricultural experiments and instruction could be carried on better with less expense in a rural region. A committee of the board of agriculture, including Marshall P. Wilder and George B. Loring, afterwards United States Commissioner of Agriculture, were among the opponents. Others wanted the land-grant fund divided among the colleges of the State and there were petitions from Amherst and Williams Colleges on this basis. The joint committee, however, favored one or at most two institutions.

A subcommittee had visited and reported on the agricultural college of Pennsylvania. Their report evidently made a deep impression on the joint committee, who concluded that " a school like that can only succeed as a large school * * * wholly disconnected with all existing institutions and separate from all large cities and towns." Otherwise manual labor, which the committee believed was a very important factor in an agricultural college, would be treated with contempt by the students.

The necessary funds " should be contributed equally by the State and individuals." The committee's report was accompanied with a bill granting one-tenth of the land-grant fund for the purchase of land for an agricultural college; and of the remainder, one-third for the Institute of Technology and two-thirds for an agricultural college under a separate board of trustees.

Three acts were passed, one accepting the land grant April 18, 1863; one incorporating the agricultural college April 29, 1863; and one dividing the land-grant fund as proposed by the committee, April 21, 1864.

A board of trustees was created consisting of 13 members elected by the legislature for life, and the governor, lieutenant governor, secretaries of the boards of education and agriculture, and the president of the college as members ex officio. In practice one member was elected from each county. The location, plan of organization, and course of study were originally made subject to the approval of the legislature but later of the governor and council. By an act of May 26, 1866, the board of agriculture was made a board of overseers, with advisory and visitorial powers.

The board of trustees was organized November 8, 1863, and set about securing funds for the college. The act relating to the land grant provided that not less than $75,000 must be raised by subscription or otherwise for buildings before one-tenth of the proceeds of the sale of the lands would be paid to the board. Funds had to be provided for livestock and other equipment, maintenance of the farm, and faculty. Under the terms of the land grant act of 1862 the State was pledged to establish an agricultural college within five years after the passage of that act. The trustees therefore petitioned the legislature in 1864 to make the land-grant funds immediately available in order that they might locate the college. They also asked for further financial aid from the State.

Henry F. French, a lawyer and judge, who had been prominent in the agricultural affairs of the State, had written a book on drainage, and had recently visited agricultural institutions in Europe, was elected the first president of the college November 29, 1864, and served two years. His successor was Paul A. Chadbourne, instructor in natural sciences at Williams College. Ill health compelled his resignation after a few months. Then came the long-time presidency of William S. Clark. He had been trained at Amherst College, including studies in geology and mineralogy under Doctor Hitchcock, had studied chemistry and botany at Göttingen, Germany, and had made special botanical observations at the Kew Gardens at London. He had then been professor of chemistry, botany, and zoology in Amherst College and a colonel in the Civil War. As representative from Amherst in the legislature between 1864 and 1867 he had an important part in determining the location of the college.

The board of trustees considered the offers made by Northampton, Springfield, Lexington, and Amherst, and decided to locate the college at Amherst, that town having agreed to raise $50,000 by taxation and $25,000 by subscription.

The State of Massachusetts received 360,000 acres in scrip. On May 11, 1864, scrip for 36,000 acres was transferred to the Massachusetts Agricultural College to be used in purchasing a site for the college. The proceeds from the sale of this scrip amounted to $29,778 and were used in part payment for the farm of 310 acres at Amherst, costing $34,999. The remainder of the scrip was sold by the State from time to time. In 1868 the land-grant fund amounted to $205,-509 and the income to $12,445, two-thirds of which was paid to the agricultural college. In 1871 by fortunate reinvestments and State grants the endowment fund for technical education became $350,000 and this was increased to $360,000 in 1876. In 1882 the legislature divided this fund into a United States grant roughly set at $219,-000, and a Commonwealth grant aggregating $141,575. The former was invested in bonds at 5 per cent, making the annual allotment of the Federal land-grant fund to the agricultural college $7,300. The college also received the income of the Commonwealth grant.

The need of State aid for the maintenance of the college was early apparent.

In 1864 the legislature granted the college $10,000, provided that repayment would be made from the income of the land-scrip fund (but this was illegal) and by an act of May 11, 1865, $10,000 outright.

In 1868 the legislature appropriated $50,000 for buildings and the following year the same amount for buildings and other purposes.

In 1877 the legislature gave $5,000 for current expenses, one-half to be used for paying student labor. In 1879, $32,000 was appropriated to meet debts incurred during several years. In 1882, $9,000 was granted for a drill hall and the next year a permanent appropriation of $10,000 annually for current expenses was made. In 1884, $36,000 was given for a chapel and library building and the next year $45,000 for buildings and apparatus.

At the beginning all students were required to pay tuition, fixed at $12 per term. This was soon increased to $18, and in 1874 to $25. Afterwards it was reduced to $12, but in 1885 was raised to $80 for the year. However, in the early years most of the agricultural societies paid the bills of one or more students. Free scholarships were from time to time provided by State appropriations and these increased in number until practically tuition was free to students from within the State.

The buildings erected when the college opened were a hall for classrooms, library, museum and dormitory; a chemical laboratory; a botanic museum, and a boarding house. The same year a fine group of glass plant houses was given to the college by Nathan Durfee and a fund of $10,000 was provided by L. M. and H. F. Hills, the income of which was to be expended for seeds, plants, etc. In 1868 another dormitory was built, and the following year a barn costing $9,000 was constructed and the chemical laboratory was extensively enlarged to provide a chapel, classrooms, and drill hall. In 1883 a separate drill hall was erected and two years later a chapel and library.

In their report for 1866 the trustees set forth their view of the purpose and organization of the college. " Our first duty we apprehend to be, to make the college distinctively an agricultural institution, to establish a course of study, which if faithfully pursued shall make every graduate a scientific and practical farmer." There must be also—

the best discipline of the mind, physical training, esthetic and moral culture, and military tactics. The college should have departments of agriculture and horticulture, physics, mathematics and engineering, natural history, chemistry, political economy, intellectual philosophy and Christian morals, comparative anatomy and animal physiology (including veterinary surgery and medicine), modern languages and literature, and physical education, including military tactics. The applications of science to farm labor, roads, bridges, irrigation, drainage, and surveying should be taught, as well as architecture. Special attention should be given to the training of teachers and to experiments and investigations to advance knowledge. Manual labor was to be required primarily for the education of the student and not for profit. The student should practice such labor as he does not understand.

In addition to the regular long course there should be short courses and popular lectures. To lay out the farm and conduct its operations Levi Stockbridge, a farmer in the near-by town of Hadley, was elected farm superintendent.

The board of agriculture continued to show great interest in the college, and in 1866 was made its board of overseers, whose duty it was to visit the college and advise on its affairs. It immediately decided to locate its cabinet and library at the college. In 1867 it urged the agricultural societies in the State to maintain scholarships at the College, and in 1869 eighteen societies were doing this.

It also provided for lectures at the college by its secretary and Charles L. Flint lectured four years on dairy farming. As a member of this board Louis Agassiz for several years visited the college and in 1871 spoke at its first commencement.

Lecturers from outside, including Doctor Hitchcock and other members of the faculty of Amherst College, on different phases of literature, science, and agriculture were employed and members of the faculty gave more or less instruction not included in the terms of their professorships. For example, Professor Goodell lectured on entomology in 1869 and was instructor in zoology, anatomy, and physiology from 1869 to 1871. In 1869, Henry E. Alvord, major of the Regular United States Army, was detailed as military instructor. He was thus given an opportunity to study agriculture at the college and in 1885 became professor of agriculture there.

The college was opened October 2, 1867, and 47 students were in attendance during the first term. The faculty consisted of William S. Clark, president and professor of botany and horticulture; Levi Stockbridge, instructor in agriculture; Ebenezer Snell, professor of mathematics; and Henry H. Goodell, professor of modern languages and instructor in gymnastics and military tactics. Charles A. Goessmann came in 1868 as professor of chemistry and the faculty was soon increased to 11 members.

In 1871 Selim H. Peabody, afterwards regent of the University of Illinois, became professor of mathematics, physics and civil engineering, and in 1872 Henry James Clark became professor of comparative anatomy and veterinary science. He was a graduate of New York University and Lawrence Scientific School, a student and assistant under Agassiz, adjunct professor of zoology in Harvard College, and a professor in the Pennsylvania Agricultural College and Kentucky University.

In 1874 Samuel T. Maynard, a graduate of the college in 1872, was elected gardener and assistant professor of horticulture and afterwards served for many years as professor of botany and horticulture.

In 1883 Manly Miles, who had been professor of agriculture in the Michigan Agricultural College and the University of Illinois, succeeded Professor Stockbridge as professor of agriculture at the Massachusetts College, and served in that capacity for three years.

In 1886 Charles H. Fernald came from the Maine State College to be professor of zoology and lecturer on veterinary science. That year the faculty included President Goodell and eight professors, an associate professor, and two lecturers.

Candidates for admission must be at least 15 years of age and were examined in English grammar, geography, arithmetic, and history of the United States. From 1874 algebra to simple equations and afterwards to quadratics was required. The academic year began on the second Thursday of September and included three terms of 13 weeks each.

The first course of study occupied four years and led to the degree of bachelor of science. It included in freshman year algebra, geometry, human anatomy and physiology, chemistry, botany, English, and French; sophomore year, commercial arithmetic, bookkeeping, trigonometry, mensuration, surveying, chemistry, zoology, English, German and drawing, and agriculture; junior year, physics, agricultural chemistry, botany, astronomy, English, French or German, drawing, horticulture; senior year, geology, political geography, civics, political economy, history, engineering, and intellectual and moral philosophy. At different times during the courses there were lectures from persons outside the resident faculty on crops, livestock, dairy farming, market gardening, landscape gardening, horticulture, forestry, rural law, entomology, diseases of animals, etc. Exercises in gymnastics and military tactics were also required during the course.

In 1873 this course had been changed to include regular instruction in agriculture throughout the four years; chemistry in freshman and sophomore years; zoology and entomology in sophomore and junior years; botany in junior and senior years; veterinary science throughout senior year; French in freshman and sophomore years; German throughout junior year. Thereafter changes were made from time to time in the order in which the subjects were taught, but the content of the course as a whole remained practically the same.

All students were required to perform manual labor six hours a week without compensation and voluntary work for wages of from 10 to 15 cents per hour was also provided. The first senior class went on a strike because they thought the compulsory labor was not educational. Apparently thereafter greater efforts were made to relate manual work more definitely to the classroom work. Here, as elsewhere, there was much difficulty in working a satisfactory labor system and about 1883 compulsory labor ceased to be required uniformly of all students.

From the beginning special students were admitted to pursue certain studies either in connection with the regular classes or by special arrangement with individual instructors. The number of such students was relatively large during the early years of the college.

Graduate students were reported first in 1874. Their number ranged 2 to 13 each year between 1874 and 1886. The total number of students was 147 in 1872, but declined until 1877 when there were 88. Increase in the number of free scholarships brought the number up to 141 in 1878. It went down again to 79 in 1883 and was only 110 in 1885.

The number of graduates began with 27 in 1871, but did not reach that level again until 1881 when there were 31. Otherwise up to 1886 the number fluctuated between 24 in 1872 and 1876, 7 in 1878, and 4 in 1884. The general catalogue of the college, 1862–1886, enumerates 237 graduates and 406 nongraduates, a total of 643. Of both graduates and nongraduates 175 engaged in agriculture and kindred pursuits, 221 in various forms of business, 25 were teachers, 18 were chemists, 7 were veterinarians, 22 were physicians, and 25 were engineers.

Much of the instruction was given through lectures, but in the natural sciences a considerable amount of laboratory work by the students was developed. Practical observations and exercises in the field were employed to a certain extent, in addition to the routine manual labor of the students in agriculture and horticulture. Textbooks were also used.

The conditions prevailing in the early years of the Massachusetts and other agricultural colleges as regards the instruction in agriculture are well set forth in the report of President Clark for 1869. The instruction of the students—

in all the practical details of the farm, and of business connected therewith, as well as in the principles that underlie all intelligent, successful practice, devolve to great extent on the farm superintendent and professor of agriculture. * * * In consequence of the crude and undigested condition of our agricultural knowledge, of the lack of suitable textbooks, and a generally accepted system of agriculture, his duties should be so arranged as to give him the necessary time and freedom of thought for investigating and establishing agricultural facts, and to instruct his pupils individually in everything that relates to the most correct practice. In the present condition of the institution this officer is the "man of all work."

The following extract from Professor Stockbridge's report for 1873 illustrates the prevailing methods of instruction in agriculture:

Our method of instruction in the theory of agriculture is by lectures, which are continued through more than three years of the college course, keeping the subject of agriculture prominently before the student much the largest portion of the time while he is connected with the institution. These lectures are conversational in manner and are intended to give a thorough knowledge of the fundamental principles which are the basis of all correct, rational practice in the management of soils, and the production of plants and animals, and to qualify the student to engage in agriculture, or the pursuits related thereto, as a personal vocation, with intelligent satisfaction and success, or to judiciously superintend and direct agricultural operations. The entire course is systematically arranged by topics, commencing with "The importance of Agriculture as an occupation, and its influence on private and public welfare and improvement" (171).

When the agricultural college was established there was much objection in Massachusetts to the support of higher education by the State and in 1870 a determined effort was made to stop all further grants of State funds to this college. A resolution adopted by the house of representatives directed the secretaries of the boards of education and agriculture " to devise a plan, if practicable, by which the college may without expense to the Commonwealth be recognized as an independent institution in analogy with other colleges in the Commonwealth and that they inquire whether the term of study in said college should not be reduced."

In 1871 the first class, having 27 members, was graduated. At the graduating exercises Senator Morrill and Marshall P. Wilder delivered addresses. Boating was then the leading form of athletics in the New England colleges and there was great excitement in college circles when the "aggies" won their race with Harvard and made a record for a 3-mile race. This event did much to give the agricultural college standing as a real college. That year the legislature gave the college an appropriation of $50,000 for its debts and other expenses and the permanent endowment fund was increased to $350,000.

In 1875 an arrangement was made with Boston University, by which a student at the agricultural college " might become a member of the university and receive its diploma in addition to that of the college, and many of the students have done this " (159).

President Clark went to Japan in 1876 at the invitation of the Imperial Government to organize the Sapporo Agricultural College and took with him several graduates of the Massachusetts college to be professors in this new college. Among these was William Penn Brooks of the class of 1875, who served as professor of agriculture until October, 1888, when he returned to the Massachusetts Agricultural College to hold a similar position for many years.

In 1879 President Clark resigned the presidency of the Massachusetts college. The college then entered on a period of difficulty and uncertainty regarding its future.

On April 24 the legislature passed an act granting $32,000 to the college to pay existing indebtedness, and at the same time made the trustees personally responsible for any debt thereafter incurred in excess of the income of the college. June 12 the trustees, owing to the diminished income, sold at auction all the blooded stock belonging to the college, except the Ayrshire herd. Current expenses were reduced $10,000 a year; one professorship was abolished; the president's salary was withheld; and the salaries of the professors and treasurer were cut down.   *   *   *

An act passed by the legislature in 1879 constituted the governor and council a commission to examine the status of the institution with the intention of severing its connection with and releasing the State from its obligation and guarantees to the General Government respecting the college. This committee submitted its report to the legislature in 1880, practically recommending that the college, with its real and personal estate and the trust funds received from the United States for its specific support, should be given to Amherst College, and that any further effort toward its maintenance by the State should be abandoned. This proposition, although strongly advocated by Governor Long, was so radical and so subversive of the integrity of the State that it gained no favor at the hands of the public, and no effort was made by the legislature to accept this report. This attempt by those opposed to the college to destroy its independence as an agricultural college seemed to attract to the college the sympathy and support of the agricultural community and the friends of agricultural education (*159*).

In this crisis for about a year Charles L. Flint, long-time secretary of the State board of agriculture and of the board of trustees of the college, served as president without pay. From 1880 to 1882 Levi Stockbridge was president and then Paul A. Chadbourne was for a short time president for a second term and died in that office. His successor in 1883 was James Carruthers Greenough, a graduate of Williams College and principal of the Rhode Island Normal School. By the time President Greenough took office in 1883 confidence in the usefulness of the college as a State institution had been restored and under his administration considerable appropriations for new buildings and extensive repairs and improvements in old buildings were made, the standard of scholarship was raised, and the course of study was extended.

In 1883 the legislature passed a resolve: That there shall be paid annually from the treasury of the commonwealth to the treasurer of the Massachusetts Agricultural College at Amherst, the sum of ten thousand dollars, to enable the trustees of said college to provide for the students of said institution the theoretical and practical education required by its charter and the law of the United States relating thereto. Eighty-three scholarships were also established, two for each senatorial district, the candidates to be recommended by the senator of the district.

In 1886 Henry H. Goodell, who had served as professor of modern languages and in other capacities from the beginning of the college, was elected president and continued in that office until his death in 1905. During his term the college was greatly strengthened and had a much broader influence as an institution for higher education in science and agriculture.

Experimental work was begun on the college farm by Professor Stockbridge as soon as the college was established. The early experiments with fertilizers led to the issuing in 1876 of his special formulas for commercial fertilizers which were widely used. The first money which he obtained for royalties was used for experiments at Amherst and laid the foundation for an experiment station there. Among other experiments made by him were those on the "dust mulch," the sources of soil moisture, and the origin of dew. President Clark's experiments on the circulation of sap in the sugar maple and other species of trees and with the "squash in harness" to determine the expansive force of a growing plant, attracted much attention. Soon after Professor Goessmann came to the college he began investigations on the culture of sugar beets and the manufacture of beet sugar, the results of which were published in four important papers between 1871 and 1879. Among his other early investigations were those on the utilization of salt marshes, the relative value of several varieties of corn for feeding purposes, the value of Early Amber sorgo as a sugar-producing plant, and the chemistry of fruit culture. His report on commercial fertilizers, including his own analyses of those in the local market, was largely instrumental in bringing about the first law in the United States requiring an official inspection of fertilizers. This was passed May 26, 1873, and Professor Goessmann as chemist of the State board of agriculture became the State inspector of fertilizers. In 1878 when Professor Stockbridge's gift of $1,000 became available the organization of an experiment station at the college was attempted but lack of funds prevented its continuance until by a State act of May 12, 1882, the Massachusetts Agricultural Experiment Station was established. Goessmann was made its director and chemist. This station was independent of the college in its organization and management but was located on the college grounds and under a nominal lease used college land and buildings. Plans were immediately made for field and feeding experiments and for chemical work. Analyses of fertilizers, forage plants, feeding stuffs, milk and other dairy products, drinking waters, etc., were made for farmers and others. The experimental work at the college was enlarged to include field and feeding experiments with legumes and other forage plants for soiling, feeding experiments with milk cows, and with pigs. The list of experiments carried on from 1870 to 1884 published in the annual report of the college for 1884 shows quite a range of work. Thus the way was prepared for the larger development of experiment-station work under Federal and State laws.

In Massachusetts extension work was carried on through annual " country meetings " of the State board of agriculture, beginning with 1863, and through meetings of the county and local agricultural societies. In December, 1868, the country meeting of the board, which resembled a farmers' institute, was held at Amherst. Among the speakers at this meeting was Louis Agassiz. He was also chairman of a committee of the board, who attended examinations of students and inspected the operations of the college. A few months before this the New England Agricultural Society had held a trial of plows at the college. From 1878 the State agricultural societies held farmers' institutes under the direction of the

State board. Members of the faculty of the Massachusetts Agricultural College participated to a certain extent in these meetings of the State board and the societies. Information regarding the experimental work at the college was also disseminated through the annual reports of the college and the agricultural and other press.

Through the experimental and other activities of its small but efficient faculty the Massachusetts Agricultural College exerted a considerable and wide influence on the development of agricultural education and research in this country. The number of its students was not large during the first 20 years of its operation and only a small share of these devoted themselves to agricultural careers. The graduates of this college during this period who became teachers, investigators, or administrative officers in agricultural institutions in different parts of the country, did much useful work in the promotion of the agricultural interests of the Nation. This college gave at this time relatively strong instruction in languages, mathematics, chemistry, botany, and zoology, and coupled this with definite teaching of the relations of the natural sciences to agriculture and horticulture and of the practices of these arts.

IOWA STATE AGRICULTURAL COLLEGE

In 1848 the Iowa Legislature asked Congress to grant to the State the site and buildings of Fort Atkinson in Winneshiek County, with two sections of land, for an agricultural college. Nothing came of this movement, but on December 28, 1853, the State agricultural society was organized by people interested in agricultural education and the following year Gov. James W. Grimes favored the establishment of a State school of applied science. Petitions for an agricultural college multiplied and finally on March 22, 1858, Governor Lowe approved a bill for a State agricultural college and farm.

The act carried an appropriation of $10,000 and put the management of the college under a board of trustees of 11 members, one for each judicial district. The board held its first meeting December 10, 1859, and issued a notice for the purchase of land for the college. Proposals were received from six counties. The farm selected is located in Story County, near the village of Ames. It contains 648 acres and cost $5,374.

Story County voted $10,000 of county bonds and subscribed $4,320 in individual notes. Boone and Story Counties together gave 861 acres of land, valued at $6,015, and their subscriptions, together with the appropriation of $10,000 by the State, amounted to $31,355. The five sections of land in Jasper County, comprising 3,200 acres and granted to the State by the Federal Government for the erection of capitol buildings, were diverted with the consent of Congress to the use and benefit of the college (*132*).

The bad financial conditions of the State and the advent of the Civil War prevented further State appropriations for several years. In 1860 an attempt was made in the legislature to repeal the act establishing the college.

Iowa was the first State to accept the provisions of the Morrill Land Grant Act. This was done on September 11, 1862, by the legislature in special session. The State thus became entitled to 240,000 acres of Federal land. A competent agent was appointed by the governor to locate the lands, which were immediately approved and certified to the State.

These lands were leased at about 8 per cent on an appraised valuation of $1.50 to $3 per acre. This gave at once a satisfactory income to the Iowa Agricultural College. The college financial agent managed the grant so well that, through buying, selling, and renting the lands, investing and reinvesting the income, on June 30, 1914, the principal amounted to $686,817.97 and the income accruing to the college was $35,191.86. In 1864

An earnest effort was made to divert these lands from the agricultural college, and to use them to increase the endowment of the State university, upon the condition that a department of agriculture should be established, an experimental farm be purchased, and an agricultural course in the university be provided for such as wished to pursue it (*131*).

The board of trustees as constituted in 1865 included the governor and president of the State agricultural society as ex officio members, in addition to those appointed from the judicial districts. The erection of the first college building was then begun, for which the legislature appropriated $20,000 in 1864 and $91,000 in 1866. For small buildings, farm expenses, etc., $47,750 was appropriated in 1868, and in 1870 an additional amount of $68,500 of which $50,000 was for extending the original college building, $5,000 for a chemical and physical laboratory, $5,000 for a workshop, and $4,500 for professors' houses.

The main college building was to have sufficient accommodations for the board and lodging and tuition of 200 students, and the required number of professors. The structure was 5 stories high, 156 feet long, and 70 feet wide. The wings were capable of extension to meet any future demands for space. The equipment of the college was gradually increased and in 1886, besides the original building, there were on the campus special buildings for chemistry and physics, agriculture, zoology and botany, horticulture, domestic economy, veterinary medicine, engineering, and administration, together with a workship, creamery, two barns, and six dwellings. The farm had been enlarged to 900 acres.

In connection with the determination of the faculty and new course of study, a committee consisting of Governor Stone, Lieutenant Governor Gue, and Peter Melendy, president of the State agricultural society, was appointed to visit the agricultural and other scientific and industrial institutions of other States, inquire into their operation, and nominate a president and faculty for the Iowa college.

The course of instruction was provided for in the organic law creating the college, as follows:

The course of instruction in said college shall include the following branches, to wit: Natural philosophy, chemistry, botany, horticulture, fruit growing, forestry, animal and vegetable anatomy, geology, mineralogy, meteorology, entomology, zoology, the veterinary art, plain mensuration, leveling, surveying, bookkeeping, and such mechanic arts as are directly connected with agriculture. Also, such other studies as the trustees may from time to time prescribe, not inconsistent with the purposes of this act.

The board of trustees was also given the right to establish professorships.

Tuition in the college was to be forever free to pupils from the State who were over 14 years of age and who had been residents of the State for six months previous to their admission. The law also provided that—

Applicants for admission must be of good moral character, able to read and write the English language with correctness, and also to pass a satisfactory examination in the fundamental rules of arithmetic.

By 1883 the minimum age of admission had been raised to 16 years and the scholastic requirements for admission to the freshman class included English grammar and analysis, arithmetic, human physiology, and algebra through simple equations. Preparatory or sub-freshman classes were maintained until 1887.

The trustees were given authority to establish rules regulating the number of hours, to be not less than two in winter and three in summer, which must be devoted by the students to manual labor, and the compensation therefor, and no student was to be exempted from such service except in cases of sickness or infirmity. At first this meant chiefly ordinary labor on the farm or in the erection, repair, or care of buildings. But later an effort was made for a number of years to distinguish between instructive and uninstructive labor. Gradually the latter was reduced and from 1884 was no longer required. Work in the laboratories or in the field was thereafter more closely related to the plan of instruction in the several scientific and technical departments.

Iowa Agricultural College and farm formally opened for the admission of students March 17, 1869. The first year 253 students were enrolled. Adonijah Strong Welch was the first president and held that office from 1868 until 1883. He was a native of Connecticut and a graduate of the University of Michigan and had been principal of the Michigan State Normal School at Ypsilanti and president of the Michigan State Teachers' Association. He was greatly interested in agriculture, especially animal breeding, and being an attractive speaker was often called upon to address farmers' meetings.

Only two courses were offered at first, one in agriculture and the other in the mechanic arts or engineering. Women were permitted to enter either course.

The agricultural faculty consisted of Norton S. Townshend, professor of agriculture and horticulture, and President Welch, who lectured on landscape gardening, and the second year on farm animals. In 1870 this faculty consisted of James Mathews, professor of pomology, and Charles E. Bessey, instructor in botany and horticulture (vegetable gardening), while the duties of the vacant professorship in agriculture were delegated to Professor Mathews, President Welch, and Issaac P. Roberts, who came to Ames as farm superintendent in 1869. The next year Mr. Roberts was made professor of practical agriculture and "did much to give impetus, tone, and real scientific and practical value to agricultural teaching in the Iowa Agricultural College."

Though the requirements for admission to the college were at first necessarily low, much preparatory instruction was given. The first year there were 59 men and 21 women in the preparatory classes as compared with 97 men and 76 women in the freshman class.

The college year began in February and closed the end of October following. A few days of vacation were given in July. The winter vacation permitted the students to go out and teach and also made unnecessary the heating of the college building which was an expensive undertaking.

In 1870 the purpose of the college was stated to be "to make proficients in the sciences which underlie the various branches of industry and by manual labor to produce experts in all its various applications to the operations of the garden, farm, and workshop."

In 1871 the college faculty included 13 professors and assistants, and the student body had 220 members. Of these 147 were in the freshman class, 40 in the sophomore class, and 33 in the junior class. Agricultural students were not differentiated until sophomore year when there were 18 and the same number in junior year. The following year there were 265 students and a class of 26 was graduated, of whom 17 were in the agricultural courses, 8 in mechanic arts, and 1 in the women's course.

No agriculture was taught in freshman year, but there was instruction in physics and physiology. The sophomores had physics, chemistry, zoology, botany, and horticulture, with lectures in stock breeding and farm engineering. The juniors had agricultural chemistry, entomology, vegetable physiology, orchard culture, landscape gardening, and farm engineering. The seniors had mineralogy, geology, comparative anatomy and physiology, meteorology, cultivation and rotation of crops, fruit culture, forestry, management of stock, veterinary science and practice, and political economy. The horticultural course was somewhat different in senior year and there was a special nursery course running through sophomore, junior, and senior years. Manual labor was required for two and one-half hours each day. For farm labor, students were paid 3 to 9 cents per hour and for labor in horticulture 3 to 7 cents.

Professor Roberts describes the method of teaching agriculture at the Iowa college as follows:

I began to tell the students what I knew about farming. It did not take me long to run short of material and then I began to consult the library. I might as well looked for cranberries on the Rocky Mountains as for material for teaching agriculture in that library. Thus, fortunately, I was driven to take the class to the field and farm, there to study plants, animals and tillage at first hand. * * * I fell into the habit of taking the students to view good and poor farms; to see fine herds and scrub herds in the country around about, even though they had to travel in freight cars. I suppose I was the first teacher of agriculture to make use, in a large way, of the fields and the stables of the countryside as laboratories. * * * One day, being short of lecture material, I went to the fields and gathered a great armful of the common weed pests. Handing them around to the class I asked for the common and the botanical names, and the methods of eradication. * * * This experiment provided material for a week's classroom talk and led me to place still more emphasis on field laboratory work—"walks and talks," we called them (315).

Finding the horse books in the library out of date, he dug up the remains of horses which had died of an epidemic in the neighborhood and with these specimens taught students "the fundamental principles of horse dentition."

There was one graduate student in 1873 and in 1876 authority was given the college to grant advanced degrees. The first of these degrees was given the next year to J. C. Arthur, afterwards for a long time botanist and investigator of plant diseases at Purdue University in Indiana.

On the resignation of Professor Roberts in 1873, to become professor of agriculture at Cornell University, Miliken Stalker was appointed superintendent of the farm and assistant professor of agriculture. Three years later in 1876 he was promoted to the chair of agriculture and veterinary science. During 1875 G. E. Morrow had been appointed professor of agriculture, but in 1876 he resigned to accept a similar position in the Illinois Industrial University.

In 1877 agriculture and veterinary science were separated into two distinct departments and two years later a school of veterinary science was established. Doctor Stalker was given veterinary science and Seaman A. Knapp was appointed professor of practical and experimental agriculture. In 1877 J. L. Budd came to the college as professor of horticulture and forestry.

The drift of this and other land-grant colleges toward becoming mainly scientific institutions is shown in a paper on the true work of national industrial schools, which was read by President Welch at a meeting of presidents of State universities and agricultural colleges in the West at Chicago, November 23, 1877. It is a plea for having these colleges educate specialists in the sciences relating to agriculture and other industries and is reported to have been approved unanimously by the convention. A course in industrial sciences was developed at the Iowa college and for a considerable period this was the most prominent feature of the institution. At first this amounted to an elective system by which juniors and seniors might specialize in particular sciences.

The following is quoted from an historical sketch, issued for the semicentennial celebration of the college, June 6-9, 1920:

Prior to 1882 only 6 per cent of the men then living who had graduated from the college became identified with either practical farming or professional agriculture while nearly 40 per cent entered law, medicine, or the ministry, 17 per cent engaged in teaching or similar professional work, 3 per cent became veterinarians and only 9 per cent engineers or mechanics. The dreams of the founders of the institution for a college which would send its graduates into the industries had not yet been realized.

The pressure for better recognition of agriculture resulted in giving marked emphasis to that major line of work by conferring the degree of bachelor of scientific agriculture on students completing this course. Three men received this degree in 1883, which was the first year it was conferred at this institution. During the next few years a considerable number of men graduated with the B. S. A. degree and in later years nearly every one of them achieved positions of honor and influence in professional or practical work along agricultural or horticultural lines. (*136*.)

The renewed interest in agriculture was shown by the organization of agricultural clubs in the college and by the issuing of a monthly bulletin, called the Students' Farm Journal.

In 1879 the college was divided into schools of agriculture, horticulture, veterinary science, domestic economy, literature and langauge, mathematics and physics, chemistry, biology, philosophy, mechanical engineering and architecture, and civil engineering. And it was announced that students might pursue exclusively the studies of any single school. But the next year this organization was modified so as to include only the course in sciences related to the industries and schools of agriculture, engineering, and veterinary science. In 1883 the college had 319 students of whom 69 were women. Nine were in the veterinary school and 48 in the sub-freshman class. That year President Welch, who had been sent by the United States Commissioner of Agriculture to study agricultural schools in Europe, was succeeded by Professor Knapp as president of the college.

At that time there were 13 professors, assistants in zoology and entomology and chemistry, an instructor in mathematics and book-keeping, a preceptress, a lecturer on domestic economy, a teacher in the workshop, and a teacher of instrumental and vocal music. The agricultural faculty consisted of professors of practical and experimental agriculture, horticulture, and veterinary science. In 1885 it was reported that only one-fifth of the students had the intention of becoming farmers. In 1887 the student body included 219 men and 74 women. The graduates numbered 39, divided as follows: Sciences, 11; agriculture, 5; mechanical engineering, 2; civil engineering, 6; veterinary science, 12; and ladies' course, 3. The smallest number of graduates was 15 in 1873. The total number of graduates from the opening of the college to 1887 was 386. The occupations chosen by the members of the graduating class of 1887 were veterinary medicine, 12; agriculture, 9; civil engineering, 6; mechanical engineering, 3; practical chemistry, 2; pharmacy, 1; dentistry, 1; business, 1; law, 3; teaching, 3; and medicine, 1. In 1885 President Knapp was relieved of the presidency and in 1886 also retired from the professorship of agriculture. Leigh S. J. Hunt was president in 1885–86, but was compelled to resign on account of ill health. William I. Chamberlain, who had been secretary of the Ohio State Board of Agriculture, was president from July, 1886, to 1890.

From 1883 to 1890 there was a marked falling off in enthusiasm and in efficiency. It was a period of administrative instability. The total enrollment declined, the agricultural clubs disappeared, and the Students' Farm Journal was discontinued.

Experimental work on the college farm was begun as soon as the institution was established. In 1870 there was a special item of $500 in the budget for seeds and plants for experiments, and the next year there was a report on tests of varieties of wheat, rye, and oats. Experimental orchards of apples and other fruits and plantations of small fruits and vegetables were established. By 1880 about 40 acres were devoted to field experiments. That year $600 was allotted for such work and $800 in 1881, when the experiments included the cereals, potatoes, and green manuring. Analyses of grasses and studies of rusts and other blights of grain were made. In 1883 Professor Knapp reported experiments with different methods of setting milk for cream, a milk record of cows, feeding experiments with calves and colts, field experiments with wheat, oats, corn, millet, soybeans, potatoes, and grasses, durability of different kinds of wood for posts, sorgo for sirup and sugar, etc. In 1885 the annual appropriation for experiments was $1,500, equally divided between agriculture and horticulture.

The policy of disseminating information by means of lectures and demonstrations was early established. Farmers' institutes at Cedar Falls, Council Bluffs, Muscatine, and Washington were conducted during the winter of 1870–71. Extension work of this character was gradually strengthened and enlarged.

ALABAMA AGRICULTURAL AND MECHANICAL COLLEGE (POLYTECHNIC INSTITUTE)

The Alabama Polytechnic Institute had its origin in the East Alabama College, which was established by the Alabama Conference of the Methodist Episcopal Church, South, and opened for students October 1, 1859, "with a faculty composed of some of the ablest and best-known southern educators. It was well equipped for a classical college, with apparatus and appliances, and had a prosperous career until it suspended in 1862. In 1866 it was reopened and was in operation with a full faculty and respectable patronage " in 1872.

The State legislature, by an act approved February 26, 1872, accepted an offer of the Alabama Conference of the Methodist Episcopal Church, South, donating to the State the college building, apparatus, and good will of the East Alabama Male College, and located the Agricultural and Mechanical College at Auburn (77).

Conditions due to reconstruction after the Civil War caused Alabama to delay acceptance of the Morrill Land Grant Act until December, 31, 1868. The State then received scrip for 240,000 acres of land, which was sold during the next three years by a commission for 90 cents per acre, thus creating a fund of $216,000. This was invested in Alabama State bonds at 85 cents on the dollar, giving the fund a face value of $253,500 with interest at 8 per cent. Up to 1879 the interest was paid in Alabama State certificates and afterwards in currency. From this source the college has had an annual income of $20,280. However, the State paid only $2,560 " of the first installment of interest due the college and a large debt was incurred the first year, which severely hampered the work of the institution for several years." Moreover, for some time the interest was paid in depreciated certificates. The first State appropriation for the college was made under an act of February 28, 1883. This amounted to $30,000 for buildings, equipment, and an experiment farm. In 1885 a second appropriation of $12,500 was made by the legislature to establish a department of mechanic arts.

The college had only one substantial building until 1884 when an audience hall and a mechanic arts laboratory were erected. In 1886 a building for the forge and foundry departments was added. On June 24, 1887, the main building with all its contents was burned. With the insurance and a State appropriation of $50,000 a new building was erected, together with a chemical laboratory.

The Agricultural and Mechanical College was organized by the new board of trustees March 22, 1872. Its first faculty included the members of the old faculty, two new professors and a commandant. L. T. Tichenor was president and professor of moral philosophy. There were seven other professors, including W. C. Stubbs, professor of chemistry, geology, and mineralogy, and W. H. Jemison, professor of practical agriculture. The next year the president became professor of agriculture and his faculty was reduced to four professors and an assistant professor. Mr. Stubbs was called professor of natural science and secretary of the faculty.

In 1878 W. H. Chambers became professor of agriculture and served until his death in 1881.

The program of instruction as stated in the catalogue for 1872 included a classical and scientific course of three years. In this course agriculture was to be taught in the second term of the second year and the first and second terms of the third year by lectures and excursions. The aim was " to educate scientific agriculturists." Additional higher courses of two years in agriculture, civil and mining engineering, and literature and science were offered.

For admission to college classes the student was to be examined in geography, English grammar, arithmetic, algebra to equations of the second degree, and geometry (first book). For the literary course Latin and Greek (including grammar, lessons and two books of Cæsar) were added. In the college in 1873 were a one-year preparatory course, three and two year courses in agriculture, and four-year courses in literature, science, and civil engineering. The agricultural course leading to the degree of bachelor of agriculture included French, German, natural science (particularly botany and chemistry), mathematics, surveying, political and moral philosophy, and lessons in practical agriculture throughout the course. With some modifications this program was continued until the end of President Tichenor's administration in 1882.

The number of students attracted to this college in its early years was small, though special inducements were offered. The minimum age for admission was 14 years. Sons of ministers or those preparing for the ministry were given free tuition and this was also offered to two students from each county provided they took the course in agriculture or engineering. In 1875 the catalogue gives the number of students as 88, of whom 4 were seniors, 9 juniors, 18 sophomores, 18 freshmen, and 38 preparatory. In agriculture there were only 7 juniors and 1 sophomore. During the first decade the average number of students in college classes was 100; total number of graduates was 101, of whom 16 had the B. S. A. degree.

In 1882 William Leroy Broun, who had been a professor in Vanderbilt and Georgia Universities, and had taken part in the organization of the Georgia Agricultural College, became president and, except for one year, held this position until his death in 1902. J. S. Newman, of the Georgia Agricultural College, was elected professor of agriculture in 1883 and President Broun thereafter served also as professor of physics and astronomy. Four-year courses in agriculture and chemistry, mechanics and engineering, literature and science were organized. There were also two-year courses in agriculture and mechanic arts. The long course in agriculture was the same as that in literature during the first two years except that modern languages might be substituted for ancient languages. In the last two years the subjects were mechanics, physics, botany, astronomy, meteorology, geology, mineralogy, zoology, entomology, agricultural chemistry, vegetable physiology, cattle feeding, and practical husbandry. Some lectures on agricultural subjects were given to the students in all the courses. There were also field observations, especially of the work on the college land.

The number of students in the college increased slowly up to 1887 and comparatively few gave special attention to agriculture. In

1884–85 out of 120 students there were only 1 senior and 12 juniors, in agriculture. The total number of students in 1887 was 185. In the short and long courses in agriculture there were 95 students as compared with 90 in mechanic arts. From 1883 to 1887, inclusive, there were 59 graduates, of whom 10 received the B. A. degree, 30 the B. S. degree, 4 the B. S. A. degree, 10 the B. E. degree, 3 the C. E. degree, and 2 the M. S. degree.

Experimental work in agriculture was begun by the college in 1875, and was carried on at Auburn and for a time at a branch station in north Alabama, where 10 acres were used for this purpose. A bulletin recording experiments with fertilizers on cotton at the north Alabama station was published in the president's report for 1875. The college farm at Auburn was used principally to grow crops for observations by the students and farmers of the vicinity, but a few experiments were carried on during the early years of the college and the results published in the president's reports.

In 1882 when Professor Stubbs was acting professor of agriculture, the first separate and systematic report on experiments at the college was published. This was a bulletin of 89 pages on the vineyard and analyses of grapes, strawberry culture, peaches, cowpeas, grasses, wheat, oats, fertilizers on potatoes,[1] corn, and cotton, analyses of fertilizers, cottonseed hull ashes, cottonseed, meteorological data, etc.

In 1883 a State experiment station was established in connection with the college, with Professor Newman as director and Professor Stubbs as chemist. In 1885 a State department of agriculture was established and the office of the commissioner was located at the college. One-third of the net proceeds of the sale of fertilizer tags was paid to the college for the maintenance of its agricultural and mechanical departments, on condition that it would make fertilizer analyses and furnish the commissioner a report on the work of the experiment station for publication by the State department. With State funds a farm was purchased near the college and was equipped with livestock and the necessary appliances for experimental work. A branch station was established at Uniontown in the canebrake region. Prior to the reorganization of the station under the Hatch Act in 1888, 32 bulletins were published, recording the experimental work at Auburn and Uniontown. The work included experiments with varieties, fertilizers, methods of planting and cultivation on corn, cotton, oats, sweet potatoes, sugar cane, vegetables, and strawberries, analyses of soils, fertilizers, etc.

Through its experimental work the college greatly increased its influence among the farmers of the State. The college also disseminated useful information among farmers by the participation of members of its faculty in meetings of agricultural societies and otherwise.

UNIVERSITY OF MISSISSIPPI AND THE AGRICULTURAL AND MECHANICAL COLLEGE OF MISSISSIPPI

The State of Mississippi first accepted the Morrill land grant on October 30, 1866, but this was not recognized as valid by the Federal Government. The State constitution adopted in 1868 provided for a State board of education and a public school system and that " the legislature as soon as practicable shall provide for the establishment of an agricultural college or colleges," to which shall be given the Morrill land-grant fund.

On May 13, 1871, Congress passed a time-extension amendment and the same day the reconstructed State legislature under Governor Alcorn again accepted the grant and conferred two-fifths of the fund on the University of Mississippi, and three-fifths on an institution for negroes established by the same act and called Alcorn University (215).

This action was satisfactory to Washington—

and scrip for 209,920 acres was given to the State. This was sold for 90 cents per acre and the fund was so managed that in 1876 it amounted to $227,150, which was invested in 5 per cent State bonds. In 1878 the legislature incorporated the Agricultural and Mechanical College, to which it transferred one-half of this fund. Fifteen thousand dollars was used to purchase a college farm near Starkville, and the new college annually received the interest on $98,575, which was increased to 6 per cent and amounts to $5,914. The institution for negroes, reorganized in 1878 as Alcorn Agricultural and Mechanical College of the State of Mississippi, was given the other half of the land-grant fund (215).

The University of Mississippi had its origin in a State act of February 20, 1840, which gave it the proceeds of the sale of one township granted to the State for a seminary of learning under the act of Congress of February 20, 1819.

In 1841 Oxford was selected as the site of the university, which was incorporated in 1844 and opened for students November 6, 1848. It was at first governed by a self-perpetuating board of 13 trustees, but in 1870 the governor, who had been an ex officio member from 1857, began to appoint members of the board, and in 1876 their number was increased to 15. The first faculty had a professor of natural sciences, J. N. Millington, who was expected to teach chemistry, botany, geology, mineralogy, and natural philosophy. In 1853 instruction in analytical chemistry and agriculture in the second half of the senior year was scheduled. An act of March 5, 1850, provided for a State geological and agricultural survey to be connected with the university. This survey was first put in charge of Professor Millington. The first report, issued in 1857, was prepared by Lewis Harper, who had been professor of geology, agriculture, and analytical chemistry at the university from 1854 to October, 1856. From October, 1855, the assistant State geologist had been Eugene W. Hilgard, a native of Rhenish Bavaria, who had received the degree of Ph. D. from Heidelberg University in 1853 and had served a short time as chemist in the Smithsonian Institution at Washington. An act of January 31, 1857, separated the survey from the university. Harper was then reappointed State geologist and served until March, 1858, when he was succeeded by E. W. Hilgard, who held that office until October, 1866, and again from 1870 to 1873. His first brief report was issued in 1858 and this was followed in 1860 by a " Report on the geology and agriculture of the State of Mississippi," of 391 pages, including a chapter on the principles of rational agriculture, treating of soils, principles of agricultural chemistry, manures, methods of culture, restoration of exhausted soils, maintenance of fertility, etc. Work on the survey was continued until October, 1874, but provision for a final report was not made.

The Civil War caused the suspension of the university from 1862 to October, 1865. When it was reopened Doctor Hilgard acted as professor of chemistry, mineralogy, and geology and was made professor of chemistry a year later. When the university received the land-grant fund in 1871 a department of agriculture was established with a chair of agricultural and economic chemistry and the special geology and agriculture of Mississippi, and this chair was filled by Professor Hilgard. A preliminary course of lectures on agriculture was delivered by him in 1871–72. A 4-year course was organized in October, 1872, including mathematics, English literature, political sciences, ethics, physics, chemistry, mineralogy, geology (soils), meteorology, botany, zoology, and agricultural and economic chemistry. Daily lectures in general and special agriculture were scheduled throughout the four years, including field crops, horticulture, animal husbandry, rural engineering, and architecture, landscape gardening, rural economy, and the agriculture and zoology of Mississippi. This course was explained by Professor Hilgard in an address before the Mississippi Agricultural and Mechanical Fair Association in 1872 (*209*). Professor Hilgard attended the meeting of the presidents and professors of agriculture held in Chicago in 1871 and on August 29 of that year made a report to the chancellor of the University of Mississippi on the organization of the department of agriculture and mechanic arts, in which he summarized what he had learned at that meeting. His general conclusions regarding the desirable character of a college course in agriculture are stated as follows:

While, therefore, access to the direct benefits of the institution should be as easy as consistent with its limited funds, we should stoutly insist that its main object is to impart, besides a general education, a thorough knowledge of the principles of agriculture, combined with such an acquaintance with its practice as will enable its graduates not only *to know how things should be done, but to do them themselves in the field.* But beyond the practice requisite to attain this end, the mechanical operations should not be made to encroach upon the time of the student; nor should the farm, upon which this practice is to be acquired, be considered otherwise than as a means of instruction, both by way of exercise and example, in the details. In the latter respect it should and must be a "model," but not in the sense of pecuniary success; it being fully understood that the latter can only result from a judicious application of the general principles to local circumstances infinitely varied. * * * The labor required for the cultivation of the college farm should be provided for independently of the obligatory labor of students. Nevertheless, it is undoubtedly desirable that those who may wish to perform agricultural labor, beyond that required as a part of instruction, should be afforded opportunity of doing so (*210*).

To organize properly a department of agriculture and mechanic arts Dr. Hilgard advised the appointment of—

a professor of practical agriculture in all its branches, including dairy-farming, stock-raising, and fruit-culture; a professor of technology and the mechanic arts; and a superintendent of the farm.

This minimum array of employees presupposes, of course, that—
1. The chair of civil engineering be filled; also,
2. The chair of botany, and zoology; horticulture to be included in the same,
3. That agricultural chemistry, as well as the special agriculture and economic geology of the State, be otherwise provided for.

Lack of means prevented the carrying out of this plan. An assistant professor of agriculture and farm superintendent was appointed and some field experiments were conducted for several years on about 20 acres. An attempt to get State funds for the department of agriculture failed. Insufficient funds combined with the fact that the course offered was too advanced and technical to fit in well with educational conditions in the State and that the atmosphere of the university was not favorable to industrial education prevented the success of this enterprise. Only five students in agriculture and mechanic arts are reported in 1873 and three in 1874, but it is doubtful if any students took the work in agriculture. Professor Hilgard withdrew from the university and after a short period on the faculty of the University of Michigan began in 1875 his long-time service as professor of agricultural chemistry and head of the agricultural work of the University of California. In 1876 an attempt was made to revive the agricultural course at the University of Mississippi but without success. The farmers of the State, especially as represented by the granges, became very much dissatisfied with the course taken by the university in this matter and repeatedly urged the legislature to withdraw the land-grant funds from the university and establish on agricultural college.

THE AGRICULTURAL AND MECHANICAL COLLEGE

The Agricultural and Mechanical College of the State of Mississippi was established as a separate institution by a State act of February 28, 1878, and was located near Starkville, whose citizens contributed $9,000 to it. It was opened for students in 1880.

The act under which it was established directed that it should be—

a first-class institution, at which the youths of the State of Mississippi may acquire a common-school education and a scientific and practical knowledge of agriculture, horticulture, and the mechanic arts; also of the proper growth and care of stock, without, however, excluding other scientific and classical studies, including military tactics.

Connected with it was to be an experimental farm of not less than 160 acres. In addition to the income from the land-grant fund the legislature made the following appropriations for its buildings, equipment, and maintenance during the first five bienniums: 1880, $85,000; 1882, $120,000; 1884, $65,000; 1886, $50,000; 1888, $35,320. The reduction in 1888 was part of a general policy of retrenchment in State expenditures and was due to depression of agriculture and dissatisfaction with heavy taxation. The principal buildings erected during this period were a large main building, chemical laboratory, dormitory, mess hall, hospital, seven professors' houses, barn, and creamery. The college campus and farm included about 1,750 acres. The board of trustees included the governor as president ex officio, and nine other members.

On April 1, 1880, Stephen Dill Lee was elected president of the college and served in that capacity 19 years. He was born in Charleston, S. C., September 22, 1833, graduated at West Point in 1854, was in the United States Army until 1861, and served with great distinction in the Confederate Army throughout the Civil War, attaining the rank of lieutenant general. Afterwards he engaged in farming in Mississippi and was a State senator for two years. His election to the presidency gave the college immediate favorable recognition in the State and his strong and wise management put it upon a firm foundation and made it an important institution of its class from the beginning. Prior to the opening of the college a faculty was chosen, which included professors of English, and (in one chair) horticulture, biology, vegetable physiology, and animal husbandry. From the Michigan Agricultural College R. F. Kedzie and F. A. Gully were called to be professors of chemistry and agriculture, respectively. A professor of military science and tactics was detailed from the War Department. There were also a principal and four assistants for the preparatory department, an instructor in writing, a farm foreman, and a steward. During the first college year the total attendance was 354, of whom 267 were in the preparatory department, 73 in the freshman class, and 14 in the sophomore class. During the first 10 years the attendance fluctuated between 257 and 415, about half the students being in preparatory classes. The total number of individuals during this period was 1,832. The college graduates from 1883 to 1890 numbered 104, about half of whom engaged in farming, teaching agriculture, or experiment-station work. The student body was organized on a military basis and General Lee enforced strict military discipline. During the early years—

The College work was confined to a single course of study, extending over two years of preparatory, afterwards reduced to one year, and four years of collegiate, and regular farm work was made compulsory as a part of the daily program. The college boys worked in the fields, grubbed stumps, cleared land, filled ditches (and they were numerous), and attended to the stock three hours a day, at 8 cents an hour for their work. Conditions at that time were very crude and primitive. At night the students brought in their own coal to their rooms in the dormitory and made their fires; they drew their water from the deep wells on the campus with rope and bucket and carried it to their rooms for all bathing purposes; and their rooms were lighted with kerosene oil lamps. The mess hall, kitchen, and dining room were in the basement of the old chapel building with only dirt and brick floors (212).

The college course included for freshmen natural philosophy in first term, agriculture and horticulture in second term; for sophomores chemistry all the year, agriculture in third term; for juniors, anatomy and physiology in first term, horticulture, veterinary science, and agricultural chemistry in second term, entomology and botany in third term; for seniors, chemical physics, and zoology in first term, geology and agriculture in second term, meteorology and botany in third term. The period in the course in which the several subjects were taught was shifted from time to time. In addition to these scientific and technical subjects the course included algebra, geometry, analytical geometry, mechanics, trigonometry, surveying, civil engineering, astronomy, English language, composition and literature, history, United States Constitution, moral science, and military science and tactics. Some elementary instruction in agriculture was given to preparatory students and after a time Professor Gully formulated this in a textbook entitled "First Lessons in Agriculture." Commenting on this instruction President Lee said that "work and contact with the experimental farm, college herds, creamery, and gardens illustrate what is taught and give even these beginners a good idea of improved and progressive agriculture."

Field experiments were begun at the college in 1883 and were gradually increased in variety and extent, leading up to the organization of an experiment station in 1888. The early experiments included variety and fertilizer tests on corn and cotton, feeding experiments with steers and dairy cows, use of silage, variety tests of apples, peaches, pears, plums, apricots, mulberries, Japanese persimmons, grapes, strawberries, and vegetables. Dairying was promoted by means of a college creamery.

The college also joined in the farmers' institute movement and undertook the holding of several institutes annually in different parts of the State. In 1886-87 the trustees allotted $500 of college funds to this work. The college was in close touch with the granges, farmers' alliance, and other agricultural organizations.

During its first decade the Mississippi college became firmly established and demonstrated that under conditions existing in the South an institution for white students which had the promotion of agricultural education as its primary interest could be successfully organized and managed. Its influence soon began to be felt in the agricultural affairs of the State and was extended to the other States similarly situated.

AGRICULTURAL COLLEGE OF PENNSYLVANIA (STATE COLLEGE)

The Pennsylvania Legislature accepted the provisions of the Morrill Land Grant Act of 1862 on April 1, 1863. Judge Watts, Mr. McAllister, Doctor Pugh, and others connected with the Farmers' High School (p. 67) had been active in promoting the passage of this act and its change of name to the Agricultural College of Pennsylvania in 1862 had undoubtedly been largely brought about to enforce the presumption that it would receive the benefits of the Federal grant. The college was at first given the income from the land-grant fund tentatively because other institutions were claiming at least a share of it.

This matter was not finally settled until the act of February 19, 1867, gave the college one-tenth of this fund for experiment farms and the income of the remainder annually, provided three experiment farms were maintained, one at the college and the others in the eastern and western parts of the State.

In the act accepting the grant of 780,000 acres in scrip, the surveyor general of the State was instructed to obtain the scrip, to sell it, and to invest the proceeds. The governor, auditor general, and the surveyor general were appointed a committee to prescribe rules and regulations for its management. The surveyor general realized $439,186.80 from its sale. About 10 per cent, $43,886.50, was used to purchase experimental farms for the college and the balance was invested in United States and Pennsylvania State bonds bought at a premium and giving $381,500 face value of investment. The assembly on April 3, 1872, ordered these bonds sold and a 50-year State bond for $500,000 at 6 per cent interest issued to the college to represent the land-grant endowment fund. Pennsylvania State College receives $30,000 a year income from this source (1).

By the act of April 11, 1866, the legislature directed that payment of expenses of disposing of the land scrip be paid from the State treasury and authorized the trustees to borrow $80,000 to complete the college building and "consolidate" the college debts. This mortgage was a serious incubus on the college until 1878 when the legislature made an appropriation for its payment. The college also incurred floating debts which caused it much embarrassment for many years. No further aid was given the college by the State until 1887.

Originally the entire charge to students for board, room rent, tuition, etc., was fixed at $100 per year, but in 1864 it became necessary to double this and two years later it was raised to $260.

The college was housed in a substantial stone building, which as completed some years after the opening of the institution was 240 feet in length, 80 feet in average width, and five stories in height, exclusive of attic and basement. In this building were the administrative offices, chapel, library, cabinets, laboratories, classrooms, and a large number of dormitories. Its internal arrangements were changed from time to time to meet the necessities of the developing institution. In 1885 two frame buildings were erected for work in mechanic arts. The other buildings on the college land were professors' houses, barns, and smaller farm buildings. Not until 1887 did the State provide funds for other college buildings. About 1875 students began to rent rooms in the little village which was growing outside the college campus.

During the progress of the struggle to retain the land-grant fund for the agricultural college Doctor Pugh came to realize that in Pennsylvania a beneficiary of the land grant act would be expected to maintain a broad "industrial college." Therefore in 1864 he made an elaborate report to the trustees regarding the financial and educational requirements of such an institution (*359*). To this was added an argument against giving the land-grant fund to more than one institution in the State.

The professors and assistants required for complete organization of an industrial college are as follows:

(1) A professor of pure mathematics and the higher mechanics and astronomy. (2) A professor of civil engineering and applied mathematics. (3) A professor of natural philosophy and astronomy, mechanics and physics; an assistant, to prepare experiments for lectures, and to teach classes in the physical laboratory, where students would learn the art of experimentation with philosophical apparatus. (4) A professor of pure chemistry; an assistant to help prepare lectures and look after classes in the laboratory; a subassistant to take charge of the chemicals, and to help in the laboratory, with no other salary than free tuition. A chemical department, embracing laboratory instruction, can not be efficient with less aid than one professor and two assistants. (5) A professor of agricultural chemistry and geology; an assistant to help with field experimentation and work in the laboratory. (6) A professor of metallurgy, mining and mineralogy and chemical technology; an assistant, to prepare lectures and help in the laboratories. (7) A professor of anatomy, physiology and veterinary. (8) A professor of natural history, more particularly of zoology, comparative anatomy and entomology. (9) A professor of botany, horticulture and entomology; one assistant, to take charge of the greenhouse, and give field instruction in horticulture, and a gardener, to take charge of the garden. (10) A professor of practical agriculture; as assistant, he should have a practical farmer of the highest attainments in his art, and the latter should be assisted by two good farm hands, and by all the students in the college. (11) A professor of the English language and literature. (12) A suitable professor to take charge of a commercial department. (13) A professor of modern languages.

To these thirteen professorships or departments, he would advise the adding of (14) a professor of the Latin and Greek languages and literature; (15) a professor of military art and science and teacher of military tactics; (16) a treasurer, bookkeeper and librarian.

Omitting the organization of the culinary department, the summary of the staff of such an institution would be as follows:

President and professors _____ 16
Librarian and treasurer _____ 1
Assistants _____ 10
Superintendents _____ 2

Total _____ 29

There should be suitable buildings and laboratories as well as large collections of apparatus, natural history objects, etc. Means for scientific investigations should be provided and scholarships for needy and deserving students. Owing to lack of proper secondary schools this college must give preparatory courses. The college courses proposed are (1) agricultural science and practice; (2) engineering and architecture; (3) industrial courses for instruction in such subjects as metallurgy, technological chemistry or pharmacy; (4) practical short course; (5) commercial course; and (6) a literary department.

The financial requirements (evidently for the time being) of such an institution are set forth as follows:

Expenditures:

Sixteen professors at $1,500	$24,000.00	
Ten assistants	4,000.00	
A farm superintendent	700.00	
Janitor and helps	1,000.00	
		$29,700.00
For addition to museums, to scientific apparatus and to library		5,000.00
For scientific investigation		5,000.00
For indigent students, orphans of soldiers, free scholarships, etc		7,000.00
For repair of buildings		1,000.00
Total expenditures		47,700.00

Income:

Four hundred students, at $50 per annum	20,000.00
Income required from endowment	27,000.00
	47,000.00

Very soon after this report was prepared Doctor Pugh died. The college retained the land-grant fund but had many difficulties in establishing itself firmly and getting adequate financial support. A period of instability in the administration of the college ensued.

Late in 1864 the presidency was filled by the election of William H. Allen, who had been long associated with Girard College in Philadelphia. Then John Fraser, who had been professor of mathematics at the Pennsylvania College, served as president for part of the year 1867. He was succeeded by Thomas H. Burrowes, former State superintendent of public instruction, who died in 1871.

There was a great lack of secondary schools in the State and the rural schools in many localities were so weak that children from the farms had great difficulty in getting sufficient education to enable them to enter the college, though its requirements for admission were low. The location of the college, which in its early years was over 20 miles from a railway station, was long a hindrance to getting any considerable number of students. In fact their number declined, and when President Burrowes was elected the college was nearly empty. A circular of the college issued in 1870 gives a list of 59 students, of whom 40 were in the first year, but in 1871 when President Burrowes died the actual attendance was reduced to 37. After the reorganization of the college by his successor, the number of students rose to 148 in 1872, including 7 seniors, 10 juniors, 21 sophomores, 42 freshmen, and 68 preparatory students. There were 125 men and 23 women. These numbers had only minor variations for the next decade.

Up to 1867 only one course of study had been in effect and each student had been required to perform three hours of manual labor per day on the farm or about the college building. After the acceptance of the land-grant fund military drill was required and at first took the place of one day's manual labor per week. There was much dissatisfaction regarding the labor requirement and in September, 1866, the trustees ordered "that the rule requiring every student to work three hours daily on the farm, having proved uniformly injurious to the financial and educational interests of the college, shall cease to be enforced at the end of the present term." Voluntary labor of students with pay was provided. For students in the college departments daily military drill was required and preparatory students were to have one hour's exercise daily in a gymnasium. According to a circular issued by the United States Bureau of Education in 1902 (*345*) the college announced that—

Agriculture will be taught as an experimental science, and will be placed under the care of a professor of agriculture, who will give instruction by means of books and lectures in the class room, numerous experiments on the farm, and agricultural excursions. Every student in this department will be required to assist in the work connected with the experiments and to record them in a memorandum book, which will be examined from time to time by his instructor.

The college year, which had been practically one session beginning about the middle of February and ending early in December, was divided into two terms of 20 weeks each. Three 4-year courses, general science, agriculture, and literature, were established. A graded system of military instruction for all students was adopted. This program was too elaborate to meet the financial condition of the college and President Burrowes was obliged to curtail it.

Practically but one course of study was maintained, and the former arrangement of sessions and vacations and the manual labor system were restored.

The first two years included work in arithmetic, algebra and geometry, chemistry, botany, physiology, geography, history, English, Latin, and Greek, with practice in agriculture and horticulture. The third year as arranged for an agricultural class included trigonometry, analytical geometry, surveying, civil engineering, botany, chemistry, civil government, history, English literature, and ancient languages, with lectures and practice in agriculture. At the end of three years the student might graduate with the degree of B. S. A. or go on in a scientific or literary course for another year to obtain the degree of B. S. or a fifth year for B. A. An elective system was practiced to a certain extent, particularly with reference to the ancient and modern languages. For admission to college courses the student must be 15 years of age and have a common-school education. President Burrowes gave the instruction in practical agriculture.

James Calder became president early in June, 1871, and served in that capacity until 1880. During his administration changes were made which broadened the work of the college and brought it more into line with other educational institutions in the State. This was emphasized by the change of name in 1874 to the Pennsylvania State College. Two women were admitted in 1871 and their number increased to 23 the following year and to 47 in 1881.

Three college courses of study were again organized—scientific, classical, and agricultural. Preparatory and music courses were continued. Instruction in military tactics was added to the curriculum in 1875 and two years later an Army officer was detailed by the War Department to take charge of the military department. Manual labor was required, but for seniors and juniors this consisted of laboratory work. No class was graduated in 1872 and from that time the college year began in August and ended in July. In 1876 the long vacation was transferred from winter to summer.

In 1870 John Hamilton, a farmer living near the college, who had been a soldier in the Civil War, was made military instructor and the next year when he graduated from the college he became professor of agriculture. The course in agriculture as revised at that time began with general agriculture in freshman year. The sophomores had plant culture, soils, and horticulture; the juniors had fertilizers, animal husbandry, farm machinery, rural laws, and agricultural chemistry; the seniors had veterinary science, rural architecture, rural economy, landscape gardening, and essays and discussions on agricultural subjects. Botany, zoology, and general and agricultural chemistry were included in this course. Ancient languages and French were elective. All the students in the college were expected to take the work in general agriculture in freshman year. Professor Hamilton soon relinquished his military work, but was largely employed as business manager and treasurer of the college and general superintendent of the three experimental farms. Few students were attracted to the upper classes in agriculture, where the instruction had little scientific basis. The inadequacy of such instruction was recognized by Professor Hamilton in his final report as professor of agriculture in 1880 and he advised that his successor be a man trained in agricultural chemistry. At this time the State grange also expressed dissatisfaction with the agricultural work of the college.

From its beginning to 1880 the number of graduates was 122, of whom 43 had taken the degree of bachelor of agriculture but only 14 after leaving college had become farmers. Among them was also a professor of agriculture, a professor of horticulture, and an officer of the United States Department of Agriculture.

About July 1, 1880, Joseph Shortlidge became president of the college but continued in that position only a short time. He was succeeded by James Y. McKee as acting president. The faculty now undertook a revision of the educational program of the college. Meanwhile Whitman H. Jordan, who had studied agricultural chemistry under S. W. Johnson in the Yale Sheffield Scientific School and had taught at the Maine Agricultural College, had become professor of agriculture and agricultural chemistry. His influence is seen in the reorganized curriculum. The work in the preparatory department was to be made more like that of a high school. The first two years of the college course were to be largely devoted to instruction in mathematics, fundamental sciences, and other basal subjects. Technical instruction was to be given in the junior and senior years. A new chair in civil engineering was created. Systematic instruction in mechanic arts was begun. New special courses in natural history, chemistry and physics, and civil engineering were scheduled.

The course in agriculture included, for juniors, mechanics, civil government, mineralogy, agricultural chemistry, cryptogamic botany, zoology, entomology, fertilizers, crops, and agricultural engineering; for seniors, mental philosophy, political economy, ethics, history of English literature, geology, horticulture, anatomy and breeding, feeding, dairy and sheep husbandry, veterinary medicine, and farm economy. Laboratory and field practicums were included throughout the course.

In 1881 the board of trustees asked the legislature to appoint a committee to investigate the college. A joint committee of the two houses was appointed and made a report which on the whole was favorable. On the practical features of the instruction given at the college the committee comments as follows:

In connection with the usual studies of the class-room, we find that there is carried on a very extensive and progressive system of practical training in the applications of knowledge, which, for extent and thoroughness, is equaled by few, if any institutions, of which we have information. The student in agriculture, for example, goes into the laboratory until he becomes a well-trained analyst, and into the field and barn to observe processes or to conduct investigations. The student in horticulture works in the gardens and vineyards. The student in mechanic arts goes into the shop, and is trained in the use of tools, as well as the principles of mechanics. The student in civil engineering acquires a knowledge of the instruments and the methods of his profession by actual work in the field; and similarly, in every department that admits of it, subjects are taught with constant reference to their practical application in the various industries of life. When the institution was first opened to students, a considerable amount of manual labor was required of all. This system was abandoned after a trial of several years, and the practical work now required is regarded as educational, rather than a matter of manual labor, though it evidently serves the two important ends of giving physical exercise and skill in manipulation (*348*).

George W. Atherton became president of the college in 1882. He was a native of Massachusetts and a graduate of Yale College after service in the Army in the Civil War. He taught at St. John's College, Annapolis, Md., and at the Illinois Industrial University and had been professor of political economy in Rutgers College in New Jersey for 14 years. He had a broad understanding of the economic and industrial situation in the United States and believed that the land-grant colleges had great opportunities in training men in science and the arts, who would be useful in the future development of the country. In Pennsylvania existing conditions favored the immediate development of instruction in the State college along the lines of the natural sciences and mechanic arts. In agriculture economic conditions and the lack of scientific knowledge relating to this art made the outlook for securing any considerable number of students in agricultural courses of college grade quite unfavorable. The experiment-station movement had, however, proceeded far enough to show that research on agricultural subjects was likely to produce important scientific and practical results. An increasing body of intelligent farmers was becoming interested in such investigations and was calling on the college for information concerning their results. President Atherton laid emphasis on strengthening instruction at the college in science and mechanic arts and improving the equipment for such work. He also encouraged the enlargement of the work of the college in agricultural research and the prompt publication and dissemination of its results. He joined with the representatives of the other land-grant colleges in seeking further Federal aid and actively promoted the movement which resulted in the Hatch Experiment Station Act. He urged upon the State its responsibility for the maintenance and development of the college and aroused sufficient public sentiment in its favor to bring about substantial appropriations by the legislature for buildings and other equipment.

The educational program of the college was conservatively modified from time to time in an effort to meet existing conditions. In the annual report of the college for 1882 the president stated that the program of the preparatory department had been too elaborate, with the result that comparatively few students had been encouraged to enter the regular college classes. He therefore advised that the program of this department be narrowed so as to be strictly preparatory. The catalogue for 1883–84 gives the following four-year courses: General science, Latin-scientific, classical, a general course in agriculture and special courses in agriculture, chemistry, and physics, civil engineering, and natural history. There were also two-year courses in agriculture and in mechanic arts. Students were admitted to the college courses at the age of 15 years and the entrance requirements for the agricultural courses included only arithmetic. English grammar, geography, and spelling.

In the general course in agriculture the first two years were devoted to mathematics, surveying, the general principles of the natural sciences, modern languages and rhetoric, with Latin as an elective. The applications of the sciences to agriculture and the technical agricultural subjects were included in the program for the last two years.

The courses in agriculture offered at this time were evidently too scientific and technical to meet the economic and educational conditions existing in the State. In 1882 there were 20 students in agriculture, in 1884 three, and in 1887–88 five.

Meanwhile the work of the college in the natural sciences and mechanic arts was being strengthened. In 1884 teaching of Greek was dropped and the course in mechanic arts was reorganized. Two years later a course in mechanical engineering was established. The efforts of President Atherton to secure more substantial equipment for the college came to fruition in a State act of June 3, 1887, in which there were appropriations of $100,000 for buildings and equipment, including $35,000 for a chemistry and physics building, $20,000 for a drill hall and assembly room, and $5,000 for a greenhouse and botanical laboratory.

The number of students as recorded in the catalogue in 1883–84 was 128 (graduates 5, postgraduates 2, seniors 5, juniors 9, sophomores 9, freshmen 27, in special courses in agriculture 1 and in chemistry 1, preparatory classes 69); in 1886–87 140 (preparatory 63) and in 1887–88, 176 (preparatory 77).

Before the Farmers' High School of Pennsylvania was opened to students it was planned to have the institution carry on analytical and experimental work relating to agriculture. In the State act of May 20, 1857, provision was made for the analysis at the college,

without charge, of all soils and manures which shall be sent by citizens of this Commonwealth for that purpose and a correct report of the result of said analysis, accompanied by such information as may be useful in the case and the college was directed to "furnish reports of the results of all experiments with trees, shrubs, plants, seeds, soils, and breeding and rearing of stock, to at least one newspaper in each county in the Commonwealth for publication." Between 1857 and 1867 the experimental work was to a large extent horticultural, but included some observations on the cultivation, fertilization, and growth of varieties of agricultural plants and on various kinds of farm implements. Some meteorological observations were also made. Most of the experiments were simple but some involved research in the chemical laboratory.

By the State act of February 19, 1867, the college was obliged to maintain three farms, one near the college, and the others east and west, respectively. Under this act 100 acres of the college farm were set aside for experiments and similar tracts were obtained in Chester and Indiana Counties. For about 15 years field experiments were carried on under this plan. These included experiments in variety testing, rotation, planting, cultivation, fertilizing, and harvesting of corn, barley, oats, potatoes, clover, timothy, etc. At the college the experiments were under the immediate direction of the professor of agricultural and were systematically conducted. The outlying farms were largely controlled by local committees and had frequent changes of personnel and plans of work with unsatisfactory results. In 1887 the legislature authorized the sale of these farms.

After the appointment of Professor Jordan in 1881 a new program of field experiments at the college was introduced, a more careful checking of the field experiments was made, and laboratory research became an important element in the work. A number of experiments in the production of feeding stuffs and the feeding of domestic animals were also made. In 1884 the professor of agriculture was appointed chemist of the State board of agriculture, and in that capacity made the analyses necessary in the fertilizer control maintained by that board. In 1885 Professor Jordan was succeeded by William Frear, who remained in charge of the work until 1887, when he became vice director and chemist of the experiment station then organized under the Hatch Act. In 1882 the publication of bulletins was undertaken and 15 were issued prior to the organization of the station.

President Burrowes in 1870 instituted a meeting at the college which resembled what is now called farmers' week. It was then known as the "annual harvest reception," which occupied the last four or five days of the spring term.

Members of the faculty attended and addressed meetings of the State and county agricultural societies and the granges and after the organization of the farmers' institutes under the State board of agriculture also took part in these assemblies of farmers. In 1882 a two weeks' course of about 30 lectures was given at the college under the title of a farmers' institute and this was continued for several years. Beginning with 1885 the State made an appropriation of $1,000 for the institutes in different parts of the State held under the direction of the State board of agriculture, and this was increased to $3,000 in 1887.

CORNELL UNIVERSITY IN NEW YORK

New York accepted the provisions of the Morrill Land Grant Act May 5, 1863, and received scrip for 989,920 acres. Meanwhile numerous educational institutions within the State had sought to have the legislature give them at least a portion of this fund. The People's College at Havana (now Montour Falls) and the State Agricultural College at Ovid, both of which had been active in promoting the passage of the land grant act, pressed their claims most actively. By an act of May 14, 1863, the legislature decided to give all of this fund to the People's College. (See p. 56.) This was done, however, on condition that within three years the college

should meet all the requirements of the Morrill Act, should have at least 10 professors, a farm of 200 acres supplied with stock and agricultural machinery, shops and machines, a building for at least 250 students, a suitable library and all needed scientific apparatus, all of which was to be fully paid for by the college trustees; and that commencing in 1868 the college was to receive students from the different counties of the State free of tuition.

The number of free students was to be determined from time to time by the regents of the University of the State of New York and they were to be chosen for scholarly excellence.

In spite of financial difficulties the college was opened in 1864. An investigation by a committee of the regents of the University of the State of New York in February, 1865, showed that the college was not able to meet the conditions imposed by the legislature. Its faculty was therefore disbanded that year.

Meanwhile the friends of the State Agricultural College at Ovid (see p. 51), which had been closed since 1862 and was financially bankrupt, appealed to Ezra Cornell, who was a trustee of this college and a member of the New York Senate, to aid in securing the land-grant fund, or at least a part of it, for this college.

As a member of the State senate Mr. Cornell favored a division of the land-grant fund between two institutions but was opposed in this by Andrew D. White, who had come from Onondaga County as a senator in January, 1864. Cornell was chairman of the committee on agriculture and White of the committee on literature. The problem of the disposition of the land-grant fund was finally referred to these two committees for their joint action. White overcame Cornell's objection to making the grant to a single institution and on February 7, 1865, introduced a bill establishing Cornell University at Ithaca and giving it the entire land-grant fund. He supported his bill in an elaborate speech in which he described the unfortunate condition of the colleges at Havana and Ovid and said that while he had favored the People's College he was now convinced that the plan proposed in his bill offered the only practicable solution of the problem. This bill was opposed by Horace Greeley and other friends of the two colleges but became a law April 27, 1865. The matter having been thus settled, Horace Greeley and Erastus Brooks, trustees of the People's College, and William Kelly and J. B. Williams, trustees of the State Agricultural College, became members of the first board of trustees of Cornell University.

There thus came into the organization of Cornell University a combination of the influences represented in the long effort of the State agricultural society to establish an agricultural college, in the more recent attempt of the mechanics' organization to organize an industrial college which had been modified particularly by the activities of Horace Greeley and Amos Brown so as to make a plan for a much broader institution, and in the personal attitude of Andrew D. White, which was the result of his connection with Yale College and the University of Michigan and his acquaintance with the European universities.

Mr. Cornell was also familiar with the Illinois plan for industrial universities and had corresponded with Turner about it.

The act establishing the university had been drafted by Cornell, White, and Charles J. Folger, chairman of the judiciary committee of the State senate. It created a body corporate to be known as Cornell University, the leading object of which was to teach such branches of learning as are related to agriculture and the mechanic arts, including military tactics, but also such other branches of science and knowledge as the trustees might deem useful and proper. The government of the university was intrusted to a board of 24 trustees, including the governor, lieutenant governor, speaker of the assembly, superintendent of public instruction, and president of the State agricultural society, ex officio.

The university was required to receive annually one student from each of the 128 assembly districts in the State free from any tuition fee or incidental charge. This number was afterwards increased to four students from each of 150 districts. "Persons of every religious denomination, or of no religious denomination, shall be equally eligible to all offices and appointments." The farm and grounds must consist of not less than 200 acres, and two years were granted for the provision of suitable buildings and equipment.

The income of the land-grant fund was given to the university on condition that Mr. Cornell give it $500,000 and also $25,000 to the Genesee Seminary at Lima, N. Y. This last provision was a concession permitted by Mr. Cornell on account of the persistent effort of the seminary to secure a portion of the land-grant fund. Mr. Cornell's announcement, which was inscribed on the seal of the university, contained a far broader conception of a university than had hitherto been thought of in educational circles. To found "An institution where any person can find instruction in any study" seemed at that time to educators and college men generally not only to be impracticable but to be contrary to any reasonable educational policy. It was thought that its organization would be so loose and its instruction so diffuse as to break down all proper standards for higher education. Guided by the practical wisdom of Mr. Cornell and by the sound judgment and broad educational training and experience of Doctor White the institution was established on a sound basis financially and educationally.

The State controller, who was charged with the sale of the land-grant scrip, had sold 76,000 acres for $64,400 when Mr. Cornell undertook to acquire the remainder for the benefit of the university. In 1865 he bought 100,000 acres for $50,000 and the next year made a contract with the State to purchase the rest of the scrip for 30 cents per acre, and to pay an additional 30 cents per acre to the State whenever scrip or land was sold, the sum thus obtained to be the land-grant fund, and with the balance of the profits to constitute an endowment fund for the university which would not be subject to the restrictions of the Morrill Land Grant Act. He first sold 6,080 acres and located 525,920 acres, mostly in timberland in Wisconsin, and had to pay for its location, taxation, and protection against timber thieves. In 1868 and 1869 he was persuaded by the trustees to sell 381,920 acres still in the hands of the controller, which netted $128,499.20 for the Cornell endowment fund and increased the land-grant fund by $229,152. The propriety of Mr. Cornell's transactions was disputed and it was not until October, 1874, that they were finally approved by the land commissioners.

The rest of the land was kept off the market at tremendous expense and when Mr. Cornell proposed to transfer the land to the university, with the cost of its purchase, location, and care, amounting to over $576,000, from $50,000 to $90,000 was required to meet the annual charges against this land. For seven years the university bore the burden of this unproductive investment and had to borrow from its endowment fund to carry it. To Henry W. Sage, chairman of the board of trustees, is due in great measure the final success of this enterprise. He persuaded the board to hold the land until after 1880, and fortunately the price of pine timber rose so rapidly that when the university sold 140,000 acres in 1881 and 1882 they brought over $2,300,000. When the land was all sold the total endowment secured to the university through Mr. Cornell's plan was about $5,460,000. In addition he gave the 200 acres on which the university was located and other gifts, amounting to over $650,000. The land-grant fund finally amounted to $688,576.12.

The private gifts by him and other individuals amounted to $1,433,457 five years after the opening of the university and at the end of 30 years to about $9,500,000. The State made no direct appropriations to the university until 1893. In 1873 the income of the university was $101,000, including $18,000 from tuition fees, and in 1881 it was only $100,000. Friends of the university kept it from going into bankruptcy until the great land sales of 1881-82 made its financial status stable.

For buildings the university had at first one which was originally intended for a water cure (now Cascadilla Hall) and a new stone building, afterwards known as Morrill Hall. A large temporary wooden building was erected in 1869. Six other substantial buildings for the use of students were erected during President White's administration.

Through purchases in Europe by President White and in other ways an unusually large equipment in apparatus, collections, and other facilities for instruction in science and the arts was obtained during the early years of the university. Its library in 1868 contained about 12,000 volumes and grew rapidly in variety and extent.

The plan for the organization of the university presented to the trustees by Doctor White October 21, 1866, had the following main features: The university should have two great divisions; 1, special sciences and arts (including (*a*) agriculture, (*b*) mechanic arts, (*c*) civil engineering, (*d*) commerce and trade, (*e*) mining,

(f) medicine and surgery, (g) law, (h) jurisprudence and political science, and (i) history); 2, science, literature, and the arts in general. Twenty-six professors were needed, but for the present 16 resident and 10 nonresident professors would suffice. In the department of agriculture there should be professors of the theory and practice of agriculture, agricultural chemistry, general and analytical chemistry, geology and mineralogy, zoology and comparative anatomy, botany, civil engineering, veterinary surgery and breeding of animals, and physiology, hygiene, and physical culture. There should be an experimental farm. Courses of 4, 3, and 2 years would be offered.

The salaries of professors should range from $1,750 to $2,250. Manual labor by students should be elective. There should be a gymnasium, with an instructor; baseball and boating should be encouraged. Military education should be encouraged or made compulsory. The university should have a vital connection with the school system of the State. Dormitories should be erected for only a limited number of students.

The division of courses into "general" and "special" was kept up during President White's administration. At its close in 1885 there were five general courses; arts, literature, philosophy, science, and science and letters; and 11 special courses; agriculture, architecture, analytical chemistry, chemistry and physics, civil engineering, electrical engineering, mechanic arts, mathematics, natural history, medical preparatory, and history and political science. At first students who chose to take the "optional course" were allowed to select freely the subjects they were to study but before long it was apparent that this plan was not working well. Then a more limited scheme of electives within the regular courses was adopted and in most courses the electives were confined to junior and senior years. More latitude was permitted in the general than in the special courses.

To give the university at the outset good standing educationally it was Doctor White's plan to obtain a number of experienced and apparent that this plan was not working well. Then a more limited courses of lectures during the college year and to employ as resident professors comparatively young men of good training and promise. In the selection of such men he consulted especially Louis Agassiz. Among the first nonresident professors were Agassiz in natural history and Goldwin Smith in English history, and among the resident professors were George Chapman Caldwell in agricultural chemistry, Burt Green Wilder in comparative anatomy and zoology, Albert Nelson Prentiss in botany, horticulture, and arboriculture, James Law in veterinary medicine and surgery, and John L. Morris in mechanic arts. Doctor White was professor of modern European history.

The year the university opened there were 15 professors, 3 assistant professors, and 6 nonresident professors. The limited income of the university prevented rapid growth of the faculty until after 1880. In 1885 there were 56 teachers and in 1889 there were 99.

At first men only were admitted as students in the university. Mr. Cornell, however, favored coeducation, and Mr. Sage offered an endowment and a residence hall for women. They were formally admitted in 1874.

No preparatory classes were organized in the university. For admission to the freshman class the requirements applying to all courses were at first English, geography, arithmetic, and algebra to quadratics, with Latin and Greek for the arts course, and Latin for the course in philosophy and literature.

After 1876 a modern language or advanced mathematics was required for the courses in letters and in science. For the courses in agriculture, architecture, and engineering only the primary requirements were in force until 1887.

The first year 414 students were matriculated in the university, but this number was not reached again until the twentieth year, when there were 457. The smallest number, 125, was in 1880-81. The matriculation, attendance, and degrees at several times within the first 20 years were as follows:

Year	Matricu-lates	Attend-ance	First degrees	Advanced degrees
1868–69	414	414	16	
1872–73	188	539	95	3
1877–78	180	529	67	3
1882–83	153	406	65	6
1887–88	457	1,022	137	12

During the administration of President White the university developed most strongly in the courses in natural science, where the attendance of students was greatest. Between 1868 and 1886 482 students received the degree of bachelor of science. On its mechanical side the largest development during this period was in civil engineering, in which 171 students received their first degree, as compared with 65 in mechanical engineering.

In 1885 Charles Kendall Adams came from the professorship of history in the University of Michigan to the presidency of Cornell University. He was especially interested in the humanities and during his administration of seven years, while the work of the university and its scientific and technical departments prospered, there was an especially marked increase in the interest in humanistic studies. In his report for 1888–89 President Adams said:

Within four years the number of classical students in the university has increased by about fivefold. This increase is plainly owing to the superior instruction offered, to the enlarged equipment of the seminary rooms for advanced work in the ancient classics, and to the very gratifying atmosphere of confidence and enthusiasm that has come to surround linguistic studies.

THE COLLEGE OF AGRICULTURE

The general principles on which Cornell University attempted to establish a college of agriculture were stated by President White in an address before the New York State Agricultural Society February 10, 1869. It should be built on the experience of the farm and the workshop and the common school and make master farmers thoroughly based in the sciences relating to agriculture. The principles of accounts should also be taught. The trustees at the outset were of the opinion that under the Morrill Land Grant Act all students in the university should be required to take some instruction in agriculture. It was therefore decided that no student should receive a diploma who had not attended lectures on general agriculture. Before the opening of the university a beginning was made of organizing an agricultural faculty. George Chapman Caldwell was elected professor of agricultural chemistry. He was a native of Massachusetts and a graduate of the Lawrence Scientific School, who had also studied at the universities of Göttingen and Heidelberg, Germany, and the agricultural college at Cirencester, England, had taught chemistry at Columbia, Antioch, and Pennsylvania State colleges and had been vice president of the Pennsylvania college.

As one of the results of President White's tour in Europe in 1868 James Law was persuaded to come to the university as professor of veterinary medicine and surgery. He had taught anatomy and materia medica in the Veterinary College at Edinburgh and in the Albert Veterinary College at London, had practiced veterinary medicine in England and Ireland, and was widely known as the author of a work on the Anatomy of Domestic Animals.

Joseph Harris, editor of the American Agriculturist, was appointed professor of agriculture, but did not undertake the work. Governor Frederick Holbrook, of Vermont, was asked to be the nonresident professor of agriculture, but also performed no service.

Albert N. Prentiss was called from the Michigan Agricultural College to be professor of botany, horticulture, and arboriculture.

Lewis Spaulding was appointed assistant professor of agriculture and farm superintendent February 18, 1869, and served in that double capacity for a year. John Stanton Gould, who had been president of the State agricultural society, was appointed that year nonresident professor of agriculture and for several years delivered two courses of lectures, one on general agriculture and the other on mechanics as applied to agriculture.

Rooms were assigned to the agricultural faculty in the new building, afterwards known as Morrill Hall, and the headquarters of the agricultural college were in this building for many years.

The college farm of about 200 acres was gradually developed and used in connection with the classroom work, partly for observation of crops, animals, machinery, and agricultural operations and partly to furnish labor for a limited number of students under the voluntary paid-labor system of the university. For a long time this farm had only an equipment of ordinary farm buildings. The library was well provided with books and journals on agriculture and related sciences. A special agricultural library was given to the university by Mr. Cornell. For admission to the college of agriculture students were required to pass examinations in English grammar and orthography, geography, arithmetic, and algebra to quadratic equations.

The first 4-year course in agriculture was scheduled as follows: For freshmen, algebra, geometry, English, French, human physiology, botany, and history; for sophomores, bookkeeping, experimental mechanics, trigonometry and surveying, English, German, chemistry, vegetable physiology, geology, and physics; for juniors, English, agricultural and economic botany, agricultural chemistry, horticulture, arboriculture, veterinary anatomy and physiology, veterinary medicine and surgery, entomology, strength and preservation of materials, and practical agriculture; for seniors, English, drafting, astronomy, psychology, history, political science, constitutional law, architecture, building and building materials, entomology, landscape gardening, rural economy, and practical agriculture.

Two and three year courses were also offered.

Under the elective system "more than two-thirds of the students in the first academic year received instruction in one or more agricultural branches, although but 30 devoted their entire attention to the subject."

After the retirement of Assistant Professor Spaulding there was a vacancy for a year in the department of practical agriculture. In 1871 Henry H. McCandless, who had been connected with the Royal Agricultural College at Glasnevin, Ireland, was appointed professor of agriculture and served until 1873. The separate office of farm superintendent was created. The course in agriculture was somewhat changed; the strictly agricultural subjects began with soils in the third term of junior year, and manures, farm implements, field crops, animals, farm management, buildings, and accounts were scheduled in senior year. Horticulture was an elective in sophomore and junior years. Professor McCandless was not well acquainted with American agriculture and was unable to adjust himself to the conditions then existing in the university. Interest in agricultural instruction declined during his term and in 1873 there were only seven students in agriculture.

Then Isaac P. Roberts was called from the Iowa Agricultural College as assistant professor of agriculture and was made full professor the following year. He arrived at Ithaca in January, 1874, and was much discouraged by the lack of interest at the university in its agricultural department. In his autobiography (315) he says that—

in 1874 there were only three senior students in agriculture at Cornell University and a few strays to whom I gave an hour of instruction per day, five days in the week for the rest of that year * * *. At that time the trustees had not much interest in the farm and did not know enough about it to appreciate my difficulties.

Because of the trouble they had had in managing the university farm the trustees had leased it to an ordinary farmer and it was in poor condition. It contained less than 100 acres of arable land and the livestock consisted mainly of 12 " miserable " cows. The barn erected by the former professor was not at all suitable for such a farm.

Professor Roberts had been brought up on a farm in western New York and was thoroughly acquainted with the agriculture of that region. He developed the university farm as well as he could with the means at his disposal, conducting it on a system of mixed farming with dairy husbandry as its most prominent feature. In 1880 he erected a large barn of a good type at a cost of $7,000 and he gradually brought in improved livestock. Besides managing the farm, he engaged in instructional work, which he has described as follows:

From 1880 onward I lectured five times a week throughout the year and spent two afternoons in each week with my class in the fields or shops or barns. Beside this I gave one lecture a week to the students in veterinary science and three lectures per week and some laboratory work to the winter course students.

Following the plan begun in Iowa he sometimes took his students on tours of inspection of farms in different places.

The agricultural faculty was strengthened by the coming of John Henry Comstock as instructor in entomology in 1873, who was made professor of entomology in 1876, and by the employment of William Rane Lazenby, a graduate in agriculture at the university in 1874, first as instructor and in 1877 as assistant professor of horticulture, previous to his long service as head of that department in Ohio State University.   Henry Hiram Wing, also a graduate of this college in 1881, served as assistant in dairying in the college before going to the University of Nebraska in 1884 as assistant professor of animal husbandry.   In 1888 he came back to Cornell University as deputy director of the experiment station and for many years was professor of animal husbandry in the agricultural college, becoming emeritus professor after 40 years' service.

The 4-year course in agriculture in which Professor Roberts and his associates participated, as it was scheduled in 1881-82, included for freshmen, French or German, rhetoric, geometry, algebra, trigonometry, freehand drawing, hygiene, and general chemistry; for sophomores, French or German, analytical and agricultural chemistry, zoology, anatomy, botany, entomology, surveying, and one elective; for juniors, mechanics and physics, analytical chemistry, agricultural botany, vegetable physiology and histology, arboriculture, landscape gardening, entomology, veterinary science, and surgery; for seniors, agriculture (lectures and field work), botany, horticulture, geology, building materials and construction, American law, and one elective.   There was also a 3-year course not leading to a degree.   Beginning about 1885 special students were allowed to take limited courses without passing entrance examinations.

But in New York as elsewhere for a long time conditions within and without the university were not favorable for bringing many students into the College of Agriculture.   The number ranged from 17 in 1874 to 36 in 1888.   In the latter year there were 3 seniors, 8 juniors, 12 sophomores, and 13 freshmen.   The total number of students in the university at that time was 1,211.   In his annual report for 1891-92 President Adams described the College of Agriculture as

almost purely a technical school. Its design is to educate young men to be farmers in a large sense of the term, or to be teachers of some one of the branches of agriculture in an agricultural college. Professors in the College of Agriculture, with two exceptions, devote most of their time to giving instruction to students not enrolled in that course. * * * Our function in the College of Agriculture seems to have been very largely to educate professors and teachers, and notwithstanding the smallness of the number of students enrolled in the college it is probable that no other department in the university can now show so large a list of alumni who have risen to distinction in their respective vocations.

Among the graduates of this college during the first 20 years were D. E. Salmon, Chief of the Bureau of Animal Industry, and A. M. Farrington, assistant chief of that bureau; Clinton D. Smith, head of the department of agriculture of the Michigan Agricultural College; and Veranus A. Moore, director of the State Veterinary College at Cornell University.   It is also interesting to note that L. O. Howard, Chief of the Bureau of Entomology, graduated in a scientific course at the university in 1877.

The department of veterinary science was separated from the College of Agriculture in 1896 and became the New York State Veterinary College at Cornell University. In a similar way a State college of forestry was established there in 1898 and afterwards transferred to Syracuse University. In 1904 the State took over the College of Agriculture and provided for its equipment and maintenance but left it at Cornell University.

Experimental work on the college farm was begun soon after Professor Roberts came to the university in 1874 and in 1879 this and related work was organized as an experiment station, under a board of control consisting of the faculty of the College of Agriculture and representatives of the State agricultural society, the State grange, and six other farm organizations. Professor Roberts was president of the board and Professor Caldwell was director of the station.

The only special fund which the station had at first was $250 contributed by Miss Jennie McGraw for the printing of the report. In 1881 the trustees of the university appropriated $1,100 for the station, and this was followed by $1,145 in 1882 and $750 in 1883.

Three reports were issued by the station before it was reorganized under the Hatch Act in 1888. The first report, issued in 1880, gives an account of field experiments by Professor Roberts with wheat, corn, oats, grass, and mangel-wurzels. Some of these experiments were begun in 1874. There were also reported experiments by Professor Caldwell with fertilizers on corn and with cows with reference to the influence of the ration on the composition of milk; experiments in dairying, including some on the curing of cheese, by S. M. Babcock; experiments in horticulture and investigations in entomology and in agricultural chemistry. Work in the same general lines was described in the succeeding reports.

Members of the agricultural faculty almost from the beginning addressed meetings of farmers to a limited extent. Professor Roberts was particularly active in this direction and kept in close touch with the State agricultural society and other farm organizations. Under the leadership of Professor Roberts and J. S. Woodward, of Lockport, the first farmers' institute in New York was held at the university February 16 to 18, 1886. It asked the State agricultural society to assume responsibility for future institutes. Several were successfully held by the society during the following winter with the result that the legislature made an appropriation for their continuance. From this time members of the agricultural faculty were prominent in the institutes.

ILLINOIS INDUSTRIAL UNIVERSITY (UNIVERSITY OF ILLINOIS)

Illinois accepted the provisions of the Morrill Land Grant Act February 14, 1863, and received scrip for 480,000 acres. Then a bitter controversy ensued regarding the disposal of this grant within the State. Some favored its distribution among several agricultural colleges and others desired to have it all given to some existing institution. Meanwhile the followers of Jonathan B. Turner were active in promoting the establishment of an industrial university which should receive all the Federal land grant.

In 1863 several existing colleges attempted to get a share of the land-grant fund, but under Turner's leadership action on this fund by the legislature was deferred until 1865. During this interval those who favored an industrial university were very active through lectures, press articles, and resolutions at agricultural, horticultural, educational, and industrial meetings. The State teachers' association and the State agricultural and horticultural societies favored one institution. In July, 1864, Governor Yates was persuaded to appoint a commission to report plans for dividing the land-grant fund between an agricultural college centrally located and a mechanical college in Chicago. So much opposition from the farmers was aroused by this action that the governor disbanded the commission before it had taken action. However, when committees representing the agricultural organizations met at Springfield December 6, "a large and influential delegation from the mechanics of Chicago" came to this meeting and presented arguments for a mechanical school. Then Turner and a few of his friends drafted a bill which provided for the use of the land-grant fund by a single university whose location was to be determined by a commission. This bill was introduced in the house January 10, 1865, and during consideration there was amended so as to locate the university at Urbana, Champaign County, and to give the trustees authority to establish a mechanic arts department in Chicago, and an agricultural department in southern Illinois. The amended bill passed the house but was defeated in the senate.

For the origin of the movement to locate the university at Urbana it is necessary to go back to January, 1859, when a company which was attempting to establish seminaries in different parts of Illinois sent a representative to that town. The company proposed to purchase 200 acres of land between Urbana and West Urbana (in 1860 named Champaign) and to erect a substantial building. The land not needed for the school would be divided into lots and sold. Committees from the two towns assisted in securing the land and in getting subscriptions to the company's stock. Eight acres were set apart for the seminary and the construction of a building was begun. In January, 1861, a memorial signed by 62 citizens of the two towns was presented to the legislature asking that an agricultural seminary and bureau be established in Champaign County, and given a portion of the tax fund from the Illinois Central Railroad. The legislature on February 21, 1861, granted a charter for the Urbana-Champaign Institute, as "a seminary of learning comprehending an agricultural or other departments as the public may demand." No State aid was given to this institution. The Civil War brought financial difficulties and work on the seminary building was suspended. After the passage of the land grant act the project to use this building for the agricultural and mechanical college was revived. The board of supervisors of Champaign County passed resolutions May 4, 1864, asking the legislature to locate such a college in that county and entered into negotiations to purchase the seminary property if the legislature granted their request. They also sought the aid of the Illinois Central Railroad, provided a fund to be used in securing the location of the college and asked authority to borrow money and issue bonds to complete this transaction. Their agent visited Springfield December 6, 1864, conferred with the farmers' committee advocating the industrial university, and brought about the amendment to their bill which located the university at Urbana. A joint committee of the legislature visited Urbana January 21, 1865, and reported favorably on the offer of Champaign County, which included the completed seminary building and grounds and 100 acres of land.

In September, 1865, the executive board of the State agricultural society decided to call a convention of agriculturists, mechanics, and manufacturers at Bloomington to consider measures for the location of the land-grant college. This convention met December 14, 1865, and through a committee of which Turner was chairman adopted resolutions favoring " one university of the highest order " to receive all of the congressional grant and " the general principles adopted and approved by all parties at the last session of the legislature." A later resolution provided for a committee to revise the bill presented at the last session of the legislature and get pledges from candidates for the next legislature to support this bill.

Presidents of existing colleges in the State had a meeting in Chicago in October, 1865, and passed resolutions favoring division of the land-grant fund among institutions in different parts of the State.

In September, 1865, the supervisors of Champaign County decided to submit to the people a proposition to bond the county for $100,000 to purchase the seminary building and a farm for the industrial university and to bear other expenses necessary to secure the location of the university in this county. The people approved this proposition by a vote of 4,601 to 1,085. C. R. Griggs was elected representative to the legislature from that district with the understanding that he would push the university measure. A lobby from Champaign County was established at Springfield when the legislature met and an active propaganda involving the use of considerable money was carried on. When it became clear that the interest at the legislature would center chiefly in the location of a single university other counties took action to secure consideration. Definite offers were finally made on a financial basis from Morgan, McLean, and Logan Counties. Turner was especially interested in the offer from Morgan County, which involved the use of Illinois College at Jacksonville, where he had formerly taught. The McLean County proposition was for a site adjoining the Normal University.

A joint committee of the legislature which visited the four counties in February, 1867, reported the value of the offer as follows: Champaign, $285,000; McLean, $470,000; Logan, $385,000; and Morgan, $315,000, or including the Illinois College property, $419,000. But the thorough organization and persistent efforts of the Champaign County forces prevailed and the legislature located the university at Urbana.

Two acts regarding the university were passed in 1867. The first was an act of January 25, 1867, which provided—

That any county, city, township, or incorporated town of said State, may, by taxation, as well as by voluntary subscription of its citizens, raise a fund to secure the location of said university at any point whatever; and any other corporation in this State may make bids and subscription for the purpose of securing said location at any point whatever (117).

The second was the act of February 28, 1867, for the organization and maintenance of the Illinois Industrial University. Under this act the general management of the university was vested in a board

of trustees consisting of the governor, superintendent of public instruction, president of the State agricultural society, and the regent
of the university as members ex officio, five members from each of the
three grand judicial districts of the State, and one member from
each of the 13 congressional districts, to be appointed by the governor with the consent of the senate, for a term of 6 years, except
that the first members were to be divided into three classes to serve
2, 4, and 6 years, respectively. The board was given power to establish branches of the university at different places in the State but
could not grant to such branches any portion of the Federal land-
grant fund or funds donated by the county, city, or town near the
university. The regent was to be elected for two years, be president
of the board and the faculty and have general supervision of the educational facilities and interests of the university. A corresponding
secretary was to secure "instructive information from persons in
various counties skilled in agricultural, mechanical and industrial
arts" and prepare an annual report on the progress of the university,
with accounts of experiments and State industrial and economical
statistics, to be published in editions of 5,000 copies. The trustees
might establish "model farms" and such departments and professorships as might "be required to teach in the most thorough manner,
such branches of learning as are related to agriculture and the mechanic arts, and military tactics, without excluding other scientific
and classical studies." They might accept voluntary contributions
for the endowment of professorships or departments. The minimum
age of students was fixed at 15 years, and before entrance they must
pass examinations in "the branches ordinarily taught in the common
schools of the State." Free tuition was to be given to one descendant
of a soldier or seaman from each county who has been in the United
States military service during the Civil War and to such other persons as the trustees should decide on without embarrassing the finances of the university. No degrees could be given but "certificates
of scholarship" might be awarded. The trustees must permanently
locate the university at Urbana, in Champaign County, whenever
that county should convey to the university the buildings and lands
of the Urbana and Champaign Institute and other near-by lands, including in all 970 acres, $100,000 in Champaign County bonds bear-
ing interest at 10 per cent, $2,000 in fruit, shade, and ornamental
trees and shrubs donated by M. L. Dunlap, and $50,000 in freight
donated by the Illinois Central Railroad. The governor was directed to transfer the Federal land scrip to the treasurer of the university, who was given authority to sell it under the direction of the
board of trustees.

The trustees met for the first time March 12, 1867, took the oath
of office, which under the constitution of 1848 required them to pledge,
among other things, that they would not engage in dueling, and
elected as regent, John Milton Gregory (1822–1898), who, through
successive elections, served 13 years. He was a native of Sand Lake,
N. Y., graduated at Union College, studied law and theology, held a
pastorate in a Baptist church, and had been principal of a classical
school in Detroit, editor of the Michigan Journal of Education, State
superintendent of education in Michigan, and president of Kalamazoo College. He was in full sympathy with those who would
establish a broad university and as chairman of a committee ap-

pointed by the board prepared a comprehensive outline for the departments and courses to be developed. The agricultural department was to include courses in agriculture and in horticulture and landscape gardening.

The report of this committee aroused a prolonged discussion through the State and much opposition to the university in its early years, especially among the friends of agricultural education. This was intensified by the disappointment of Turner and his associates at the outcome of the struggle over the location of the university, by the difficulties attending the organization of the agricultural work of the university, and by an apparent emphasis laid on ancient and modern language requirements for college classes. In March, 1869, the legislature passed resolutions alleging that the university was being diverted to an ordinary academic and classical school and declaring that—

its leading and essential objects should be the teaching of such branches of learning as relate to agriculture, horticulture, and the mechanic arts and the consequent promotion of the industrial classes in the various pursuits of life by imparting to them a liberal and practical education.

In 1870 at a convention of delegates from the several county agricultural societies to consider conditions at the university, Professor Baker explained the act creating the university and its work under that act, and the committee, including Turner, appointed to visit the university on the invitation of Doctor Gregory made a report which greatly helped it. They found that the university was doing more for the promotion of agriculture and mechanic arts than they had believed was being done, and that out of a student body of 194 men and 14 women 50 were in agricultural and horticultural courses and 54 in mechanic arts and civil engineering, while only 20 were taking Latin, and none were studying Greek.

The land scrip given the university was rapidly put on the market until 455,000 acres had been sold at an average of about 70 cents per acre, giving a fund of $319,178. Invested at from 8 to 10 per cent this brought the university an income of from $25,000 to $30,000 per year until about 1877, when as a result of the panic of 1873 the interest rate was considerably lowered. This, combined with the refusal of the legislature to make appropriations for current expenses, brought about the necessity of reducing salaries and otherwise greatly embarrassed the university during the closing years of Doctor Gregory's administration. In 1881 the legislature was persuaded to appropriate $11,400 to help cover the loss due to reduced interest on the endowment, and during the next four bienniums $14,000, $24,000, $32,000, and $40,000 were granted for current expenses.

The university was at first housed in the brick building donated by Champaign County. This had a 125-foot front, was 40 feet in depth, and 5 stories high, with a wing. In 1869 the legislature appropriated $60,000 for the biennium, including $25,000 for farm houses, barns, and other farm buildings, fencing, draining, farm equipment, livestock, and fruit and forest trees; $20,000 for buildings, equipment, trees, plants, etc., for the horticultural department, $5,000 for the chemical department, and $10,000 for books and apparatus. In 1871 a drill hall and mechanical shop was built and that year the legislature gave $75,000 toward the erection of a large main building which was completed in 1873. A chemical laboratory was built in 1878 and a small astronomical observatory in 1882.

At its first meeting the board of trustees also empowered members to receive contributions for a polytechnic branch at Chicago. A proposition from the common council of that city to donate $250,-000 for the endowment of this branch, if the legislature would give authority to issue bonds for this purpose, was later accepted but nothing came of this offer.

The university was opened March 2, 1868, and 77 students attended the first term, of whom 45 were from Champaign County. The first faculty consisted of William M. Baker, professor of English language and literature and instructor in natural philosophy; George W. Atherton, professor of history and social science and instructor in Latin; A. P. S. Stuart from Lawrence Scientific School, professor of theoretical and applied chemistry; Thomas J. Burrill, assistant in natural science. The subjects actually taught the first term were algebra, geometry, natural philosophy, history, rhetoric, and Latin. Mr. Burrill was a native of Pittsfield, Mass., and a graduate of the Illinois Normal School. He was superintendent of the public schools at Urbana when he was drafted to aid in opening the university. He was soon elected assistant professor of natural science and later became professor of botany and horticulture. Willard F. Bliss, who had studied at Yale College and was engaged in farming in Illinois, joined the faculty later in 1868 as professor of agriculture and instructor in French. Samuel W. Shattuck also came that year as assistant professor of mathematics and instructor in military tactics; Edward Schneider was instructor in bookkeeping and German; Jonathan Periam was head farmer and superintendent of practical agriculture.

In compliance with the law establishing the university, students were admitted on examinations in arithmetic, geography, English grammar, and United States history. To these subjects a natural science was added when such studies became by law part of the curriculum of the Illinois common schools. Under Doctor Gregory's guidance the trustees took the position that while they could not prevent students entering the university from the common schools it was necessary to prescribe other subjects for entrance to courses of college grade. The entrance requirements for such courses were therefore gradually raised to the high-school level, and about 1880 students began to be admitted from accredited high schools without examination.

Preparatory classes were organized at the university from the beginning and for a considerable time at least half the students were in such classes. In 1875 a regular one-year preparatory course was established. A free elective system was adopted at first, but it was soon found necessary to modify this and to require students desiring to graduate to complete a regular course of study. The trustees did not have authority to grant degrees until 1878, but before that gave " certificates of scholarship " to students who had completed certain courses. Manual labor from one to three hours a day was at first required of all able-bodied students, for which a maximum compensation of 8 cents per hour was given or for additional voluntary work 12½ cents. There were the usual difficulties in enforcing such a regulation and before long all such labor was made voluntary unless it was directly connected with instruction. Women were first formally admitted in 1870, and the university has been coeducational since that time. In 1869 Stillman W. Robinson was elected professor of mechanical engineering and "in January, 1870, a mechanical shop was fitted up with tools and machinery." The number of students increased rapidly, and in 1870 the university was divided into colleges of agriculture, mechanic arts and engineering, chemistry, natural history, and literature, science, and art. In 1873 the number of colleges was reduced to four and the organization was as follows:

The college of agriculture, which included the schools of agriculture and horticulture; the college of engineering, which included mechanical, civil, and mining engineering, and architecture; the college of natural science, which included the schools of chemistry and natural history; and the college of literature, arts, and science, which included the schools of modern language and literature, and ancient language and literature. Besides these there were the schools of commercial science, military science, and domestic economy (123).

The number of men students increased to 326 in 1873 but did not reach that number again during the next 15 years. The number of women was 24 in 1871 and 90 in 1874 but declined to 70 in 1886. The number of preparatory students up to 1888 ranged between 131 and 71. During the first 20 years 3,023 students attended the university, of whom 799 were in preparatory classes, and 2,224 were college students, including 1,818 men and 406 women. The graduates were 403 men and 107 women. About 50 of the graduates became farmers. The institution tended rapidly to lose its distinctive character as an industrial university. With the growth of the high-school system in the State and the giving up of tuition charges by the university, the number of students taking work in the college of literature and science rapidly increased and that college became the largest major unit in the university. In 1875-76, when the total student body numbered 386, there were 199 in that college. The agricultural and mechanical courses had each about 50 students. The following year when the student body was about as large there were 114 in preparatory classes. Largely through the influence of the alumni the name of the institution was changed to University of Illinois in 1885. The trustees appointed by the governor had been reduced from 28 to 9 in 1873 and in 1886 a law was enacted providing for their election by vote of the people. Under this law the governor and State superintendent of education were made members ex officio and women became eligible for election to the board

In June, 1880, Doctor Gregory resigned and Selim Hobart Peabody was elected regent pro tempore. The following year he became regent and served in that capacity 10 years. Under his administration the university gradually grew stronger and somewhat broadened its work. In 1879-80 there were 434 students and 26 teachers, of whom 15 were of professorial rank; in 1890-91 there were 519 students and 40 teachers, including 24 professors. Doctor Peabody was born at Rockingham, Vt., and graduated at the University of Vermont in 1852. For the next 25 years he was engaged in secondary-school work most of the time but was professor of physics and civil engineering in the Massachusetts Agricultural College from 1871 to 1874. In 1878 he became professor of mechanical engineering and physics in the Illinois Industrial University, and except for a few months in 1880 continued in that position after becoming regent. He naturally took much interest in the College of Engineering, which was considerably developed during his administration. He also systematized the financial business of the University and secured substantial increases in its income.

AGRICULTURAL WORK OF THE UNIVERSITY

Originally the university had somewhat over 1,000 acres of land but soon sold about 400 acres. In 1871 the land being used by the university was divided as follows: Campus, 13 acres; horticultural plantations, 130 acres; experiment farm, 70 acres; and stock farm, 410 acres. Jonathan Periam, as head farmer and superintendent of practical agriculture, was expected to develop the farms and supervise student labor on them. He held this position less than two years, and then Willard F. Bliss, the professor of agriculture, became also farm superintendent. One of the major units of the university was the department of agriculture. It was expected that ultimately there would be two distinct courses in this department, (1) general agriculture, and (2) horticulture, fruit growing, and landscape gardening. A somewhat detailed schedule of the subjects to be covered by these courses was given in the first catalogue. The general subjects were choice of farm and its arrangement, farm structures, farm implements, roads and bridges, soils, subsoil, fertilizers, useful crops and products, weeds, propagation and improvement of plants, domestic animals, noxious animals, stock raising, veterinary surgery and medicine, rural laws, history, literature and economy of agriculture. A course of three years was laid out, as follows: First year, the farm, plant culture, English, surveying, drawing, botany, and French; second year, soils, fertilizers, climate, roads, fruit culture, animal husbandry, mechanics, chemistry, zoology, entomology, mineralogy, and German; third year, agricultural economy, agricultural bookkeeping, rural law, veterinary science, landscape gardening, rural architecture and engineering, foreign agriculture, history and literature of agriculture, geology, meteorology, physical geography, inductive logic, political economy, history and civil politics, and English literature.

The studies will be pursued partly by lectures, accompanied by courses of reading and examinations, and partly by the regular study of textbooks. Practical exercises and experiments on the farm and in the gardens, nurseries, and fruit plantations will constitute a part of the course.

In addition to the regular instruction a course of 12 lectures on vegetable physiology and fruit growing by John A. Warder, a prominent pomologist in Ohio, was announced. The method of instruction has been described by Henry M. Dunlap, who entered the university in 1868, as follows:

Our instruction in the classroom consisted in having a chapter in "How Crops Grow" read and commented on by the professor of agriculture. Wearisome hours were spent in this unprofitable work in reading books.

Professor Bliss resigned in June, 1870, and it was then announced that Manly Miles would be his successor. He was to divide his time between the Michigan and Illinois Colleges, serving in the latter during the fall and winter months. This arrangement was not consummated and for several years makeshifts of various kinds were made in the effort to continue agricultural instruction. " The regent and various members of the faculty gave assistance, such as it was, in class instruction." Professor Burrill continued to give instruction in horticulture. H. J. J. Detmers was lecturer in veterinary science and was succeeded in 1873 by F. W. Prentice. That year Charles W. Silver, a graduate of the university in 1872, who had studied agricultural science at the University of Halle, Germany, was appointed instructor in agricultural chemistry with the expectation that he would become professor of agriculture, but he resigned at the end of the year. Then in 1875 Doctor Miles became professor of agriculture and instructor in agricultural chemistry, at the double salary of $5,000. This arrangement lasted only one year.

The college of agriculture was organized with schools of agriculture and horticulture. The courses in these subjects had been lengthened to four years. In agriculture the technical and scientific subjects were arranged as follows: For freshmen, botany, chemistry, vegetable physiology, trigonometry, and surveying; for sophomores, agricultural chemistry (soils, plants, fertilizers, and foods), entomology, and zoology; for juniors, agricultural engineering and architecture, animal anatomy and physiology, animal husbandry, veterinary science, and landscape gardening; for seniors, rural economy, history of agriculture, and rural law. A 1-year farmers' course was also offered. In horticulture the course was the same as in agriculture, except that instead of instruction relating to field crops and animals, in junior year there was pomology, forestry, and landscape gardening, and in senior year floriculture, horticultural history, and rural law.

In 1876 George Espy Morrow (1840–1900) was elected professor of agriculture and became dean of the college of agriculture in 1878, serving in that capacity for 16 years. He was born in Warren County, Ohio, was educated at Maineville Academy and in law at the University of Michigan, and was a soldier in the Civil War. After several years' experience as editor of agricultural papers he became professor of practical agriculture at the Iowa State College. He was a very industrious worker and a man of very fine spirit. His long-time associate, Professor Burrill, has spoken of him as follows:

He was singularly gifted in many ways, and these included qualifications needful in the arduous and difficult work which he undertook to perform. He harmonized opinions, coordinated interests, gained the confidence and good will of those in authority and of others with whom he worked. Himself an editor in his earlier career, he secured a favorable attitude on the part of the agricultural press. He was unequaled at the time as a lecturer at home and abroad upon agricultural themes, and his devotion to his subject was limitless in time and boundless in endeavor (121).

Under Professor Morrow the general plan of the college course in agriculture was not altered materially, except that instruction in the elements of agriculture was brought down to the freshman year. Unfortunately his term of service at the Illinois college covered the period when economic, agricultural, and educational conditions were not conducive to bringing any considerable number of students into the regular collegiate courses in agriculture.

The published statistics of the attendance of students in the agricultural department of the Illinois university during the first 20 years are somewhat difficult to interpret, but it appears that in 1871 there were 60 agricultural students and in 1876 there were 45. After the more formal organization of the College of Agriculture, it reported in 1879 only 17 students and in 1888 it had 23. Apparently these numbers included students in both agriculture and horticulture, for the number recorded in agriculture alone in 1882 was 4 as compared with 24 in horticulture, and in 1884 there were 10 in agriculture and 15 in horticulture. After the bachelor's degree began to be conferred by the university, one student in the college of agriculture received that degree in each of the years 1878, 1885, and 1888 and 3 in 1884. Among these were M. A. Scovell, Thomas F. Hunt, and Harry S. Grindley, who became members of the faculty of the university. Professor Scovell was afterwards for a long time director of the Kentucky Agricultural Experiment Station and Professor Hunt served as a professor of agronomy in the New York College of Agriculture at Cornell University, professor and dean in the Pennsylvania State College and Ohio State University, and dean of the College of Agriculture of the University of California.

In Illinois, as elsewhere, the foundations for a much broader work of agricultural instruction in college classes were being laid by efforts in other directions.

From its beginning the university undertook to establish agricultural and horticultural experiments on its lands at Urbana and set apart tracts for these purposes. In 1871 the trustees made an annual appropriation of $2,500 for the agricultural experiments. A plan was made for field experiments with cover and other crops, on the treatment of soils, and on the feeding of animals. A beginning of such experiments was reported in 1872 and further reports were made in succeeding annual reports of the university.

In 1875 experiments with silage were reported; sugar beets were also being tested. After Professor Morrow came, the experimental work was further systematized. Special attention was given to corn, but there were also experiments with other grains, sorgo for sugar making, crop rotation, steer feeding, etc. Experiments in horticulture, begun almost as soon as the university opened, were conducted by Professor Burrill. These included variety plantations of apples, pears, and other orchard fruits, small fruits, and ornamental plants. There was also a plantation of forest trees. He made valuable botanical studies and collections of the flora of the State and undertook investigations of plant diseases. In 1876 he reported the discovery of bacteria in great numbers in the blighting bark of pear and apple trees. Two years later he announced that through inoculations he had discovered that bacteria caused the disease and this was confirmed by him through more thorough investigations conducted later, the results of which were published in 1880.

Professor Weber made chemical studies of soils, sugar beets, sorgo, etc., and Professor Scovell also made studies in agricultural chemistry. Accounts of the experimental work at the university were published in its annual reports, particularly from 1880.

Through such work a considerable foundation was laid for the Illinois experiment station, which was organized at the university in 1888.

The agricultural extension work of the university began almost as soon as it was organized. Its first annual report contains an article of over 100 pages on Illinois agriculture, compiled from the replies of 34 farmers in different parts of the State. "Following the precedent of the Yale agricultural lectures" of 1860, the "First annual course of lectures and discussions" was held at the university January 12 to 22, 1869, and was attended by the students and many farmers. An account of this meeting, covering 240 pages, was published in the second report of the university. The following year 4-day courses for farmers, which were essentially farmers' institutes, were held at the university and at Centralia and Rockford. In 1871 the legislature appropriated $500 for such courses and they were held that winter in four places. Then they were called farmers' institutes, and five were held in 1872 and seven in 1873. The regent and members of the faculty often addressed other farmers' meetings and Professor Morrow was particularly active in this work. An institute held at the university in 1879 was well attended and an exhibit of animals from the university at the Fat Stock Show in Chicago in 1881 attracted much favorable attention. The management of the farmers' institutes was transferred to the State board of agriculture, but university officers participated in these meetings. In 1888 Professor Morrow attended 28 institutes and sent papers to 3 others.

Part 4. PREPARATION FOR LARGE UNDERTAKINGS IN AGRICULTURAL EDUCATION, 1871–1900

The lack of a satisfactory body of agricultural knowledge with special reference to American conditions made the agricultural courses in the land-grant colleges during the first 25 years after the passage of the Morrill Act of 1862 unsatisfactory from a pedagogical point of view, and the methods of teaching, chiefly by textbooks and lectures, combined with the labor requirement, made them unattractive to students. Other causes, such as the economic depression of agriculture due to the rapid development of farming on virgin soils west of the Alleghenies and the demand for engineers and factory managers due to the building of railroads and industrial plants, led the development of these colleges to follow mainly scientific and engineering lines and turned the attention of the farm youth to pursuits other than farming.

Those who had been the chief promoters and supporters of the college land grant act of 1862 had expected that the colleges thus endowed would do much to advance agricultural knowledge by experimental work. After these colleges were established it was soon apparent that a large amount of such work would be required before a satisfactory body of agricultural knowledge which might be used in teaching would be available. The success of agricultural research in Europe, and to a certain extent in the United States Department of Agriculture, stimulated the colleges to a desire to undertake more work in this direction, provided funds could be obtained. They also began to realize that united action was very desirable in order to plan and conduct the work in the best way and without unnecessary duplication of effort. It would also aid them in securing more adequate financial support. Such motives as these led to the meeting of representatives of the land-grant colleges, at Chicago, in 1871, which has already been mentioned. (See p. 127.) This meeting started a movement which had three very important ultimate results: (1) Federal endowment of agricultural experiment stations under the Hatch Act of 1887, (2) further Federal endowment of the land-grant colleges under the Morrill Act of 1890, and (3) the formation of the Association of American Agricultural Colleges and Experiment Stations in 1887.

THE CHICAGO MEETING OF 1871

The convention of friends of agricultural education at Chicago, August 24 and 25, 1871, was in pursuance of an invitation signed by representatives of 12 land-grant colleges and the agricultural college at Guelph, Ontario. The purpose of the meeting was stated as follows:

After correspondence with those more immediately interested it has been decided to call a convention of presidents of agricultural colleges, professors of

192

agriculture, or other persons in the United States or British Provinces, who are engaged or interested in promoting the art or science of agriculture by experiments in the field or laboratories, for the purpose of organizing, consulting and cooperating in the great work of advancing the cause of agricultural knowledge and education, especially by experimentation with similar crops under similar conditions at all the agricultural colleges (*118*).

Twenty-nine persons attended this convention, including the following representatives of land-grant colleges: J. M. Gregory, of Illinois; Manly Miles, of Michigan; D. C. Gilman, of Connecticut (Yale Scientific School); A. N. Prentiss, of New York; John Hamilton, of Pennsylvania; E. W. Hilgard, of Mississippi; W. W. Daniels, of Wisconsin; W. W. Folwell, of Minnesota; S. H. Peabody, of Massachusetts; A. S. Welch and I. P. Roberts, of Iowa; Joseph Denison, of Kansas; and G. C. Swallow, of Missouri. The Missouri Board of Agriculture was represented by its secretary, C. W. Murtfeldt, and there were also representatives of six farm papers. The convention was organized with J. M. Gregory, regent of the Illinois Industrial University, as president, and A. N. Prentiss, professor of botany at Cornell University, and John Hamilton, professor of agriculture at the Pennsylvania Agricultural College, as secretaries. There was much discussion at this convention about cooperation of the colleges in experimental work, and a committee brought in a plan which included experiments (1) to test variation of soil on adjacent plats, (2) planting of corn in hills and drills, and (3) uniform application of manures on adjacent plats. The relations of the schools of applied science to one another and to other institutions were also discussed and this led to a warm debate on the kind of education which the agricultural colleges should give, particularly as to the relative importance of science and practice in agricultural instruction.

W. C. Flagg, corresponding secretary of the board of trustees of the Illinois Industrial University, brought up the question of a permanent organization to meet from year to year or oftener for consultation in regard to experimental work and perhaps to go further and become " an organization of agricultural colleges and the technological schools." A committee appointed to consider this matter reported through E. W. Hilgard that such an organization at this meeting would be premature, but recommended that the officers be an executive committee to draft articles of association and call another meeting to consider them. There was a long discussion, during which suggestions were made that such an organization might be connected with the National Education Association or be confined to consideration of experiments, but the general sentiment seemed to favor a broader and separate organization. Mr. Flagg moved " that the object of the organization to be formed at this meeting shall be the advancement of the interests of industrial education by assembling together persons engaged in agricultural and mechanical experiments and education and with a view of disseminating industrial knowledge." Finally this motion was laid on the table with the understanding that the officers of the meeting would further consider the matter.

W. C. Flagg then offered a resolution that the examples of the European agricultural experiment stations " make us believe the establishment of not less than one such station in each of the several States of the Union would be eminently beneficial to the agricultural interests of the country" and "that a committee, consisting of one from each of the several States in which an institution founded on the national grant has been organized, be appointed by the President, whose duty it shall be to memorialize Congress and the several State legislatures for the speedy establishment of such stations throughout the country." This was adopted by the convention and had an influence on events which followed the adjournment of this meeting.

THE WASHINGTON CONVENTION OF 1872

In 1871 Frederick Watts, long-time president of the board of trustees of the Pennsylvania Agricultural College, became United States Commissioner of Agriculture.

On December 20, 1871, Commissioner Watts issued a call for a convention of two delegates from each agricultural college, State agricultural society, and State board of agriculture to meet at Washington, February 15, 1872 (410). At this meeting 32 States, the District of Columbia, and the Territories of Montana, Dakota, and Utah were represented. Messrs. Gilman, Gregory, Folwell, Swallow, Hilgard, Prentiss, Hamilton, Denison, and Welch, who had been at the Chicago meeting, were delegates, and among the men especially prominent then or in the events which followed were S. W. Johnson, of Connecticut; W. S. Clark, of Massachusetts; T. C. Abbott, of Michigan; George H. Cook, of New Jersey; Ezra Cornell, of New York; W. O. Atwater (then of Tennessee); J. Sterling Morton, of Nebraska (representing the State horticultural society); and Senator J. S. Morrill, of Vermont. George B. Loring, of Massachusetts, was made permanent chairman. When the delegates convened Judge Watts in an introductory address said that the main purpose of the meeting was to bring about cooperation of the colleges and societies with the Department of Agriculture.

Commissioner Watts suggested the following matters for the consideration of the convention: (1) The expediency of seeking further land grants from Congress for the promotion of colleges of agriculture and the mechanic arts, (2) the establishment of experimental farms and stations for the promotion of agricultural knowledge, (3) the modification of military instruction in the national colleges of agriculture and mechanic arts, and (4) the best methods of cooperating with one another and with the Department of Agriculture.

In an address on equalization of land grants President Folwell, of Minnesota, favored asking Congress for a land grant of from 500,000 to 2,000,000 acres per State on the basis of relative area. This new grant should be available for university purposes, but with the proviso "that any institution whatever which fails to conduct the departments of agriculture and the mechanic arts in the most efficient manner practicable shall forfeit the whole endowment." Doctor Gregory, of Illinois, said that President Folwell's proposition had been presented in printed form. He also called attention to the bill granting the net proceeds of the sales of public lands for common schools which had passed the House of Representatives and he opposed its passage by the Senate. He favored the use of the public-lands fund for education but would have it distributed on the following basis: One-third for teachers or school libraries apportioned according to the number of children between 6 and 15 years in the several States; one-third for normal schools or normal classes in high schools; and one-third for agricultural, polytechnic, and other State colleges and universities, to be apportioned one-half according to population and one-half according to area of the State. To consider this matter a committee on equalization of land grants was appointed, consisting of Messrs. Folwell, Bowman (Kentucky), Gilman, Abbot, and Fielder (Georgia). This committee reported in favor of an additional grant of not less than 1,000,000 acres to any one State for the institutions receiving the benefits of the act of 1862. After much debate and many alternative propositions the report of the committee was rejected. Later Senator Morrill introduced a resolution " that, as a sense of this convention, we deem it of paramount importance to ask of Congress, as we do earnestly, for an additional donation of land, or proceeds of land, sufficient to found a professorship of some of the branches of practical science in each of the colleges now wholly or in part sustained by the previous land grant of Congress." This resolution was adopted. Reference is also made in the published proceedings to a committee of six on appropriations, but the members of this committee are not recorded.

The convention also had a committee on experiment stations, including Hunter Nicholson, of East Tennessee University; Daniel Needham, of the New England Agricultural Society; John Hamilton, of the Pennsylvania Agricultural College; S. W. Johnson, of the Yale Scientific School; and L. F. Allen, of the New York State Agricultural Society. This committee had the cooperation of the committee appointed at the Chicago convention. The joint report, read by W. O. Atwater, dwelt on the importance of speedily establishing experiment stations in the United States with the help of individuals, agricultural societies, the States, and the Federal Government. To aid this it was recommended that the committee be continued, that Professor Johnson prepare a further report on the character, value, and practicability of experiment stations, and that the Department of Agriculture be asked to cooperate in preparing, publishing, and disseminating this report. This recommendation was approved by the convention. The convention adjourned to meet in February, 1873, and Commissioner Watts sent out an invitation for this meeting, but for some reason it was not held.

THE MOVEMENT FOR FEDERAL AID TO COMMON SCHOOLS

After the Civil War and the passage of the amendments to the Constitution giving the rights of citizenship to the negroes, much public sentiment was created in favor of granting Federal aid to promote their education. It was also realized that the Southern States had a heavy burden in establishing school systems which would provide even an elementary education for great numbers of both white and black children for whom there had been no schools. Under the leadership of George F. Hoar, of Massachusetts, a bill " to establish an educational fund and to apply the proceeds of the public lands to the education of the people," passed the House of

Representatives on February 8, 1872. Under this bill the net proceeds of the public lands were annually to be invested by the Secretary of the Treasury in United States 5 per cent bonds to constitute a perpetual fund. One-half of the net proceeds of the public lands for the previous year and the income of the educational fund were to be apportioned to the several States and Territories and the District of Columbia on the basis of population between the ages of 4 and 21 years, provided that for the first 10 years the distribution was to be on the basis of illiteracy. For the first year half of the fund and thereafter 10 per cent might be used for normal schools.

This bill did not pass the Senate, but it affected unfavorably the effort of the land-grant colleges to secure additional Federal endowment. Some of its language was embodied in subsequent bills relating to these institutions.

THE MORRILL EDUCATIONAL BILLS, 1872–1888

The committee appointed by the agricultural convention of 1872, with knowledge of the common-school bill, immediately drafted a bill for additional Federal aid to the land-grant colleges. Senator Morrill introduced this bill February 23, 1872, (S. 693) with the statement that it had been presented to him " by a committee representing a convention of a body of men of high character, and hardly ever surpassed in this country for their intelligence. While I have not examined the bill in detail I cordially approve of its general scope and purpose " (546).

This bill provided in three sections for the more complete endowment and support of the colleges of agriculture and the mechanic arts established under the act of Congress of July 2, 1862, an appropriation to each State in which such colleges had been or might be established, of 1,000,000 acres of public lands. On certification of the governor that at least one such college had been established in his State, the Secretary of the Interior was to issue to the board of control of the college warrants for that amount of land or its equivalent in value if the price had been doubled in consequence of railroad grants. This bill was referred to the Committee on Education and Labor and reported back by Mr. Morrill March 11, 1872, with amendments.

On May 14, 1872, Mr. Morrill, evidently influenced by the passage in the House of the common-school bill, presented an amendment in the nature of a substitute for his bill of February 23. This substitute appropriated to each State and Territory in which land-grant colleges have been or may be established within five years from the passage of this act, the proceeds of the sale of 500,000 acres of public lands, estimated at $1.25 per acre, on the conditions prescribed in the act of July 2, 1862. Annually the Secretary of the Treasury must ascertain the net proceeds of sales of public lands for the preceding year and invest the same, as far as they come under this act, in 5 per cent registered United States bonds, or he may issue such bonds to the college but keep them in the Treasury and pay the interest semiannually to the college trustees.

More than six months elapsed before this bill was considered in the Senate. Meanwhile apparently Mr. Morrill pursued the course which had proved successful in the case of the original land-grant bills. That is, with the aid of representatives of these colleges and other friends of increased Federal endowments to them, including State legislatures, he ascertained quite definitely which Senators would steadily support his measure. There was also an understanding that the friends of this measure would not take much time for speeches in the Senate but would press for a vote as soon as it seemed best to do so. When Mr. Morrill thought that he had a majority in its favor he brought the bill before the Senate. The debate on it began December 5, 1872, with an introductory statement by Mr. Morrill. He defended the equal grants to each State as necessary to build strong colleges everywhere and said that the colleges themselves originated and indorsed this proposition. The bill then went over to January 13, 1873, when it was attacked by several of the most influential men in the Senate, including Sherman and Thurman, of Ohio; Windom, of Minnesota; Morton, of Indiana; Conkling, of New York; and Hamilton and Vickers, of Maryland. There was evidently much sentiment in favor of Federal grants to common schools, as expressed by Wilson, of Massachusetts; Howe, of Wisconsin; and others. Mr. Morrill strongly resisted efforts to amend the bill, but agreed to omission of the Territories. It passed the Senate January 14, 1873, by a vote of 39 to 14. In the House a substitute bill was passed without debate, with a vote of 120 to 70. The substitute was drawn to conciliate those who wanted something done for the common schools. It provided that one-fourth of the proceeds of the public lands should annually be invested in United States bonds, the interest on which should be paid to the colleges and they should also have an additional quarter of these proceeds. This left one-half of these proceeds to be otherwise used by the Government. This bill came up in the Senate February 24, 1873, when there was a prolonged struggle over it. The opponents endeavored to kill the bill by indefinite continuance of the discussion and continual offering of amendments. Senator Sherman made the most comprehensive speech against the bill. He declared permanent appropriations were against the policy of the Government from the time of Thomas Jefferson; the public lands have always been considered a source of revenue; the proposed distribution of funds is unequal and unconstitutional because it disregards the relative wealth and population of the States; this grant is a palpable discrimination against existing colleges supported by State and private funds; this measure will lead to practical abandonment of the homestead and preemption laws; it has never been considered by the people and faces a deficiency of revenue. A proposal by Senator Windom to nonconcur with the House and send the bill to conference was finally accepted by Mr. Morrill in desperation. The friends of aid to common schools prevented the House from going to conference. The bill, therefore, died with the close of that session of Congress.

Mr. Morrill was evidently impressed with the strength of the movement for Federal aid to common schools. Therefore his next bill introduced December 15, 1873, not only provided " for the further endowment of national colleges for the advancement of general, scientific, and industrial education," but was also intended to " establish an educational fund and apply the proceeds of a portion of the public lands to the support of public education." In introducing this bill Mr. Morrill attempted to conciliate those Senators who feared a deficiency in Government finances in view of the great panic then distressing the country by stating that the bill would not take any funds from the Treasury the coming year. This bill was referred to the Committee on Education and Labor, but was not printed so that we do not know its exact nature.

And now an attempt was made to discredit the land-grant colleges (*502*). On February 2, 1874, the House, on the motion of James Monroe, then a professor in Oberlin College, adopted a resolution for an investigation of those colleges by the Committee on Education and Labor. A favorable report of this investigation was presented by Mr. Monroe January 13, 1875, and he became a steadfast friend of these institutions.

On January 25, 1875, Senator Morrill introduced a bill which was printed and laid on the table. This bill is interesting as being a measure which with various modifications was under consideration in Congress at different times within the next 15 years. It was essentially a combination of the bill for Federal aid to common schools, which had passed the House in 1872, with the bill for aid to land-grant colleges which had also passed the House in 1873, but which the Senate had refused to accept. One half of the annual proceeds of public lands were to be made a perpetual educational fund invested in 5 per cent United States bonds. The other half of these proceeds was to be allotted to the States, Territories, and District of Columbia for common schools. The income of the educational fund was appropriated to the land-grant colleges, one-half in equal shares to each State and one-half in proportion to the number of their Senators and Representatives in Congress, until the amount equaled 5 per cent on 400,000 acres of land at $1 per acre and in addition 30,000 acres for each Senator and Representative. Thereafter the remainder of the income of the educational fund would be given to common schools. For every $200 received under this act a competitive scholarship covering tuition was required.

On January 25, 1876, Senator Morrill again introduced this bill with slight modifications, reducing somewhat the maximum amount to be given each State. This bill was reported back with amendments by the Committee on Education and Labor, February 17, 1876.

A substitute bill was submitted April 20, 1876, by Senator Maxey, of Texas. This was a somewhat simpler measure following the general lines of Senator Morrill's bill. The States or Territories must partially offset the Federal fund granted to the colleges.

On April 26, 1876, the bill was considered in the Senate. Senator Morrill again spoke at considerable length. He defended the policy of giving Federal aid to common schools, but claimed that college education in agriculture, mechanic arts, and military tactics was also much needed, and many more teachers of these subjects should be trained. Senator Maxey followed Morrill and dwelt especially on the long-established Federal policy to aid schools and the need of the South for more education. Nothing further was done with these bills.

On March 24, 1879, Senator Burnside, of Rhode Island, introduced Morrill's bill and this was reported back February 19, 1880, with amendments. This bill differed from former bills principally in adding proceeds from patents, reducing interest to 4 per cent, and permitting the Secretary of the Treasury to accept gifts for educational purposes. On March 8, 1880, Senator Morgan, of Alabama, offered an amendment requiring admission of women to land-grant colleges.

On December 14, 1880, this bill was discussed in the Senate by Messrs. Burnside, Morrill, Brown, Teller, Hoar, Blair, Bailey, and Ingalls. Amendments including admission of women and training of teachers were adopted. The word " national " as a designation of land-grant colleges was stricken from the title of the bill. It passed the Senate December 17, 1880, by a vote of 41 to 9. The House refused to consider this bill.

Senator Morrill, however, persisted in his efforts to secure the passage of an educational bill. On January 23, 1884, he reintroduced the bill which had passed the Senate in 1880, except that one-half the annual returns from railroads was substituted for the receipts from patents. This bill was reported back March 12, 1884, considered momentarily three times in the Senate, and put to sleep on the calendar January 5, 1885. The same bill was reintroduced by Senator Morrill February 17, 1886, and May 1, 1888, but in both cases was laid on the table.

The friends of Federal aid for common schools were not satisfied with the proposals for that purpose in Senator Morrill's bills. Under the leadership of Senators Blair and Hoar several large bills for this purpose were considered in the Senate. These bills attracted much attention in and out of Congress and had the active support of many people. In the end public sentiment crystallized against the use of Federal funds for common schools.

Mr. Morrill's attempts to utilize the sentiment in favor of Federal aid to common schools to float appropriations for the land-grant colleges proved a mistaken policy, but he persisted in this course until 1890.

THE MORRILL LAND-GRANT COLLEGE BILLS OF 1890

On March 25, 1890, Senator Morrill introduced a bill (S. 3256), which had the same title as previous bills but in which the allotment to the land-grant colleges of one-half of the educational fund accruing from the proceeds of public lands and railroads was made more prominent by being placed ahead of the common-school grant (546). The college fund was to be permanent with interest at 4 per cent, which was to be given in equal shares to each State and Territory up to a maximum of $25,000 annually, the remainder going to the common schools. This was the first indication that Senator Morrill did not consider the connection of the land-grant college grant with that to common schools so important as he had hitherto.

He now had the active assistance of the executive committee of the agricultural college association and " with the hearty concurrence of Senator Blair " the college bill was rewritten and again introduced April 30, 1890. It was now a bill " to apply a portion of the proceeds of the public lands to the more complete endowment and support " of the land-grant colleges. It carried an appropriation of

$15,000 to each State and Territory and an annual increase of this sum by $1,000 for 10 years, after which the annual appropriation would be $25,000. No distinction of race or color was to be made in the admission of students, but where separate colleges for white and colored students were maintained this would be considered a compliance with the act provided the fund was equitably divided between the two races. Reports of finances and work were to be made annually to the Secretaries of Agriculture and the Interior. None of the Federal fund was to be spent for the purchase, erection, preservation, or repair of buildings. The Secretary of the Interior was charged with the administration of the act.

This bill was referred to the Committee on Education and Labor, of which Senator Blair was chairman, and was favorably reported by him, with amendments, May 17, 1890. " After being discussed at length for three days and considerably amended the bill passed the Senate June 23 by a practically unanimous vote."

The next day it was read in the House of Representatives and referred to the Committee on Education, by whom it was favorably reported, without amendment, on July 12. Under a special order it was considered August 19 and passed in the House, with one amendment, by a vote of 135 to 39. The Senate concurred in the amended bill on August 20. The amendment adopted in the House restricted the use of the Federal funds to the teaching of " agriculture, the mechanic arts, the English language, and the various branches of mathematical, physical, natural and economic science, with special reference to their applications in the industries of life and to the facilities for such instruction." It was prepared by the executive committee of the association to meet the views of the National Grange on this matter.

The act was approved by President Harrison, August 30, 1890.

Opposition to the use of any available money in the United States Treasury for the benefit of the land-grant institutions gradually died out, and in an act of May 17, 1900, providing for free homesteads on the public lands, it was expressly declared that if the proceeds of the sales of public lands shall not be sufficient to meet the payments " provided for agricultural colleges and experimental stations " by the act of August 30, 1890, " such deficiency shall be paid by the United States."

THE EARLY AGRICULTURAL EXPERIMENT STATIONS AND MEETINGS OF AGRICULTURAL TEACHERS

Meanwhile the agricultural forces interested in teaching and research were strengthening their position and making a beginning of united action. Following the convention at Washington in 1872 there was increased activity in agricultural experimentation in the United States Department of Agriculture and the land-grant colleges. Beginning with 1875 agricultural experiment stations were organized, first at Middletown, Conn. (transferred to New Haven in 1877), and during the next 10 years in Alabama, California, Colorado, Indiana, Kentucky, Louisiana, Maine, Massachusetts, Minnesota, Nebraska, New Jersey, New York (Geneva and Ithaca), North Carolina, Ohio, Tennessee, and Wisconsin. Of these 18 stations, 7 were organized separately under State laws, but all except those in Louisiana, New York (Geneva), and North Carolina were established at or near the land-grant colleges.

In 1880 under the leadership of W. J. Beal, of the Michigan Agricultural College, the Society for the Advancement of Agricultural Science was organized. The same year on the invitation of G. E. Morrow, of the University of Illinois, agricultural teachers in a number of the land-grant colleges assembled at Champaign, Ill., and formed an association entitled " The Teachers of Agriculture." This organization held meetings at agricultural colleges in Michigan (1881), Iowa (1882), Ohio (1883), New York (Cornell, 1884), and Indiana (Purdue University, 1885). Its proceedings were informal and were not published. At the meeting in 1881 there were present Professors Morrow, of Illinois, Knapp and Budd, of Iowa, Shelton, of Kansas, Porter, of Minnesota, Tracy, of Missouri, Thompson, of Nebraska, Georgeson, of Texas, and Henry, of Wisconsin.

THE WASHINGTON CONVENTIONS OF 1882 AND 1883

On July 1, 1881, George Bailey Loring, long-time president of the New England Agricultural Society and a lecturer at the Massachusetts Agricultural College, became United States Commissioner of Agriculture. He had presided at the Washington agricultural convention of 1872 and had been a Member of the Forty-fifth and Forty-sixth Congresses, when Senator Morrill's bills for Federal aid to the land-grant colleges were pending there. Within a month after he entered the Department of Agriculture he issued a call for a series of four 2-day agricultural conventions to meet at the Department of Agriculture at Washington January 10–18, 1882 (418). These conventions were to consider matters relating to (1) agricultural education and organizations and the principles of farming, (2) animal industries, (3) cereal crops, and (4) the management of vineyards and the manufacture of wines. Delegates from the State agricultural colleges and societies were invited, and 19 States were represented at the first roll call. Among those present who were prominent in the affairs of the agricultural colleges and experiment stations, were Atwater and Gold, of Connecticut; Peabody and Morrow, of Illinois; Fairchild, of Kansas; Fernald, of Maine; Porter, of Minnesota; Cook, of New Jersey; Caldwell and Roberts, of New York. Commissioner Loring was made chairman and H. E. Alvord (then from the private experiment station at Houghton Farm, N. Y.) was one of the secretaries.

Professor Cook read a paper on agricultural education in New Jersey, in which he dwelt especially on the work of the experiment stations. Professor Caldwell spoke on the experiment station as the educator of the farmer, and Professor Atwater described cooperative experiments with fertilizers carried on for five years in nine States. A committee on cooperative experiments was then appointed which recommended that the Department of Agriculture prepare a digest of foreign experiments, endeavor to bring about cooperative experiments in this country on a carefully prepared plan, and ask Congress to appropriate money for this work. Regent Peabody, of the University of Illinois, discussed the legitimate work of the land-grant institutions, holding that their primary business was to teach, but that their curricula should include many subjects besides agriculture and mechanic arts.

A second series of three conventions on agricultural education, animal industry, and cotton was held at Washington January 22–29, 1883 (*419*), at which 29 States and Utah Territory were represented. Among those present at the meeting on agricultural education were Messrs. Brewer, of Connecticut; Knapp and James Wilson, of Iowa; Abbot, of Michigan; Folwell, of Minnesota; Law, of New York; and Atherton, of Pennsylvania. Senator Morrill was a delegate representing the Vermont State Agricultural Society. At this meeting there was much discussion of the difficulties which the land-grant colleges were having, including the problems of student labor.

H. W. Wiley, then representing Purdue University in Indiana, read an extract from an address by E. E. White, president of that institution, in which he summed up the existing status of the land-grant colleges.

* * * it may be safely said that the results actually accomplished by the national grant in the two decades now closing are not satisfactory, though promising more complete success in the future. The best results thus far attained have been in the direction of scientific training and investigation. The founding of the national schools has caused the study of science to assume new importance in all higher institutions, and a greatly increased number of students are taking the so-called scientific courses of study. Radical changes have also been made in the methods of teaching science, and enlarged facilities for scientific study and investigation have been provided.

The most unsatisfactory results are in technical training, both in agriculture and the mechanic arts. The contributions made to agricultural science have been small, and the promising work of agricultural experiment is still in its infancy, even in the institutions first organized, and in most of them it has not been seriously undertaken. Comparatively few students have taken distinctively technical or industrial courses, and the small number of well-trained technologists sent into the industries of the country is at once a surprise and a disappointment. The great majority of the students receiving either an agricultural or mechanical training are found in the few institutions which have only industrial courses of study.

It is not difficult to account for this unsatisfactory progress in industrial training and investigation. The importance of technical education for the farmer and artisan is not generally realized, and, as a consequence, the demand for such training is limited, though happily increasing.

Professor Wiley also read a paper on "The true relation of the sciences to the industries and arts," which led to considerable discussion regarding experimental work in agriculture. In the course of this discussion, Thomas H. Dudley, representing the New Jersey State Agricultural Society, made the following statements:

I shall be very glad to see the time when every State in this Union shall have established an agricultural experiment station in connection with a farm for carrying on practical field experiments.

It is a practical subject which the Government should take up; and not only the General Government, but I would be glad to see a large appropriation sufficient to establish an experiment farm and an agricultural experiment station upon it in every State, so that both might be carried on for the people of the whole State.

As the final outcome of the interest in agricultural experimentation aroused in this meeting a resolution indorsing the bill of Congressman Carpenter of Iowa for the establishment of agricultural experiment stations in connection with the State agricultural colleges introduced by Seaman A. Knapp (fig. 10), at the request of President Abbot of the Michigan Agricultural College, was adopted.

A committee of five was appointed to prepare a statement on this subject for presentation to the Committee of Agriculture of the House of Representatives. Messrs. Knapp and Abbot, together with

FIG. 10.—Seaman A. Knapp

Stephen D. Lee, of the Mississippi Agricultural College; Paul Chadbourne, of the Massachusetts Agricultural College; and E. E. White, of Purdue University, were appointed on this committee.

THE CARPENTER AND HOLMES EXPERIMENT STATION BILLS

Prior to the convention in 1883 Professor Knapp had drafted a bill for Federal aid to agricultural experiment stations. Charles E. Bessey, then a professor in the Iowa Agricultural College, wrote the section defining the work of the stations. C. C. Carpenter, of Iowa, introduced this bill in the House of Representatives in the Forty-seventh Congress (May 8, 1882), and it was referred to the Committee on Agriculture but not reported back. It was considered by the committee of the 1883 convention and with some modification was again introduced in the House by A. J. Holmes, of Iowa, on December 10, 1883. It was entitled "A bill to establish national experiment stations in connection with the agricultural colleges of the various States." Its text was as follows:

Be it enacted by the Senate and House of Representatives of the United States of America in Congress assembled, That in order to enable the Department of Agriculture to fulfill the design and perform the duties for which it was established, as declared in the organic act creating the said Department, to-wit, "to acquire and diffuse among the people of the United States useful information on subjects connected with agriculture in the most general sense of that word, and to procure, propagate, and distribute among the people new and valuable seeds and plants," institutions shall be established in connection with each of the agricultural colleges in the States providing such colleges, with an improved farm in connection therewith, and placed under the conduct of such colleges, to be called and known as "national experiment stations."

SEC. 2. That it shall be the object and design of the said national experiment stations to conduct original researches or verify experiments on the physiology of plants and animals, the diseases to which they are severally subject, with the remedies for the same; the chemical composition of useful plants at their different stages of growth; the comparative advantages of rotative cropping as pursued under a varying series of crops; the capacity of new plants or trees for acclimation within the isothermal limits represented by the climate of the several stations and their vicinity; the analysis of soils and waters; the chemical composition of manures, natural or artificial, with experiments designed to test their comparative values for raising crops of different kinds; the composition and digestibility of the different kinds of food for cattle; the scientific and economic questions in the production of butter and cheese; and all other researches or experiments bearing directly on the agricultural industry of the United States.

SEC. 3. That the said experiment stations shall be placed under the general control of the regents or trustees of said agricultural colleges, who shall have power to employ a professor for each agricultural college who shall act as superintendent of the experiment stations established under this act.

SEC. 4. That the said professors shall make such reports to the Commissioner of Agriculture from time to time as he may direct. The general character of the work and of the experiments to be performed at each station shall be determined by the Commissioner of Agriculture, the president of the college where the station is located, and the professor in charge of said station.

SEC. 5. That to each agricultural college providing for experiment stations under this act, to pay the salaries of the professors and superintendents of the said experiment stations, the wages of the laborers employed in their operations, and the cost of the experiments and researches connected with their conduct as heretofore specified, the sum of fifteen thousand dollars is hereby appropriated, out of any money in the Treasury not otherwise appropriated, or so much thereof as may be necessary to cover expenditures actually made for said purposes; the money to be drawn quarterly from the Treasury of the United States, upon a certified statement of the amounts actually expended at each station, properly indorsed by the college board of audit, the professor in charge, and the Commissioner of Agriculture.

SEC. 6. That upon the passage of this act, before the agricultural college in any State can draw any funds as provided, the legislature of such State shall pass an act accepting such trust and agreeing to conduct an experiment station in accordance therewith.

As chairman of the committee and president of the Iowa Agricultural College, Doctor Knapp issued a circular (41, 201), in which he briefly stated the history of the bill, gave the names of the committee appointed by Commissioner Loring, presented reasons for establishing agricultural experiment stations in the several States because of the diversity of their climate and agricultural production and the broad range of problems to be solved, as well as the desirability of aiding the Department of Agriculture in its researches and in obtaining useful seeds and plants for distribution in different parts of the country. He thought the stations should be connected with the agricultural colleges because (1) it would be economical to take advantage of their organization, faculties, buildings, and equipment and (2) the investigations would greatly benefit the students "as object lessons and would perfect and give practical value to the work of the colleges, as contemplated in the original law creating them." The supervision to be exercised by the Commissioner of Agriculture "will systematize their work throughout the United States and will avoid too much repetition of experiments at different stations."

From this time the efforts of the friends of agricultural education in the land-grant colleges, the agricultural societies, the grange and other organizations were concentrated on securing the passage of an experiment station act by Congress.

The Holmes bill was not generally acceptable to the colleges largely because it seemed to make the stations virtually branches of the Department of Agriculture and put them to a considerable extent under the control of the Commissioner of Agriculture. It was therefore remodeled, and when it had been considered and modified by the Committee on Agriculture of the House of Representatives it was favorably reported from that committee by Mr. Cullen, of Illinois. It was still a bill (H. R. 7493) to aid the Department of Agriculture in acquiring and diffusing agricultural knowledge, but the stations were to be distinctly departments of the land-grant colleges and under the control of their governing bodies and were to make their reports to the governors of the States. It was expressly provided that nothing in the act "shall be construed to authorize said commissioner to control or direct the work or management of any such station except as to the standard of valuation of commercial fertilizers." He might furnish forms for the tabulation of results of experiment, indicate lines of inquiry, and "in general furnish such aid and assistance as will best promote the purpose of this act." Sections were added which required the stations to publish and distribute bulletins every three months, gave them the franking privilege for their publications, and required the trustees of the colleges to agree to spend the Federal money according to the provisions of the act, to maintain a farm of at least 25 acres, and to give a bond "for the faithful expenditure and accounting for all moneys so received." One-fifth of the first year's appropriation might be spent for the erection, enlargement, or repair of station buildings but only 5 per cent thereafter. If any money was not expended during the fiscal year of its reception, that amount was to be deducted from the next annual appropriation. Nothing in the act was to impair or modify the legal relation between the college and the State. A group of college presidents were in Washington in the winter of 1884–85 to forward the passage of this bill, but Congress was not ready to take action.

THE WASHINGTON CONVENTION OF 1885

Doctor Loring's administration of the Department of Agriculture came to an end on March 3, 1885. He was succeeded by Norman J. Colman, of Missouri (fig. 11), who as editor of the Rural World and member of the State board of agriculture, had for many years shown his friendship for agricultural education and research. On May 6,

FIG. 11.—Norman J. Colman

1885, he issued a call for a convention of "representatives of the different agricultural colleges and allied State institutions" to consider cooperation with the department in the work of the experiment stations, the best means for bringing about congressional action, and other cognate questions.

This convention met July 8, 1885, and was organized under the presidency of Commissioner Colman. (Fig. 12.) At least 28 States and 3 Territories were represented. Among the men prominent in promoting the work of the colleges and stations were President Atherton, of Pennsylvania; Professor Armsby, then of Wisconsin; H. E. Alvord, of the Houghton Farm station in New York; Professor Cook, of New Jersey; Doctor Dabney, of North Carolina;

FIG. 12.—Meeting in Washington of representatives of agricultural colleges and experiment stations, July 8 and 9, 1885

President Fernald, of Maine; President Fairchild, of Kansas; Professor Goessmann, of Massachusetts; Mr. Gold, of Connecticut; Professor Knapp, of Iowa; President Lee, of Mississippi; Professor Roberts, of New York; Professor Townshend and C. E. Thorne, of Ohio; and President Willits, of Michigan. A committee on order of business and resolutions, consisting of Messrs. Alvord, Lee, Knapp, Fernald, Atherton, and Willits, largely determined the business of the convention. Its resolution regarding the experiment station bill, introduced early in the session and unanimously adopted, was as follows:

Resolved, That the condition and progress of American agriculture require national aid for the investigation and experimentation in the several States and Territories, and, therefore, this convention approves the principles and general provisions of what is known as the Cullen bill of the last Congress, and urges upon the next Congress the passage of this or a similar act (*420*).

There was much discussion regarding cooperation of the department and the stations. A series of resolutions on this subject, proposed by the committee on business, was adopted with amendments. This recommended that the department create a division of intercommunication and exchange between the colleges and stations, which would have charge of the details of cooperation, issue a periodical bulletin on "the progress of agricultural education, investigation, and experimentation in this and in all other countries," and issue uniform blanks for reports of the operation of the schools and experiments. It was also resolved to petition Congress for the necessary funds to carry out this plan. A committee on legislation consisting of Messrs. Atherton, Willits, and Lee was appointed. Near the end of the convention an advisory committee consisting of one representative from each State and Territory and the Department of Agriculture was appointed. President Atherton was elected its chairman and was authorized to choose five other members, who with him would constitute an executive committee to determine the time and program of the next convention and a plan for permanent organization. He selected Messrs. Cook, Knapp, Peabody, Curtis (Texas) and Newman (Alabama).

THE HATCH EXPERIMENT STATION ACT

The committee cooperated with Commissioner Colman in securing the interest of William H. Hatch, of Missouri (fig. 13), in the experiment station bill and at the next session of Congress he introduced it (in somewhat modified form) on January 7, 1886, when it was referred to the Committee on Agriculture, of which he was chairman, and reported back favorably March 3, 1886.

Meanwhile a similar bill had been introduced in the Senate December 10, 1885, by J. Z. George, of Mississippi. This bill was considered there in detail and was amended in many important particulars. It passed the Senate January 27, 1887, and was accepted by the House on Mr. Hatch's recommendation in lieu of his bill. This amended bill, which made the stations quite completely State institutions in charge of their own governing boards, was approved by President Cleveland March 2, 1887. In most States the benefits of this act went without question to stations organized as departments of land-grant colleges. In a few States the stations had been organized as separate institutions, which felt strongly that they should receive the Federal funds granted under this act. Under the leadership of J. H. Brigham, president of the Ohio State Board of Agriculture and master of the State Grange, and with the aid of Senators

John Sherman, of Ohio, and Dawes, of Massachusetts, an amendment to this effect was embodied in section 2 of the Hatch Act.

It is also interesting to note that while the Carpenter and Holmes bills provided for a direct appropriation from the Treasury the Hatch bill stipulated that the station fund should come from the sales of public lands, thus following the precedents set in the educa-

FIG. 13.—William H. Hatch

tional bills which had been before Congress during the previous 15 years.

The Hatch Act became a law March 2, 1887. To the surprise of many who had not followed this legislation closely, it was soon discovered that in this act Congress had only authorized, but had not made an appropriation. This caused some difficulties in carrying the work of stations already established. The first appropriation under the Hatch Act was made in 1888 and at that time a precedent was established, which has since been followed, of including this fund in the annual appropriation act for the Department of Agriculture.

THE ORGANIZATION OF THE ASSOCIATION OF AMERICAN AGRICULTURAL COLLEGES AND EXPERIMENT STATIONS

The executive committee appointed at the Washington convention of 1885, which had actively promoted the passage of the Hatch Act, saw that many problems would arise regarding the interpretation and administration of this act, the relations under it of the land-grant colleges, experiment stations, and Department of Agriculture, and the more comprehensive organization and management of experiment stations in all the States and Territories. President Atherton, as chairman of this committee, therefore called a meeting of representatives of the colleges and stations, which met at Washington, October, 18–20, 1887. (499).

At this meeting the Association of American Agricultural Colleges and Experiment Stations was organized and the constitution proposed by the executive committee was adopted with few amendments. As stated in its constitution—

The object of this association shall be the consideration and discussion of all questions pertaining to the successful progress and administration of the colleges and stations included in the association.

At any regularly called meeting of the association each college established under the act of Congress approved July 2, 1862, and each experiment station established under State or congressional authority, and the Department of Agriculture, shall be entitled to one delegate; but no delegates shall cast more than one vote. * * *

The officers of this association shall be a president, five vice presidents, and a secretary, who shall act as treasurer. * * *

The president, secretary, and five persons, to be chosen by the association, shall constitute an executive committee, which shall elect its own chairman.

The executive committee shall determine the time and place of the next meeting of the association, shall issue its call for said meetings, stating the general purpose thereof, not less than thirty days before the date at which it shall be held; shall provide a well-prepared order of business and programme of exercises for such meeting, and shall make seasonable issue of said programme. * * *

The executive committee shall be charged with the general arrangement and conduct of the meeting called by it; at which meeting, before its adjournment, a new executive committee shall be chosen.

In 1889 an amendment provided for permanent committees, and a committee on college work was appointed, out of which was developed in 1890 a section on college work. The Office of Experiment Stations was made a member of the association, with a voting delegate.

President Atherton, of Pennsylvania, was elected first president of the association, and Charles E. Thorne, of Ohio, secretary and treasurer. The executive committee included Henry E. Alvord, of Massachusetts; Edwin Willits, of Michigan; James K. Patterson, of Kentucky; Charles W. Dabney, of Tennessee; Charles K. Adams, of New York; and Charles E. Thorne, of Ohio.

The form of organization adopted in the Association of American Agricultural Colleges and Experiment Stations has greatly promoted continuous and effective efforts for the improvement of the educational and material conditions of the land-grant institutions. The annual conventions have afforded a broad basis for personal contacts of leading officers of these institutions and the Federal departments dealing with their affairs and for the discussion of many important problems relating to the organization and work of the institutions represented in the association.

The executive committee with broad authority to act during the intervals between conventions, as well as temporary and standing committees for the consideration of different phases of the work of the colleges and stations, have been able to keep the association in continuous action in many important ways.

The inclusion of members from Federal departments in the conventions and committees of the association had many advantages. This was particularly true with reference to agricultural education and research, in the promotion of which the United States Department of Agriculture, and especially the Office of Experiment Stations, established October 1, 1888, cooperated actively and effectively.

The proceedings of the association at its annual conventions for 21 years (1889–1909) were published as bulletins of the Office of Experiment Stations, thus insuring their regular appearance and distribution, as well as official sanction. Summaries of these proceedings and other information about the educational work of the colleges were also given in the Experiment Station Record.

One of the first pieces of work which this office undertook in 1888–89 was the collection of information, documents, and photographs from the agricultural colleges for a report and exhibit at the Paris Exposition of 1889. There were thus brought together, though imperfectly, considerable data regarding the history and status of these institutions, and in this way their appreciation of the fact that they collectively constituted a unique system of agricultural education with great possibilities was considerably strengthened.

Thus there came about a general movement for the accumulation of new agricultural knowledge, its reduction to pedagogical form, the enlargement of agricultural faculties, the broadening and specialization of agricultural courses, the securing of better and more adequate buildings, apparatus, and other equipment, and much wider and more effective measures for enlisting the confidence and support of the agricultural people and giving them aid and information which they greatly appreciated.

In the conventions of the association for the first decade after the preliminary meeting in Washington in 1885 questions relating to the funds, organization, and work of the experiment stations naturally occupied a large place on the programs and in the discussions. However, from the beginning educational problems were more or less discussed, and gradually arrangements were made for their orderly and continuous consideration.

EARLY WORK OF THE ASSOCIATION OF AMERICAN AGRICULTURAL COLLEGES AND EXPERIMENT STATIONS RELATING TO AGRICULTURAL EDUCATION

The Morrill bill of 1890 was not brought to the attention of the individual colleges or their association until after its introduction by Senator Morrill. The executive committee of the association, of which Henry E. Alvord was chairman, then worked actively in its support and was assisted by representatives from most of the col-leges. Coming so soon after the passage of the Hatch Act, the second Morrill Act greatly strengthened the educational work of the land-grant colleges. Encouraged by this new recognition of the value of these colleges by the Federal Government, the State legis-latures were more easily led to make liberal appropriations for build-ings and facilities for instruction in these institutions. The friends of agricultural education became more active in urging their claims upon faculties, boards of management, and legislatures, and met with increasing success in securing for agriculture a larger recog-nition in the college curriculum. The establishment of the experi-ment stations had attached to these colleges a much larger and stronger body of men whose prime interest was on the side of agri-culture, and the increased financial revenues of the colleges made it possible to utilize the service of many more instructors in agri-cultural subjects. The economic condition of agriculture did not, however, favor an immediate increase in the number of agricultural students, or tend to hold those who began agricultural studies until they had completed the four years' course.

The section on college work of the association reported at the New Orleans meeting in 1892 that engineering courses were much more popular than those in agriculture. In Illinois, for example, there was that year a decrease of 11 students in agriculture and an increase of 50 in mechanic arts. In Indiana there was an increase of 15 in agriculture but of 87 in engineering. Many colleges were erecting buildings for mechanic arts. At this meeting Professor Henry, of Wisconsin, urged that there should be greater specializa-tion of instruction in agriculture, that it should be made more prac-tical, and that short courses should be organized to attract agri-cultural students and meet the actual needs and conditions of a large body of farm youth. He had already had considerable success in these directions, having organized at the Wisconsin College a short course in 1886 and a dairy school for the practical instruction of men to manage creameries and cheese factories. (See p. 75.)

At the New Orleans meeting of the association in 1892 there was much discussion about the agricultural curriculum. President Fair-child, of the Kansas Agricultural College, in a paper on " The relations of technical to general courses of study " gave the plan followed at his institution: (1) Admit directly from the common schools; (2) give as early as possible, with English and mathematics, an introduction to nature through drawing and botany, with me-chanical training in simple construction; (3) with chemistry and mineralogy apply science in agriculture, horticulture, economic ento-mology, and household economy, with practice in all; (4) with mathematics, mechanics, agricultural chemistry, and physics, give training in surveying and common engineering; (5) give general problems in thinking and reasoning, illustrated by everyday facts and practice in the arts of construction and production; (6) keep students thinking along the line of the industries; (7) make the faculty a unit in their sympathy for the purpose and methods of the college; (8) interest the students in the objects and arouse their pride in the college; (9) bring the college to the people; (10) culti-vate the interest of the alumni.

S. W. Johnson, of Connecticut, favored a fundamental course in the sciences underlying both agriculture and the mechanic arts, with instruction in greenhouses, laboratories, shops, and barns, and a post-graduate course for special training. W. M. Hays, then from North Dakota, called attention to the specialization of agricultural education in the colleges in Michigan and Wisconsin, the dairy schools in Wisconsin and Minnesota, and the secondary school of agriculture in Minnesota.

P. M. Harwood, of Michigan, argued for the organization of agricultural instruction in one college department with assistants in " vegetable economy and animal industry." At the Michigan college the freshmen had instruction on breeds of livestock, the sophomores on field crops, the juniors on animal husbandry, and the seniors on special agricultural subjects. Student labor was made educational by making it experimental.

The statistics of the land-grant colleges in 1894 as published in Circular 27 of the Office of Experiment Stations showed that 17 colleges had less than 25 students in agricultural courses, 13 had less than 75, and 6 less than 150. The States in which there were more than 150 students were Kansas with 460, Mississippi 216, Massachusetts 204, Texas 187, Michigan 181, Iowa 179, and Minnesota 175. In these statistics there was no differentiation of students in long and short courses. The total number of students in agricultural courses in all the land-grant colleges that year was 3,847 and the number of graduates was 229. Fourteen colleges had no graduates in agriculture, 21 had less than 5, 4 had less than 10, and only 7 had over 10. The latter included Alabama with 12, Kansas 39, Massachusetts 34, Michigan 14, Minnesota 20, Rhode Island 12, and Wisconsin 20.

In 1893 at Chicago Professor Henry, of Wisconsin, in his presidential address before the association urged a division of labor as regards teachers and investigators. The latter should do only a little teaching of advanced students. At that year's meeting the Chicago exposition largely engrossed the attention of the association. The cooperative exhibit of the agricultural colleges and experiment stations, with the Office of Experiment Stations, did much to strengthen the feeling of unity of interest in the nation-wide system of agricultural education and a desire to do more to promote its improvement.

At the Washington meeting in 1894 there was great interest in the plans of the Department of Agriculture with reference to the supervision of the Hatch fund, which had been given to it by Congress at the request of Secretary Morton. The inspection of the work and finances of the stations inaugurated that year by the Office of Experiment Stations had unexpected results as regards agricultural instruction. The annual visits to the stations were made for a number of years by the director and assistant director of the office. They were thus enabled not only to discover what relations existed between the stations and the teaching departments of the colleges but also to learn much about the status of agricultural instruction in these institutions. At that time they were often called in conference with boards of trustees or their committees, presidents, and heads of departments, especially at the younger colleges, and were consulted about the qualifications of teachers, courses of instruction and equipment for agricultural teaching, as well as about station affairs. The Office of Experiment Stations was thus put in a position to aid the movement for agricultural education in a broad way.

In 1894 the association also opened the way for a systematic study of educational problems. In his address as acting president, Professor Morrow, of Illinois, deplored the lack of agricultural students due to the economic depression of agriculture, and pointed out the need of making agricultural courses more attractive through studies on methods of teaching and the devising of improved apparatus. He referred to an informal society which he and other teachers of agriculture had formed and kept up for several years before the national association of agricultural colleges was organized and said that Professor Hunt, of Ohio, had written him that something ought to be done to systematize instruction in agriculture.

W. T. Harris, United States Commissioner of Education, speaking at this meeting also laid stress on reducing agriculture to pedagogical form.

REPORT OF THE COMMITTEE ON ENTRANCE REQUIREMENTS

A. W. Harris, then president of the Maine State College, on behalf of the section on college work, brought about the appointment of a committee of five members on entrance requirements.

The committee was Charles S. Murkland, of New Hampshire; Abram W. Harris, of Maine; George W. Atherton, of Pennsylvania; J. M. McBryde, of Virginia; and Thomas F. Hunt, of Ohio. The final report of this committee was made in 1896 (*499*). This took the general position that Congress intended that the land-grant institutions should be " collegiate in scope " and that their work under the act of 1862 " should be as far as practicable uniform in scope and character in the different States and Territories " though it might be " somewhat limited or conditioned by the environment of each college."

The steadily increasing tendency to ignore and obliterate all State lines in scientific and educational work; the free intercourse in social and industrial life among the people of the several States, and, in consequence, the steadily broadening field of usefulness and activity open to the graduates of educational institutions; the association of the land-grant colleges into a national organization for the protection and promotion of their common interests; the increasing recognition by the National Government of the importance and promise of the work of these colleges—all these considerations made it desirable that the degree or degrees awarded by these colleges should represent work approximately uniform in character and scope; should be, in other words, degrees of such recognized value as to pass current, each the equivalent of the others, in any State or Territory.

The defective school system in some States made it impossible, according to the committee, for the time being " to prescribe uniform requirements for admission into the colleges of this class." But the colleges should protect " their standards of work and graduation " by special efforts and through educational work within the institution. Since it was not practicable for students in the United States to get liberal training in preparatory schools the colleges " must include in their courses for graduation certain elements of a liberal (or general) education," along with technical subjects.

On the foregoing basis, the committee recommended that colleges in the association " should unite in requiring for the bachelor's degree, or degrees, at least the following general studies (*499*):

Mathematics.—At least through algebra, geometry, and trigonometry.
Physics and chemistry, with laboratory work in each.
English language and literature.—At least two years' work.
Other languages (one, at least, modern).—Four years.[2]
Mental science and logic or moral science.—One year.
Constitutional law.
Social, political, or economic science.—One year.

As regards amount of work it was thought that—

it is not too much to require the equivalent of 15 hours per week of recitations and lectures, together with 10 hours per week of laboratory work or practicums, including the time devoted to military science and drill. Upon this basis, the above-mentioned general studies should be assigned a relative importance approximately as follows:

	Hours		Hours
Algebra	75	Modern languages	340
Geometry	40	Psychology	60
Trigonometry	40	Ethics or logic	40
Physics (class-room work)	75	Political economy	60
Physics (laboratory work)	75	General history	80
Chemistry (class-room work)	75	Constitutional law	50
Chemistry (laboratory work)	75		
English	200	Total	1,285

The total number of hours included in a four years' course, allowing 15 hours per week for 36 weeks, would be 2,160; with 10 hours' laboratory work or practicums added, 3,600. In general terms, therefore, the foregoing general studies should comprise about two-fifths of the work required for a bachelor's degree.

Only the degree of bachelor of science should be conferred for a technical course of four years but the diploma might indicate the particular kind of course pursued, e. g., engineering, chemistry, etc.

Recognizing differences in the character of the school systems in the several States, the committee suggested standard and minimum requirements for entrance. The standard requirements included:

(1) Physical geography.
(2) United States history.
(3) Arithmetic, including the metric system.
(4) Algebra, to quadratics.
(5) English grammar and composition, together with the English requirements of the New England Assoc.ation of Colleges and Preparatory Schools.
(6) Plane geometry.
(7) One fore'gn language.
(8) One of the natural sciences.
(9) Ancient, general, or English history.

For minimum requirements the first five subjects in the standard requirements were suggested.

At this meeting a paper by J. E. Stubbs, of Nevada University, showed that of 46 colleges reporting 30 had preparatory departments and as regards entrance requirements 18 had standard high school requirements in English, while 28 required only work done in eighth or ninth grades of elementary schools; 38 required arithmetic; 34 algebra to or through quadratics; 46 history of United States; 20 at least part of plane geometry; and 8 a reading knowledge of French or German; physics, chemistry, botany, or physiology was required in from 8 to 17 colleges.

---

[2] The statement " four years " means 340 hours. These may be distributed over four, three, or two years, or confined to one year.

ORGANIZATION AND EARLY WORK OF THE COMMITTEE ON INSTRUCTION IN AGRICULTURE

The report of the committee on entrance requirements formed a basis for the work of the committee on methods of instruction in agriculture which was established by the association in 1895. The appointment of this committee was preceded by a discussion on what studies should be embraced in the 4-year course for the degree of bachelor of science. President Ellis, of Colorado, favored a cultural course in literature, mathematics, and the sciences, and Professor Hilgard, of California, thought the land-grant colleges should make their degree courses of high scientific grade as their main object should be to train leaders and teachers, but courses in agriculture of lower grade should be provided in secondary schools or in the colleges.

T. F. Hunt, of Ohio, in a paper on methods of teaching agriculture (*521*) expressed a preference for textbooks rather than lectures, but thought that students should have practice in agricultural operations which they had not had before coming to college. The report of the section on college work showed that changes in curriculum and additions to agricultural faculties were proceeding in the colleges and " indicates its interest in agricultural work by discussing means for increasing attendance in agricultural courses." The association was thus prepared to consider favorably some regular method of promoting agricultural instruction in the colleges and readily adopted a proposition advanced by Professor Connell, of Texas, for the appointment of a committee on methods of instruction in agriculture. The following resolution was passed:

That a standing committee of five be appointed, whose duty it shall be to report annually upon the best methods used in the various colleges of the world for the instruction of students in the practical and scientific facts relating to agriculture with a view to bringing instruction in agriculture into pedagogic form.

The committee appointed was J. H. Connell, of Texas; A. C. True, of the Office of Experiment Stations; T. F. Hunt, of Ohio; H. T. French, of Idaho; and H. H. Wing, of New York.

The Office of Experiment Stations cooperated actively with this committee. The director of that office became secretary of the committee and from 1902 its chairman. The first report of this committee was presented to the association at its meeting in Washington, November 11, 1896 (*499*). Data regarding the status of agricultural instruction in the United States had been collected from about 50 colleges. It was thus—

plainly shown that there exists at present in this country no standard for instruction in agriculture. There is a bewildering variety as regards the topics taught, the time devoted to each topic, the order in which the different topics occur in the course, the relative amounts of class-room work and laboratory or practical exercises, etc., Granting all that ought to be conceded because of local conditions, it is nevertheless obvious that general progress in the teaching of agriculture in college courses can hardly be expected until there is greater uniformity in planning and conducting the course of study in this subject.

One great obstacle to the intelligent discussion of the scheme of agricultural instruction and the methods of agricultural teaching is the lack of a definite nomenclature of the subject. This confusion of terms is evident in the data collected by the committee, as well as in much of the current discussion of this subject which appears in the public prints.

To aid in removing this difficulty the committee proposed a tentative classification of the subjects commonly taught under the head of agriculture, as follows:

Agriculture
1. Agronomy, or agriculture (technical). { Climate, soils, fertilizers, and crops; plant production.
2. Zootechny, or animal industry. { Animal physiology and animal production.
3. Agrotechny, or agricultural technology. { Agricultural industries, e. g., dairying, sugar making.
4. Rural engineering, farm mechanics, or farm equipment. { Roads, drains, irrigation systems, farm buildings, etc.
5. Rural economy, or farm management. { General policy of farm management, rural law, agricultural bookkeeping, etc.

The committee had also examined the courses in agriculture in foreign institutions, its secretary had visited a number of agricultural schools in Germany, France, Belgium, and Holland, and Professor Woll of Wisconsin, had done similar work in Denmark, Norway and Sweden. The report with its accompanying papers was published in Circular 32 of the Office of Experiment Stations. It shows that in many of our colleges the professor of agriculture or his assistant taught all that was included under agronomy and zootechny, to which were added dairying in 15 colleges, farm engineering in 17, and rural economics in 14.

That year the section on agriculture and chemistry reported that in 35 land-grant colleges there were only 117 instructors in agriculture, of whom 48 were assistants, and 36 colleges had 2,963 students in agricultural courses, of whom 1,355 were in the long courses, 237 in a 2-year course, 1,238 in short courses, and 113 in graduate work.

In 32 colleges there were 61 instructors in agricultural chemistry, of whom 23 were assistants. Twenty-five of these colleges had 925 students in agricultural chemistry as a special subject, outside the regular agricultural course.

In its second report, in 1897 (499), the committee on instruction in agriculture suggested that on the basis of the previous report of the committee on entrance requirements with reference to the mathematics, sciences, languages, and other cultural subjects to be included in a 4-year college course, there should be added in the course in agriculture leading to a bachelor's degree the following subjects:

	Hours
Agriculture	486
Horticulture and forestry	180
Veterinary science, including anatomy	180
Agricultural chemistry, in addition to general requirement	180
Botany (including vegetable physiology and pathology)	180
Zoology (including entomology)	120
Physiology	180
Geology	120
Meteorology	60
Drawing	60
Total	1,746

Under "agriculture" the following division of time among the main branches was proposed:

	Hours
1. Agronomy, or plant production	132
2. Zootechny, or animal industry	162
3. Agrotechny, or agricultural technology	72
4. Rural engineering, or farm mechanics	60
5. Rural economics, or farm management	60
Total	486

In three following reports this committee gave in some detail syllabi of courses in agronomy, zootechny, dairying, rural engineering, and rural economics.

In its fourth report (*499*) the committee pointed out that "the arrangement of the topics to be taught under each head in a logical and pedagogical order has been deemed of fundamental importance," though this might be a different order from that followed in existing manuals.

It makes little difference whether some unfortunate "professor of agriculture" is compelled to bear the heavy burden of guiding the student through the entire course or whether numerous specialists give their combined energies to the task. * * * But on the other hand, we are inclined strongly to contend that in the courses in agriculture a comprehensive scheme of instruction should be adopted, and that all the topics should be included which are necessary to a clear understanding of the proper relations of the different parts of the subject. We hold that there is such a thing as a science of agriculture, secondary and complex in its nature, and deriving its facts and principles very largely, if not wholly, from other primary sciences, but after all to be differentiated as a distinct entity from the other sciences, however dependent it may be on them for its materials. And we urge that one radical defect of agricultural instruction thus far has been that so much of the teaching of agricultural subjects has been done in a disjointed way by experts in different branches of science. The student has therefore often not had the subject of agriculture presented to him as a connected whole with related parts, and has for this reason failed to appreciate that there was any such thing as a science of agriculture, or has not learned to make any useful application of what he has learned in various sciences to either the theory or the practice of agriculture. Thus, we believe, for example, that however much the student may have learned or will learn about the physiology of plants, or the physics of soils, or the chemistry of fertilizers, at some period in his agricultural course he should have all these subjects grouped together in a course in agronomy and there learn their relation to each other and to the methods employed in the production of crops in actual agricultural practice. * * * If generally and efficiently taught in our colleges it will do much to counteract the pernicious influences of a narrow specialism which has in recent years been fostered by a false eclecticism. This requires, however, that agriculture in its scientific and practical aspects shall be treated as a distinct entity and not be hopelessly dismembered in the scheme of college instruction.

While these reports were tentative and crude in many particulars and represented in the usual way compromises of statement growing out of differing views of members of the committee, they laid the foundation for a wide discussion on agricultural courses in the colleges and did much to strengthen the position of the teachers of agriculture as distinct from the sciences related thereto. They also helped to increase the specialization of agricultural instruction, enlarge the agricultural faculties, and secure more ample equipment of buildings, land, livestock, apparatus, etc., for this work. Agriculture as a subject of college instruction was thus helped to outgrow its subordinate place in the curriculum, and the agricultural course became much more than the teaching of the relations of the sciences to agriculture.

The need of more than an undergraduate course for the training of experts in agricultural and scientific subjects was beginning to be appreciated and some of the stronger colleges began to have a considerable number of graduate students. For several years prior to 1900 the association had a committee that endeavored to secure some arrangement by which graduates of the land-grant colleges might make use of the special facilities for study and research in the Government establishments in Washington. At one time it seemed as if this might be aided through an office in the Smithsonian Institution, but finally the authorities there decided that this would contravene their established policy of not engaging in educational activities.

The United States Department of Agriculture undertook in 1899 to aid this movement by establishing in cooperation with the Civil Service Commission a register of " scientific aids," which would enable graduates of colleges having proper qualifications to earn a small salary for work in different bureaus, with the understanding that a part of their time would be given to studies outside their regular duties. This arrangement continued for several years and afforded a number of students opportunities to continue studies in special lines and in some cases to enter the permanent service of the Government. After a time, however, difficulties in the administration of such an arrangement, which involved a somewhat limited competition under civil service regulations, led the commission to withdraw its consent to its continuance.

Part 5. EXPANSION AND DEVELOPMENT OF AGRICULTURAL COLLEGES, 1900–1914

GENERAL CONDITIONS FAVORING GROWTH OF AGRICULTURAL COLLEGES

By the opening of the twentieth century a period of unparalleled general prosperity of American agriculture had set in. Economic conditions favored the multiplication and enlargement of industries and the expansion and diversification of agriculture. Settlement in new agricultural regions in the West increased, and the rising prices of products and land in the country generally encouraged young men to work on farms and acquire land for the establishment of homes in the country. Special difficulties which hampered production in various regions called attention to the desirability of more scientific farming and the need of a knowledge of the means of controlling plant and animal diseases and insect pests as such means were being developed by the United States Department of Agriculture and the experiment stations.

While the relative number of people engaged in agriculture as compared with the number in other industries decreased, the total number of farmers increased, and conditions, including the invention and wide use of much farm machinery, favored a great increase in the efficiency of American farmers as measured by the yield of products per man.

The experiment stations and the United States Department of Agriculture were reaching great numbers of the more intelligent farmers and were assembling a great body of tested knowledge for use in agricultural education. Not only were very many official publications freely distributed, but agricultural journals, manuals, and textbooks were rapidly increasing in numbers and extent of distribution.

In the colleges agricultural faculties were growing larger, and more adequate material equipment for their work was being provided. The general content of the agricultural courses had been fairly well defined comprehensively, and specialization, particularly in the branches connected with agricultural production, was proceeding. There was much discussion of the problems connected with curriculum making for both long and short courses. The number of agricultural students was increasing, and their standing in the colleges and universities was much improved.

DEVELOPMENT OF COLLEGE ORGANIZATION

As the faculties and student bodies in the agricultural divisions of the land-grant institutions grew and the variety of duties of these institutions increased, the necessity for a more complex organization became apparent. The presidents of the universities and of the

220

larger colleges ceased to function as teachers. The universities were usually divided into colleges, among which was a college of agriculture. The special officer at the head of this college was usually called a dean. The college had a faculty, in which the workers in agriculture and the sciences directly relating thereto were usually employed full time, but often divided their time between teaching and research. The teachers of other subjects were either wholly in the service of that college or were wholly or partially engaged in other colleges of the university. Thus, for example, general chemistry might be taught in the college of arts and sciences and agricultural chemistry in that college or in the college of agriculture. Each college was divided into a number of subject-matter departments. At first all of the agricultural instruction was given in one department, but gradually it was divided and subdivided into departments of agronomy, horticulture, soils, animal husbandry, poultry, dairying, rural engineering, rural economics, etc.

Each department was given a head or chairman, who had general supervision of its work and to a greater or less extent the choice and management of its personnel.

The agricultural and mechanical colleges had an organization which approximated that of the university in so far as the size of the college and the variety of its duties necessitated a more or less elaborate organization.

When the agricultural experiment stations were organized, under the Hatch Act of 1887, they became distinct departments of the college or university as the Federal law required. The title of director had come into use to designate the head of an experiment station organized as a separate institution. That title was carried over to the college stations. For fear of weakening the authority of the chief officer of the college or for what was supposed to be proper economy in the use of funds, the president of the institution or the dean of the agricultural college was at first often designated also director of the station. His position was often made more attractive by increase of his salary on account of the new duties involved in the management of the station.

While this arrangement seemed justified at first on account of the conditions prevailing at many of the land-grant colleges it often did not work well as a permanent arrangement. The president sometimes had little knowledge of agricultural science or practice, and even the deans were greatly hindered in giving the stations efficient management by the increase of duties relating to teaching and the discipline of students or by reason of their lack of real interest in agricultural research. The Hatch Act brought to the agricultural colleges what for the time was an unusually large fund for research, and when to this were added considerable amounts of State funds, which often imposed regulatory as well as experimental duties on the station, its management really required the full time of a specially trained and capable director. The college presidents gradually withdrew from the station directorships, but the custom of giving this designation to the deans persisted and has not yet been altogether abrogated. Various arrangements have been made in efforts to strengthen the station administration through the appointment of vice directors or other administrative assistants or by giving the heads of the subject-matter departments broader administrative functions.

In some cases the station was made a more or less separate organization attached to the college, with a director who reported to the president or even to the trustees, and had a staff with a considerable number of members wholly under his control and others detailed from the college departments to the station for part of their time. This was not a very satisfactory arrangement, since the station and the teaching division of the college needed to have close and well-correlated relations.

The growth of the extension work of the colleges brought about the employment of technically trained persons and clerks who gave their whole time to this work. Many college and station officers and other employees also engaged in this work part of the time. This development created new administrative problems in the colleges. At first the extension workers were attached to the different subject-matter departments and did their work under the supervision of the heads of these departments. But it was afterwards necessary to locate authority for their schedules of travel, attendance at meetings, and other extension business in some central organization within the college to avoid administrative confusion and friction. Faculty committees on extension work were sometimes appointed, but these did not prove very satisfactory. Then extension departments or divisions were created. Whereupon an administrative problem arose, similar to the one previously created by the establishment of the experiment stations. The extension department was in some cases made a distinct division of the college with a separate force; in other cases it was composed of members of the subject-matter departments, forming a somewhat loose organization under the supervision of the dean or station director.

When it became evident that a Federal law would be enacted under which large grants of money from different sources would be given to the colleges for the maintenance of a broad system of extension work, thus making such work a large and permanent function of the land-grant colleges, the organization of this work was actively discussed in the several colleges and in their association. There was great variety of opinion and practice, but the discussion more and more definitely went on around the proposition that the whole agricultural work of a land-grant institution should be administered by a dean, under whom there should be directors of research, resident teaching, and extension work, respectively.

This plan was definitely stated in a paper by the director of the Office of Experiment Stations at a conference on extension teaching in agriculture at the Southern Commercial Congress in 1912. The main features of the plan may be summarized as follows:

The State colleges in which agriculture was taught were institutions broadly organized to give instruction in many subjects, and in 20 States the agricultural college was a part of the State university. It was generally agreed that the agricultural work of the institution should be organized as a distinct unit, to which the name college of agriculture was commonly given. Within this college were three main lines of activity—research, resident teaching, and extension work. It would be desirable, therefore, that three administrative divisions be made within the college to which the names agricultural experiment station, division of instruction, and extension division might be given. But it was also appropriate, and indeed essential, that the college as a whole should be divided according to the subject matter included within its curriculum into departments such as agronomy, animal husbandry, dairying, etc.

Since it was highly important that the information on any subject given to the students and public should represent the views of the institution as a whole, all the experimenters, teachers, and extension workers should be grouped by departments representing the specialties in which they were working. Thus the department of agronomy should embrace all the agronomists employed by the college, whether engaged in experimenting, teaching, or extension work. Each department was to be presided over by a chief, who would have authority to assemble all the workers in the subject for consultation regarding the subject matter of their work, methods of instruction, etc. All the workers were expected to keep in close touch with their respective departments, so as to be fully acquainted with the work of their associates and the progress of knowledge in their subjects.

On the other hand, each member of a department was also to be a member of a division, or in some cases of two or three divisions, and was expected to report to one or more division directors who would have authority to control the whole or parts of his time and assign him to duties as experimenter, teacher, or extension worker. This dual responsibility was already recognized in many institutions in regard to the experiment station and teaching work and needed only to be extended to cover the extension work. As far as possible it would be desirable that the individual devote himself primarily and chiefly to one line of work, and as the extension work increased it would be necessary more and more to have men working exclusively in that department. This was already true with regard to the experiment-station work.

To carry out such an organization several classes of administrative officers would be required. The general management of the university or State college as a whole was to be vested in a president. Under him would be a number of deans, one of whom would have charge of the college of agriculture. Under this dean there would be three directors—(1) the director of the experiment station, (2) the director of the teaching division, and (3) the director of the extension division. Each of these directors was to have administrative control of his division. Where the work and staffs of the division overlapped or cooperative action was desirable, the three directors would constitute a general administrative committee under the chairmanship of the dean. The directors were to arrange for the division of the individual worker's time and his assignment to duties within the respective divisions.

The general program for the work of the college was to be made up by the faculty, consisting of the dean, directors, heads of departments, and other professors whose rank entitled them to faculty membership under the general policy of the institution. This program was to include conferences of the workers in each department, under the chairmanship of the head of the department.

The same plan was briefly presented at the meeting of the agricultural college association in 1913. In a general way this plan was approved in 1917 by the committee on college organization and policy of the association after an extended study made in cooperation with the Bureau of Education by C. D. Jarvis (*499*). The results of this study were incorporated in the following recommendations:

1. That the individual specialist, capable of working independently, should be regarded as the unit of organization.

2. That the group of working specialists on any one of the recognized subjects, regardless of the kind of service, should constitute the subject-matter department.

3. That specialists should devote their time mainly to one kind of service, but provision should be made for exchanges for the mutual advantage of each.

4. That one member of each department should be designated as chairman or administrative head.

5. That the members of the subject-matter department should be given a voice in the designation of their chairman or administrative head.

6. That authority for subject-matter should be confined to the group of specialists comprising the subject-matter department, and that administrative control should be limited to the amount and method of work.

7. That the distribution of administrative authority should be on the basis of the kind of service.

8. That the three kinds of service, each in charge of a secondary administrative officer, should be coordinated under a chief executive who, in the case of a large institution composed of several faculty groups, should be an officer other than the president.

9. That the official designation " dean " in an agricultural college should be applied only to the chief executive officer who is responsible for the coordination of the three phases of agricultural service, and that of " director " should be applied to the coordinate officer in charge of each of the three lines of service—resident instruction, research, and extension.

10. That when one individual performs the duties of two or more offices his official designation should identify clearly the officer with the respective offices assigned.

11. That the leaders in charge of the various phases of the extension service should be regarded as administrative officers and should not usurp the duties of the specialists in the various subjects. Where an individual serves both as specialist and administrative leader a dual responsibility should be recognized.

12. That in the promotion of extension projects controlled by either connected or cooperative colleges the same administrative relations with the subject-matter departments concerned should exist as with departments that are organically connected.

13. That incoming correspondence, except that of an administrative nature, should be referred to the subject-matter departments concerned and there referred to the individual best qualified to study the desired information.

14. That specialists in whatever kind of service should be on an equal basis from the standpoint of rank and official designation. If differentiation of extension and research specialists is desirable, the prefixes " extension " and " research," respectively, may be used in connection with the customary professional titles.

The complicated organization and varied local conditions in the several land-grant colleges have so far prevented the general acceptance of this plan of organization. It is, however, followed substantially in a number of the larger institutions and approximately in others.

This movement has been helped by the determination of the Department of Agriculture, announced in 1914, to differentiate its research, extension, and regulatory work more definitely and modify its organization to meet the new conditions caused by the expansion of its activities. This has resulted in the appointment of directors of scientific, extension, and regulatory work, who, under the Secretary of Agriculture, have general charge of these phases of the work, the bureau organization of the department remaining as before.

COLLEGE BUILDINGS FOR AGRICULTURE

One of the important factors in strengthening the agricultural work in the land-grant colleges during the decade beginning about 1900 was the erection at many institutions of distinctive and substantial buildings for use in that work.

These were either large buildings to house most of the agricultural work in progress when they were erected or smaller buildings for different branches of the work such as horticulture or dairying. To the students and in considerable measure to the general

FIG. 14.—Townshend Hall, Ohio State University

public such buildings on the college campus typified the dignity and importance of the agricultural work of the institution. This was particularly true where the college of agriculture was part of a university.

The first large agricultural building of the new type was Townshend Hall, at the Ohio State University. (Fig. 14.) This was erected in 1898 at a cost of about $77,000 and was named for N. S. Townshend "as a memorial of his public services and his work in advancing the cause of agricultural education." It was 260 feet in length and varied in width from 64 to 78 feet. It had a basement and two main floors. In its original use the basement contained the dairy department, with rooms for testing and pasteurizing milk and for butter and cheese making.

At the opposite end of the basement were a lecture and livestock-judging room with adjacent stalls for animals, and a storage room for soils, near an outside glasshouse for experimental study of soils and crops. The first story contained the offices, classrooms, laboratories, reading room, library, and museum of the department of agriculture. At one end was a large soil physics laboratory with special apparatus of a new type. The second floor contained the departments of agricultural chemistry and veterinary medicine, an assembly room, and an office for the editors of the Agricultural Student.

The building for the College of Agriculture of the University of Illinois was opened in 1901. It consisted of a main portion 248 feet in length, from 50 to 100 feet in depth, and three stories in height, and with three wings, each 45 by 117 feet and each two stories in height, connected with each other and with the main portion by corridors, all built around an open court. The entire floor space amounted to a little over 2 acres. This building contained an assembly hall, offices, classrooms, laboratories, seminar rooms, etc.

At the Department of Agriculture of the University of Minnesota, located on a farm between the cities of Minneapolis and St. Paul, there were erected buildings for horticulture, animal husbandry, dairying, veterinary science, agricultural chemistry, and finally a great administration building, completed in 1907 at a cost of $250,000, which included among other things, classrooms and laboratories for the work in agronomy, farm accounts, and entomology, and an auditorium seating 1,000 people.

Before 1900 the College of Agriculture of the University of Wisconsin had a substantial dairy building with a dairy laboratory and rooms devoted to creamery practice, cheese making and curing, pasteurizing, farm dairying, etc.; and in 1896 completed a unique horticulture-physics building to which were attached large glasshouses. The work in agricultural physics included meteorology, drainage, irrigation, road building, construction of farm buildings, and soil physics. In 1901 the State legislature appropriated $150,000 for an agricultural building.

When the State of New York undertook to maintain the College of Agriculture at Cornell University the legislature in 1904 provided a building fund of $290,000. A group of three buildings connected by covered loggias and a detached building for the department of animal husbandry were constructed and were dedicated April 27, 1907, in connection with the celebration of the centennial anniversary of the birth of Ezra Cornell. (Fig. 15.)

The group of agricultural buildings dedicated at the Pennsylvania State College, November 22, 1907, cost about $300,000, and included an agricultural building for the departments of agronomy, horticulture, agricultural chemistry, animal husbandry, animal nutrition, and agricultural extension; a dairy building with rooms and equipment for work with milk, the making of butter, cheese, and ice cream, farm dairying, bacteriology, etc.; and a respiration-calorimeter building.

The Iowa State College erected in 1904 a dairy building, 110 by 60 feet, with three stories and a basement, which provided rooms and equipment for work similar to that provided for at the Pennsylvania State College. To this was added in 1909 a monumental agricultural building, 230 by 78 feet, with a semicircular wing containing an assembly room seating 1,000 people. The building and its furniture cost about $375,000.

Before 1910 substantial agricultural buildings were also provided for the colleges in Kansas, Texas, Indiana, New Hampshire, Oregon, South Carolina, Vermont, Oklahoma, North Carolina, Georgia, Maine, Michigan, Montana, and California; dairy buildings in Mississippi, Missouri, Kansas, and Nebraska; horticultural buildings in Massachusetts and Kansas; and the quarters for instruction and research in the various branches of agriculture and related sciences were much improved in other buildings used by the colleges in many States.

SPECIAL BUILDINGS

Special buildings for use in agricultural instruction and research became quite numerous on the grounds of the agricultural colleges. One of such early structures was the insectary built at the New

FIG. 15.—New York State College of Agriculture, central group

York College of Agriculture in 1888. This was a two-story cottage with greenhouses attached, and contained a laboratory, workshop, dark room for photography, and cold room for the storage of hibernating insects. It was provided with various pieces of apparatus devised at the station, among which were a root cage and various forms of breeding cages.

As the work in agronomy, horticulture, plant physiology and pathology, and entomology grew, glasshouses increased in variety and extent. Sometimes laboratories and workshops were connected with these houses, and some of them were so arranged that classes of students could work in them. Pot experiments were also carried on in such houses, often with special arrangements for transferring the pots into the open air without disturbing them.

In connection with the work in animal husbandry barns of different kinds were erected. Sometimes these were large and expensive structures. In other cases they were built to illustrate barns such as prosperous farmers might have. With the specialization of the work separate barns for different kinds of animals were built. There was a special development of dairy barns in the effort to make them sanitary and provide good ventilation and convenient feeding arrangements.

During this period there was great activity in the use of silage, and various kinds of silos, as regards form, size, material of construction, etc., were built at the colleges. Where large numbers of animals were fed and the climatic conditions permitted more or less elaborate feeding sheds and lots were used. Piggeries of various kinds were constructed, as well as poultry houses. The latter were often equipped with trap nests and contained special rooms for work with incubators.

The great interest in stock judging developed during this period led to the construction first of special rooms for this work and then to the erection of separate stock-judging pavilions. In 1901 the Iowa college built such a pavilion, circular in form, 65 feet in diameter, with a seating capacity of 300, and containing a judging pit 50 feet in diameter. The great popularity of stock judging, especially as the colleges increased their participations in competitive tests at fairs and particularly at the International Livestock Show at Chicago, led to the erection of larger and more elaborate stock-judging pavilions at these institutions.

Grain judging also became an important factor in agronomy courses and special arrangements for this were made in the college buildings. In 1908 at the Nebraska college a substantial building devoted to stock and grain judging work was erected.

When a department of farm mechanics was established at the Iowa college a building for its special use was erected in 1903 at a cost, including equipment, of over $65,000. It contained wood and iron working shops, large operating testing rooms for the study of farm motors, binders, mowers, planters, plows, wagons, and other farm machines, as well as rooms for classes, drafting, reading, offices, etc. Buildings for similar purposes were erected at other colleges, and in Colorado in 1909 a building in which considerable space was devoted to the work in irrigation engineering.

EQUIPMENT FOR INSTRUCTION IN AGRICULTURE

In both agriculture and the related sciences the equipment of the agricultural colleges became more and more extensive and varied as the number of students and the funds for their instruction increased. The work of the experiment stations connected with these colleges called for the employment and devising of many unusual kinds of equipment. The college students, especially those in the advanced work, had at least the opportunity of observing this equipment and the methods and results of its operating. A considerable number of students were employed to some extent in the stations and thus came into intimate contact with their equipment. In the natural sciences the laboratory method of instruction became universal in the American colleges, and many of the agricultural colleges had excellent equipment for work in these sciences.

For the study of soils there was the devising and use of much special apparatus. For example, the equipment for soil study in

Townshend Hall of the Ohio State University included apparatus for studying the specific gravity of soils, volume weight of soils, power of loose and of compact soil to retain moisture, rate of flow of air through soils, rate of percolation of water through soils, effect of mulches on evaporation of water from soils, effect of cultivation on evaporation of water from soils, power of dry soil to absorb moisture from the air, and the capillary rise of water through soils. Mechanical analyses were also made of typical soils. A large glasshouse with its equipment of pots, trucks, and tracks afforded opportunity for the student to test the adaptability of crops to various soils, the fertilizer requirements of soils, and to experiment on various other problems of crop growth.

At the same time in the agricultural building of the Illinois college there were separate laboratories for work in soil fertility, soil physics, and soil bacteriology.

For the study of farm crops the Minnesota agricultural college had a seed-breeding laboratory, which furnished facilities for special instruction in field seeds and in laboratory work in plant breeding. The college possessed a stereopticon with several hundred lantern slides, including illustrations of crops, implements, machinery, processes of drainage, etc.; imported models of wheat and of clover flowers and seeds; many charts of root systems and illustrations of floral organs which had been drawn at this institution; also maps and designs of farm plans, both for laying out new farms and for reorganizing old ones.

There were also in a number of colleges collections of many different kinds of grasses, cereals, and other crops, and of seeds of useful and noxious plants, as well as a great variety of farm implements and machinery.

Domestic animals of different kinds were increasingly kept by the colleges for instructional purposes, and the students also had many opportunities for observing breeding and feeding experiments, and participating in the judging, care, and management of such animals. With dairy cattle different kinds of stalls and fixtures were often used. In the latter part of the period milking machines were installed. For the handling of milk and the making of butter and cheese many of the colleges began to have equipment which compared favorably with that in commercial establishments.

The libraries of the agricultural colleges also made material growth during this period. Not only were there large collections of the publications of the United States Department of Agriculture, Bureau of Education, and other Government establishments and of the experiment stations and State departments of agriculture and education, and reports of similar institutions in foreign countries, but also numerous scientific and agricultural books and journals published in this and other countries. More attention was also paid to the arrangement and cataloguing of these collections and the facilities and personal service which would make them readily available to teachers and students.

Much was done during this period in the preparation and publication of textbooks and manuals on agriculture and related sciences. The Annual Report of the Office of Experiment Stations for 1903 contained an article on the development of the textbook of agriculture in North America up to 1900, by L. H. Bailey. This was followed by the report of the bibliographer of the Association of Agricultural Colleges at its meeting in November, 1906, which contained a list of 389 books, the work of 198 men and women at some time connected with agricultural colleges and experiment stations. In this list was included Bailey's Cyclopedia of American Horticulaure, published in 1906, which was soon followed by his Cyclopedia of American Agriculture.

COLLEGE FARMS

As the agricultural work of the college became more extensive and diversified the amount of land used in connection with instruction increased. Part of this land was used for the growing of crops with which to feed the college livestock and, in some cases, the students. Fields were also set aside for the growing of crops that were being tested with reference to their adaptability to the region, or for the demonstration of different methods of planting, fertilizing, cultivating, draining, irrigating, and harvesting. Orchards of different kinds and varieties of fruits, and plantations of small fruits, vegetables, and flowers occupied considerable space. At some colleges there were small plantations of forest trees. There were also the more or less extensive fields, orchards, and series of plats used by the experiment stations on which numerous varieties of many kinds of plants were grown under a great variety of conditions. At some institutions there were botanic gardens in which were grown many native and foreign plants, particularly those of some economic importance.

At some colleges the farms were under a single general management, portions of the farm being temporarily assigned to the experiment station and different college departments. In other cases the experiment-station land was permanently separate, and in a few institutions there were permanent assignments of land to the different departments which assumed their management for special purposes. While the old compulsory manual-labor system for students disappeared, there was a considerable amount of required labor on a field-laboratory plan. A certain number of students were employed and paid for part-time work on the college and station lands. The students generally observed the station experiments and thus became familiar with whatever useful progress in new directions the stations were making. The use of large tracts of land in connection with agricultural instruction and experimentation marked a somewhat radical departure from the conception that higher agricultural education should be very largely a matter of lectures and laboratory work as was held by some of the early leaders in this movement, e. g., by S. W. Johnson and E. W. Hilgard.

The acreage of land used in 1910 by some agricultural colleges, largely as farms and experiment grounds, was as follows: Illinois 620 acres, Iowa 1,200, Kansas 800, Massachusetts 400, Minnesota 420, Mississippi 2,000, New York 638, Oregon 180, Pennsylvania 600, and South Carolina 1,544.

INCREASED FEDERAL FUNDS FOR AGRICULTURAL RESEARCH

The growth of public interest in the agricultural colleges, the enlarged faculties and student bodies, and the provision of more elaborate buildings and equipment brought upon the experiment stations additional burdens which they could not bear satisfactorily without more well-trained workers and larger financial support. Attention was called to the needs of the stations in the report of the Director of the Office of Experiment Stations for 1902.

So rapidly has the demand for the services of agricultural experts spread in different directions that the workers in this service have in many instances been overworked, or at least have been forced to dissipate their energies in attempts to cover too many fields. There is therefore a most urgent necessity that the number of workers in our agricultural institutions should be increased so as to permit proper specialization of work. * * * It is of little use to construct expensive laboratories and equip them with elaborate apparatus unless they are manned with first-class investigators.

An editorial by E. W. Allen, published about this time in the Experiment Station Record, was cited, which pointed out that—

the character of the work of the stations is gradually undergoing a change. The simpler and more superficial problems in many lines of agriculture have been solved to a large extent and demonstrated beyond doubt. The more complex and intricate investigations involving deeper and more time-consuming research will be the field more largely occupied by the leading stations in the future.

At the meeting of the Association of American Agricultural Colleges and Experiment Stations at Atlanta, Ga., October 7, 1902, a resolution offered by Eugene Davenport, of Illinois, was adopted, which instructed the executive committee—

if in its judgment it should seem expedient, to urge upon Congress at the earliest practicable date that the appropriation to the several States under the Hatch Act be increased by the sum of $15,000 annually.

The increased importance of the experiment stations was also brought out at this meeting through an amendment to the constitution of the association offered by W. A. Henry, of Wisconsin, and adopted the next year, which provided for a section on experiment station work.

The executive committee decided that it would be unwise to attempt legislation for increased Federal endowment of the experiment stations in the Fifty-seventh Congress, but laid the foundation for future action in this direction by asking the Director of the Office of Experiment Stations to present in his next annual report a statement of the present conditions and work of the experiment stations and of the need of additional funds for their work. Such a report was made in 1903. Nothing further was done in this matter at the Washington meeting of the association that year, but immediately thereafter W. A. Henry called on his long-time friend, Henry Cullen Adams (fig. 16), former dairy and food commissioner in Wisconsin, and then a new member of the National House of Representatives. Mr. Adams readily agreed to undertake to secure the passage of a bill giving additional Federal aid to the experiment stations. With the aid of the Director of the Office of Experiment Stations a bill for this purpose was drawn and introduced in the House by Mr. Adams on January 4, 1904. Stress was laid by Dean Henry and the writer on the need of funds especially for research. The Adams bill was therefore so worded as to restrict the use of this new fund to paying the expenses of original research in agriculture.

FIG. 16.—Henry C. Adams

The executive committee of the association cooperated actively with Mr. Adams, and his measure had widespread support from the agricultural press and farm organizations. It also early received favorable consideration from a large number of Congressmen. But the leaders in Congress had set themselves firmly against increase of Federal appropriations. Therefore this bill made no progress during the Fifty-eighth Congress. It was reintroduced in somewhat modified form by Mr. Adams early in the first session of the Fifty-ninth Congress, and on January 15, 1906, he was able to make a favorable report on this bill from the House Committee on Agriculture. It then made relatively rapid progress through both houses, was passed without dissenting votes, and was approved by President Roosevelt March 16, 1906.

Mr. Adams, by great tact and patience, had achieved a notable legislative victory through the final passage of this important measure. He had long worked under a serious handicap of poor health, and on July 9, 1906, he passed away, to the great regret of all who understood his profound interest in agriculture and the farming people.

THE ADAMS ACT

The Adams Act appropriated $5,000 for the year ended June 30, 1906, an annual increase of this sum by $2,000 for five years, and thereafter $15,000 annually to the experiment stations organized under the Hatch Act in each State and Territory, " to be applied only to paying the necessary expenses of conducting original researches or experiments bearing directly on the agricultural industry of the United States." The Secretary of Agriculture was " charged with the proper administration of this law."

The details of this administration have been carried out by the Office of Experiment Stations. The stations were persuaded by the director of this office annually to submit their plans for work under this act to the Office of Experiment Stations in advance of payment of the Adams fund. These plans have taken the form of limited and specific projects and have been approved only when it has appeared that they involved original research. The Adams Act has therefore given the stations a substantial financial basis for carrying on research and in general has greatly strengthened them.

PROMOTION OF GRADUATE STUDY

Some leaders in the colleges perceived that something more than an ordinary undergraduate course with a bachelor's degree was required for the preparation of college teachers, investigators, and experts in various agricultural lines. Some graduate work was being offered in certain institutions, but as yet it was not well organized.

THE SUMMER GRADUATE SCHOOL

While Thomas F. Hunt, dean of the College of Agriculture and Domestic Science of Ohio State University, was attending the convention of the Association of American Agricultural Colleges at San Francisco, Calif., in July, 1899, it occurred to him that it would be a good plan to organize a graduate school of agriculture.

This proposition met with the approval of President W. O. Thompson, of the university, and on his recommendation the trustees in April, 1900, took action in favor of the establishment of such a school.

In explaining this matter to the association in November, 1900, President Thompson made it clear that it was the purpose of the Ohio State University to inaugurate a movement in which the colleges represented in the association would be expected to cooperate. "The proposition would be to have a faculty of instruction gathered from the colleges and experiment stations represented in this convention." It was to be "an intercollegiate school of agriculture" and to have "a migratory character" if experience showed that it was best "to take it from institution to institution."

The association referred this matter to its executive committee, which at the convention in November, 1901, reported its approval of the plan suggested by the Ohio State University and recommended the holding of the first session of the school during the summer of 1902 "under the control of the president of the said university, with the expectation of adopting the school as a cooperative enterprise under the control of the convention should the success of the first session seem to justify the continuance of the school."

In 1900 the board of trustees of Ohio State University had made an appropriation of $1,000 to finance such a school, and the next year the authorities of the university, having learned in advance of the decision of the executive committee of the college association, took some preliminary steps toward its organization. The Secretary of Agriculture expressed his approval of this project and his willingness to have the Director of the Office of Experiment Stations act as its dean and other officers of the department to be members of the faculty.

Many of the officers of the colleges and stations expressed their interest in the school in response to a circular letter from the university. With this and other information before them the association approved the report of its executive committee. The university then took prompt action to hold the first session during July, 1902. The writer was made dean, and Thomas F. Hunt acted as registrar. The school was opened July 7, 1902, and continued for four weeks. At the inaugural exercises addresses were made by James Wilson, Secretary of Agriculture; H. C. White, president of the Georgia College of Agriculture, as chairman of the executive committee of the association of agricultural colleges; and the dean.

Courses were offered in three main lines—agronomy, zootechny, and dairying. A special course in plant and animal breeding was also planned and arrangements made for general exercises in agricultural pedagogy and on special topics to be held in the Saturday morning periods.

The university authorities put at the disposal of the school the large and well-appointed building devoted exclusively to the instruction given in the college of agriculture of the university, known as Townshend Hall. This building contains well-appointed lecture rooms, thoroughly equipped laboratories, and an agricultural library. Animals of different kinds and breeds were obtained from leading breeders in Ohio for use in demonstration exercises. A matriculation fee of $6 for each student for the whole session or any part thereof was asked, this being the fee regularly charged by the Ohio State University for each term. Arrangements for board and lodging were made in the neighborhood of the university for from $5 to $7 per week, and the north dormitory of the university was open to the school, where board and lodging were provided at $5 per week and for table board at $4 per week.

The faculty included 35 men, of whom 26 are professors in agricultural colleges, 7 are leading officers of the Department of Agriculture, and 2 are officers of the New York State Experiment Station. Seventy-five students were in attendance. These were drawn from 28 States and Territories, including such widely separated regions as Maine, Oregon, California, New Mex.co, and Alabama. There was 1 student from Canada and 1 from Argentina. There was also 1 woman, and the colored race was represented by teachers from the Tuskegee Institute and the North Carolina Agricultural College. Twenty-seven of the students are professors or assistant professors of agriculture in agricultural colleges, 31 are assistants in the agricultural colleges and experiment stations, 9 are recent college graduates, and 8 are engaged in farming.

The lectures and other exercises given at the school were as a rule of a high order. Much new information was presented, as well as useful reviews and summaries, with special reference to the needs of different students. There was a large amount of interesting and profitable discussion among students and the faculty both inside and outside the lecture rooms. The course of study was pursued with great earnestness by both faculty and students and it was even necessary to restrain the faculty and students from too prolonged exercises. The Saturday morning conferences proved to be of great interest. Among the topics treated in these exercises were the organization of agricultural education in colleges, secondary schools, nature-study courses, correspondence courses, farmers' institutes, and various forms of university extension, what constitutes a science of agriculture, the educational values of courses in agriculture, and methods and values of cooperative experiments (*499*).

The broad aim of this school, which in considerable measure, was justified by its results, was thus stated by its dean at the session in 1902 (*439*):

In an unusual measure we believe this school will furnish inspiration and up-to-date knowledge to workers in our agricultural institutions, gathered out cf many States and Territories; but beyond this, we believe that in its ultimate results this school will greatly aid in the formation of public opinion in favor of the more thorough and rational organization of agricultural education and research in the United States.

The school will aim to solidify and amplify the organization of education and research in agricultural subjects on the basis of agriculture itself, considered as both a science and an art. It will seek on the one hand to help on the movement for grouping the results of investigation in many scient fic lines into a fairly well-defined body of knowledge, to be known as the science of agriculture, comparable with such sciences as geology, geography, and medicine, and on the other hand to quicken and broaden the movement for the direct application of science in manifold ways to the art of agriculture. While we expect to pursue our work with high standards of scientific and pedagogical effort, we will not for a moment lose sight of the farmer and the requirements of practical agriculture. All our labor will be counted as in vain if it does not issue sooner or later in the growing of plants and animals better adapted to the uses of men and the evolution of a system of farming in which the financial returns shall be more satisfactory to the intelligent and thrifty farmers, and under which the general level of intelligence, comfort, and upright and harmonious living of our rural population shall be perceptibly and increasingly raised.

The fundamental basis of the development of courses of instruction in agriculture was also presented with some elaboration by the dean in a paper on the science of agriculture and in one on educational values of courses of agriculture. Both these papers were published in the Report of the Office of Experiment Stations for 1902 (*439*) and the latter in Bulletin 19 of Ohio State University. The science of agriculture was compared with geology, geography, and medicine, as a science which is made up of materials derived from other more fundamental sciences such as chemistry, physics, botany, zoology, etc. It may be defined as—

that body of knowledge (gained and verified by exact observation and correct thinking, methodically formulated and arranged in a rational system) in which the facts relating to the production of plants and animals useful to man and the uses of these plants and animals are accurately set forth, and a rational explanation is given of the phenomena and laws involved in such production and uses. It is obvious that this body of knowledge may be variously subdivided according to different purposes of study or application.

Agriculture may be divided into plant production, animal production or zootechny, agricultural technology or agrotechny, rural engineering, and rural economics.

Under plant production is included whatever relates to the natural or artificial environment (i. e., climate, soil, water, fertilizers) of useful plants, their structure, composition, physiology, botanical relations, varieties, geographical distr.bution, culture, harvesting, preservation, and uses, and the obstructions to their growth, preservation, or use. Plant production may be subdivided into agronomy, which deals with what are commonly called field or farm crops; horticulture, which deals with vegetables, fruits, and ornamental plants, especially as grown in gardens, small plantations, or parks; and forestry, which deals with trees and shrubs grown in large tracts.

Animal production includes—

whatever relates to the anatomy, physiology, zoological relations, domestication, types and breeds, breeding, feeding, hygiene, management, and uses of useful animals. It may also include * * * diseases and other impediments to the production of animals, i. e., veterinary medic!ne, though this is in itself a large and distinct body of knowledge.

Animal production may be subdivided according to the different kinds of animals or into such branches as animal breeding, animal nutrition, and animal management.

Agrotechny includes whatever relates to the conversion of raw materials produced in agriculture into manufactured articles for use in commerce and the arts. It may also include the processes of handling these raw materials in connection with their commercial uses, as in the case of milk and cream sold for consumption. It also involves whatever relates to departures from standards set for manufactured articles, i. e., adulterations and sophistications, in somewhat the same way that the diseases of plants and animals are related to agronomy and zootechny. Agrotechny is naturally divided into specialities according to the kinds of materials, e. g., foods and feeding stuffs, liquors, oils, textiles, and leather. The subdivision of most importance as a subject of school instruction in the United States is dairying.

Rural engineering includes those branches of civil and mechanical engineering which relate to the locating, arranging, and equipment of farms and the construction and operation of farm implements and machinery. It embraces the surveying of farms, the location of farm buildings and works, the construction of buildings, water, irrigation, drainage, and sewage systems, and roads. It also involves the principles of mechanics as applied to farm machinery and the use of different kinds of power for agricultural purposes.

Rural economics may be more or less broadly defined according to the point of view. It at least includes whatever is related to agriculture considered as a means for the production, preservation, and distribution of wealth by the use of land for the growing of plants and animals. It may include the development of agriculture as a business (history of agriculture), as well as the facts and principles of farm management under present conditions.

The practical advantages of organizing agricultural instruction on a science of agriculture rather than on the relations of the fundamental sciences to agriculture were pointed out.

The differentiation of the body of knowledge, which may fairly be called the science of agriculture, from the other sciences will lead to profound changes in the methods of teaching agricultural subjects, the equipment for such instruction, and the arrangement of courses to meet the needs of different classes of students. We are, in fact, already in the midst of such changes. The most obvious result of this movement thus far is the division of the subject of agriculture among several instructors in a college, so as to make at least the beginnings of a real agricultural faculty. Thus we now have quite commonly in our agricultural colleges professors of agronomy, animal husbandry (zootechny), dairying, horticulture, and veterinary science. When a group of instructors is thus formed the natural consequence is a special building in which they may work, to a certain extent at least, in cooperation. When the building is provided it is seen to be appropriate and desirable that it should contain special arrangements, facilities, apparatus, etc., suited to the requirements of the subjects to be taught in it. This leads the instructors in several branches of agriculture to set their wits to work to devise special arrangements and apparatus which will improve the quality and thoroughness of their instruction. Along with this there is more study of the relation of the different topics to each other in a scheme of instruction, the rearrangement of courses, the improvement of methods of teaching, and the discussion of the whole subject of the pedagogy of agricultural science.

According to President Eliot, of Harvard University, the essential constituents of education in the highest sense are as follows: " We must learn to see straight and clear; to compare and infer; to make an accurate record; to remember; to express our thoughts with precision, and to hold fast on lofty ideals." "There is also," he says, " general recognition of the principle that effective power in action is the true end of education rather than the storing up of information or the cultivation of faculties which are mainly receptive, discriminating, or critical."

School courses, especially in high school and college, should therefore particularly promote the development of each pupil's dominant interests and powers, and further should seek to render these interests and powers subservient to life's serious purposes, which include self-support or some worthy form of service, and intelligent, active participation in human affairs.

A properly constituted agricultural course, taken as a whole, will include both cultural and vocational studies. The educational value of two-thirds of the course would not be disputed. As regards the strictly agricultural portion of the course, much of it consists of materials drawn from physics, chemistry, various biological sciences, engineering, and economics. The objects, facts, and phenomena brought before the student of agricultural science are of such a kind as to test his capacity to " see straight and clear " in a very high degree. There is also abundant opportunity " to compare and infer " and make " an accurate record " of what is learned, as well as to exercise the memory and to express thoughts with precision.

It also may be fairly claimed that the study of agriculture in its human relations may have an ethical side of much educational value. We should teach men in our agricultural colleges to be intelligent farmers, not simply that they may thus make a better living, but also that they may be leaders in making agriculture a live, progressive art, which in the future shall provide a more stable and satisfactory basis for thrifty, intelligent, and refined rural communities, as well as a stronger guaranty for the manufactures, commerce, art, literature, and science of a higher civilization, in which industrial and civil peace, and not war, shall be the established order.

Full responsibility for this enterprise was then assumed by the Association of American Agricultural Colleges and Experiment Stations and a committee on graduate work was appointed to have general charge of the school. This committee reported in 1904 in favor of holding sessions biennially, and advocated that each college contribute a small sum toward its maintenance. On this plan the second session was held at the University of Illinois in 1906, with a faculty of 35 leading agricultural teachers and investigators. Ninety-one students and 40 visitors from 34 States and Territories,

Hungary, and India were enrolled. Courses were given in agronomy, horticulture, plant physiology, zootechny, and plant and animal breeding.

The third session was held at the New York College of Agriculture, in cooperation with the New York Agricultural Experiment Station, with a faculty of 50 members, in addition to 18 speakers at special meetings. On the faculty, besides officers of the agricultural colleges and stations, were the United States Commissioner of Education, the New York commissioner of agriculture, the State entomologist, and representatives of Teachers' College of Columbia University, the Carnegie Institution, Sheffield Scientific School, and the Royal Agricultural College at Berlin, Germany. The students numbered 164, including 15 women registered in the Graduate School of Home Economics. They came from 37 States, the District of Columbia, Canada, China, and India, and included at least 40 heads of departments in agricultural colleges and stations. " Probably never before had there been gathered together for so extended a period so large and enthusiastic a body of scientific men interested in agriculture." Courses were given in biochemistry, agronomy, horticulture, entomology, dairy husbandry and dairying, poultry, and veterinary medicine.

At the fourth session, held at the Iowa State College in 1910, the courses included plant physiology and pathology, agronomy, horticulture, animal husbandry, poultry, dairying, and for the first time rural engineering, rural economics, and sociology. The faculty numbered 57, including representatives of the Carnegie Institution of Washington, Harvard University, University of Pennsylvania, the Royal Imperial College of Agriculture, Vienna, Austria, the University of Edinburgh, Scotland, and the Ontario Agricultural College. The students numbered 205, including 15 women and 3 negroes, from 39 States, the District of Columbia, Canada, Scotland, Cuba, Denmark, Russia, and the Transvaal.

The fifth session, at Michigan Agricultural College in 1912, had a faculty of 48 instructors, including representatives of Harvard University, Yale University, Carnegie Institution, Rothamsted Experiment Station, Cambridge University, England, and the Hygienic Institute at Munich, Germany. The students numbered 180, including 41 women enrolled in the Graduate School of Home Economics. They came from 34 States, Porto Rico, Canada, Russia, China, and Japan. There were courses in soils, plant physiology, animal physiology, agronomy, horticulture, beef and dairy cattle, swine, poultry, rural engineering, rural economics, and farm management.

The sixth session, at the University of Missouri in 1914, had courses in genetics, agronomy, animal husbandry, horticulture, immunity and disease resistance, rural economics, and farm management. The faculty was purposely limited to 29 members, including representatives of the Carnegie Institution, University of Wisconsin, Harvard University, New York Veterinary College, University of Edinburgh, and the Imperial Institute, Dahlen, Berlin, Germany. The students numbered 132, and came from 32 States, District of Columbia, Canada, and Scotland.

The seventh and final session was held at the Massachusetts Agricultural College in 1916. The courses were restricted to two main subjects: (1) The fundamental factors involved in the growth of plants and animals, and (2) the economic and social factors affecting profitable agriculture and country life. There were 45 persons who gave instruction as lecturers or leaders of seminars and about 40 others participated in the formal presentation of matters in the seminars and conferences. Outside of the land-grant colleges and United States Department of Agriculture, the faculty included representatives of the Missouri Botanical Garden, Amherst College, the Young Men's Christian Association at Springfield, Mass., the Massachusetts State Board of Education, the Vermont Department of Agriculture, the Kalamazoo (Mich.) Normal School, the London Hospital Medical Service, and the Ontario Agricultural College. About 150 students were enrolled, together with 48 visitors, but only 66 persons came from outside the Massachusetts Agricultural College. However, 27 States, District of Columbia, Porto Rico, England, Canada, and the Transvaal were represented.

At each session of this graduate school there were a number of important conferences on vital problems in agricultural research, teaching and extension work. At the Iowa college in 1910 there were " by far the largest and most important assemblies of persons directly connected with the extension work of our agricultural colleges." Secondary education in agriculture also occupied a new and important place in this session. A number of scientific agricultural associations held special meetings at the graduate school. Out of the session at the Illinois college in 1906 came the National Association of Dairy Instructors and Investigators, and the session at the Iowa college led to the formation of the American Farm Management Association.

The growth of graduate instruction in the agricultural colleges and conditions arising from the World War made it very difficult to continue this graduate school, and it was abolished by the association on the advice of its committee on graduate study. However, there has been nothing to take its place as a meeting place for officers of colleges and stations and advanced students from the whole country to discuss at some length vital problems of agricultural education and research.

It is believed that the graduate school had much influence in stimulating the establishment of more thorough agricultural courses in the land-grant colleges based on the science of agriculture broadly considered and on the sciences related to agriculture. It also promoted the raising of standards for the undergraduate courses and the institution of regular graduate work. It showed the necessity of thorough training for agricultural teaching and research. At the same time it aided the development of research and extension work in agriculture and the spread of agricultural teaching into the secondary schools. In a way its courses and conferences represented the progress of the movement for a broader and better American system of agricultural education and research. Its membership drawn so widely from different parts of the country carried its influence throughout the land-grant colleges and it thus furnished much material for the discussion of curricula, methods of teaching, lines of research, organization and conduct of extension work which went on in these institutions during the period of its existence.

DEVELOPMENT OF COURSES IN AGRICULTURE

SPECIALIZATION OF BRANCHES OF AGRICULTURE

The division of the agricultural work of the colleges into departments began with the separation of horticulture from general agriculture. Then came departments of animal husbandry and dairying. The great emphasis during this period was on agricultural production. Matters relating to agricultural engineering or economics occupied a subordinate place and were often associated with the department of agriculture or agronomy. In 1901–2 in the Illinois college, in which under the leadership of Dean Davenport, the specialization of agriculture had gone furthest, the technical portion of the courses leading to graduation occupied about half the time. There were 20 instructors in technical subjects, of whom 16 gave entire time to agriculture. In agronomy there were 6 instructors, in animal husbandry 3, in dairy husbandry 3, and in horticulture 5. Under agronomy there were 18 courses, including soils, farm crops, drainage, irrigation, farm buildings, machinery, roads, farm management, and history of agriculture. Under horticulture there were 19 courses, including orchard and small fruits, vegetables, viticulture, floriculture, nut culture, forestry, landscape gardening, and economic botany. Under animal husbandry there were 20 courses, including breeding, feeding, and management, and special courses on beef cattle, sheep, swine, and horses. Under dairy husbandry there were 13 courses, including breeding, feeding, and care of dairy cattle, milk, butter, cheese, ice cream, dairy bacteriology, and factory management. There were also 2 courses in thremmatology and 3 in veterinary science.

In 1903 the committee on instruction in agriculture of the Association of American Agricultural Colleges and Experiment Stations stated that the reorganization of faculties and courses on the basis of agriculture as a science was continuing.

One effect of this movement has been to change the relation of the natural sciences to agriculture in the scheme of instruction in the agricultural colleges. As long as agriculture was taught almost wholly on a practical basis and without much regard to its pedagogical formulation, the teachers of the natural sciences were called upon not only to develop the relations of these sciences to agriculture in their courses of instruction, but to give instruction in strictly agricultural subjects, and this was done to a considerable extent, especially in chemistry and botany (441).

Formerly the relations of the natural sciences to agriculture had formed the bulk of the courses in agriculture and this had been supplemented by only a limited amount of instruction on the practice of agriculture. On the other hand, in some subjects and particularly chemistry, too much emphasis was laid in the general course in agriculture on technique used by specialists. This was true, for example, in teaching analysis of fertilizers and feeding stuffs, as if the students generally were to become experts in control work.

Under the old system the emphasis was often laid so much on analytical work that the colleges produced many analysts and but few agricultural experts.

Another unfortunate result of the old arrangement of courses in our agricultural colleges was that the study of the general principles and outlines of the various natural sciences was often unwisely abridged in order to give more attention to their economic applications.

The general readjustments of science teaching which are demanded by the present development of our agricultural colleges are, therefore, first, the more thorough teaching of the foundations of the natural sciences; secondly, the clearer differentiation of the courses in natural science associated with the courses in agriculture from those which are intended for the training of experts in various economic specialties related to agriculture; and, thirdly, the separation from the science courses of those subjects which may be more appropriately taught by the instructors in the various branches of agriculture itself.

On the basis of the standard entrance requirements as previously stated, a general scheme for a 4-year college course in agriculture was presented in which were courses in general physics and chemistry on the assumption that these would naturally precede the study of plants and animals, whether in a general way under the head of botany, physiology, or zoology, or in a special way under the different branches of agriculture. Some knowledge of physics and chemistry is also essential to a proper understanding of even the elements of meteorology and geology, as provided for in this course. Botany has been so placed as to run along with agronomy, and physiology and zoology with the more scientific presentation of zootechny.

Most of the course was prescribed, but some electives were allowed in the senior year, to permit specialization in some branch of agriculture.

Agricultural experts can not, however, expect that any properly adjusted undergraduate course will fully meet their needs for training along their chosen lines. Persons who expect to enter positions in our Department of Agriculture, experiment stations, or agricultural colleges should attain at least the master's degree. And erelong the doctor's degree will be a prerequisite to entrance on the career of agricultural teacher or investigator in our colleges and universities and the National Department of Agriculture.

The outline of the course is as follows:

Agricultural course in college

Freshmen		Sophomores		Juniors		Seniors	
Subjects	Hours	Subjects	Hours	Subjects	Hours	Subjects	Hours
Physics	150	Agriculture:		Agriculture:		Agriculture:	
Chemistry	150	Zootechny 60		Agronomy 50		Dairying 70	
Geometry and trigonometry	155	Agronomy 90	150	Zootechny 100	150	Farm mechanics 60	190
English	120	Meteorology	60	Geology	120	Rural economics 60	
Modern language	180	Agricultural chemistry	180	Botany	60	Veterinary medicine	180
		Botany	120	Physiology	180	Horticulture and forestry	180
		English	80	Zoology	120	History and political economy	190
		Modern language	100	Psychology	60	Ethics	40
		Drawing	60	Modern language	60		
	755		750		750		780

The number of clock hours assigned to each subject includes the time given to laboratory exercises, each of which would occupy two hours.

The arrangement of the college course here suggested proceeds on the assumption that it is best for the student to devote his time largely during the first two years to language, mathematics, and the fundamental sciences, physics, chemistry, and botany. He will thus be prepared for a better understanding of the more complex sciences of agriculture, zoology, animal physiology, and veterinary medicine in the second half of his course.

The course in agriculture has been arranged with reference to taking up first in sophomore year some of the simpler topics in zootechny, such as stock judging and types of breeds, which do not require scientific knowledge, but are well calculated to arouse the interest of the student in agricultural subjects. Agronomy may then be taken up systematically and run along with the study of meteorology, agricultural chemistry and botany, and the more scientific study of zootechny may be parallel with the study of physiology and zoology (*441*).

A course in the natural sciences was outlined, based on the presumption that there would be instruction in elementary physics in

Fig. 17.—Class in farm crops studying grain sorghums, Kansas Agricultural College

the secondary school. The sciences included physics, chemistry, botany, physiology, zoology, geology, and meteorology.

At the same time a committee of the section of botany and horticulture of the association presented a plan for an introductory course in botany and showed how this might be fitted into the general course in agriculture by increasing the hours for botany and making modifications in the time for other subjects.

AGRONOMY

The department of agronomy, which in many cases included subjects within the field of agricultural engineering or farm management, was gradually restricted to production of farm crops and then was in some cases divided by the establishment of separate departments of soils and farm crops. (Fig. 17.)

The syllabus of a course in agronomy reported to the Agricultural College Association by its committee on instruction in agriculture in 1898 defined agronomy as including the "theory and practice of the production of farm crops. In agronomy we need to consider the several kinds of plants grown as farm crops under the following subjects: Structure (anatomy), composition, physiology and environment. Plant production in agriculture has for its object the adaptation of environment to the anatomy and physiology of the plants under cultivation, with a view to securing crops which are best suited to the uses of man or the domestic animals." The environment of the plant was said to consist of factors above ground (climate) and under ground (soil). Under climate the relation of light, heat, moisture, and air to plant growth were to be considered. Under soil the main subdivisions were functions, origin, properties (chemical and physical), temperature, air, moisture (sources and amounts from the water table, hydroscopic moisture, rainfall, and irrigation), drainage, tillage, fertilizers, waste, and renovation.

Farm crops were then to be considered in a general way with reference to their classification and methods of improvement by breeding and selection. Finally each farm crop selected for study was to be treated with reference to its structure, composition, physiology, botanical relations, varieties, geographical distribution, culture, harvesting, preservation, uses, preparation for use, obstructions to growth, preservation or use (weeds, fungi bacteria, insects, birds, quadrupeds, and the means for their repression), production, marketing, and history.

In 1903 the Office of Experiment Stations published an account of typical courses in agronomy at six land-grant institutions.

At the Alabama Polytechnic Institute agronomy was included in the general course in chemistry and agriculture. Agronomy was given during the second and third terms of the sophomore year and included lectures (with the use of books and other literature as reference material), two hours per week on soils and on the staple crops of Alabama, forage crops adapted to the South, and plants valuable for the renovation of soils. Two afternoons per week were devoted to farm practice. Three small barns and a gin room served partly as laboratories for students when engaged in indoor work. Plats on the experiment station farm and collections of varieties were used as object lessons. Instruction was given by means of lectures and laboratory practice.

At the Michigan Agricultural College instruction in agronomy was given by the professor of agronomy and one assistant during four years and was supplemented by instruction in botany, bacteriology, and chemistry. Until the end of the first term of junior year all four-year agricultural students pursued the same studies but were allowed to specialize during the rest of their course.

The courses in agronomy began with lectures on soils in freshman year, illustrated with samples, lantern slides, and field observations. In the first term of sophomore year there were lectures and laboratory work in agricultural physics, including mechanical analysis of soils, moisture determination of soils and plants, and subjects relating to rural engineering and farm mechanics. The second term of sophomore year was devoted to farm crops. In junior year there was one elective course on "agricultural experimentation" and in senior year on soil physics. Lectures were supplemented by practice in the laboratory and on the college farm. There were laboratories for agricultural physics and mechanical analysis of soils, and a soils laboratory containing considerable special apparatus, soil samples, etc. The college farm had over 250 acres devoted to grasses, roots, cereals, forage crops and pasture. There was a large collection of modern types of implements and machines.

At the Department of Agriculture of the University of Minnesota agronomy was taught in the secondary school of agriculture and in college courses. In the first two years of the college course the sciences related to agriculture were taught. The technical agricultural subjects were mainly elective in junior and senior years. The college course in agronomy included soil physics, field crops, and seed and plant breeding. Instruction in soil physics was given in the divisions of agricultural physics and agricultural chemistry, and the rest of the course was given mainly by the professor of agriculture.

There was a special laboratory for work on seeds and plant breeding. Lantern slides were extensively used, together with maps and designs of farm plans. Collections of dried weeds, grasses and forage plants, and seeds were made for the use of students. Much farm machinery was available on the college farm and the vicinity. About 150 acres were devoted to college and station work. The plant-breeding experiments were extensive and involved the use of special machinery. Students assisted in these experiments. Farms in the vicinity served as a basis for designing farm plans and working out problems in farm management. Instruction was almost entirely by lectures. Students were required to write theses.

At the Industrial College of the University of Nebraska in freshman year all courses were required, but after that the courses were mostly elective. Agronomy courses included "soils, field crops, farm management and the care and use of farm machinery." There were general courses on soils and field crops, followed by a laboratory course on the properties of soils and elective courses on methods of investigation with soils and with crops, plant food in the soil (with a series of pot experiments), production and movement of crops as affecting prices, and sugar-beet culture. Instruction was carried on by lectures and laboratory practice, and through the use of reference books and experiment station literature. There were special laboratories for field crops, soils, and seeds. About 50 acres of land were used for purposes of instruction, in addition to the extensive experimental fields.

At the College of Agriculture and Domestic Science of Ohio State University the course in agronomy was preceded in the freshman and sophomore years by instruction in agricultural chemistry, physiology, economic botany, plant pathology, and horticulture. The courses in agronomy were given by the professor of agriculture and the instructor in agronomy and included two elementary courses in junior year and two advanced elective courses in senior year. There was first an elementary course in soils. This included lectures and recitations on the origin, formation, kinds, and physical properties of soils and their improvement by cultivation, fertilization, drainage, and irrigation. There were laboratory practicums once a week on physical properties of soils and mechanical analyses. The elementary course in farm crops dealt in a similar way with the history, production, cultivation, harvesting, and marketing of farm crops, and there were practicums with growing and dried specimens of grasses, clovers, and other forage crops. The advanced course in soils consisted of lectures and recitations once a week on the physical properties of soils; the relation of soils to heat, air, and moisture; the effect of fertilizers on soil structure and fertility; and consideration of practical methods of tillage, as affecting the crop-producing power of the soil. There were laboratory and field experiments during two periods each week. The advanced course in farm crops dealt similarly with the effect of climate, soil, and markets on the distribution and adaptation of farm crops in the United States, the best methods of crop production, and the consumption of farm crops, with practicums twice a week. The soil-physics laboratory was equipped with special apparatus, much of which had been devised at the college. There was also a large glasshouse with tracks, trucks, and pots for tests with soils and fertilizers. Mechanical analyses of typical soils were made. In the study of crops use was made of dried specimens and a grass garden. Observations and studies were also made on the college farm.

At the College of Agriculture of the University of Illinois, of 130 credits required for graduation 15 were required to be in agronomy. and there were also elective courses in that subject. In the department of agronomy 15 courses were offered (not including those in farm mechanics) in drainage and irrigation, farm crops—quality and improvement, farm crops—germination and growth, special crops, field experiments, soil physics and management, special problems in soil physics, soil bacteriology, fertilizers, rotations and fertility, investigation of the fertility of special soils, history of agriculture, comparative agriculture, German agricultural readings, special work in drainage and machinery, investigation and thesis.

The department of agronomy had four principal divisions—soil fertility, soil physics, soil bacteriology, and farm crops. Instruction was by the laboratory method as well as by textbooks, lectures, and reference readings. Two well-equipped laboratories were provided for work in soil fertility, an analytical laboratory and a pot-culture laboratory in a greenhouse. There were also two laboratories for soil bacteriology and two for work on farm crops. Several acres of land were devoted to plat experiments by the students. In the department of agronomy there were six regular instructors, besides several student assistants.

The number of teachers and investigators in the field of agronomy grew rapidly during the early years of the twentieth century. According to Carleton, in 1900 there were 3 agronomists at the land-grant colleges, in 1905 there were 50, and in 1908 there were 99. That year about as many more were employed in the United States Department of Agriculture. These technical workers, in a field which by that time was fairly well defined, formed the American Society of Agronomy on December 31, 1907. The two great divisions of the subject were represented in the choice of the principal officers. M. A. Carleton, of the Bureau of Plant Industry, who dealt with farm crops, was elected president, and Thomas L. Lyon, who in

1906 had been made professor of soil technology at Cornell University, was elected secretary. Through its proceedings, which were published in four volumes (1909–1912), and its journal, issued continuously since that time, this society has contributed much toward the systematization of agronomy and the classification and development of its various divisions. At its meetings there have been a considerable number of papers and discussions on courses of study and the progress of the science as shown in the technical papers has suggested many items which have been incorporated in the later courses of study in this field.

During this period the study of soils was profoundly affected by the physical researches of such investigators as King and Whitney and by the development of soil bacteriology. This led to the classification of soils on a much broader basis than had been attempted by the geologists and chemists. The elaboration of soil surveys and the beginning of conducting them on a nation-wide plan stimulated interest in soil work on the part of both teachers and students. The revival of the Mendelian theory gave greatly increased interest to the study of plant breeding. Studies of methods of conducting plat experiments (such as ear-row plantings and the centgener method), devices for seed testing, the development of a system of seed inspection, the treating of seeds and plants to prevent diseases, the devising of methods and score cards for the judging of grain are examples of the things by which the programs of courses on farm crops were improved and enriched.

HORTICULTURE AND BOTANY

In the early days of the agricultural colleges the work in botany was often organically associated with that in horticulture. The first of the colleges to develop horticulture as a separate subject were those in Michigan (1867), New York (1874), Ohio (1876), and Iowa (1876). As research and instruction in plant physiology and pathology developed, the relations between courses in botany and horticulture became in some respects more intimate; even though work in these lines was given in separate departments. This intimacy was recognized in the Association of Agricultural Colleges when in 1892 a section on horticulture and botany was established. For several years this section dealt principally with subject matter relating to plant pathology. However, in 1895 the section was represented in the general session of the association by a paper on the teaching of horticulture. From this and the discussion which followed it appeared that only in a few colleges was there much laboratory or practical work connected with the courses in horticulture. Interest in practice work in laboratories, greenhouses, and fields was promoted by this section during the next few years by papers describing what was done in some States. In the general course in agriculture proposed by the committee on instruction in agriculture in 1897 horticulture and forestry were allotted 180 hours. In 1902 the report of the section on horticulture and botany showed that in most of the colleges horticultural instruction began with the sophomore year and that there was a decided movement to emphasize laboratory and field work and "to replace the lecture with the practicums."

A committee of this section reported in 1905 in favor of dividing the 180 hours assigned to horticulture in the general agricultural course proposed by the committee on instruction in agriculture as follows: Propagation 20, pomology 50, olericulture 50, floriculture 30, landscape horticulture 30. They also advised that the study of horticulture should begin before the senior year in order to give opportunity to take advantage of elective courses in that subject, most of which were given in the last two years.

A schedule for a horticultural course, parallel with that in general agriculture, was also given. This provided 270 hours of botany, equally divided between the first three years, 175 hours of electives in senior year, and horticulture as follows: Sophomores, propagation, 60 hours; juniors, pomology, 120; olericulture, 120; seniors, pomology, 80; floriculture, 75; landscape gardening, 60; forestry, 40. A table was presented, showing the number of required and elective hours in horticulture in nine colleges. The required hours varied from none at the New York college to 266 in Massachusetts. The aggregate number of hours of electives in the different colleges were as follows: New York, 360; Illinois, 900; California, 180; Michigan, 430; Pennsylvania, 342; Missouri, 162; Massachusetts, 638; Ohio, 450; New Hampshire, 270.

The statistics of the land-grant colleges show that in 1903 there were in the separate horticultural courses of four years 539 students, and in short courses 367. For some reason the number of students specializing in horticulture declined for several years, and in 1909 there were 158 in the 4-year courses and 233 in short courses. Then the number began to rise again, and in 1911 there were 243 in the 4-year courses and 565 in short courses.

As specialization proceeded in the agricultural colleges separate departments of horticulture were provided, and during the period now under consideration professorships were created for different branches of horticulture. Pomology most commonly received this recognition. The Massachusetts Agricultural College established a division of horticulture with separate departments of pomology, floriculture, and landscape gardening.

Relatively little attention was given to instruction in vegetable growing prior to 1908, though Bailey's Principles of Vegetable Gardening, the first textbook on this subject for college students, appeared in 1901. In 1908 "there were not more than four or five vegetable specialists in the colleges." From that time interest in this subject increased. "In 1912 five institutions offered for 4-year students as many as three to five courses in vegetable gardening, 9 offered two courses, and 21 offered single courses."

When investigations in plant pathology led to the invention of practical methods of control of plant diseases through spraying, seed treatment, etc., much attention was often given to these matters in connection with courses in horticulture, though the broader and more technical phases of this subject were usually treated in the department of botany or one of its subdivisions.

In 1887 Joseph C. Arthur began service at Purdue University as professor of vegetable physiology and pathology.

FORESTRY

As late as 1897 the only instruction in forestry in American colleges consisted of lectures on dendrology and forest geography in connection with courses in botany and similar work, together with some practical matters connected with the growing of ornamental trees and farm wood lots, in horticultural courses.

The first professional school of forestry was established at Cornell University in 1898, and about the same time the private school at Biltmore, N. C., was organized. The following year the Pinchot family endowed the Forest School in connection with the Sheffield Scientific School at Yale University. Meanwhile the National Government had entered on the policy of making reservations of large areas of public land for forests and parks, and these reserves were administered by the Department of the Interior.

The United States Department of Agriculture, through its forestry division under B. E. Fernow and later Gifford Pinchot, was broadly stimulating interest in the study of forest problems. By 1900 there were State offices for forest work in 13 States. The American Forestry Association, with the Secretary of Agriculture, James Wilson, as president, was in active operation. That year some instruction in forestry was reported from land-grant and other colleges in 39 States.

At the meeting of the Agricultural College Association in 1905 a resolution was passed urging "that the national forestry policy of this country should include provision for education and experimentation in forestry by the agricultural colleges and experiment stations of the different States and Territories " (499).

In 1905 the management of the national-forest reserves was transferred from the Department of the Interior to the Department of Agriculture, and the Bureau of Forestry became the Forest Service.

Under the broad conservation policy of President Roosevelt the area of the national forests was greatly increased. Considerable areas of private forests were also put under management recommended by the Forest Service. While in 1898 the division of forestry employed only 11 persons, of whom 2 were professional foresters, in 1905 the employees of the Forest Service numbered 821, of whom 153 were professional foresters, and in 1909 there were 2,012 employees. There were also many persons employed in forestry work in other ways.

One result of this expansion of forestry work was much greater interest in forestry instruction in educational institutions. Students flocked into the forestry classes in order to prepare themselves for civil-service examinations or other opportunities for work in this line. Whereas in 1907 the reports of the land-grant colleges showed 114 students in 4-year courses in forestry and 79 in short courses, in 1911 there were 449 in the long courses and 411 in the short courses.

The civil-service examinations for the Forest Service helped to set standards for the courses in forestry in the colleges. Further effort in this direction was made at a conference held in Washington in 1909, in which 15 universities and colleges participated. A committee, of which Henry S. Graves was chairman, formulated a plan for the standardization of education in forestry and made a report at a second conference in 1911. It soon appeared that thorough professional training in forestry was expensive for the colleges and required more than undergraduate work, and that the number of positions open to the students in the advanced courses was quite limited. It therefore seemed best to most of the colleges to confine their forestry work to such courses as would prepare men for positions as rangers and other subordinate work in forest services, or fit farmers to properly manage their wood lots.

In an article on forest education, by Henry S. Graves and R. Zon, of the Forest Service, published in 1911, the schools teaching forestry were listed in four groups: (1) Graduate schools, including the Yale Forest School, course of forestry at the University of Michigan, and the division of forestry in the School of Applied Science at Harvard University; (2) undergraduate schools at the universities of Minnesota, Montana, and Washington; Colorado College, Biltmore, N. C., Pennsylvania State Forest Academy, and land-grant colleges in 11 States; (3) ranger schools, including a number of short courses in undergraduate schools; (4) courses in forestry in 21 land-grant colleges and three others; and (5) six secondary schools. In 1910, 144 normal schools were also reported as giving some instruction in forestry.

ANIMAL HUSBANDRY

In 1899 the committee on agricultural instruction presented to the Association of Agricultural Colleges a syllabus of a course of zootechny framed with reference to its incorporation in the 4-year college course in agriculture. The term zootechny had been adopted from foreign usage, particularly in Germany, as indicating more definitely the scientific character of this course but this term did not acquire general usage in the colleges in this country, the more easily understood expression " animal husbandry " being commonly used. The committee defined zootechny as the theory and practice of the production of animals useful to man (exclusive of the diseases of animals usually taught in a separate department under the head of veterinary science). The animal was to be studied in a general way under anatomy, physiology, and management, which included animal types, breeding, feeding, hygiene, and systems of management. " Animal production in agriculture has for its object the securing and growing of animals which, in themselves or in their products, are best suited to the uses of man." (*499*). The topics included were mammals, birds, fishes, beneficial insects, frogs, oysters, snails, etc. Then followed the principles governing the choice and breeding of animals, types and breeds of different kinds of animals, principles of feeding, practice in feeding different kinds of animals, principles of hygiene and management, and practice in the management of different kinds of animals. The committee, however, stated that there were " some important considerations which may be urged in favor of teaching the principles of the different branches of zootechny together before taking up the application of any of them to different kinds of animals." By this time animal husbandry had an important place in the general agricultural course, and through the elective system students had opportunities for specializing in breeding, feeding, or management, or on particular kinds of animals.

In animal husbandry much interest was developed in the study of types and breeds of different kinds of animals. Some of the colleges acquired considerable numbers of animals of different kinds and breeds. Purebred stock was brought into the college herds, and the animals often had excellent records. Great importance was attached to the judging of animals, and students were given much practice in this work, which was also promoted on a wide scale by competitive tests. More attention was also given to studies of the principles of breeding, and these studies were stimulated by the experiments in breeding conducted at many of the experiment stations. Instruction in feeding was put on a strictly scientific basis, and much attention was paid to the compounding and use of rations for different purposes. The preparation, storage, and use of silage and the kinds of crops best adapted to this purpose were carefully considered. Many colleges undertook the preparation of animals for exhibition at fairs, and their success in competition with practical livestock men, notably at the International Livestock Show at Chicago, undoubtedly increased the prestige of the colleges among farmers and greatly stimulated the interest of students in animal husbandry. Some of the colleges employed special instructors for different kinds of animals. This was particularly true with reference to dairy cattle. In some institutions dairy husbandry was united with dairy manufacture in a single department. In most colleges there was some instruction regarding poultry, and in some cases a separate poultry department was established. Both meat and egg production were studied, as well as breeding for these purposes, and training and practice were given in caponizing, treatment of diseases, use of incubators and brooders, construction of poultry houses, etc.

AGROTECHNY

While no college organized a department of agrotechny there was more or less instruction in scientific or agricultural departments of the land-grant colleges on subjects within that field and particularly with reference to those matters which were locally important. These included such things as sugar making, vegetable and animal oils, vinegar, concentrated foods and feeds, canned goods, textiles, leather, fertilizers, etc.

DAIRYING

In many States dairying was so important that a separate department was established for that subject, and in some cases this was subdivided and a number of specialists were employed as instructors. Interest in dairying was greatly stimulated by the invention of the Babcock milk tester (fig. 18) in 1890 and the growing movement for the establishment of creameries and cheese factories, the increase of scientific knowledge, particularly in bacteriology, regarding the requirements for the sanitary handling of milk and other dairy products, and the consequent control measures under public laws and regulations. Thus there was offered a broad opportunity for the agricultural colleges to do useful public service by giving instruction in farm dairying and also by training managers and operators of the milk business and the manufacture of butter, cheese, and ice cream, as well as public officials for the inspection services relating to dairy products.

A general course in dairying as a part of the 4-year agricultural course was formulated by the committee on instruction in agriculture in 1900. This included the raw material (milk), its source,

FIG. 18.—Original Babcock milk tester

standards, handling and uses; milk and cream for consumption (preparation for sale, and delivery and sale); butter and cheese making (processes and equipment); butter and cheese properties, standards, handling, marketing, and uses.

Special courses in the science and practice of dairying had already been established at a few colleges, and these were increased in number and variety in after years. In some cases the dairy department was run largely on a commercial basis for the production, purchase, and delivery of milk and the manufacture and sale of other dairy products. The practical study of economic problems relating to an agricultural industry may be said to have begun in some of the dairy departments of these colleges.

The equipment of the dairy departments often included much scientific apparatus for chemical, physical, and bacteriological studies and outfits of machinery and other appliances on a scale approximating those of commercial concerns. In some institutions special buildings were erected for the dairy departments.

For rural engineering as part of a general course in agriculture the committee on instruction in agriculture outlined a tentative syllabus in 1900. This subject was then defined as "the science and art of laying out farms, designing and constructing farm buildings and works [including water, irrigation, drainage, and sewage systems, and roads], and the construction and use of farm machinery." The committee also urged the "need of the establishment of thorough courses in rural engineering in some of our higher institutions, in order that well-trained rural engineers may be produced to act as leaders in the advancement of engineering enterprises for the benefit of agriculture."

In 1901 the committee again called the attention of the Association of American Agricultural Colleges and Experiment Stations to this subject, pointing out that up to this time "there has been comparatively little development of courses in rural engineering in our colleges and universities" though there were beginnings of such courses at a few institutions. "For example, a department of irrigation has recently been established at the University of California and arrangements have been made for special courses in irrigation at the Colorado Agricultural College." Irrigation was a live subject at this time because of its growing development in the West. The activities of the Office of Experiment Stations through its irrigation investigations, begun in 1898 and extended to both arid and humid regions in cooperation with the agricultural colleges, were stimulating interest in this matter in these institutions. In 1902 the association appointed a standing committee on rural engineering. Their report in 1903 showed the opportunities for education and research in the different branches of agricultural engineering and recommended "the creation of separate departments of rural engineering in the colleges." That year the report of the Office of Experiment Stations describes courses in various branches of rural engineering at the colleges in Illinois, Minnesota, North Dakota, and New York. In Wisconsin, where instruction in this subject had been given for several years in the department of agricultural physics, the State legislature had made an appropriation of $15,000 for a farm engineering building, and an assistant professor of agricultural engineering had been appointed. At the Iowa college a department of farm mechanics had recently been established and a substantial building erected for its use.

In 1904, 125 students were enrolled in this department of the Iowa college, and Indiana, Kansas, Nebraska, and Wyoming were added to the list of States in which instruction in this subject was given.

Special buildings for this work had been erected in Minnesota and Nebraska. In 1905 the committee on rural engineering called attention to the need of more adequate attention to this subject in the colleges in general and advised that a few institutions should establish independent departments of rural engineering to be manned by persons with engineering training, who should be given full professorial rank. The American Society of Agricultural Engineers was organized in December, 1907, at the University of Wisconsin.

In 1906 a subcommittee of the committee on instruction in agriculture reported that at least 32 colleges were offering " some instruction which may be classified under the head of ' Rural Engineering,' " but in general it was not well organized.

This committee in 1909 called attention to the necessity of distinguishing between a short course in agricultural engineering as a part of the general course in agriculture and a long professional course for the training of engineers qualified to pursue some branch of rural engineering. In 1910 Iowa State College offered a 4-year course leading to the degree of bachelor of science in agricultural engineering. For the most part the agricultural colleges have been content to give limited courses in this subject. Only a few colleges have erected special buildings for this work or offered degree courses in rural engineering.

RURAL ECONOMICS

Rural economics was recognized as a division of the science of agriculture in the first report of the committee on instruction in agriculture in 1896 and in 1897 was given 60 of a total of 486 hours allotted to agriculture in the general course of study. A brief syllabus was presented in 1900.

The early treatment of this subject by this committee was evidently crude and tentative. However, these reports stimulated interest in this subject and helped the movement for greater recognition of the economic problems of agriculture in the agricultural colleges. There had been some teaching of subjects in the field of rural economics in these colleges from the beginning but for the most part this was incidental and not well organized. In 1901 the committee again called attention to this subject.

It is hoped that some of our stronger agricultural institutions will soon take a more active interest in the establishment of courses in rural engineering and rural economics. These subjects embrace matters of great importance to our agriculture, and their serious consideration in our higher institutions for agricultural education may do much to promote the best development of our agriculture. We need to broaden our agricultural courses along these two general lines. (499).

By 1903 the beginnings of distinct courses on the economic problems of agriculture were in operation in colleges in Wisconsin, Massachusetts, and some other States. At the Ohio State University a course on the history of agriculture and rural economics was offered, and H. C. Price, who succeeded T. F. Hunt as dean of the College of Agriculture, was also designated professor of rural economy. In the Department of Agriculture of the University of Minnesota a course in " agricultural economics " was offered. In the reorganized curriculum of the New York State College of Agriculture at Cornell University rural economy was given as one of the main branches of agriculture, and courses were offered in farm accounting and the economics and history of agriculture.

At the Rhode Island College of Agriculture and Mechanic Arts courses in farm management and rural economics were given, and President Butterfield prepared for the report of the Office of Experiment Stations in 1903 an outline of a short course in agricultural economics suitable for incorporation in the general college course in agriculture. That report also contained an article describing the courses in rural economics in European agricultural schools. At that time H. C. Taylor, as instructor in commerce at the University of Wisconsin, was giving a course in agricultural economics. Meanwhile the Office of Experiment Stations was studying legal and economic problems in connection with its irrigation investigations, and in 1905 Doctor Taylor was employed in this work. This afforded an opportunity to begin a department of rural economics in the Experiment Station Record, with Doctor Taylor as editor. The same year his book entitled "Introduction to the Study of Agricultural Economics" was published.

At the meeting of the American Association for the Advancement of Science, at St. Louis, Mo., in December, 1903, a session of the section on social and economic science was devoted to a discussion of the economic aspects of agriculture.

Interest in the economic problems of agriculture was greatly increased by the address of President Roosevelt at the semicentennial of the Michigan Agricultural College in 1907 (*499*), his great conference on the conservation of our natural resources at the White House in May, 1908, and the work and report of the Country Life Commission appointed by him in August of that year (*409*).

The purpose of the commission, as stated in the President's message to Congress transmitting the report of the commission, was "not to help the farmer raise better crops, but to call his attention to opportunities for better business and better living on the farm."

In commenting on the work of this commission, an editorial in the Experiment Station Record (vol. 20, p. 601) stated that it—

broadly emphasizes the need, hitherto chiefly felt within a comparatively narrow circle, of broadening the scope of our agricultural colleges and the State and national departments of agriculture. So far these institutions have directed their energies mainly toward stimulating agricultural production.

The time has now come for exact and comprehensive studies of the economic and social conditions of agricultural communities.

The awakening of interest in the economic and social problems of agricultural comunities which is bound to follow the inquiries of the Commission on Country Life will have only a transient effect unless it is succeeded by the establishment of permanent institutions for the study of such problems and the preparation of experts in these lines. When we consider the vast extent of our country and the varied character and environment of our agricultural people it can hardly be expected that any satisfactory solution of the complex economic and social problems of different regions can be reached until after many years spent in the most careful study of local conditions by thoroughly trained experts. At present we have neither the facts nor the experts.

To secure the experts it will be necessary to broaden the work of our agricultural colleges and build up in them strong departments of agricultural economics and sociology. A beginning has been made in this direction, but present provision for such studies is wholly inadequate. It seems likely that the same process of evolution must go on in these departments as has occurred in the departments for agricultural production. First, a few men will roughly block out the problems and attempt instruction on them. Then the need of research will be apparent, and fragmentary efforts will be made in this line. But the departments of instruction in agricultural economics and sociology will never be in satisfactory condition until agencies for systematic research in these lines are established and have done considerable work.

Herein lies a great opportunity for the National and State Departments of Agriculture and the agricultural colleges. It is the joint work of all these agencies which alone will secure the best results.

The work in rural economics in the agricultural colleges grew slowly. The new knowledge necessary as a basis for strong courses in this subject was accumulated in only small measure prior to the World War, and only a few men devoted themselves to investigations in this field.

A group of men whose training and experience had been chiefly in the field of agronomy undertook studies in farm management and following some foreign precedents were inclined to regard this subject as a distinct branch of knowledge outside of rural economics. Discussion of this and other matters relating to the courses in rural economics arose in the colleges. The committee on instruction in agriculture undertook an investigation of this subject in 1910. That year the American Farm Management Association had been formed and had—

adopted in a tentative way an analysis of the rural problem as outlined by President Butterfield, viz: (1) The technical aspect—farm practice or agriculture; (2) the business aspect—farm administration or farm management; (3) the scientific aspect—agricultural science; (4) the industrial aspect—agricultural economy; (5) the community aspect—rural sociology (*499*).

This was taken as a basis for work of the committee. The views of a number of the leading officers of the agricultural colleges especially interested in rural economics and farm management were obtained and published. Foreign works on these subjects were also examined.

The committee's conclusions as stated in its report in 1911 (*499*) were that the term rural economics should be used to include "the general field of economics in its relation to agriculture and rural communities," while farm management may properly be restricted to that phase of rural economics which deals with the business organization and direction of individual farm enterprises. Rural sociology was differentiated from rural economics. Rural law and legislation, history of agriculture and comparative agriculture were considered more or less distinct subjects.

While the terminology of this subject has since varied considerably the general arrangement of courses in rural economics has proceeded on the basis suggested in the report of this committee.

In 1913 the bibliographer of the agricultural college association reported that courses of study in rural economics (often combined with some instruction in rural sociology) had been organized in practically all the agricultural colleges and that outside the colleges interest in these subjects was very widespread. The literature of these subjects available to teachers and students of these subjects had greatly increased.

RURAL SOCIOLOGY

As the work of the agricultural colleges progressed and they came into closer touch with the farming people, particularly through

various forms of extension work, it became apparent that these institutions should deal with the social problems of the rural communities. Many of these problems were interrelated with economic
problems. Therefore the courses in rural economics often dealt to
a certain extent with social matters. Meanwhile the study of social
problems in general was bringing about a more or less specialized
body of knowledge which was being formulated and sometimes
taught in educational institutions under the title of sociology. It
naturally occurred to some students of this new science that one of
its divisions should be rural sociology. This was particularly impressed on President Butterfield, who was teaching rural economics
at the Rhode Island College of Agriculture and Mechanic Arts.
When he was asked in 1903 to prepare an article for the Office of
Experiment Stations on "Agricultural Economics as a Subject of
Study in the Agricultural College," he included

a plea for a broader view of the question and for urging agricultural educators to consider as a unit the whole subject of what, for want of a better
term, we may call rural social science, and therefore to permit just as much
attention to the study of rural sociology as to the study of agricultural economics. We need more well-equipped leaders on the farm, and these leaders
will find that the questions confronting them are in no small degree sociological. Farmers' organizations, better communication in rural districts, the
country school, the country church, all the broad phases of agricultural education, are pressing problems in each farm community. They need the leadership of trained minds. Viewed in all broader aspects, these sociological questions are of the greatest importance (416).

He suggested that if it was not feasible to give a separate course
in rural sociology, at least a chapter on this subject might be added
to the course in rural economics. For this he suggested the consideration of such subjects as " movements of the farm population; improvements in communication in rural districts—trolleys, telephones,
mail delivery, roads; the country church; the rural school; agricultural education; farmers' organizations and societies; and cooperation of the factors."

Following this up in 1904 at the meeting of the agricultural college association he presented a paper on " The Social Phase of Agricultural Education," in which he urged that " the college shall con-
sciously purpose to stand as sponsor for the whole rural problem."
This involved the development of extension work, as well as research and resident teaching, in order to give the college leadership in solving the rural problem. " The social sciences in their
relation to the rural problem particularly must receive a consideration commensurate with the importance of the industrial, the political, and the social phases of the farm question." Herein was a
new field for research and, as regards teaching, " in every agricultural course the social problems of the farmers should have due
attention."

In the report of the Office of Experiment Stations for 1904 President Butterfield presented an outline of a course in rural sociology.
This was divided into two parts, (1) the rural social status, including
movements and social condition of farm population, the social psychology of rural life, and the social aspects of current agricultural
questions, e. g., tenant farming, farm labor and machinery, immigration; and (2) social factors in rural progress, including means

of communication in rural districts, farmers' organizations, rural education, the rural church, and the social ideal for agriculture.

L. H. Bailey was also greatly interested in the social problems of the farmers. In a paper read before the agricultural college association in 1905 he argued that agricultural education should not be severely technical but rather " education for country life."

It stands also for all the social and economic relations of the farm to its community. It stands for the discussion of the rural church, the rural school, rural literature, sanitation, good houses, good roads, organization, and all the laws that govern trade in farm products.

The importance of the development of courses in rural economics and sociology was also emphasized, as previously stated, in the report of the Country Life Commission in 1908.

Courses in rural sociology were offered in a number of the agricultural colleges. At the Massachusetts Agricultural College a professorship of rural sociology was created in 1906, and in 1911 a division of rural social science was established, which included both economics and sociology.

AGRICULTURAL CHEMISTRY

As defined by H. E. Woodward, of the United States Bureau of Chemistry, in the Americana—

agricultural chemistry deals with the chemical composition of plants and animals and with the chemical changes involved in the life processes. It includes the chemistry of the air, water, soil, manures, fertilizers, insecticides, fungicides, plants, animals, and metabolism or the chemical changes taking place in living things as well as the chemistry of milk and other dairy products.

The relations of chemistry to agriculture attracted the attention of scientists almost as soon as that science took a definite form. Reference has already been made to the work of early investigators and writers on subjects within the field of agricultural chemistry. Before the agricultural colleges were established in this country a considerable literature on these subjects had grown up.

In the early days of agricultural education the province of agricultural chemistry was not clearly defined. This was pointed out by S. W. Johnson (1830–1909), of Connecticut, in an article on agricultural science in the Country Gentlemen of 1856.

Hitherto teachers and authors have usually classed together under the designation agricultural chemistry the whole subject of agriculture as connected with science, both theory and practice * * * But agricultural chemistry is only a part, although indeed the larger part of this subject. Vegetable and animal physiology figure quite extensively in it i. e., in agricultural science.

Thus at Yale College Professor Norton, a chemist, was first appointed in 1846 as professor of agriculture, but his title was soon changed to professor of agricultural chemistry. However, in 1850 his book was named Elements of Scientific Agriculture. Professor Johnson had a somewhat similar experience. He was primarily a chemist but taught agricultural science somewhat broadly and entitled his books, which were essentially treatises on agricultural chemistry, " How Crops Grow " (1868) and " How Crops Feed " (1870). In the same way F. H. Storer, of the Bussey Institution, published "Agriculture in Some of its Relations with Chemistry " in 1887. This book had a broad influence on the teaching of agriculture in the colleges for many years. It was enlarged as the science of agriculture developed and reached a seventh edition in three volumes in 1897.

Agricultural chemistry as a distinct branch of chemistry was only beginning to be recognized in this country when S. W. Johnson, who had studied at the universities of Leipzig and Munich, partly under Liebig, undertook his experimental work in the laboratory of the Yale Scientific School in 1855. In a course of lectures on agricultural chemistry at the Smithsonian Institution in 1859 he treated these subjects: (1) The composition and structure of the plant, (2) the atmosphere and water in their relation to vegetable life, (3) the soil as related to agricultural production, and (4) improvement of the soil by tillage, drainage, amendments, and fertilizers. He said that there ought to be a chapter on manures but this was "as yet unwritten." In later years going extensively into problems connected with the composition, valuation, and use of fertilizers he laid the foundation for the agricultural experiment stations, which at the outset were very largely concerned with problems in agricultural chemistry, particularly the analysis of fertilizers, soils and plants. He also taught agricultural chemistry and in 1875 became professor of theoretical and agricultural chemistry in the Yale school. For many years he was active in teaching and investigating in the field of agricultural chemistry and promoted the establishment of the Connecticut Agricultural Experiment Station, of which he was made director in 1877. He had a broad influence in the movement for agricultural education and research in this country. While the Yale school did not attract large numbers of students because the work done there was too severely technical and advanced for the time, yet a considerable number of men who afterwards became leaders in agricultural education and research were trained there. Among these were Peter Collier, W. O. Atwater, H. P. Armsby, and E. H. Jenkins.

At the Michigan Agricultural College, L. R. Fisk, as professor of chemistry, began work in 1858, and the following year a department of agricultural chemistry was established. Professor Fisk was made head of that department in 1861, but when Robert Clark Kedzie (1823-1902) was appointed in 1863 his title was professor of chemistry.

Doctor Kedzie was a graduate of Oberlin College and of the medical department of the University of Michigan. He carried a heavy burden of instruction in both general and agricultural chemistry for many years, but found time for important investigations relating to wheat, sugar beets, etc., and to act for several years as president of the State board of health. Many men afterwards prominent in agricultural education were among his students.

When Cornell University was established a professorship of agricultural chemistry was created and was filled in 1868 by George Chapman Caldwell (1834-1907), a graduate of the Lawrence Scientific School of Harvard University, who had also studied at the agricultural college at Cirencester, England, and at the universities of Göttingen and Heidelberg and had taught chemistry at Columbia College in New York, Antioch College in Ohio, and the Pennsylvania State College. During his long service at Cornell he did much to develop both the science and the teaching of agricultural chemistry.

At the Massachusetts Agricultural College Charles Anthony Goessmann (1837–1910) was elected professor of chemistry in 1868. He was a native of Naumburg, Germany, and received the degree of doctor of philosophy at the University of Göttingen. He also lectured on organic chemistry in the university for five years and made important investigations in this field. In the Massachusetts college "for 15 years he gave unaided all the instruction in chemistry and chemical physics, both in the classroom and the laboratory," and after the establishment of an assistant professorship, continued "to lecture to the senior class on the chemistry of fertilizers, the commercial industries, and on organic chemistry." In 1882 he became director and chemist of the Massachusetts Agricultural Experiment Station. In this position he did much to promote the elaboration and organization of agricultural chemistry, while his work as a teacher had an important influence on the development of instruction in this subject in our agricultural colleges.

In California Eugene Woldemar Hilgard (1833–1916) became professor of agricultural chemistry and director of the agricultural experiment station at the University of California in 1875. He was a native of Zweibrücken in Rhenish Bavaria and had studied in universities at Zurich, Freiberg, and Heidelberg, receiving the degree of doctor of philosophy at the latter place in 1853. In California besides teaching agricultural chemistry he made extensive investigations on the chemistry and physics of soils, with special reference to arid conditions and the reclamation of alkali lands. He also conducted an investigation of the soils of the cotton-growing States in connection with work on the Tenth Census and made broad studies of the agricultural practices and possibilities of the regions of the Pacific slope. For many years he was active in promoting agricultural education and research and had much influence on the national movement in these fields.

The United States Department of Agriculture began chemical investigations in 1862 and for a long time gave special attention to sugar-producing plants. The investigations of Peter Collier on sorghum and those of Harvey W. Wiley on sugar beets were especially important. Wiley's manual on the "Principles and Practice of Agricultural Analysis" of soils, fertilizers, insecticides, and agricultural products is an extensive work in three volumes, the first of which was issued in 1894.

Through the work of the above-mentioned investigators, and others in this country and abroad, a large body of knowledge in the field of agricultural chemistry was accumulated prior to the establishment of the agricultural experiment stations. When a number of States had established agencies for the control of fertilizers and other agricultural materials the Association of Official Agricultural Chemists was formed in 1884 and gave special attention to analytical problems.

After the passage of the Hatch Act the number of chemical workers at the agricultural colleges rapidly increased. This was also the case in the United States Department of Agriculture and in the State regulatory offices. The agricultural colleges were therefore led to specialize their teaching work in chemistry, by creating departments of agricultural chemistry and by offering a considerable number of special courses for the training of analysts and investigators in different branches of this subject, as well as by broadening the chemical instruction given in connection with the general agricultural courses. While much instruction was given through lectures, a considerable number of special textbooks and manuals were published and used, and a great variety of apparatus for special purposes was developed.

Special buildings for the departments of agricultural chemistry were erected at some colleges, and at others well-equipped laboratories of different kinds were constructed. Structures for pot experiments and other purposes were sometimes built. The amount and variety of required or optional laboratory work for students, especially in advanced courses, constantly increased. Graduate courses were offered at many colleges.

In a paper on the teaching of chemistry in American agricultural colleges, by W. A. Withers, of the North Carolina college, in 1910, it was stated that for students in the general agricultural course instruction in chemistry began in the freshman year in 32 colleges and in the sopohomore year in 16 colleges, and included training in qualitative analysis in 40 States and in quantitative analysis in 16 States. Agricultural chemistry was taught to agricultural students in connection with general chemistry or in specialized courses in quantitative analysis and plant and animal nutrition. The required course in chemistry for such students usually covered one year, but in six colleges it continued during a second year. There were, however, many elective courses for advanced students which were chosen under a group system.

Originally the professor of chemistry or agricultural chemistry in the agricultural colleges gave most or all of the scientific instruction related to agriculture, but when agriculture itself as a science had been systematized and subdivided and men had been trained to teach its several branches, much chemical instruction was included in the courses given by teachers of agronomy, soils, animal husbandry, dairying, etc. Professor Withers stated that in 1910 probably for this reason in 17 States agricultural chemistry, as such, was either not taught to agricultural students or not required of them. To a considerable extent since that time teachers of agricultural chemistry have restricted their work to the preparation of analysts or other specialists.

Meanwhile chemists have been employed as teachers and investigators in the departments of agronomy, soils, dairying, animal husbandry, etc., in a number of the agricultural colleges.

ENTOMOLOGY

The foundations for instruction on insects related to agriculture were laid before the establishment of the agricultural colleges. In 1831 Thaddeus William Harris prepared a catalogue of insects for Hitchcock's Report on the Geology of Massachusetts and in 1841 made a report on insects injurious to vegetation. In 1854 Ebenezer Emmons, State geologist of New York, with the aid of Asa Fitch, published a volume on insects injurious to vegetation in the "Natural History of New York." That year Doctor Fitch was appointed entomologist for the New York State Agricultural Society under a State appropriation of $1,000 and continued to make reports until 1871.

The United States Commissioner of Patents appointed Townend Glover in 1854 to collect statistics and other information on seeds, fruits, and insects. He resigned in 1859, but came back in 1863 as entomologist of the Department of Agriculture and served until 1877. He was succeeded by C. V. Riley (1843–1895), who had been State entomologist in Missouri since 1868. From 1878 to 1881 Riley was chief of the United States Entomological Commission, with A. S. Packard, jr., and Cyrus Thomas, and then at the head of the entomological division of the United States Department of Agriculture until June, 1894. In Illinois, Walsh, Le Baron, and Thomas were successively State entomologists, beginning in 1868, and S. A. Forbes took this position in 1882.

Alpheus Spring Packard, jr. (1839–1905), a graduate of Bowdoin College and the Maine Medical School, was a student and assistant under Agassiz in the Lawrence Scientific School and afterwards director of the Peabody Academy of Science at Salem, Mass., and professor of zoology and geology at Brown University, entomologist on the Maine Geological Survey in 1861, State entomologist of Massachusetts, 1871–1873, and lecturer on entomology at the Massachusetts Agricultural College beginning with 1869, when his book, entitled " Guide to the Study of Insects," was first published.

The first professor of entomology in the United States was H. A. Hagen, who began his service in 1873 in connection with the museum of comparative zoology at Harvard University.

John Henry Comstock (1849–   ) was educated at Cornell University, where he became instructor, assistant professor, and in 1882 professor of entomology and invertebrate zoology. From 1878 to 1881 he was entomologist of the United States Department of Agriculture. With his wife, Anna Botsford Comstock, he made important contributions to economic entomology and in 1894 published a book entitled " Manual for the Study of Insects."

The entomologists who have been mentioned, with their associates and other workers, built up a large body of knowledge regarding the morphology, classification, life history, and food habits of insects, beneficial or injurious to agriculture, and discovered or successfully applied many devices and means for controlling them. The largest amount of work was developed by the United States Department of Agriculture under the leadership of Riley, but there were important centers of original investigations in some States, particularly New York, Massachusetts, and Illinois. These three States took the lead in teaching economic entomology and preparing students to teach this subject or to become investigators. In a number of agricultural colleges in other States there was some teaching of entomology, usually in connection with zoology, botany, or horticulture, prior to the establishment of the agricultural experiment stations.

The Hatch Act enabled the State experiment stations to greatly increase their entomological work, and the employment of entomologists at the stations led to the employment of these men in many cases on a part-time basis to teach entomology in the agricultural colleges.

In 1889 the American Association of Economic Entomologists was formed. Their proceedings were published by the United States Department of Agriculture, partly in the journal of the division of entomology, entitled "Insect Life" (1888–1895) and then in the Journal of Economic Entomology, established in 1908. A "permanent committee" on entomology was formed in the Association of Agricultural Colleges in 1889, and from this developed a section on entomology in 1890, which continued to hold annual meetings until 1903. Its proceedings were published with those of the association. At the meetings of both these organizations there were from time to time presentations of the organization of the entomological work of the colleges and stations and of the methods of teaching entomology.

In 1888 entomology was a separate branch of instruction in only three colleges, but there were 25 men doing entomological work in 20 experiment stations. Two years later there were 35 entomologists in 28 States. By 1892 entomological work was developing strongly at the colleges in Colorado, Illinois, Iowa, Kansas, Massachusetts, New Jersey, New York, and Ohio, and in 1898 there were courses in entomology in every section of the United States. Five colleges were offering graduate courses.

In 1894 the experiment stations in 42 States and Territories employed 28 entomologists and 49 other persons doing entomological work in connection with zoology, botany, horticulture, etc. One person was specially devoted to bee culture. The openings for persons trained in entomology were greatly and rapidly increased in number by the growing work of the United States Department of Agriculture, the State stations, and inspection services, and the teaching of nature study in public and private schools.

In 1912 there were 101 entomologists on the station staffs, and not less than 112 persons were engaged in entomological work in the agricultural colleges and State universities. That year there were 215 technically trained entomologists in the Bureau of Entomology, as compared with 16 employees in 1894. The Federal and State funds devoted to instruction, research, and inspection work in 1912 aggregated about $1,600,000.

In 1900 the students of entomology in the University of California numbered 250, most of whom were preparing to teach nature study. At that time all the agricultural colleges for white students, except those in Wyoming and Arizona, had distinct courses in entomology. In the smaller colleges a practical course in economic entomology covering from one to three terms was given, with lectures and laboratory work, and often there was some opportunity for students specially interested in this subject to take advanced work. In some larger colleges and universities there were courses largely elective and covering 2, 3, or 4 years. At Cornell University in 1911 there were six men teaching different branches of entomology, and 29 courses were offered. Degrees of bachelor of science, master of science, and doctor of philosophy were given students whose major study was entomology. At the Massachusetts Agricultural College Charles Henry Fernald, who had come there as professor of zoology, gave special attention to entomology, and his early work in the campaign against the gypsy moth attracted wide attention. This and the establishment of the experiment stations caused the entomological work to develop rapidly. In 1893 a course leading to the master of science degree was organized at the Massachusetts College, and in 1898 work leading to the degree of doctor of philosophy was offered. A separate professorship of entomology was established in 1899.

In 1914 in the Bureau of Entomology the largest number of technically trained men came from the Massachusetts Agricultural College and Cornell University, and of 306 entomological workers in the agricultural colleges and experiment stations in 1915, 68 had studied at Cornell University, 33 at Ohio State University, 27 at Massachusetts Agricultural College, 15 at the University of Illinois, and 12 at the Michigan Agricultural College.

Instruction was given in the colleges generally through lectures and laboratory work. Packard's and Comstock's manuals were generally used, and there were also several other American textbooks on entomology issued during this period. The entomological publications of the United States Department of Agriculture and the experiment stations became numerous. Collections of insects grew rapidly and at some colleges were extensive. Spraying machinery and other devices for controlling insects became common at the colleges. In 1888 the first house for breeding and rearing insects, commonly called an insectary, was built at Cornell University. By 1901 such houses existed in at least 12 States. Field practice was more and more required, especially with advanced students. Opportunities for such work became numerous in connection with the experiment stations, Bureau of Entomology, or State inspection services.

VETERINARY MEDICINE

Between 1855 and 1860 veterinary medicine was taught to a few students in short-lived private schools in Boston and Philadelphia. The New York College of Veterinary Surgeons opened in 1864 and the American Veterinary College in 1875. These were proprietary institutions until 1899, when they were consolidated under New York University.

The St. Louis Veterinary College was incorporated in 1875. Schools on a private foundation were also formed in Chicago, Kansas City, Cincinnati, Baltimore, Washington, Detroit, and other cities, which gave short courses representing two years of five or six months each.

In 1868 Illinois Industrial University (now the University of Illinois) established a professorship of veterinary science and appointed to this position, F. W. Prentice, a graduate of the London Veterinary College. At first it was not intended to give a full veterinary education, but instruction in this subject was part of an agricultural course covering four years. The principal lectures were on entomology, physiology, and general veterinary science. For clinics sick animals were brought in from the neighborhood and treated free of charge.

Cornell University also established a chair of veterinary medicine in 1868, and brought into this position James Law. He, too, was a graduate of the London Veterinary College, and was already author of a work, The Anatomy of Domestic Animals. He soon became veterinary editor of the New York Weekly Tribune and consulting veterinary surgeon to the State agricultural society. Excitement caused by the appearance of Texas fever among cattle about this time strengthened public interest in his work. A 4-year course leading to the degree of bachelor of veterinary science was established, of which the last two years were devoted to veterinary studies. Teachers in the agricultural department of the university gave instruction in anatomy, physiology, histology, zootechny, hygiene, botany, toxicology, pharmacy, and therapeutics, and Professor Law taught principles and practice, surgery, obstetrics, surgical pathology and anatomy, examination of soundness, and principles of shoeing. To receive the degree of doctor of veterinary medicine the student was obliged to pursue two additional years of graduate study.

For a number of years most of the students of veterinary courses took these as a part of their work for the degree of bachelor of agriculture. At the end of nine years only two students had been given veterinary degrees. In 1894 the veterinary department was made the New York State Veterinary College, with a separate building and faculty.

Veterinary departments were established at the Iowa State College in 1879, Ohio State University in 1884 (became College of Veterinary Medicine in 1895), the University of Minnesota in 1890, and the University of California in 1895. By 1877 lecture courses in veterinary science were given as part of the agricultural course in land-grant colleges in Massachusetts, Maryland, New Hampshire, Pennsylvania, and Vermont. At the Michigan Agricultural College lectures on this subject were begun in 1881, but a department of veterinary medicine with authority to grant the degree of doctor of veterinary medicine was not provided until 1907 and was not put into operation as a division of the college until 1910.

At the Kansas Agricultural College a veterinary department was organized in 1872 but was discontinued in 1874 " for want of means and room " and was not revived until 1888.

At the Massachusetts Agricultural College lectures on diseases of domestic animals were begun in 1869, but a professorship of veterinary science was not established until 1890. A separate veterinary building and stable hospital were erected in 1898.

At the Washington Agricultural College a school of veterinary science was established in 1896.

In the United States Department of Agriculture the first appropriation for the investigation of diseases of animals was made in 1878, and the Bureau of Animal Industry was established in 1884, with D. E. Salmon, a graduate of the veterinary department of Cornell University, as chief (*433*). This bureau developed quite rapidly. By 1900 there were also veterinary inspectors in the larger cities and State veterinarians in a number of States. The passage of the Hatch Act in 1887 brought about an increase of veterinarians in the experiment stations. In 1899 there were 32 veterinarians, most of whom had professional degrees, at the agricultural colleges and experiment stations. That year there were 17 veterinary schools in 12 States, as compared with 6 schools in 1888. These schools had 249 instructors, of whom 156 had the rank of professor; 16 schools had authority to grant degrees. Only 6 were separate institutions. In 1898 there were 123 graduates.

In response to growing demands that professional standards should be created—

the United States Veterinary Medical Association adopted in 1891 an article providing that all applicants for membership should be graduates of a recognized veterinary school with a curriculum of at least three years of six months each and a corps of instructors comprising at least four veterinarians. The next step in advance came in 1895 when the New York Legislature enacted that at least a high-school diploma representing four years of high-school work should be offered for admission to a veterinary school, that the veterinary curriculum should embrace three full years and that only those who had met both requirements could be admitted to the regents' veterinary examinations for license to practice in the State. (*313.*)

By 1908 the Bureau of Animal Industry was employing over 800 veterinarians. It was therefore vitally interested in the professional training of its employees. Its action in this matter has been described in the history of the bureau by U. G. Houck as follows (*433*) :

In order to obtain men thoroughly qualified by education to fill positions in the bureau it was deemed advisable to prescribe a standard of veterinary education for schools that desired to prepare their graduates to qualify to take the civil-service examination for positions in the bureau. The Civil Service Commission approved this arrangement, and in February, 1908, the Secretary of Agriculture appointed a committee, consisting of five leading veterinarians of the country, for the purpose of obtaining information regarding the courses of instruction then given at the various veterinary colleges, and to make recommendations as to lengthening and arranging the courses of instruction properly to qualify graduates of these colleges for positions in the bureau.

This committee visited the veterinary colleges in the United States and Canada and made recommendations as to faculties, equipment, and teaching, which were approved by the American Veterinary Medical Association.

The minimum requirements for matriculation and the college course in veterinary medicine were fixed and a course of instruction to cover three years of not less than six months each, with a minimum of 150 days of actual teaching in each year and a minimum of 3,200 hours for the three years, was outlined. The matriculation examination should include spelling, arithmetic, letter writing, penmanship, copying from plain copy, United States history, and geography of the United States and its possessions, with a passing grade of not less than 70 per cent. This has since been modified to include at least four years' high-school education, of at least 14 full units or their equivalent.

The subjects and hours in the course were outlined as follows:

Anatomy, major subject: Lectures, 200; laboratory, 300; total	500
Histology: Lectures, 40; laboratory, 100; total	140
Embryology: Lectures, 10; laboratory, 20; total	30
Zoology: Lectures, 20; laboratory, 20; total	40
Total for subject	710
Physiology, major subject: Lectures, 80; laboratory, 20; total	100
Principles of nutrition	10
Hygiene	10
Animal locomotion	5
	25
Total for subject	125

Zootechnics, major subject:
Breeds and breeding_____ 30
Judging _____ 30
Feeds and breeding_____ 30
Dairy inspection_____ 10
Jurisprudence_____ 10

Total for subject_____ 110

Chemistry, major subject: Lectures, 50; laboratory, 150; total_____ 200
Physics (elementary)_____ 20
Physiological chemistry—urine analysis, 10; milk analysis, 10_____ 20

Total for subject_____ 240

Materia medica, major subject: Lectures_____ 70
Pharmacology, lectures and laboratory_____ 50
Botany_____ 30
Toxicology_____ 10

Total for subject_____ 160

Pathology, major subject: Lectures, 40; laboratory, 100; total_____ 140
Bacteriology: Lectures, 20; laboratory, 90; total_____ 110
Parasitology: Lectures, 50; laboratory, 10; total_____ 60
Post-mortem examination_____ 10
Meat inspection_____ 50
Laboratory diagnosis_____ 50

Total for subject_____ 420

Practice of comparative medicine, major subject: Lectures_____ 250
Diagnostic methods and clinics_____ 400
Therapeutics_____ 100
Control of infective diseases_____ 25

Total for subject_____ 775

Surgery, major subject: Lectures, 100; surgical exercise, 80; total_____ 180
Surgical diagnosis and clinics_____ 300
Surgical restraint_____ 30
Soundness _____ 20
Lameness_____ 50
Shoeing and balancing_____ 10
Dentistry (lectures)_____ 20
Obstetrics _____ 50

Total for subject_____ 660

The faculty in the veterinary college was to contain at least five
qualified veterinarians, each with three years' experience in teaching
or practicing veterinary science subsequent to their graduation at a
veterinary college, and not more than three of them were to be graduates of any one veterinary college. These veterinarians were to teach
anatomy, pathology, practice of comparative medicine, surgery, and
materia medica or physiology.

On January 21, 1909, the committee's plan was approved by 12
veterinary colleges in conference with the Bureau of Animal Industry.
This was followed by another visitation of the veterinary colleges by
a special committee of the bureau.

Generally the veterinary colleges cooperated willingly with the bureau, and
they deserve much credit for the splendid spirit displayed and the effective
manner in which they met the bureau's requirements.

Private schools predominated in number up to the year 1918, when there were 23 schools in the United States which gave full courses in veterinary medicine. Twelve of these schools were private institutions and eleven were connected with State colleges or received State aid. There were also two State agricultural colleges which gave two-year courses on veterinary subjects. As the private schools were sustained entirely by tuition fees, there was keen rivalry among them, and this, in some instances, led to a laxity in accepting matriculists. Usually the private schools did not maintain such high standards of veterinary education as the colleges which received State aid. At present (July 1, 1923) there are only three private veterinary schools in the United States and it may be expected that eventually they will cease to exist, as it is difficult for a private veterinary school to maintain the required standard and compete with colleges that receive financial aid from the States.

Following are the names of the veterinary colleges in the United States which were on the accredited list July 1, 1923:

Alabama Polytechnic Institute, College of Veterinary Medicine, Auburn, Ala.

Colorado State College, Division of Veterinary Medicine, Fort Collins, Colo.

Georgia State College of Agriculture, Veterinary Division, Athens, Ga.

Indiana Veterinary College, Indianapolis, Ind.

Iowa State College, Division of Veterinary Medicine, Ames, Iowa.

Kansas State Agricultural College, Veterinary Department, Manhattan, Kans.

Michigan Agricultural College, Division of Veterinary Science, East Lansing, Mich.

New York State Veterinary College, Cornell University, Ithaca, N. Y.

Ohio State University, College of Veterinary Medicine, Columbus, Ohio.

St. Joseph Veterinary College, St. Joseph, Mo.

State College of Washington, Veterinary Department, Pullman, Wash.

Texas Agricultural and Mechanical College, School of Veterinary Medicine, College Station, Texas.

United States College of Veterinary Surgeons, Washington, D. C.

University of Pennsylvania, School of Veterinary Medicine, Philadelphia, Pa. (*433*).

HOME ECONOMICS

Even before the passage of the land grant act of 1862 some of the friends of higher education in agriculture and other industries desired that women as well as men should have the opportunity to study in such institutions and favored making them coeducational. This was impressed on the leaders of the movement for the People's College in New York by certain prominent women. It was also favored in the North Central States, where coeducation in the secondary schools was well-nigh universal. As the land-grant colleges were organized the admission of women was sought. This began in Kansas in 1863, in Minnesota in 1868, in Iowa in 1869, in Illinois and Michigan in 1870, in Nebraska in 1871, and in New York in 1872.

Between 1870 and 1880 there was practical instruction in cooking and sewing in the agricultural colleges in Iowa and Kansas, with some lectures on the chemistry of food and nutrition.

In 1882 Mrs. Nellie Sawyer Kedzie, a graduate of the Kansas college in 1876, was employed there to teach household economy and in 1887 was made professor of household economy, a position she held for 10 years. She greatly developed and improved the work, especially along the more practical lines, and made that college a strong center for the training of teachers of home economics.

At the Illinois Industrial University (now the University of Illinois) the catalogue of 1871–72 announced a " School of Domestic Science and Art." No work in home economics was done until Lou C. Allen, a graduate of the State normal school of Bloomington, Ill., was appointed " instructor in domestic science " in 1874. After spe-

cial study in the East she announced in the catalogue for 1875–76 the
first course in domestic science of college grade, as follows:

COURSE OF DOMESTIC SCIENCE

Required for degree of bachelor of science in school of domestic science.

FIRST YEAR

1. Chemistry, trigonometry, drawing (full term), British authors.
2. Chemistry, designing and drawing, American authors.
3. Chemistry, designing and drawing, rhetoric.

SECOND YEAR

1. Botany; physiology, German or English classics.
2. Food and dietetics (simple aliments), botany and greenhouse, German or
English classics.
3. Food and dietetics (compound aliments and principles of cooking, etc.),
zoology, German or English classics.

THIRD YEAR

1. Domestic hygiene, ancient history, German or French.
2. Physics, mediæval history, German or French.
3. Physics or landscape gardening, modern history, German or French.

FOURTH YEAR

1. Household æsthetics, mental science, history of civilization.
2. Household science, constitutional history, logic.
3. Domestic economy, usages of society, etc., political economy, home architecture, graduating thesis or oration or essay (117).

Miss Allen not only taught domestic science and gymnastics but
was also virtually what is now called dean of women. She was a
thorough teacher and had high ideals for her work. She was sufficiently successful in her work at the university to be advanced to the
position of "professor of domestic economy." She married John M.
Gregory, the first regent of the University of Illinois, and went with
him when he retired in 1880. A new professor for this department
was not secured until 1900.

In 1890 only four land-grant colleges had departments of home
economics; namely, those in Kansas, Iowa, Oregon, and South Dakota. In the next 15 years such departments were organized in 18
of the land-grant colleges for white students. With the exception of
the institutions in Connecticut and Tennessee these colleges were in
the North Central and Western States. There was also some elementary instruction in home economics in 11 land-grant institutions
for colored students.

The work and publications of Mrs. Ellen H. Richards, teacher of
sanitary chemistry at the Massachusetts Institute of Technology,
between 1873 and 1890, and her kitchens at Boston and the Chicago
exposition of 1893, at which food was prepared and sold on the
basis of its nutritive value, did much to promote scientific teaching
of food and nutrition (34). The investigations and writings of
W. O. Atwater, professor of chemistry at Wesleyan University and
from 1894 in charge of nutrition investigations in the Office of
Experiment Stations of the United States Department of Agriculture, spread widely in this country the results of research on food

and nutrition abroad and added materially to the knowledge of these subjects obtained here.

The separate agricultural colleges, with their lower entrance requirements and definite vocational aims, early developed comparatively strong departments of home economics on a practical basis, but these were often relatively weak on their scientific side. In the land-grant institutions which were universities, the tendency was to minimize the practical work and make the instruction largely theoretical in order to gain for the home-economics departments proper recognition as of college grade. There was no uniformity as regards nomenclature or content of the courses offered in the different institutions. This applied not only to the land-grant institutions but to other colleges attempting to teach this subject and in great measure to the normal and secondary schools.

Perceiving the weakness and confusion thus created in the movement for education in home economics Mrs. Richards undertook to create an agency for the study of the problems of definition and organization of such education.

This resulted in the conferences held annually at Lake Placid, N. Y., and elsewhere from 1899 to 1908 (43). These conferences were attended by a considerable number of teachers in the land-grant colleges and public schools. They fixed the term home economics as the name of the general subject which included food, nutrition, clothing, and household equipment and management, and through reports of committees, discussions, and bulletins exerted a considerable influence on the systematization of the subject and the improvement of courses of study. Out of these conferences grew the American Home Economics Association in 1909.

Meanwhile the development of departments of home economics in the land-grant colleges and universities had proceeded, and the relations between these departments and the agricultural side of these institutions, which had been intimate from the first, became closer and more important. In a number of the universities the department of home economics was organized in the college of agriculture. This closeness of relations was brought about because both branches represented the same type of education, both dealt largely with agricultural products, and both depended on the same fundamental sciences for the foundations of their college courses. The agricultural experiment stations were engaged in researches which bore on the problems of home economics. This was particularly true with reference to food and nutrition, bacteriology, entomology, etc. Moreover, in agriculture the work and interests of the home are indissolubly connected with those of the farm. Thus the friends of agricultural education had a most powerful incentive for promoting home-economics education.

At the very time that the American Association of Home Economics was being formed the American Association of Agricultural Colleges and Experiment Stations through its committee on instruction in agriculture was preparing a 4-year course in home economics, with the aid of a college teacher of that subject. After the Home Economics Association was organized the agricultural committee asked that association to appoint a committee to join in this work. Such a committee consisting of representatives of the home-economics departments in land-grant institutions was appointed in 1910, and the two committees agreed on a report which was submitted to their respective associations at their next annual meetings. The courses outlined in that report were as follows:

The standard undergraduate college course in home economics leading to a bachelor's degree should include the following subjects:

Required subjects

(1) Home architecture and sanitation.
(2) Home decoration.
(3) Textiles.
(4) Selection and preparation of food.
(5) Economic uses of food.
(6) Household management.

Subjects from which choice must be made

(7) Advanced cooking.
    Dressmaking or millinery. } At least one of this group.
    Art needlework.
(8) Dietetics.
    Food and nutrition. } At least one of this group.
    Art in the home.

Such other electives in home economics as the college can offer.

The order of presentation suggested above is not essential but the subjects should be taught in some definitely related order.

For students who have not had instruction in home economics in preparatory schools the following minor college course is suggested, to be required of candidates for a bachelor's degree.

(1) Plain sewing and garment making.
(2) Cooking.
(3) Home architecture and sanitation.
(4) Home decoration.
(5) Textiles.
(6) Selection and preparation of food.
(7) Economic uses of food.
(8) Household management.

College students taking either of these courses in home economics should be required to add to them such groups of studies in mathematics, languages, science, economics, sociology, etc., as will make their whole college course a well-rounded scheme of liberal education, comparable with the degree courses in other lines, and at the same time contribute to the thoroughness of their work in home economics. Students taking the minor courses in home economics might be allowed to elect additional work in home economics during the latter part of their college course.

Short courses and extension courses, not leading to a degree, should be arranged for separately, and are not taken into account here (*499*).

The Home Economics Association then undertook a study of the content of home economics as a distinct branch of knowledge and in 1913 issued an elaborate " syllabus of home economics," which outlined the subject under four main divisions, (1) food, (2) clothing, (3) shelter, and (4) household and institution management. The first three subjects were subdivided into (*a*) selection, (*b*) preparation, and (*c*) use, and the fourth into (*a*) material basis, (*b*) social contacts, (*c*) activities and functions, and (*d*) aims and results. The syllabus " does not represent an outline for a course of instruction, but rather a classified list of topics from which courses can be made." It served, however, to show how much the field of home economics had broadened in the thought of those who were promoting education in this subject. Home economics no longer was being developed on the basis of physics, chemistry, and the biological sciences only but included much in the field of economics and sociology.

Another agency for the discussion of the problems of higher education in home economics which had considerable influence in strengthening the work in the land-grant colleges was the summer graduate school of home economics. This had its beginning in 1902 when Professor Atwater invited teachers of home economics to study four weeks at his laboratory at Middletown, Conn., primarily to become acquainted with the nutrition investigations, but also to listen to lectures by various experts and to confer with each other on home-economics problems. That same year the Graduate School of Agriculture was begun at Ohio State University. In 1906 the two schools cooperated in a session at the University of Illinois and this was continued at Cornell University in 1908, at Iowa State College in 1910, and at the Michigan Agricultural College in 1912. The American Home Economics Association assumed responsibility for this school in 1909. There was, however, difficulty in providing for the necessary expenses of this enterprise, and the increase of regular graduate work at the colleges and universities lessened the need for this summer school, which at its best served principally to stimulate a desire for more advanced study. It was therefore discontinued.

The equipment for instruction in home economics at the land-grant institutions was greatly improved during the first 15 years of the twentieth century. At a number of these institutions substantial buildings wholly devoted to the work in home economics were erected and at others large space in old or new buildings was assigned to this department. Special laboratories, workrooms, apartments resembling those in houses, etc., were provided and well equipped. For the more scientific work special apparatus was devised. Numerous textbooks and manuals were issued, the general literature of home economics became extensive, and State and Federal publications within this field were issued in large numbers.

The basis of support for the college courses in home economics was greatly strengthened by the constantly increasing breadth of the home-economics movement in the lower schools. The Bureau of Education reported that in 1914 household arts were taught in elementary or secondary schools in over 3,000 towns and cities and in 2,400 high schools and 159 State normal schools. Some 252 colleges were giving instruction in home economics, and 43 others were offering courses in applied sciences with reference to the home. Detailed statistics from about 35 per cent of these colleges showed 5,547 students in home-economics courses, of whom 3,495 were studying for home use, 1,788 for teaching, and 264 for administrative positions as dietitians, household and institution managers, etc. In 20 colleges and universities, including 13 land-grant institutions, it was possible to take the master's degree by special graduate study in home economics departments, and at the University of Chicago the degree of doctor of philosophy was given in the department of household administration. Advanced students interested in home economics could take the doctor's degree for special courses in the science departments of many universities, and already a number of women engaged in home-economics work had taken this degree.

In 28 land-grant institutions, including 14 universities, 4-year undergraduate courses in home economics leading to the bachelor's degree were offered. While differing much in details, these courses corresponded in a general way with that proposed by the American Home Economics Association. In many of these institutions the home-economics faculty had been sufficiently developed to permit of considerable specialization, particularly in junior and senior years. In addition, there were many short courses and summer schools and much extension work.

By 1915 home-economics instruction had become a permanent part of the American educational system in all its grades from the graduate school of the university to the elementary school. It had developed courses of instruction based on both science and practice and was definitely evolving standards for the different grades of courses. Research definitely related to the problems of home economics had already furnished considerable material for courses of instruction, especially in the field of food and nutrition. In the development of this educational system, particularly in its higher ranges, the land-grant institutions had an honorable and important part.

By the Smith-Lever Extension Act of 1914 home economics was linked with agriculture as an essential part of the broad system of cooperative extension work now carried on by the land-grant colleges and the United States Department of Agriculture in all the States.

TEACHER TRAINING

As the movement for agricultural education broadened and instruction in agriculture was introduced into secondary and elementary schools many teachers resorted to the agricultural colleges, chiefly for short courses, and a considerable number of students in the long courses went out from the colleges to teach agriculture.

Interest in the professional training of teachers was also becoming widespread, and colleges and universities were establishing departments of education. This movement affected many of the land-grant institutions, and some of them undertook special work relating to the training of teachers of agriculture.

In 1906 the Office of Experiment Stations reported that departments of education in which attention was given to training teachers of agriculture were maintained in land-grant institutions in Illinois, Missouri, and Washington, and normal courses were offered in Arkansas, Colorado, Connecticut, Iowa, Kansas, Massachusetts, Mississippi, New York, North Carolina, North Dakota, Oklahoma, and South Dakota. Summer schools for teachers were maintained in California, Connecticut, Georgia, Illinois, Kansas, Kentucky, Maine, Mississippi, New York, Ohio, Utah, Washington, and Wisconsin. There were also departments of education in California, Georgia, Louisiana, Maine, Minnesota, Nebraska, Tennessee, and Wisconsin.

At this time the land-grant colleges had difficulty in getting sufficient funds to meet expenses caused by their rapidly expanding work. At the meeting of the Association of American Agricultural Colleges and Experiment Stations in 1906, the following resolution, introduced by H. J. Wheeler, of Rhode Island, was adopted:

Whereas since the passage of the Morrill Act of 1890 no further Federal grants have been made for agricultural and mechanical education, notwithstanding the crying needs for such additional support: Therefore, be it

Resolved, That the executive committee of this association be authorized to cause to be introduced in Congress a measure drawn on the same general lines as the Morrill Act of 1890, providing for an increased appropriation for each of the land-grant colleges (*499*).

This led to activities in which W. M. Hays, then Assistant Secretary of Agriculture and formerly connected with the Minnesota Agricultural College, was especially prominent. Largely due to his influence, Senator Knute Nelson, of Minnesota, took this matter up and introduced on December 5, 1906, a bill for this purpose. It was also introduced in the House December 12 by Charles R. Davis, also of Minnesota. On January 16, 1907, Senator Nelson gave notice that he would offer his bill as an amendment to the appropriation bill for the Department of Agriculture, and this was done February 21, 1907. The amendment was accepted by the Senate, and, though at first rejected by the House, when the appropriation bill went to conference between the two Houses was finally accepted after considerable debate by a vote of 120 to 87, and was approved by President Roosevelt March 4, 1907. This measure provided each State and Territory with an additional appropriation under the terms of the Morrill Act of 1890. This fund began with $5,000 the first year and $5,000 more each year for four years, after which the annual sum was to be $25,000.

The appropriation was carried through on the merits of agriculture. The law itself mentions the agricultural work prominently, and the discussion in Congress hinged almost exclusively on the value and growing importance of agricultural education and the needs of developing that phase of our educational system. (439.)

Professor Hays was much interested in the extension of agricultural instruction to secondary and elementary schools, and undoubtedly suggested the proviso incorporated in the Nelson amendment to the effect "That said colleges may use a portion of this money for providing courses for the special preparation of instructors for teaching the elements of agriculture and the mechanic arts." In the statement of Mr. Nelson in explanation of his bill in the Senate and in the hearings before the Senate Committee on Agriculture and Forestry, much stress was laid on the development of secondary and elementary education in agriculture and the need of training teachers for such work. The passage of this measure quickened the interest of the land-grant colleges in establishing teacher-training courses, but the amount of the Nelson fund devoted to this purpose was disappointingly small.

During the year 1906–7 summer-school instruction in agriculture was given to 925 teachers. In 1908–9 at least 26 of the colleges provided teacher-training courses in agriculture ranging from summer schools of a few weeks to regular four-year courses with additional graduate work. Several colleges had established departments of agricultural education. In 1910, 46 of the agricultural colleges reported teacher-training work in agriculture. In more than half of these institutions the teachers' courses were four years in length, and in 29 of them summer schools for teachers were held. More than eight times as many students enrolled in teachers' courses in agriculture that year as in 1909. For further account of the teacher-training work of these colleges see page 291 and page 377.

SECONDARY EDUCATION IN THE AGRICULTURAL COLLEGES

When the agricultural colleges were first established there were comparatively few high schools or other preparatory schools easily accessible to farm children. The public, and especially the farming people, therefore thought that students from the elementary schools should be admitted to these colleges. This idea was carried over into the land-grant colleges in many States. Either the entrance requirements were kept so low that students with only the training received in the elementary schools were admitted to the freshman class of the college and the college instruction had to be largely of secondary grade, or preparatory classes were organized in the colleges. These matters were more easily arranged in the separate agricultural colleges than in the universities, which in general had entrance requirements more or less conforming to those of standard colleges of that time.

Progress in bringing the entrance requirements of the land-grant colleges generally up to proper standards was relatively slow and depended largely on the general development of the public-school system in the several States. The efforts of the Association of Agricultural Colleges through its committees to promote proper entrance requirements and actually collegiate courses in agriculture have been previously described.

When the committee on instruction in agriculture made its first report on secondary courses in agriculture in 1902 (499) it recognized that a movement was already in progress in the colleges either to raise the requirements for admission and abolish the courses of lower grade or else to raise the requirements for the bachelor's degree and differentiate the preparatory or secondary courses from those of college grade. Following the latter plan the land-grant colleges in Minnesota and Nebraska had established separate schools of agriculture of secondary grade. The committee believed—

that this is a better plan than to institute courses which are merely preparatory to the college courses given in the same institution. * * * As many of our colleges are now organized it would not at present be practicable to wholly cut off the secondary instruction. It will, however, be a great gain to have the secondary instruction in agriculture, as in other subjects, clearly differentiated from the college courses in the mind of both the students and the public.

In 1903 the Office of Experiment Stations reported that agricultural schools with a 2-year course of high-school grade had been organized at the colleges in Maine, Rhode Island, and Oklahoma, and an agricultural school with a 3-year course in Washington. The Connecticut Agricultural College, which originally had been a secondary school, was providing a special group of studies for students coming from the common schools, and at the New Mexico Agricultural College agriculture was being taught in the preparatory department. The rapid growth of the movement to differentiate secondary work in the agricultural colleges is shown by the fact that in 1909 there were similar schools or short courses in at least 29 States, as follows: Alabama, Arkansas, California, Colorado, Connecticut, Delaware, Florida, Idaho, Kentucky, Louisiana, Maine, Maryland, New Hampshire, New Jersey, New Mexico, North Dakota, Ohio, Oklahoma, Oregon, Pennsylvania, Rhode Island, South Dakota, Texas, Utah, Virginia, Washington, West Virginia, Wisconsin, and Wyoming. Such courses were supplemented to an increasing extent by brief and special courses of from a week to 10 or 12 weeks, usually in the winter. There were also summer schools for teachers and one or two year normal courses, in all of which nature study and elementary agriculture were important features. In this way the colleges attempted to meet the needs, as far as possible, of people desiring some instruction in agriculture but unable to take the regular college courses.

The number and variety of the short courses given by the agricultural colleges continued to increase throughout this period. By this means the colleges greatly increased the number of persons who through them received more or less instruction in agriculture and who principally as farmers or teachers spread the influence of the colleges in the rural communities.

In the colleges for white students in 1905 the number of persons in the shorter courses was 4,631 and in 1910 it was 11,211, without counting 1,264 who took agriculture in the summer schools for teachers.

By doing this secondary and special work the agricultural colleges did a valuable service at a time when there was little serious instruction in agriculture outside. They also helped materially to promote the spread of instruction relating to agriculture in secondary and elementary schools. Further consideration of the work of the agricultural college with relation to secondary and elementary education will be given in the chapter on the progress of agricultural instruction in the lower schools. (See p. 335.)

PROMOTION OF INSTRUCTION IN AGRICULTURE IN THE ELEMENTARY SCHOOLS

Closely connected with their extension work were the efforts of the agricultural colleges and the United States Department of Agriculture to aid the movement for the teaching of agriculture in the elementary schools. The nature-study work carried on by the agricultural college at Cornell University began in 1895. (See p. 385.) There was also some similar work by the colleges in other States. Then came the school-garden movement, and this was actively aided by the agricultural colleges and the Department of Agriculture. (See p. 385.) Both nature study and school gardening were largely taken up by the city and village schools and only affected the rural schools and farm children to a limited extent. To reach the rural schools more definitely and extensively it was found necessary to deal with the plants, animals, birds, insects, etc., which aid or hinder the farmer in his work and to make this nature study a basis for the subsequent study of agriculture in the elementary and secondary schools.

The agricultural colleges individually and through their association aided this movement by the formulation of courses of instruction for the elementary schools, training of teachers, special courses for teachers in service at summer schools, preparation of textbooks and manuals, and in other ways. Their relations to the teaching of agriculture in the elementary schools will be more fully described in a later chapter. (See p. 390.)

EXTENSION WORK

From the beginning of the twentieth century until the passage of the Smith-Lever Extension Act in 1914 the agricultural colleges were very active in developing various forms of extension work, and together with the National and State Departments of Agriculture were laying the foundations for an unparalleled system of practical education in agriculture and home economics which was to reach great multitudes of the farming people and profoundly affect the development of a better agriculture and country life in the United States. This great subject is treated in a separate monograph, and only enough will be said about it at this time to show its intimate relation to the general educational program of the colleges. (U. S. D. A. Misc. Pub. 15, 1928.)

The extension work of the agricultural colleges was an outgrowth of the addresses delivered at meetings of agricultural societies, at fairs, and at other gatherings of farmers during all the nineteenth century. From the beginning these addresses included some on the more technical phases of agriculture and its relations to the sciences, delivered by college teachers or persons having special knowledge of the subjects they treated. In 1861 the Michigan Legislature passed an act which contained a provision that " the professors of the college may give lectures to farmers away from the college."

About 1870 meetings called farmers' institutes began to be held in Iowa and Kansas, and these were gradually developed into a regular system of meetings under public control, organized and managed by the agricultural colleges or State boards or departments of agriculture, and supported by public funds. Whatever authority controlled the institutes, the officers of the agricultural colleges quite generally participated in them in the several States. The experiment stations made large use of the institutes for the dissemination of the practical results of their investigations. The Office of Experiment Stations therefore promoted the institutes and in 1903 under a special appropriation by Congress established a division for its work relating to them.

Following the decline of the lyceum movement, partly as a result of the Civil War, there began in 1874 the more systematic Chautauqua movement. This was not connected with educational institutions but consisted largely of literary and scientific circles, which were to a certain extent assisted by summer schools and correspondence courses managed by university professors. For a short time some degrees were granted by the University of the State of New York on the completion of Chautauqua courses.

Meanwhile the American universities and colleges had been influenced by the system of so-called university extension which had been begun in England in 1866 and had been taken up by Cambridge and Oxford universities and other educational institutions there and in other countries. In the United States this was first introduced through activities of city libraries, especially in Buffalo, Chicago, and St. Louis, and by 1890 it had received sufficient attention to bring about the organization of the American Society for the Extension of University Teaching.

In the next decade the universities of Chicago and Wisconsin and over 20 other institutions established departments of university extension. The extension work of the agricultural colleges was more or less influenced by this general movement.

In 1894, S. F. Nixon, assemblyman from Chautauqua County, N. Y., in response to an appeal from fruit growers there and with the cooperation of L. H. Bailey, of Cornell University, obtained an appropriation of $8,000 for horticultural experiments, instruction,

and information in western New York, and this was increased to
$16,000 the next year. Professor Bailey was put in charge of this
work. Experimental work, largely of the nature of tests or demonstrations, was conducted on a considerable number of farms, together with one or two day meetings, sometimes accompanied by
demonstrations such as orchard spraying, horticultural schools of
two to four days, and the publication of popular bulletins.

In 1896 the extension work was expanded to include (1) itinerant
or local experiments as a means of teaching, (2) readable expository
bulletins, (3) itinerant horticultural schools, (4) elementary instruction in nature study in rural schools, and (5) instruction by means of
correspondence and reading courses. This plan was so successful
that the legislature in 1897 broadened the scope of the work to
include the whole State and agriculture in general. The appropriation was increased to $25,000, to be spent under the supervision of the
director of the New York College of Agriculture (257).

That year, besides the horticultural investigations, 200 local experiments with various crops were conducted, 10,000 teachers were
reached through visits to schools, lectures at teachers' institutes, and
distribution of nature-study leaflets, 15,000 pupils were enrolled for
nature study, and 1,600 young farmers took correspondence courses.

Afterwards junior naturalists' clubs were formed, and a nature-
study monthly was issued. Reading courses for farmers and reading
courses for their wives were organized. A winter's course at the
college was also included in the extension program. An extension
division was created in the college, and there was much personal
work by college officers at meetings throughout the State.

In 1902, 29,792 persons were enrolled in the farmers' reading
course, 9,500 in the farmers wives' reading course, 1,800 in a home
nature-study course for teachers, 20,000 in junior naturalists' course,
and 26,000 in junior gardeners' course.

This extension work in New York attracted much attention
throughout the country, and the Cornell publications, which were on
many subjects and attractively presented, were widely distributed
and discussed.

The Pennsylvania State College established a reading course in
1892. This was first called the Chautauqua course of home reading
in agriculture and then home study. At first the college simply
provided books and gave the readers examinations when they desired.
After a time it was found desirable to aid the readers through correspondence, and in 1897 the sending out of printed lessons on
particular subjects treated in the books was begun.

In 1898 the name of the enterprise was changed to correspondence
courses in agriculture. On March 1, 1899, the total enrollment of
students was 3,416, including those in the Chautauqua course, but
460 had received instruction by lessons. To these over 1,800 lessons
had been sent and over 1,100 examination papers had been graded.
There were students in most of the States and in some foreign countries. Their ages ranged from 15 to 75 years and averaged about 33
years. This plan involved so much work by the college officers that
it was not found practicable to take care of a very large number of
students.

Colleges in several other States undertook similar work prior to
1900.

In 1905 the Association of Agricultural Colleges established a standing committee on extension work, of which K. L. Butterfield was the first chairman. This committee had the active assistance of John Hamilton, farmers' institute specialist in the Office of Experiment Stations, who acted as its secretary. The first report of this committee was made to the association in 1906 (*499*). It included a tentative definition as follows:

Extension teaching in agriculture embraces those forms of instruction, in subjects having to do with improved methods of agricultural production and with the general welfare of the rural population, that are offered to people not enrolled as resident pupils in educational institutions.

Four groups of such extension work appropriate to educational institutions were made: (1) Farmers' institutes; (2) itinerant lectures other than farmers' institutes, including single lectures or courses, lectures connected with special railroad trains, traveling schools, etc.; (3) literature and correspondence, including traveling libraries; (4) those efforts in which particular emphasis is laid on object lessons or outdoor practicums, including field demonstrations, cooperative tests, exhibits at fairs, and visits to colleges and experiment stations. In another group were included those activities of rural societies which have educational aspects and in which the colleges render much assistance, including the programs at meetings of the societies, study clubs, boys' and girls' clubs, etc.

The special and short courses at the colleges were not included in the work of this committee. It was found that there were over 300 centers of extension work in agriculture, including the agricultural colleges and experiment stations, other colleges, normal schools, industrial high schools, State and county departments of public instruction and agriculture, State and county agricultural organizations, granges, agricultural press, libraries, and industrial organizations. To these should have been added the United States Department of Agriculture, including the farmers' cooperative demonstration work in the Southern States. The committee recommended that each college in the association organize as soon as practicable a department of extension teaching in agriculture, or if this was not immediately practicable a faculty committee on this subject.

The association committee's report in 1907 showed that the agricultural colleges in 39 States were doing extension work. Much of this was in connection with the farmers' institutes, which in a number of States were under the direction of the college. In North Carolina, Nevada, and West Virginia faculty committees on extension work had been appointed, and in Illinois, Kansas, Maryland, Michigan, Mississippi, North Dakota, Ohio, Pennsylvania, and South Carolina the extension work of the college was under a superintendent or director.

The colleges in Indiana, Massachusetts, Minnesota, and Rhode Island were doing extension work in a number of different lines. In New York work was being done in 14 lines, and the college was getting ready to establish an extension division, which was partially done in 1908 by the creation of an extension office. The Iowa State College received a State appropriation of $15,000 for agricultural extension in 1906, when an extension department was organized with a superintendent and lecturers on soils, animal husbandry, domestic science, dairying, horticulture, and farm crops.

The extension work developed rapidly between 1905 and 1910, when the committee on extension work reported that there was organized work in 35 institutions. In over 20 of these there was an extension department or division. A number of the States were making considerable appropriations for this work, and there was also an increasing amount from local sources. It was estimated that the colleges had that year in the aggregate about $400,000 for extension work. The work had became more varied in character, and some of the newer features, such as farmers' weeks at the colleges, institutes and demonstration work for women, and boys' and girls' clubs, were becoming very popular.

The need of a greater opportunity for discussion of administrative and other problems of extension work in connection with the meetings of the Association of American Agricultural Colleges and Experiment Stations had been recognized by its committee on extension work as early as 1908, when the committee recommended the establishment of a section on extension work in the association. Objection to this was raised on the ground that the problems of extension work were so intimately associated with those of the general administration of the educational work of the colleges that it was not wise to make a separation of these interests in the organization of the association. Failing to get action on this matter, the friends of this movement secured the introduction of an amendment to the constitution of the association providing for an extension section, and this was adopted in 1909.

During the next four years the growth of the extension enterprises was greatly accelerated. The appropriations for this work from State and local and other sources aggregated about $1,000,000 in 1913. At the colleges in 38 States there were extension departments. Thirty-one of the colleges reported that 182 persons were employed full time on extension work and 217 part time. Movable schools, educational trains, country-life conferences, men and women demonstration agents, boys' and girls' clubs, boys' encampments, demonstrations at State and county fairs, and farmers' weeks were prominent features of the work. Over 7,500 farmers' institutes with a total attendance of 4,000,000 persons were held by the agricultural colleges and State departments of agriculture in 1912. The colleges were becoming more closely related to the cooperative demonstration work carried on by the United States Department of Agriculture. This work was very popular in all the Southern States and was spreading rapidly in the North and West. It was evident that a stronger and more thoroughly unified organization for extension work was needed.

The popularity of the extension work grew so rapidly from year to year that though the funds materially increased the colleges were not able to meet the demands without at least indirect encroachment on the funds given them for research and teaching. Therefore there arose a movement to secure Federal funds for extension work. This was first proposed in the report of the committee on extension work to the association in 1908 and was made more definite in 1909 by a proposal that Congress be asked to appropriate $10,000 a year to each State and Territory and additional amounts after two years conditioned on State appropriations as offsets.

The association that year approved the general principle of a Federal appropriation. The matter was then taken up by the executive committee of the association. On December 15, 1909, James C. McLaughlin, of Michigan, introduced in the House of Representa-

FIG. 19.—Asbury F. Lever

tives a bill which embodied the recommendations of the executive committee. This bill was actively supported by the association.

Meanwhile the friends of agricultural and industrial education in the secondary schools had secured the introduction of the Davis bill granting Federal funds for such schools, and there was also a bill for Federal aid to normal schools. A combination of these bills was then attempted in the Dolliver bill and later in the Page bill. (See p. 364.) This led to a long discussion in Congress regarding the policy to be pursued in granting further Federal aid to the States for educational purposes. The control of the House of Representa-

FIG. 20.—Hoke Smith

tives passed from the Republican to the Democratic Party. Asbury F. Lever, of South Carolina (fig. 19), then introduced an extension bill, and this passed the House but failed by one vote in the Senate.

On January 16, 1912, Mr. Lever introduced in the House and Hoke Smith, of Georgia (fig. 20), in the Senate a new bill for the establishment of extension departments in the land-grant colleges, which, with amendments, was passed and approved by President Wilson May 8,

1914. This measure made possible the combination of all the useful features of extension work in agriculture and home economics as carried on by the colleges and the United States Department of Agriculture and opened the way for a great expansion of such work among our farming people. (See p. 288.)

(See p. 288.)

EXHIBIT AT THE ST. LOUIS EXPOSITION

An important piece of extension work by the land-grant colleges was their collective exhibit at the Louisiana Purchase Exposition at St. Louis, Mo., in 1904. Congress appropriated $100,000, to be spent under the direction of the Government board for the exposition, in cooperation with a committee of the Association of American Agricultural Colleges and Experiment Stations (428).

A space of about 11,500 square feet was secured in the Palace of Education for the main exhibit. A supplementary exhibit in stock and grain breeding and judging was provided for in Live Stock Congress Hall in the agricultural section of the fair grounds.

In the Palace of Education there were central exhibits of the Bureau of Education and the Office of Experiment Stations showing the relations of the Federal Government to the land-grant colleges and the agricultural experiment stations and the general progress of education and research in agriculture and mechanic arts. The exhibits of the agricultural work of the colleges and stations were grouped under the different branches of agriculture and there were equipped classrooms and laboratories illustrating the methods of instruction, research, and control work. Under mechanic arts there were exhibits in civil, mechanical, electrical, and mining engineering, technical chemistry and architecture, drawing, and shop practice. The equipment of the land-grant colleges for instruction in home economics was also shown, together with the methods and courses of instruction and some of the results of the work.

The outside exhibit was organized as a school of breeding, feeding, and judging of livestock and of breeding of field crops. This school was held in two sessions of two weeks each.

The plan followed was to have 25 students from five different agricultural colleges present to act as a class for the instructors to use in demonstrating their methods of teaching live-stock judging, dressing and curing meats, judging grain, making gluten, sponge and baking trials with flour, and in grading and milling wheat (428).

This collective exhibit as a whole gave educators and the general public a better understanding of the breadth and strength of the educational work of the land-grant colleges, especially on their agricultural side, and this was emphasized by the prominent place of the exhibit among those of different classes of our educational institutions.

The farming people who visited the exposition were also impressed by the elaboration of the equipment for agricultural instruction, the wide range of the work, and its direct bearing on practical problems of the farm and home. The exhibit was thus one of the factors which in the years immediately following promoted the building up of strong agricultural colleges, especially in the great agricultural regions of the United States.

AGRICULTURE IN PRIVATE COLLEGES

In the years immediately following the passage of the land grant act of 1862, the teaching of agriculture in private colleges almost entirely ceased, and it was not until agricultural instruction became firmly established and was attracting many students in the institutions receiving the benefits of that act that private colleges in a few places offered agricultural courses. The specialization of collegiate courses in agriculture and the large equipment of land, buildings, livestock, and apparatus required for such work checked this movement and there is no present tendency for its further spread.

In 1915–16, 18 such colleges in 12 States reported to the Bureau of Education that they were giving some instruction in agriculture. In most of these institutions only one or two teachers of agriculture were employed, and the equipment was comparatively meager.

In 1919–20 only 8 private institutions in 7 States reported instruction in agriculture. Of these the most important were Notre Dame University, in Indiana, with 3 teachers and 39 students in agriculture; and Syracuse University, in New York, with 8 teachers, 106 students, and 12 graduates. The latter institution also had the New York College of Forestry supported by State funds. Yale University had a school of forestry and New York University a veterinary college.

AGRICULTURAL EDUCATION FOR NEGROES

After the Civil War it was necessary in the Southern States to establish schools for negroes, most of whom were illiterate. The burden of creating and maintaining a public-school system which involved separate schools for the two races was very heavy for these impoverished States. As far as public funds were used for negro education they were almost entirely used for elementary schools. For the training of teachers and other leaders of the negroes, private funds, largely from the North, were employed, but such funds were far from adequate. Vocational education was a very new thing in any part of the country, and in the South the schools generally followed the old academic program. Naturally, the negroes thought this should also be their educational program. The secondary and collegiate institutions for negroes in the South were for the most part under control of religious denominations and devoid of vocational instruction.

Among the very few people who thought it would be practicable to establish industrial schools for negroes was Samuel C. Armstrong, who undertook in 1865 to found such a school. This was opened at Hampton, Va., in 1868, under the American Missionary Association, but in 1870 was chartered as an independent institution called the Hampton Normal and Industrial Institute. Its officers and teachers were white, because General Armstrong believed that the negroes needed white leadership in education. Here at first elementary academic studies were combined with instruction and practice in various trades, household tasks, and agriculture. A regular agricultural course was not established until 1890. Much attention was paid to the training of teachers, and graduates of Hampton Institute went into many schools throughout the South. (Fig. 21.)

In 1872 the State of Virginia gave to Hampton Institute one-third of the interest on the land-grant fund established under the act of 1862, and after the passage of the Morrill Act of 1890 a similar share of that fund was given to this school. These funds, together with increasing amounts of money derived from private sources, enabled the institute to greatly expand its normal, industrial, and agricultural work.

In 1881 Booker T. Washington, who had studied at Hampton, opened the Tuskegee Normal and Industrial Institute, with the aid

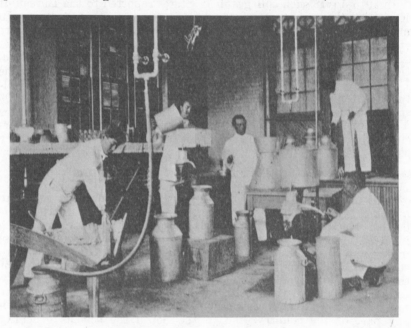

FIG. 21.—Class in dairying, Hampton Institute, Va.

of an appropriation of $2,000 from the Alabama Legislature. (Fig. 22.) This school was very successful, and had negroes as officers and teachers. It was incorporated in 1893, with a board of trustees largely composed of white persons, and was chiefly maintained with private funds, which came to it in increasing measure. The general plan of instruction was similar to that of the Hampton Institute. Considerable emphasis was laid on agricultural instruction, and under the direction of George W. Carver, a graduate of the Iowa State College, considerable experimental work was undertaken. Tuskegee Institute did not, however, receive any share of the land grant or Morrill funds.

The influence of the Hampton and Tuskegee Institutes became great throughout the South, and the separate colleges for negroes established under the Morrill Act of 1890 largely followed their plan of organization and work, as far as this was possible with the limited funds at the disposal of these State institutions. At least seven of the State colleges for negroes had their beginnings prior to 1890, but in only three of them were agricultural courses established before that time.

In 1903 the Office of Experiment Stations made a survey of the State colleges and schools for negroes which were receiving the benefits of the Morrill Act of 1890 (*423*). There were then 16 of these institutions in the Southern States, except Tennessee. They were all commonly called "land-grant" colleges, though only those in Kentucky, Mississippi, South Carolina, and Virginia participated in the benefits of the act of 1862 by receiving annually a portion of the interest on the land-grant fund.

Fig. 22.—Agricultural Hall, Tuskegee Institute, Ala.

The total revenue of the colored institutions in the fiscal year 1902–3 was $537,738.45. Of this amount $205,554.94 was received from the Federal Government, $159,264 from the States, and $172,919.51 from fees and other sources. The largest revenue ($194,046.96) was received by Hampton Normal and Agricultural Institute, and the smallest ($9,005.49) by the Delaware State College for Colored Students. The average total income per student was $88; that of the white colleges was $173—nearly twice as much.

The equipment of these institutions is valued at nearly $2,000,000, of which 67 per cent is represented by buildings. The approximate total value of farms and grounds is $300,000; of apparatus, $41,400; of machinery, $83,300; of libraries, $30,400, and of live stock, $27,600. More than half of the live stock is owned by one institution—the Hampton Institute. That these institutions are gaining in wealth is shown by the fact that more than 8 per cent of their total equipment has been added during the past fiscal year.

The total number of students in the colleges and schools for negroes in 1902–3 was 6,080; the number of graduates, 422; the number of degrees conferred, 119; the number of instructors, 346.

The statistics show that 71 per cent of the students in the negro institutions were in the preparatory courses and only 12 per cent in the collegiate courses.

But of the graduates of these institutions only 28 per cent received bachelors' degrees, and, furthermore, 269 (nearly 36 per cent) of the students reported as being in collegiate courses were in attendance at an institution which is admittedly a secondary school and grants no degrees; so it is safe to assume that not more than three or four per cent of the students in the land-grant colleges for negroes were in the four-year courses leading to bachelors' degrees. This, in itself, is not to be taken as an unfavorable criticism of the institutions, except in so far as the figures are slightly misleading, for it is known that much of the most useful work done by them is done in the secondary and special courses; but it is an indication of the grade of instruction that must be provided for nearly all of the people served in these colleges and schools (*423*).

All but one of these institutions were teaching agriculture, and more than one-fourth of their students were taking agricultural courses of some sort. In most of them, however, the agricultural work was in poorer condition than the industrial and academic work. Agricultural manuals and textbooks were comparatively few and often antiquated. Only two or three of these institutions had any laboratory equipment for teaching agriculture. Those that had farms with thoroughly modern equipment and were practicing diversified farming were the exceptions.

There were some good teachers of agriculture, but too often they were either farmers without special training or aptitude for teaching or they were men who had received theoretical instruction in northern colleges and were too scientific and impractical, not knowing how to adapt their instruction to the conditions existing in these southern schools.

Part of the weakness of the agricultural work of these schools was due to white men on their boards of trustees, who either had no real sympathy with vocational education or thought that negro students needed only ordinary negro farmers to instruct them in agriculture. Under such circumstances the negro boys, if allowed freedom of choice, avoided the agricultural course and took instruction in wood or iron working, tailoring, and other trades. They had also a powerful incentive to such a course in the fact that men skilled in the trades could immediately earn much better wages than farm laborers.

Some progress was made during the 10 years following 1903 in improving the equipment and the courses of instruction in agriculture in most of these institutions, but the number of agricultural students fluctuated considerably from year to year and did not materially increase at any time during this period.

In 1905, of a total of 6,294 students in the negro land-grant institutions 1,624 were in agricultural courses, and in 1912, of a total of 8,495 students 2,173 were in agricultural courses. Seven of these institutions in 1912 had from 8 to 58 agricultural students, four had from 100 to 181, and five from 200 to 413. That year the total number of collegiate students claimed by all these institutions was 1,544, but without doubt most of these were actually pursuing courses little if any above secondary grade. Seven institutions were giving instruction in agriculture to teachers through summer schools or special courses. The Hampton and Tuskegee Institutes began to do extension work at an early day and some of the other institutions attempted this in a small way.

After 1915 interest in these institutions grew rapidly in the Southern States and they were greatly strengthened by increased State appropriations, which in 1925 aggregated $1,455,260. The value of their buildings and equipment rose from about $2,500,000 in 1914 to nearly $8,000,000 in 1925.   Fifteen of these colleges were made headquarters for the Smith-Lever extension work for negroes and 16 received Smith-Hughes funds for the training of teachers of vocational subjects.   Of their 586 teachers in 1925, 323 were college graduates.   Including their summer schools, their students that year numbered 13,690, of whom 4,047 were in secondary work and 2,169 in collegiate courses.   In vocational agricultural courses there were 579 students and in teacher-training courses in agriculture 203 students.   An association of negro land-grant colleges had been formed, which, in cooperation with the Bureau of Education, was working toward the standardization of courses and the improvement of teaching.

Part 6. ENLARGED SCOPE OF WORK OF AGRICULTURAL COLLEGES, 1915–1925

THE SMITH-LEVER EXTENSION ACT

The Smith-Lever Cooperative Extension Act not only greatly increased the extension work of the State agricultural colleges but it also fundamentally changed their relations with the Federal Government and with the rural communities throughout the States. In its title and in its terms this act provides definitely for close cooperation between the State colleges and the United States Department of Agriculture. The nature of the work and the cooperation contemplated are clearly set forth in the act as follows:

> That cooperative agricultural extension work shall consist of the giving of instruction and practical demonstrations in agriculture and home economics to persons not attending or resident in said colleges in the several communities, and imparting to such persons information on said subjects through field demonstrations, publications, and otherwise; and this work shall be carried on in such manner as may be mutually agreed upon by the Secretary of Agriculture and the State agricultural college or colleges receiving the benefits of this act.

Ten thousand dollars annually are appropriated to each State accepting the provisions of the act and additional sums in proportion to the State's relative rural population out of lump-sum appropriations from the Federal Treasury, beginning with $600,000 in 1915 and increasing by $500,000 annually for seven years, after which this additional fund is annually to be $4,100,000. But the State will receive only so much of its annual allotment from this additional fund as is offset by sums derived from sources within the State.

The act was passed with the understanding that the county-agent system involved in the farmers' cooperative demonstration work and farm-management work carried on previously by the Department of Agriculture would be incorporated in the Smith-Lever extension work. For this reason the act permitted contributions by counties, local authorities, or individuals, as well as by States and colleges, to be used to offset Federal funds granted for extension work. The agricultural colleges were thus obligated not only to extend their instructional operations throughout the State but also to establish centers for such instruction in the counties, at least as far as cooperative funds were provided from county sources. The Smith-Lever extension system is thus radically different from the ordinary " university " extension work. It contemplates close local union of rural communities with the college and the actual permanent functioning of the college in these communities throughout the State.

To provide a practical plan for cooperation between the colleges and the Department of Agriculture in carrying on work under the Smith-Lever Act a " Memorandum of Understanding " was signed by the Secretary of Agriculture and the college presidents in 46 States, and a similar understanding was reached more informally in the other 2 States. This memorandum provides (1) that the State shall organize and maintain a definite and distinct administrative division of the college for extension work; (2) that the head of this division, commonly called extension director, shall administer all the extension work in the State as the joint representative of the college and the department; (3) that all funds for extension work in agriculture and home economics shall be expended through such extension divisions; and (4) that the department shall cooperate with the extension divisions of the colleges in such work done by the department in the States.

Congress continued appropriations to the department for farmers' cooperative demonstration work, and these were chiefly used to pay part of the salaries of State leaders and county agents. The extension system established under the Smith-Lever Act and related Federal and State legislation, therefore, brought about close cooperation, on a financial basis, between Federal, State, county, and community agencies to an unprecedented extent.

To transact the Federal business made necessary by the Smith-Lever Act the department established immediately a States relations committee and beginning with July 1, 1915, the States Relations Service. This service included the former Office of Experiment Stations and the two offices of extension work transferred from the Bureau of Plant Industry. The director of the Office of Experiment Stations was made director of the States Relations Service. The new service thus dealt in a broad way with the relations of the department with the agricultural colleges as regards their research, resident teaching, and extension work. And the continuance in this service of the chief officers, who for many years had been in close touch with the agricultural colleges throughout the country, gave assurance that the general policies of relations between the department and the colleges would be continued. This also made for an easier and more satisfactory adjustment of the details connected with putting into effect Federal and State legislation which necessitated considerable reorganization of the ·colleges, conditioned to a great extent on State and local differences of means, equipment, personnel, and methods of procedure.

As shown in the previous chapter, the colleges had developed much extension work in a considerable number of different lines and were employing many persons for the whole or a part of their time in this kind of service. The department, on the other hand, had developed the demonstration work largely on an independent basis. Over 900 counties had the services of an agricultural agent in 1914, and about 275 counties had in addition a home demonstration agent. Counting the State and district agents, about 1,400 persons were engaged in the department's extension work, and the funds from Federal, State, and private sources used in this work aggregated over $1,000,000. About 1,150 of these extension agents were employed in the Southern States. It seemed very desirable, and practically essential, to combine the extension forces of the department and the colleges in the new organization of extension work under the Smith-Lever Act. To bring this about in the best way involved a great amount of careful administrative work in the colleges, as well as in the department.

Problems connected with the organization or reorganization of extension divisions, determination of the relations of extension administrators, specialists, and county agents to college departments and faculties, adjustments of salaries of extension workers to suit varying conditions and precedents in college administration, provision of space and equipment for the extension organization in college buildings, arrangements for preparing, printing, and distributing extension publications, etc., necessarily required a large share of the time and thought of college officers and faculties for a considerable period after the passage of the Smith-Lever Act.

One interesting result of the extension system projected in that act was the closer and more permanent union of the home-economics work of the land-grant institutions with their agricultural work. In its relations with the rural communities the home-economics extension work came to function through the extension divisions of the agricultural colleges. In some Southern States where the agricultural colleges were not coeducational it was necessary to make special arrangements for the conduct of the extension work in home economics, either by creating a division for this work in the extension service or, in the case of Florida and South Carolina, by securing the cooperation of the State women's colleges. But this involved close working together of the agricultural and home-economics agents, particularly in the counties, and ultimately led in Alabama to the admission of women and the creation of a home-economics department of instruction in the Polytechnic Institute.

The reorganization and development of the cooperative extension system under the Smith-Lever Act proceeded rapidly and on the whole very satisfactorily. The work was cordially received by the farming people and through it public support of the agricultural colleges was materially strengthened. By 1917 the system in all its main features was well established. The total funds from Federal and State sources for this work increased from $3,600,000 in 1915 to $6,150,000 in 1917. The States and counties not only furnished the full offset required under the Smith-Lever Act but contributed in 1917 about $2,335,000 additional funds, of which the counties gave $1,260,000. The number of counties with agricultural agents increased from 928 in 1914 to 1,434 in 1917 and the number with home-demonstration agents from 279 to 537. The total number of persons engaged in extension work in 1917 was 4,100—2,983 men and 1,117 women. Of these, a total of 3,025—2,238 men and 787 women—were employed full time.

The extension movement and the operation of the extension system by the agricultural colleges is more fully treated in a separate monograph entitled "A History of Agricultural Extension Work, 1785–1923," published by the Department of Agriculture in 1928.

RELATIONS OF THE AGRICULTURAL COLLEGES WITH THE STATE DEPARTMENTS OF AGRICULTURE

The large development of the extension work of the colleges under the Smith-Lever Act stimulated discussion of their relations with the State departments of agriculture. Where these departments were weak and had few technically trained employees, much of the scientific work connected with the control of fertilizers, feeding stuffs, etc., and sometimes the administrative work, had been given to the experiment stations. On the other hand, the State departments had often managed the farmers' institutes. As the departments became stronger, with the passage of numerous State laws enlarging their regulatory and other functions, it became apparent that some readjustments of their work were very desirable in order that there might not be duplication of effort and friction in their relations with the colleges. This matter was taken up at a meeting of the Association of Commissioners of Agriculture in 1917, and the field of work of the State departments was outlined by a committee to include control of diseases of livestock and plants and of dairy products and foods, inspection of seeds, fertilizers, and feeding stuffs, and stallion enrollment, together with administration of State fairs, immigration and colonization, agricultural statistics, and markets. There should also be cooperation with the extension services of the agricultural colleges in "promoting constructive control projects before the people of the State." Various forms of education and extension work handled by the departments should be transferred to the colleges as soon as circumstances permitted and regulatory functions performed by the experiment stations should be transferred to the departments.

This plan was approved by that association and by the Association of Agricultural Colleges (Proc. 1917, p. 68) (*532*) and the United States Department of Agriculture. It has not as yet been fully carried out by either the State departments or the colleges, but there has been considerable progress in this direction, and as a rule the relations between these public agencies have been very good.

TEACHER TRAINING UNDER THE SMITH-HUGHES VOCATIONAL EDUCATION ACT

The agricultural colleges were vitally affected by the passage of the Smith-Hughes Vocational Education Act of February 23, 1917, which made provision for the training of teachers of agriculture for secondary schools. (See p. 377.) While the act does not specify to what institutions the funds for this purpose shall be granted, the State boards have designated the land-grant colleges in all the States.

By 1917 departments of education were in existence in many of the land-grant institutions, and there were specialists in agricultural education or distinct departments of agricultural education in a number of them. That year the Bureau of Education reported that 40 of the agricultural colleges were offering teacher-training courses with a definite amount of professional instruction and that 841 men and 18 women had been enrolled in such courses in 1916–17. From 35 colleges 513 students with special training in agricultural education were graduated in 1916, and of this number 229 engaged in teaching or directing agricultural work in the schools.

There was much variation in the methods for teacher training in the land-grant institutions. In the State universities part of the curriculum was offered by the college of agriculture and part by the school or department of education. Some institutions were offering 2-year teacher-training curricula in agriculture, but these were mainly for elementary-school teachers.

For persons preparing to teach agriculture, some institutions offer a special curriculum quite different from the regular agricultural curriculum. Others require such persons to take the regular agricultural curriculum and elect agricultural education as their major option. Some also require prospective teachers to take the regular curriculum, with a major option in some one phase of agriculture, and to carry the necessary educational courses as elective. In some cases the regular agricultural curriculum includes all or part of the educational work required for certification. Other institutions again offer a 4-year curriculum in education, with opportunity for majoring in agriculture or any other subject or subjects that the candidate expects to teach (467).

The average requirements in semester hours were as follows: Technical agriculture, 49; science, 40; cultural subjects, 26; psychology and education, 18; electives, 11; total, 144. The professional course usually included history and principles of education, educational administration, educational psychology, and agricultural education. Thirty-two institutions required two years of collegiate work before the professional studies were begun; 2 required three years, and 6 one year. Sixteen institutions required practical experience in farming before graduation. There were 104 instructors giving the whole or part of their time to the professional training of agricultural teachers in the 40 colleges, but much remained to be done in perfecting the training of agricultural teachers, with special reference to the vocational work contemplated in the Smith-Hughes Act.

The agricultural and teacher-training courses in the colleges tended more largely to have vocational aims, and the methods of instruction were modified to bring in the vocational elements more decidedly. In recent times the Smith-Hughes fund has been largely used for professional training of teachers, leaving the subject-matter of agriculture to be taught Smith-Hughes students in the regular college classes. However, the introduction of the teacher-training work under the Smith-Hughes Act has had considerable influence on the courses and methods of teaching in the agricultural colleges. This work has emphasized the desirability of general or basic courses in agriculture and the limitation of electives to such a group system as will keep the student close to his major interest in the planning of his curriculum. It has also created an enlarged interest in the problem method of teaching on the part of college teachers.

The agricultural colleges have been led to see that they are vitally concerned with the development of agricultural instruction in the secondary schools. The teachers trained in the land-grant colleges will have much to do with the success or failure of agricultural instruction in these schools, and the public will hold these colleges largely responsible for the result of the teaching of agriculture in such schools. On the other hand, through the teacher-training courses the schools are brought into much closer relationships with the colleges. If the teaching of agriculture in the secondary schools is well done by teachers trained at the agricultural colleges, not only will more graduates of the schools enter the colleges, but the colleges will be able to give students at entrance more credit for their preparatory work and some of the more elementary and practical courses in agricultural subjects will be eliminated from the college course or given only to students who have not had advantages for preparation equal to those in the Smith-Hughes schools. The establishment of Smith-Hughes courses in agriculture in many high schools has already widened the opportunities of agricultural-college graduates for employment as teachers of agriculture or principals of high schools. Such teachers, when successful, strengthen the position of the colleges in the minds of farmers and others. Their schools become centers for the dissemination of information regarding the work of the colleges and experiment stations, as well as of improved methods of agricultural practice. Thus, in another way the agricultural college is projected into the rural communities, and its educational influence is more broadly felt.

THE CRISIS IN HIGHER EDUCATION IN 1917

In a bulletin entitled "A Survey of Higher Education, 1916–1918," by Samuel P. Capen and Walton C. John, the Bureau of Education pointed out that an important epoch in the history of higher education closed with the year 1916–17 (*463*). The number of colleges and universities decreased from 594 to 574 in the previous 25 years, but 85 independent junior colleges recently organized had increased the total number of higher institutions. The distribution of collegiate institutions in different parts of the country was very uneven, and their resources and the quality of their work were very variable. Between 1893 and 1916 the national annual expenditure for higher education had risen from about $23,000,000 to over $110,000,000 and the enrollment of students from 110,000 to 329,000.

In this period college education became far more democratic. The idea that " not only should college education be open to everybody, but that nearly everybody should have it," had been widely spread, but experience had shown that the real problem was the selection by liberal and democratic methods of those who would profit by higher education. The college curriculum had been greatly expanded and liberalized. Its administration under a free elective system had been developed and pushed to an extreme, but a reaction had set in which was resulting in the adoption of the group system of electives.

There had been a closer articulation between colleges and secondary schools. The schools had been freed to a great extent from the domination of the colleges, and the colleges had liberalized their entrance requirements and had substituted in a large way accrediting systems for the entrance examination. Students had gone in increasing numbers from one institution to another, especially for professional and graduate study. Standardization of both the secondary schools and the colleges had become very important and had gone so far that there was already some danger of placing too much emphasis on the quantitative rating of education.

The strength of the liberal arts college had declined in favor of the vocational higher institution. Colleges and universities not under State control and primarily founded for the purpose of providing education in the liberal arts had been forced by public demand to add numerous professional curricula, such as commerce, journalism, business administration, and the several varieties of engineering. But in this great movement the land-grant colleges and the State universities had been the leaders.

Perhaps no institutions have grown more rapidly in power and in the public favor than the land-grant colleges. These institutions distinctly belong to the State, at the same time they are the only group of institutions with Federal affiliations. Because of this dual attachment they have played an increasingly important part in developing not only our great national resources but also a true national spirit. The important place which the applied sciences now hold in modern university curricula is in a large measure due to the progressive educational policies of the land-grant colleges (*463*).

In this movement for the broadening and liberalization of higher education the divisions of the land-grant colleges dealing with agricultural education played an important part. Here research as organized in the experiment stations had its broadest development and extension work had been most varied and far-reaching, while a comprehensive system of education in both the science and the practice of agriculture had been developed and made ready for wide expansion beyond the college into the lower schools. The agricultural colleges had come to the close of the great period of development of higher education in this country, as described by the Bureau of Education, with a strong and rapidly growing organization and with marked public approbation, as shown by the number of their students and the provision for expansion of their functions under the extension and vocational education acts. They were being drawn more and more into the general current of the movement for the improvement of higher education and were being impelled to cooperate with the other higher institutions in the study of educational problems and the working out of general plans which affected the interests and welfare of all colleges and universities. To them as to the other higher institutions the World War brought an unescapable crisis, followed by a new development of their activities.

THE STATUS OF THE AGRICULTURAL COLLEGES IN 1917

The status of the colleges giving instruction in agriculture in 1917 as regards their organization and their requirements for admission and graduation is set forth in a bulletin of the Bureau of Education, entitled "American Agricultural Colleges," by Chester D. Jarvis (*466*). In 4 States the State board of education was the governing board of the college and in 3 States the State board of agriculture. In 23 States the governing body was called a board of trustees, and in 12 States a board of regents. The number of members on the several boards varied from 4 to 41, the median number being 10. In 24 States the governor was an ex officio member of the governing board, as was the superintendent of public instruction in 25 States, and the president of the college or university in 13 States. In 44 States the governor appointed all or a portion of the members of the board, and in 4 States they were elected by the people. In only 6 States were any members of the board elected by the alumni. The term of office of board members varied from three years to life, the median term being six years.

In 17 States all higher education supported by the State was consolidated in a single university; 8 States had a single college (commonly a land-grant college); 10 States had two institutions (commonly a university and a land-grant college); and 13 States had three or more State institutions. Eight States maintaining two or more institutions had a centralized board of control.

While some of the institutions are designated "universities" and others as "colleges," the type of organization of the latter in most cases closely resembles that of the former. In other words, the institutions with the more modest designation usually are made up of two or more major divisions, each with its dean, and fairly distinct faculty (*466*).

In 37 institutions the agricultural work was administered through three coordinate divisions—resident instruction, research, and extension. In 4 States the work was administered through the heads of the subject-matter departments. In 5 States the extension service was a department coordinate with subject-matter departments. In 2 States and in Hawaii and Porto Rico the experiment station was a separate institution. In 33 institutions the extension specialists were definitely held responsible to the subject-matter departments for the correctness of their teaching, and in these institutions where the extension workers were not in the subject-matter departments it was generally understood that they would follow the recommendations of these departments in their teaching.

Students were admitted to the regular college courses largely by certification from accredited schools, but also by examination. For admission as special or unclassified students 25 institutions required applicants to be at least 21 years of age. Only 3 colleges made admission requirements of less than 14 units, but about half of the colleges lowered their standards sufficiently to admit students with one or more conditions. All the colleges prescribed for admission, English (usually 3 units) and mathematics (1 to 3½ units); 33 required physics or other sciences (1 to 3 units); 36 required history or social science (1 to 2 units); 18 required at least one foreign language (usually 2 units); Clemson College in South Carolina required 1 unit of agriculture. The number of optional units ranged from 2½ to 11, the median number being 6½. The growing liberality of the colleges with reference to optional units in vocational subjects was very noticeable. In only 10 cases was the number limited to less than 4, and in about half the institutions there was practically no limit.

In 1917 graduate instruction in agriculture was offered in 44 institutions, of which 34 gave a master's degree and 10 also a degree of doctor of philosophy. All the colleges offered 4-year curricula leading to a bachelor's degree, which in 40 institutions was designated bachelor of science.

The opportunities in the several colleges for specialization of curricula through major options ranged from less than 5 to 22 and averaged 8. Forty-four institutions offered options in animal husbandry, 43 in agronomy, 37 in horticulture, 31 in dairy husbandry, and 25 in agricultural education. The Massachusetts Agricultural College offered an option in rural sociology, Cornell University in extension teaching, and the Massachusetts and Wisconsin colleges in agricultural journalism.

Secondary curricula, made up largely of technical work and often designated "schools of agriculture," covered 4 years in one college, 3 years in 10, 2 years in 24, and 1 year in 6. Thirty-eight colleges offered winter courses of from 10 days to 5 months and summer courses of from 4 to 12 weeks. Many institutions held conferences, usually called "farmers' week." Credit toward graduation was given for some of the summer courses.

The college year in all the institutions covered 36 weeks, but the number of working days varied from about 194 to 216. In 40 institutions the session was divided into two semesters and in 10 into three terms. One hour of class work per semester or term was the credit unit. The "hour" was usually of about 50 minutes' duration. "In general one credit hour implied three actual hours of effort on the part of the student" (*466*), the distribution of this time between study, recitation, or laboratory or field work varying with the subject or course. The minimum number of hours of class work per week for which the student was permitted to register varied from 10 to 20, the median number being 15.

The requirements for graduation, as regards the amount of work in different subjects and relations of required and elective work, were so variable that comparison of institutions on any exact basis could not be made. The total credit hours required for graduation varied from 124 to 228. The median number was 157, divided among years as follows: Freshman, 41; sophomore, 41; junior, 38; and senior, 37.

In a general way the percentage distribution of the subjects required for graduation for the bachelor's degree averaged as follows: Technical agriculture, 36.5; pure science, 24.4; applied science, 6.2; social science, 4.7; mathematics, 2.4; foreign language, 2.7; English, 6.3; electives, 10.7; and military and physical training, 5.6.

English and mathematics were usually required in freshman year. At least one foreign language was required in 20 institutions. (See p. 306.) Under social science were included courses in history, civil government, economics, rural economics, sociology, and education. Forty-five institutions required at least one course in social science. generally in junior or senior year. All but three of the colleges required some work in the technical agricultural subjects in each of the four years and at least one course in applied science (i. e., agricultural chemistry, agricultural botany, agricultural bacteriology, plant pathology, economic entomology, etc.). All required some pure science in freshman and sophomore year, 45 in junior year, and 33 in senior year. General or inorganic chemistry was required by all, usually in freshman year, botany by 47, physics by 36, and geology by 39.

As a rule students select a large proportion of their elective work from among the technical courses. For this reason many of the colleges have prescribed nearly all of the nontechnical work that they expect students to carry and leave a considerable proportion of the science and technical work to be elected.

The wide difference of practice with regard to the relative proportion of prescribed and elective work offered by the institutions shows that the question of freedom of election is still a matter of contention. * * * The variation in practice concerning the placement of courses within the 4-year schedule suggests a disagreement among colleges concerning principles of education. * * * There is a growing belief that more technical work should be given early in the curriculum. * * * There is a tendency among certain institutions during recent years to emphasize the economic and sociological phases of the training, while others place the emphasis on technical efficiency (*466*).

WAR WORK OF THE LAND-GRANT COLLEGES

Before the agricultural colleges fully realized the significance of the broadening of their functions by the Smith-Lever and Smith-Hughes Acts, or had perfected their organization for work under these acts, the United States entered the World War. Immediately administrative officers, teachers, research and extension workers, and students connected with these institutions offered their services to the Government in such numbers that it was apparent that their educational work would be greatly crippled. The fact that these colleges had been giving military instruction under the land grant act of 1862 greatly intensified this situation and made the Government feel that it had a special claim on both their graduates and students. In these institutions there were also relatively large numbers of men trained in the application of various sciences to practical purposes, and this training made them valuable for war work outside of the strictly military field.

On May 5, 1917, representatives of the Agricultural College Association, four other educational associations, and 187 officers of higher institutions held a conference in Washington under the leadership of the commissioner of engineering of the advisory commission of the Council of National Defense.

The attitude of the conference was expressed in a statement of principles, in which it was urged that qualified young men below draft age and those not recommended for special service should prepare themselves in the colleges for the most effective service both during the full period of the war and in the trying times which would follow its close; that the colleges should modify their calendars and curricula to meet the war conditions; that students pursuing technical courses, such as medicine, agriculture, and engineering, should continue their training; and that the colleges should " disseminate correct information concerning the issues involved in the war and to interpret its meaning " (*463*). A permanent committee was appointed to work with the advisory commission of the Council of National Defense. On this committee the land-grant institutions were represented by Presidents Benton, of Vermont; Butterfield, of Massachusetts; Pearson, of Iowa; Stone, of Indiana; and Thompson, of Ohio. The land-grant colleges not only strengthened their military training as far as possible, but also established various emergency courses, among which were those relating to the production and conservation of food. President Wilson put the influence of the Government behind the effort of the colleges to retain their students and keep their work going in an effective way. But the exodus into military service continued. The records of the Bureau of Education show that in 38 agricultural colleges the number of students declined from 11,799 in 1916 to 7,680 in 1917; in 8 veterinary colleges from 525 to 348; and in 6 forestry schools from 484 to 236.

As the war proceeded it became apparent that more definite and drastic measures must be taken to conserve the supply of experts and of military officers. After much discussion within and outside the War Department, the Secretary of War on February 10, 1918, created the committee on education and special training, consisting of three military officers, to function under the direction of the chief of staff.

An advisory civilian board of five (afterwards seven) members was also appointed. C. R. Mann, of the Carnegie Foundation for the Advancement of Teaching, was chairman and representative of engineering education, and President Pearson, of the Iowa State College, represented agricultural education. The committee at once secured estimates from the staff corps as to the needs of the Army for technically trained men and then established 147 training centers for technicians, of which 123 were at engineering schools. Some 47 of the principal Army occupations were taught soldiers in these so-called national Army training detachments. In these intensive and practical courses under military discipline and with the compelling motives induced by the war, surprisingly rapid progress was made by the students. Job analysis and the devising of special methods of teaching to bring about the desired training were emphasized in this work.

The committee next considered the more difficult and complicated problem of keeping students in colleges and getting them ready for efficient military service. This resulted in the Students' Army Training Corps, which was at first intended to be a voluntary organization of students over 18 years of age, enlisted in the Army but kept in military training at the college until they reached the age of 21. Before this plan had gone into effect the military situation became so serious that Congress lowered the draft age to 18 years and created the necessity for a greatly increased number of officers in the Army. The Students' Army Training Corps was made an active military unit under orders from the President, and the colleges virtually came under control of the War Department, though college officers were to a certain extent responsible for the academic work of the corps. This plan, put into operation with the beginning of the college year 1918–19, lasted only six weeks, and was largely rendered useless by the influenza epidemic of that year and the ending of the war. The plan had serious defects and created much friction in the colleges, but it united the higher educational institutions of the country in a common purpose and kept them intact so that they emerged from the war in comparatively normal condition.

The committee on instruction in agriculture summarized the war work of the agricultural colleges in its report to the Association of Agricultural Colleges in January, 1919 (*499*), from which the following statements are taken:

Many of the younger men went directly into military service, many others into Federal service in positions created by the war emergency and many into war industries to take positions for which by training and education they were specially fitted. Of those resident teachers who remained at the colleges, many transferred to the extension divisions and nearly all devoted a considerable part of their time to extension work. College presidents, deans, station directors, and specialists volunteered for work in the United States Food Administration or the United States Department of Agriculture in Washington or became food administrators, or members of food commissions, State defense councils, or other emergency organization at home. There was much shifting of places but no shortening of hours of labor.

As to the shortening of the college year, there was considerable variation in practice. Several of the agricultural colleges made arrangements immediately after the declaration of war to close earlier than usual, while 10 institutions made early plans for a shorter scholastic year in 1917–18 by eliminating vacations and, in some cases, midyear examinations. Apparently, however, only seven colleges actually decreased the number of sessions in the college year.

In some cases the need for young men to work on farms was met in other ways. In Idaho and Minnesota, for example, "concentration courses" were organized. This arrangement permitted students who wished to leave college at the beginning of the growing season to devote double time to half the usual schedule and thus complete their reduced schedule in the middle of the second semester.

When war was declared in April, 1917, agricultural college students everywhere began leaving for military service, or for equally useful agricultural service in the extension organizations or on farms. Immediately questions concerning credit for college work began to arise. There was no time for long-drawn considerations. About half of the agricultural colleges met the issue promptly by permitting students to withdraw with credit for military service, for approved agricultural work, or for approved industrial work.

In some cases only seniors in good standing were permitted to withdraw with full credit, and in other cases full credit was withheld from all except seniors entering military service.

In general it may be said of existing courses carrying college credit that they were changed but little except in the direction of shortening some of them as indicated earlier in this report and of intensifying their application to the war program, to the production and conservation of food.

Only a few new college-credit courses in agriculture were conducted. These included courses for the preparation of garden supervisors in Connecticut and Massachusetts; in hippology or horse management in Indiana and Oregon; in the storing and utilization of perishable crops in Missouri and New York. There were also emergency courses for the preparation of teachers and extension workers. The short courses in farm practice, particularly in the winter, were emphasized. Special training in the operation of tractors was given in a number of States.

The greatest and most widespread work of the agricultural colleges during the war was in the extension field. With the active cooperation of the United States Department of Agriculture through its States Relations Service, and with the aid of about $11,000,000 added to the regular extension appropriations by Congress for the stimulation of agricultural production and the conservation of food, the extension organization was very rapidly expanded until there were agricultural agents in over 2,400 counties, home-demonstration agents in 1,700 counties and 200 cities, and an enrollment of 2,000,000 in the boys' and girls' clubs. A large force of specialists in the various branches of agriculture and home economics were also employed in the several States.

At the close of the war about 7,000 men and women were employed in the extension work. To cooperate in carrying on this work organizations of farming people, commonly called farm bureaus, were created in about 1,500 counties, with a membership of over 1,000,000 persons, and there was also much cooperation with the Grange, Farmers' Union, and other existing farm organizations. Through the extension agents and the farm organizations agricultural production and food conservation were greatly stimulated. Information regarding the aims and policies of the Government in the conduct of the war was widely diffused among the farming people through the extension agencies, and much knowledge of the views of these people and of the status, results, and needs of agriculture in different parts of the country was brought to the Government at Washington.

The agricultural colleges had a part in the unique educational enterprise undertaken in 1919 for the benefit of the American soldiers in France. This was planned and inaugurated by the Young Men's Christian Association and afterwards was taken over by the Army Education Commission. Part of this plan was the establishment of an organization for instruction in agriculture. This college of agriculture was located at Beaune, in east-central France, and enrolled 6,000 students, with 2,600 more at a near-by farm school at Allerey. Through a system of extension work these courses in agriculture were carried to thousands of soldiers, so that in practically every regiment some sort of agricultural instruction was given through a school, institute, short course, farmers' club, special lectures, or correspondence courses. The work was in charge of President Butterfield, of the Massachusetts Agricultural College, with whom were associated a large number of the ablest agricultural educators from the colleges throughout the United States. More than 150 others were selected from the Army, representing 40 agricultural colleges. Forty different studies were offered, grouped under agronomy, horticulture and forestry, animal husbandry, and rural economics and sociology. Numerous trips to French farms and forests supplemented the classroom work.

The agricultural colleges also had a large share in the rehabilitation of soldiers injured in the war. This work was under the general supervision of the Federal Board for Vocational Education until 1921, when it was transferred to the Veterans' Bureau. Practically all the agricultural colleges and many secondary agricultural schools were used for the instruction in agriculture. The number of such students in agriculture reached its peak in 1921, when 15,000 were enrolled. The following year there were 11,000, of whom about 2,000 were in the degree courses, 4,000 in practical courses of the unit or 2-year type, and 5,000 in special short courses.

POSTWAR WORK OF THE AGRICULTURAL COLLEGES

For two years after the close of the war there was a great increase in the number of students of agriculture in the colleges due to the return of students whose courses had been interrupted by the war, the rehabilitation work, and the general prosperity of the farmers.

In 1918–19 in the 48 State colleges for white students 9,890 men and 455 women were enrolled in the 4-year agricultural courses. In 1919–20 there were 14,750 men and 612 women, and in 1920–21, 14,679 men and 487 women. In graduate courses there were 256 men and 32 women in 1918, as compared with 744 men and 37 women in 1919 and 751 men and 71 women in 1920. In 1919, 1,133 men and 94 women students received degrees, and in 1920, 2,209 men and 87 women. In 1921, 2,417 men and 44 women were given bachelor degrees, and 195 students were given advanceed degrees. There were also 14,997 men and 1,996 women in subcollegiate work, including short courses, summer schools, and correspondence courses.

In 1922 the bachelor's degree was given to 2,339 agricultural students. At 32 institutions 265 students received the master's degree for work in agriculture, including 44 at the Iowa State College, 39 at the University of Wisconsin, 23 at Cornell University, and 22 at the University of California. For more advanced work 42 students received the doctor's degree at 8 institutions, including 16 at the University of Minnesota and 13 at the University of Wisconsin.

For some time after the war the colleges experienced great difficulties in getting properly trained teachers to meet the increased demand for agricultural instruction. Many teachers who had been in war service, as well as young graduates who might have become teachers, found more profitable employment in farming or other industries. The salaries for county agents and other extension workers and for agricultural teachers in the secondary schools were in many cases higher than those of college teachers.

The income of the land-grant colleges for instruction and administration increased from $41,500,000 in 1919 to $55,200,000 in 1920 and to $66,500,000 in 1921. A goodly share of this increase was devoted to agricultural instruction, the erection of many substantial buildings, and much equipment in apparatus, libraries, livestock, and farm machinery. The organization of the land-grant institutions is so varied and complex that it is impracticable to determine exactly how much of their income is spent on agricultural instruction. It is, however, estimated that between 1920 and 1925 this amounted to about $10,000,000 annually.

The economic depression of agriculture, which began in 1921, brought peculiar problems and intensified the desirability of more careful and thorough attention to the needs of college teaching of agriculture. The number of students began to decrease because they could not see a prospect of profitable employment in agriculture. It therefore became necessary for the colleges to study the vocational outlets for their students and to increase their courses which prepared for various special pursuits in which a knowledge of agriculture was necessary or desirable. The great demand for the teaching of rural economics, together with a definite call for instruction in rural sociology, agricultural pedagogy, and extension work, necessitated the readjustment of the curriculum to include matters relating to these subjects. The individual colleges, therefore, between 1920 and 1925 made many studies and experiments covering various phases of their curricula and teaching. Accounts of this work largely occupied the attention of the Association of Land-Grant Colleges, which also made efforts to collate the results and suggest ways for their general utilization. The Bureau of Education and the States Relations Service of the Department of Agriculture cooperated with the colleges in studies along these lines.

In the 51 land-grant colleges (including those in Alaska, Hawaii, and Porto Rico) in 1922–23 there were 13,502 men and women in the 4-year courses in agriculture, besides 588 in forestry and 525 in veterinary medicine. In 1923 in these colleges 2,413 men and 121 women were given the bacherlor's degree in agriculture; 294 students in agriculture received the master's degree and 40 the doctor's degree. There were 75 graduates in forestry and 140 in veterinary medicine.

CHANGE IN NAME AND ORGANIZATION OF THE ASSOCIATION OF AMERICAN AGRICULTURAL COLLEGES AND EXPERIMENT STATIONS

In the course of its development the Association of American Agricultural Colleges and Experiment Stations had become essentially an association of the colleges and universities receiving the benefits of the land grant act of 1862 and supplementary Federal legislation. Only in New York and Ohio were there agricultural experiment stations receiving Federal funds, which were entirely independent of these colleges.

As amended in 1912, the constitution of the association divided it into three sections on (1) college work and administration, (2) experiment station work, and (3) extension work. The voting members of these sections were (1) the presidents or acting presidents of the colleges and universities, (2) the directors or acting directors of experiment stations, and (3) directors or superintendents of extension departments of the institutions represented in the association. These voting members might, however, be represented by duly accredited proxies. Only members of the section were entitled to vote in general or sectional sessions, and " no action on public and administrative questions shall be final without the assent" of the section on college work and administration. No action of a section was valid until ratified by the association in general session. Each section was empowered to " create such divisions as it may from time to time find desirable " (499). When the representatives of the engineering and home economics departments of the colleges sought admission to the association, divisions were created for them in the section on college work and administration. This arrangement was not very satisfactory, because these departments were interested in research and extension work, as well as in college teaching and administration, and they felt humiliated by not having voting privileges in the association. They also objected to the name of the association as leaving them out of account. The feeling that the name was not right had often involved the association in much unprofitable discussion. On the other hand, the presidents of the colleges and universities found increasing embarrassment because of action taken from time to time in the association in which the votes of representatives of the stations and extension departments had been cast so as to counteract their own votes, thus making for administrative confusion. The enlarged functions of the colleges growing out of the Smith-Lever and Smith-Hughes Acts increased their apprehension because the interpretation and administration of these acts involved many new problems of relationships within and without the institutions.

This matter came to a head in connection with the meeting of the association held at Baltimore in January, 1919 (499). The presidents of the land-grant institutions held a meeting and formulated a statement which was presented to the association by President Stone, of Purdue University. In this statement it was pointed out that "the present form of organization has become too complex; that it is no longer well adapted to the needs of the land-grant colleges as a whole." A reorganization of the association was recommended, the name to be changed to The Association of Land-Grant Colleges [and Universities, added in 1926]; the legislative functions of the association to be lodged with the presidents of the land-grant colleges belonging to the association; and the sections to be retained for discussion and for recommendation and report to the legislative body of the association.

After discussion the association accepted " the principles involved in this report " and provided for a committee of nine members to report a plan for carrying the purpose of the report into effect. This committee reported definite amendments to the constitution at the Baltimore meeting, which under the constitution went over to the meeting at Chicago in November, 1919. The amendments were there discussed at considerable length and were adopted with a number of changes. The most important changes, suggested by Dean Vivian, of Ohio, created a section of agriculture in place of the sections of agricultural experiment stations and agricultural extension, made representatives of the Department of Agriculture and Bureau of Education members of the sections, provided definitely for general sessions, and gave members of the sections a vote both in general sessions and in their respective sections. The legislative branch of the association was designated " the executive body," to consist of the presidents or executive officers of the institutions having membership in the association. The officers and executive committee of the association were to be chosen by the executive body, but each section was to elect its chairman and secretary. Sections of agriculture, engineering, and home economics were expressly provided for in the constitution. When the section of agriculture was organized in 1920, provision was made for subsections of resident teaching, experiment station work, and extension service to be established.

The broadened interest of the association in vocational education was shown at the meeting in January, 1919, when the standing committee on instruction in agriculture was changed to a committee on instruction in agriculture, home economics, and mechanic arts and its membership was increased from 6 to 10, including 3 representatives of agriculture, home economics, and mechanic arts, respectively, in addition to the chairman.

EFFORTS OF THE AGRICULTURAL COLLEGES TO IMPROVE THEIR CURRICULA

In the period following the World War there has been a general desire of American colleges to meet the new educational situation by improving their curricula. The agricultural colleges have shared in this movement. In January, 1919, the United States Commissioner of Education, P. P. Claxton, called a conference of representatives of agricultural education to advise him concerning a program of agricultural instruction to meet present needs. At this meeting a subcommittee on college instruction in agriculture was appointed. Representatives of this subcommittee visited 20 of the agricultural colleges located in the different agricultural regions of the United States. Conferences were held with deans and members of the faculties individually and collectively and in some cases with groups of students. The report made in 1920 (*478*) as the result of these conferences contained the following statement regarding the attitude of the colleges toward the movement for the improvement of curricula.

It was discovered that practically all the colleges were more or less actively considering problems of their curriculum through special faculty committees or otherwise. Modifications of the curriculum had either been recently adopted or were under consideration; entrance requirements were either changed or being seriously scrutinized; readjustments of the elective system were being made or discussed. There was also a general purpose to improve the quality of college teaching and the equipment for this work. This movement was being affected by various influences. Among these were: (1) A desire to make sure that the institution would be fully of standard college grade; (2) to train students to meet more practically and fully the requirements of the particular pursuits for which they were preparing; (3) to meet new conditions in the secondary schools, especially those due to the introduction there of vocational studies, in order that the college might improve and strengthen its relations with the preparatory schools; (4) to take into account the new pedagogical theories relating to the mental fitness of students to pursue college courses, the educational value of different studies as related to the objective of the student, the problem method of instruction as related to the logical method, etc.; (5) the scope of limitations of practicums, field practice, visual instruction, lectures, textbooks, etc.; (6) new views of educators regarding the development of instruction in the fundamental and related sciences out of courses in practical agriculture so constituted as to create a desire in the student to know underlying facts and principles and to lead him on to studies of the sciences, rather than by beginning with sciences and basing instruction in agriculture on the scientific facts and principles previously acquired by the student; (7) the broadening of the agricultural curriculum to include not only agricultural production but also rural economics and sociology and, for certain students, pedagogical training.

The Bureau of Education published in 1921 the results of a study by Carl R. Woodward, of Rutgers College, in which "the fundamental principles underlying the curriculum as applying to average conditions" were summarized (557).

The need of a more thorough and comprehensive study of the problems of the curriculum was brought out at the meeting of the Association of Land-Grant Colleges in 1922 in a paper by A. R. Mann, dean of the New York College of Agriculture, on the determination of the aims and organization of the courses of study in an agricultural college. This was based on an outline of an analysis of the problem worked out by the department of rural education in that college (527).

The subcommittee on college instruction in agriculture in the report above referred to stated the objectives of the agricultural colleges as follows:

(a) The general aim of the agricultural colleges should be to prepare students to live in a rural community and work in agriculture or to work in the interests of agriculture and rural life, wherever they might live.

(b) The particular objectives of the individual college will vary with its environment, clientage, and resources, but may include training for the following pursuits in the agricultural field:

1. General or mixed farming.
2. Special farming, such as seed growing, truck growing, orchard management, greenhouse management, animal breeding (beef cattle, hogs, horses, etc.), dairy production, poultry production.
3. Teaching in colleges or schools, extension work, county agent work, journalism.
4. Research, as experiment-station work.
5. Administrative and regulatory work (478).

In the movement to improve the agricultural curricula during this period there was a strong tendency to limit early specialization. At the same time an effort was made to satisfy the reasonable demands of students who were looking forward to entering a greater variety of pursuits. This led to the offering of special courses not only for the principal branches of agricultural production but also in rural engineering, rural economics, rural sociology, agricultural education, and agricultural extension. Here and there new courses were organized to meet the requirements of various professional groups. For example, the New York college offered courses for fertilizer salesmen, poultry judges, and beekeepers; the Wisconsin college, courses for boys' and girls' club leaders and county agents; the Massachusetts college, courses for salesmanship of agricultural products, advertising agricultural products, rural social surveys, and horticultural manufactures.

There was a growing belief that while instruction in some of the sciences underlying agriculture, particularly physics, chemistry, botany, and biology, early in the college course was very desirable, teachers of these subjects should have the agricultural point of view and shape their courses to meet the real needs of agricultural students rather than to follow the traditional plan of developing their subjects logically and with the idea that the students were to become specialists in these sciences. This view was expressed, for example, by Dean Davenport, of the Illinois College of Agriculture, in a discussion of fundamental courses in science for agricultural students at the meeting of the Land-Grant College Association in 1920. He said:

> In the sciences we have yet to work out good elemental courses. The tendency is to drag too much of specialization into the beginning courses. * * * These nontechnical courses should be taught in the college of agriculture, and with special reference to the needs of the agricultural student.

At the same meeting H. F. Cotterman, of the University of Maryland, as the result of a broad study of required courses for the bachelor's degree, found a general feeling in the colleges that agricultural students seeking this degree should be required to take one or two courses in farm crops, soils, horticulture, animal husbandry, dairying, farm equipment, and farm management, and present at least the equivalent of a year's practical experience on a farm.

The results of a study in curriculum making by the faculty of the College of Agriculture of Ohio State University were presented to the Land-Grant College Association in 1923 by Dean Vivian (551). Under the plan which this faculty adopted the amount of the basic natural sciences, economics, and other so-called " arts " subjects was to be limited to that " which is necessary to give the student the foundation for his technical courses." Each student must choose one major subject on which he will spend at least three-quarters of a college year. He was to have a faculty adviser to assist him in selecting his major and the other subjects in his course. A limited number of agricultural subjects were to be taught in freshman year. Special lectures were also to be given to the freshmen describing in a general way the various lines of work. Farm experience was to be required before entrance upon the junior year.

The economic depression in agriculture beginning in 1920 brought urgent demands from various sources, including important farm organizations like the American Farm Bureau Federation, that the colleges should give more attention to the teaching of economics, with special reference to agricultural problems. The colleges had great difficulty in satisfying this demand, partly because the knowledge of this subject had been only partially reduced to pedagogical form, and partly because there were few trained teachers of this subject. The great interest in this matter in the colleges was illustrated by the discussion of the rôle of economics in the training of agricultural students by B. H. Hibbard, of the Wisconsin College of Agriculture, and Henry C. Taylor, Chief of the Bureau of Agricultural Economics of the United States Department of Agriculture, at the meeting of the Land-Grant College Association in 1923. Professor Hibbard pointed out that the organization of work in agricultural economics had been most successfully accomplished when it was a separate subject in the college of agriculture, rather than a part of the general department of economics in a college of letters and science, or distributed among several departments dealing with agricultural production. He thought that agricultural students should have courses in economics covering at least seven semester units, of which four should be given to general economics and three to agricultural economics. Doctor Taylor thought that in the 4-year agricultural curriculum the required course in economics should include economic geography, agricultural history, elementary statistics and graphic methods, farm inventories and accounts, and the outlines of agricultural economics. Elective courses should be offered in agricultural statistics, farm management and practice, marketing of farm products, cooperative marketing at home and abroad, agricultural finance, land problems, and country-life problems.

At the Massachusetts Agricultural College, where there is a division of rural social science with a curriculum of required and elective groups, in 1923–24 there were required courses in an introduction to economic principles and practice, agricultural industry and resources, and elements of rural sociology, and a considerable number of elective courses in special economic and sociological subjects.

There has in recent years been a growing appreciation that such studies as rural economics and sociology have not only practical importance but also a large measure of cultural value since they are essentially in the field of the " humanities."

The spread and improvement of instruction in agriculture in the secondary schools and the consequent giving of entrance credits for this subject by the colleges has had the effect of breaking down the insistence on at least one foreign language as a prerequisite for entrance to the college course in agriculture in the land-grant colleges. In 1924 the committee on instruction in agriculture found that " only five of these colleges now hold to a rigid foreign-language requirement for students in agriculture."

It has been seen that in the development of the 4-year agricultural curricula the colleges have generally come to the conclusion that some agriculture should be taught in freshman year. The subcommittee on college instruction in agriculture found in 1920 (*478*) that a practical compromise had been generally made between the theories that instruction in the fundamental sciences should precede the study of agricultural subjects and that the students should first deal with concrete things and make their practical knowledge of such things a basis for the study of the sciences.

Of late, basic courses in agriculture have come to have added significance and importance in connection with the training of teachers of agriculture for secondary schools and extension workers in general agricultural lines, who need broad general training in agriculture rather than specialization in one or two phases of the subject. Those in charge of teacher-training work in the agricultural colleges are quite generally agreed that basic courses in agronomy, animal husbandry, rural engineering, and rural economics are essential to best results in their field. They point out that where basic courses are lacking it is sometimes necessary for a student to take 12 to 15 semester hours in a department in order to get even a superficial view of its subject matter, and that when the work of six or seven departments is so organized it is manifestly impossible for prospective teachers to get the kind of training they need (*478*).

The colleges were quite generally agreed "that during the first two years in college students should be required to take general basic courses, which should include what the general farmer needs to know in order to carry forward work intelligently and successfully." There was, however, a lack of clear understanding regarding the essentials of such courses. The desire of the different subject-matter departments to be represented in these courses often led to too much specialization and too much detailed instruction in certain subjects. Thus some institutions would give courses in agronomy, animal husbandry, horticulture, and farm mechanics, while others would add to these courses in genetics, farm motors, farm carpentry, forging, vegetable gardening, etc. To remedy this, at least in part, some institutions developed a brief survey course for freshmen.

The subcommittee reached the following conclusion regarding basic courses:

The plan now generally followed of having basic courses in each of a considerable number of departments and spreading those courses over two years does not fully meet the need of the student who has not had a good course in agriculture in the secondary school to get a fairly good view of the general content of agriculture quite early in his course. This difficulty may perhaps be largely removed by having the basic courses in soils, crops, and animal husbandry somewhat broadly drawn and required in freshman year.

An example of a course in crops framed on this plan is that given to freshmen at the Illinois College by Professor Burlison. This course is based on the discussion of a few type crops, including cereals, legumes, and potatoes. Among the subjects treated are preparation of the seed bed, seed selection, judging, grading, improvement of varieties, weeds, insects, diseases, harvesting, storing, marketing, and cost of production.

These basic courses, together with the elementary courses in the more specialized subjects, such as horticulture, poultry, rural engineering, etc., might be spread over freshman and sophomore years. In this way a sufficient basis of general instruction in agriculture would be laid on which to build specialization through group courses beginning in junior year (478).

While there has been a general tendency in recent years to adopt the group system of electives, agreement has not been reached regarding the best way to administer this system. Usually the student has been expected to take as his major subject one of the main divisions of agriculture such as agronomy, horticulture, animal husbandry, dairying, agricultural engineering, or rural economics. But often the student desires to specialize on some subdivision of these subjects. Care has to be taken lest this specialization go too far and deprive the student of the broader training required for full appreciation of his chosen subject. Thus the student in the animal husbandry or horticultural group may not get enough of rural economics to understand the problems of economic production or marketing, and on the other hand the student of rural economics may not get enough regarding agronomy or animal husbandry to understand the proper relation of production to marketing or other economic phases of agriculture. Studies of agricultural curricula in recent years have indicated that if there is to be liberal as well as practical education relating to agriculture and country life, the agricultural curriculum must be extended down into the secondary schools, as is proposed and actually begun under the Smith-Hughes Act, and be continued in graduate courses for those fitting themselves for professional or special lines of agricultural service. This would enable the college student pursuing the curriculum for the bachelor's degree to get considerable training in all the main divisions of agriculture, namely, plant and animal production, agrotechny (especially dairying), agricultural engineering, and rural economics and sociology, with the beginning of specialization in some limited subject to be pursued more fully in graduate courses or otherwise. These are the directions in which the improvement of the college curricula in agriculture is at present tending.

One of the unsolved problems in curriculum development, which merits more attention than it has thus far received, was briefly discussed in the report of the subcommittee on college instruction in agriculture above referred to. This is the problem of connecting the various phases of scientific and agricultural knowledge which the student has considered in different parts of his college course with the actual conditions of agriculture and country life, so that he may have a fair view of the agricultural problem as a whole. The suggestion was made in this report that something might be done in this direction by formulating and giving in senior year an advanced general course in agriculture, provided persons qualified by training, experience, and outlook could be found for such work. Little has as yet been done in this direction.

This matter is connected with an educational problem which is now attracting considerable attention and which a few institutions are beginning to attack. The organization and administration of curricula in American colleges has led both teachers and students to consider the various divisions of the curriculum as complete in themselves and largely unrelated to the curriculum as a whole. When the student has " passed up " on a particular subject he has tended to let it severely alone thereafter. This has often had unfortunate results and diminished his standing as a scholar or practitioner. To remedy this it is now proposed to give " comprehensive " examinations in certain subjects at the close of the college course to test the student's acquaintance with these subjects as a whole and to determine how well he is prepared to utilize his presumptive knowledge regarding related subjects which he has studied. This is being tried in a limited way at Harvard University and a few other American colleges.

THE IMPROVEMENT OF COLLEGE TEACHING

While the equipment for college teaching has been very greatly enlarged and improved in recent years and the teachers have had more thorough technical training there has been a widespread feeling that the quality of college teaching has deteriorated. The general requirement that college teachers should have advanced degrees, and particularly the doctor's degree, has brought into our college faculties many young men who have pursued highly specialized courses and who are without training or experience directly relating to the art of teaching. The emphasis placed on research in connection with advanced courses has led many college teachers to believe that this is their primary function, and to this they have given their chief interest. Their courses of instruction and their methods of teaching have therefore been developed largely with reference to the interests of the instructors and without sufficient regard to the needs, capabilities, and aims of the students.

The recent development of departments of education in American colleges has led to consideration of the problems of teaching and sometimes to investigation of the condition of teaching in the college generally. Having recognized the importance of consideration of the problems of teaching by establishing departments of education, the colleges could hardly take the position that the study of such problems with reference to instruction in the lower schools was all sufficient. It did not take long to discover that college teaching needed improvement and that much which had been learned about principles and methods of teaching as applied to the lower schools could be used to advantage in connection with efforts to improve college teaching. The movement in this direction was quickened and intensified by certain things which came out of the brief military control of college instruction during our participation in the World War.

In the land-grant institutions not only the influence of this general movement but also the duties relating to the training of teachers of vocational subjects in consequence of the passage of the Smith-Hughes Act aroused great interest in the problems of teacher training. To a certain extent this was increased by the large demand on these colleges for persons well trained in agriculture or home economics to act as extension workers and in this capacity to do a kind of teaching which not only required a definite knowledge of the theory and practice of agriculture or home economics but also an understanding of the ways of approach to the mind of the adult accustomed to deal with the practical problems of farming or housekeeping.

The committee on instruction in agriculture, home economics, and mechanic arts, at the request of the Association of Land-Grant Colleges, undertook as its first piece of work a study on the training of vocational teachers under the Smith-Hughes Act and made a report on this subject at the meeting of the association in November, 1919 (499). In this report it was stated that provision for teacher training in the land-grant colleges under the Smith-Hughes Act had exerted—

a beneficial reflex influence on the methods and quality of instruction in subject-matter departments. * * * Quite generally it has caused a careful scrutiny of existing courses and curricula with reference to their educational values and their adaptation to particular needs. And finally it has brought into many of the college faculties instructors or groups of instructors who are primarily concerned with bringing about improved methods of instruction.

The committee undertook in 1920 an investigation on the improvement of college teaching in vocational subjects (522). Questionnaires were sent to the presidents of the land-grant colleges and to the teachers of agriculture, home economics, and mechanic arts or engineering. Those sent to the presidents related to the—

policy of the institution with reference to minimum qualifications for the initial appointment of vocational instructors, assistant professors, associate professors, and professors; means employed for following the work of teachers and encouraging improvement in methods of teaching; and the relations of resident teaching to research, extension, vocational practice, and outside employment for these teachers.

The teachers were asked to give information regarding " their qualifications as to academic, technical and professional training, their teaching experience and the number of subjects they are now teaching; methods of teaching, difficulties in doing good teaching, and measures of success in teaching; bases for the promotion of teachers and relations of resident teaching to research, extension and outside employment.

Over 800 replies were received, of which 31 were from presidents or deans. These replies showed candidates for teaching positions in vocational subjects were usually required to have at least a bachelor's degree. However, at that time nearly 19 per cent (including principally shop instructors in engineering departments) had no college degrees, and only 14 per cent had a second degree. The doctorate was held by 8.8 per cent of the teachers in agriculture, 1.8 per cent of the teachers of home economics, 5.5 per cent of the teachers of engineering, and 15 per cent of the teachers in departments of vocational education.

Replies to the question on professional training showed that 49 per cent of the teachers answering had studied one or more subjects in education, and less than 9 per cent failed to give definite values to such studies. About 60 per cent were confining their work to one subject, and less than 12 per cent were teaching more than two subjects. The teachers of home economics were carrying more subjects than those in agriculture and engineering. The requirements regarding teaching or vocational experience before entering on college work were usually not definite or fixed.

To promote professional training the committee recommended that—

the colleges encourage students who hope to become college teachers to take courses in education; they insist upon graduate study, including courses in education, for appointment to any position higher than that of instructor, professional experience to be included in engineering; college instructors doing graduate work to prepare for teaching be urged to take work in education designed for college teachers, including methods of teaching, college organization, and supervised teaching; the colleges provide for the improvement of college teachers in service by bringing in outside lecturers and arranging for conferences or seminars among teachers to discuss methods of teaching (522).

Interest in this report was increased by a statement to the association by Dean Watts regarding the effort made by The Pennsylvania State College to improve the teaching of its staff by having William H. Kilpatrick, of Teachers' College of Columbia University, give a week's course and seminar on the principles and methods of teaching, which was attended by 95 per cent of the faculty, with very favorable results.

In its second report on improvement of college teaching made at the meeting of the association in 1921 (522) the committee dealt with the difficulties in attempting to do good teaching, the opportunities afforded for teachers to improve their work, means for keeping up to date in vocational practice, extent to which teachers should engage in other pursuits, outside employment of college teachers for pay, measures to determine the success of college teachers, and the basis for their promotion.

The difficulties in doing good teaching most frequently reported were of a material nature, and such as might have been overcome to a considerable extent if teachers had had more professional training. Apparently there was—

comparatively little systematic or conscious self-analysis, and still less application of the experimental method, such as conducting tests with different groups of students or varying the method and checking results. On the other hand, many have attempted to observe the results on students and their ability to apply knowledge, to compare their own methods with those of other teachers, and to get the opinions of students and alumni.

Besides the opportunities for study afforded by the regular vacation, ranging from 1 to 3½ months, 10 colleges granted sabbatic leaves and 17 leave by special arrangement with part-time pay or without pay. In some institutions there were apparently no opportunities for professional advancement, and in others, if they existed, they were not well understood by the teachers.

A considerable number of the teachers were attempting to keep up in vocational practice by spending their vacations in shops, on farms, in home or institution work, or in consultation, commercial, or extension work. Many were engaging in research or extension work and others were doing various kinds of work for pay. Because of low salaries many colleges were permitting this practice, but in some States the laws would not allow pay from outside sources.

To determine the success of teachers more than half the institutions were employing some kind of supervision, and others were seeking the opinions of associates, students, and alumni. The basis of promotion was largely success as a teacher and capacity for growth. Other things were, however, more or less considered, such as—

ability to do advanced work and to grasp subject matter, advanced degrees, study in other institutions, research, personality, character, the extent and character of professional studies, service to the community, initiative and originality, and ability to cooperate with other members of the faculty.

In a discussion of this subject following the report of the committee, T. H. Eaton, of Cornell University, summarized the needs of college teaching as follows:

(1) Clearly defined teaching objectives appropriate to the needs of the particular students with whom we deal as prospective participants in one or another social group.

(2) Recognition of the limitations of mental discipline.

(3) Teaching through situations more often approximating those of the prospective life and occupation of the particular students we deal with.

(4) Closer correlation and integration of courses now isolated.

(5) Greater attention to individual differences in capacity to learn and in acquired experience.

(6) Increased activity and increased satisfaction in the learning process on the part of the students.

Among suggestions for satisfying these needs were the following:

A professionally qualified teaching force: (a) Selection of ablest teachers for initial courses in departments, particularly freshman courses; (b) insistence upon professional, as well as technical qualifications, in new appointments to the teaching force; (c) requirement of professional improvement on the part of teachers in service; (d) provision of opportunities for professional improvement—in the distribution of the teaching load of the teacher, in the offering of graduate courses in sociology, economics, and education, in the organization of professionally conducted seminars in college teaching problems (513).

The third and final report of the committee on this subject was presented in 1922 (499). This dealt with methods for the professional improvement, while in service, of college teachers of technical subjects. It was largely based on information obtained from the presidents of the land-grant colleges.

The committee found that all the land-grant colleges were offering courses in general and educational psychology and other professional studies for teachers, but it did not appear that these courses were in all cases available to the members of the college faculties.

In 20 of the colleges 147 teachers of technical subjects had taken courses in education while in service. The education departments were more definitely beginning to help the college teachers to improve their teaching by personal advice and by group discussions on methods of teaching in seminars, faculty meetings, and otherwise. They had not yet been called on to any extent to analyze methods of teaching in technical departments. Twenty-three of the colleges had brought in outside lecturers on educational subjects, and some were making this a regular practice.

Results of this movement were becoming apparent, and 15 presidents had reported definite improvement. College officers and teachers were showing a more receptive attitude toward professional training for college teachers.

The committee made the following recommendations, which were adopted by the association:

(1) That the Association of Land-Grant Colleges declare this year in favor of professional training for college teachers.

(2) That beginning this year the land-grant colleges make particular efforts to improve their methods of teaching by some special means best suited to their respective facilities.

(3) That a number of colleges having strong departments of education offer immediately professional courses for graduate students preparing for college teaching, including the development of graduate work with special emphasis on its application to the technical fields of agriculture, home economics and engineering.

(4) That until such time as courses in methods of college teaching can be made readily available to teachers of technical subjects, these teachers be permitted and encouraged to avail themselves of such courses in educational psychology and the principles of teaching as are readily accessible, even though these courses are not designed primarily to meet the needs of college teachers.

(5) That the institutions with well established departments of education make an effort to offer strong summer courses, so that members of the teacher-training staffs in other colleges may be given opportunity to pursue special work in these colleges.

We believe and urge further:

(6) That greater use should be made of departments of education and that these departments should become service departments in connection with the instructional work of land-grant colleges, as well as training departments for teachers.

(7) That the land-grant colleges make definite and liberal arrangements for professional training of teachers in service and urge such teachers to take professional courses at summer schools or elsewhere for at least two successive years.

(8) That instructors in the technical departments be urged to pursue graduate work in education with particular emphasis on research in some problem of teaching in their technical fields.

(9) That frequent conferences should be held of teachers handling the same or related subjects. These conferences should aid in developing esprit de corps among the instructors, in improving teaching methods, in considering textbooks, in revising schedules of assignment and in scrutinizing teaching content.

(10) That much attention should be given by the heads of departments to guiding younger teachers. Under careful supervision beginners in teaching should be given opportunity to teach a variety of subjects, thus broadening the horizon of their interests.

(11) That experienced and successful teachers should have charge of and take part in teaching introductory and basic courses.

(12) That beginning with 1925, candidates for teaching positions in land-grant colleges be required to have at least six semester hours of professional training, including courses in educational psychology and methods of teaching. As soon as practicable this requirement should be increased (*499*).

To an increasing extent during the past decade the curriculum and instruction in agriculture have been influenced by the new theories of education. The breaking down of the theory that great importance should be attached to the disciplinary value of certain subjects, particularly mathematics and the languages, has encouraged teachers of agriculture to strengthen their courses and curricula in that subject. A curriculum of agriculture in the broad sense of that term may include much of practical scientific and cultural instruction. When the courses in the various branches of this curriculum are strongly developed and well taught the student will have a practical and liberal education, especially if a reasonable amount of pure science, literature, history, and the social sciences is combined with agriculture in the 4-year college curriculum. Considerable progress has recently been made in standardizing the curriculum for agricultural students and bringing it into conformity with the progress of educational thought and research.

One of the newer methods of teaching which has the favor of many progressive and well-trained educators is the so-called problem or project method. In higher education this has been most thoroughly and successfully worked out and applied in the " case " methods of teaching law and medicine and in certain lines of engineering.

The various branches of agriculture afford much material for the problem method of teaching, and some college teachers of agriculture are now using this method at least to a certain extent. To develop courses in which this method is to be largely used it will be necessary to make a definite and thorough analysis of the elements in the various farm undertakings; that is, to make a " job analysis " of agriculture in its various forms. Beginnings of such work have been made, particularly by the division of agricultural instruction of the United States Department of Agriculture in cooperation with the Federal Board for Vocational Education. These analyses have been made with special reference to the requirements in secondary education. They should be supplemented with more elaborate analyses on a scientific basis for use in college instruction.

The agricultural colleges have also been interested in the educational problems growing out of recent studies in psychology and exemplified by the intelligence tests used by the Army. For advising students regarding entrance to college and the studies to be pursued there, as well as for formulating and conducting courses, it is apparent that more attention should be paid in our colleges to the mental status of students individually rather than in the mass. To stimulate studies and experiments in this line, with special reference to college instruction in vocational subjects, the committee on instruction in agriculture, home economics, and mechanic arts undertook a study regarding "means of adapting instruction and rate of progress to the ability of students, with particular reference to the stimulation of scholarship." Its report on this subject was made to the Association of Land-Grant Colleges in November, 1923 (*499*). Advantage was taken of reports of similar studies and particularly of the work of C. E. Seashore, dean of the Graduate College of the University of Iowa and chairman of the committee on the gifted student in the National Research Council. It was found that sectioning of students according to ability had been tried in a number of land-grant colleges, most frequently in English and mathematics, but sometimes in physics, chemistry, agriculture, home economics, and other studies.

Sectioning was confined almost entirely to the freshman year for several obvious reasons: (1) The sectioning of freshmen is usually necessary on account of the size of the class and can be made as easily on the basis of native and acquired ability, provided satisfactory tests are available, as on any other basis; (2) most of the students in the lower levels of intelligence are eliminated in the freshman year, thus lessening the need in later years for special methods for different intelligence groups; (3) the division of second, third and fourth year students into special subject-matter groups and the elections in the upper classes decrease the need for sectioning according to ability and further stimulate effort by motivating the work (499).

One or more of the standard intelligence tests have been used in about half of the land-grant colleges.

In some cases the intelligence tests have been put to no immediate practical use but are being studied by departments of psychology for such bearings as they may have upon entrance credits and examinations and upon the relations between intelligence quotients and the standings determined by class records and final examinations. In no case on record with the committee have intelligence tests been used alone to determine the fitness of candidates for entrance to college, with the exception of a few veterans' bureau candidates. Nor have these tests been used alone in sectioning students on the basis of ability except in Connecticut in an experimental way. In most cases the intelligence tests (e. g., the Army Alpha tests) have been supplemented by other types of tests, such as standardized information tests, aptitude tests, placement tests, comprehension tests, and ordinary subject-matter tests of the kind that have long been used to measure the progress of students (499).

Special or standing faculty committees on methods of instruction are increasing in number in the land-grant colleges and are aiding in stimulating scholarship among the students.

Numerous other methods of stimulating scholarship are employed. The excess credit or " point " system whereby the A and B students are given credit toward graduation in excess of semester hours' credit is in use in 16 of the colleges. Thirty-eight of the colleges award class or commencement honors. Honor societies are found at all but three of the colleges. Student advisory systems are still on trial and occasionally amount to something more than a perfunctory signing of study cards. One type of advisory relationship is proving helpful, that is the meeting of deans or heads of departments or personnel officers with individuals or groups of students of high intellectual capacity to stimulate their working up to capacity (499).

PROGRESS IN TEACHING RURAL ECONOMICS AND SOCIOLOGY

The efforts of the agricultural colleges to organize and improve courses in rural economics and sociology have in recent years been increasingly aided by the researches in these lines carried on by the United States Department of Agriculture through its divisions now combined in the Bureau of Agricultural Economics and by the State experiment stations.

The work of the American Farm Economic Association, published in its Journal of Farm Economics, and of the American Country Life Association, contained in its proceedings, has also made a considerable contribution to the subject matter in these fields.

The rapid growth of the literature on rural economics and sociology in recent years is indicated by comparison of the reports of the bibliographer of the Land-Grant College Association in 1913 and 1921. In the former year 128 books and other separate publications issued during the previous seven years were listed. In 1921 the list included 362 titles, grouped as follows: Agricultural history and development, 21; agricultural land, 12; cooperation, 17; cost of production, 26; farm labor and wages, 17; farm management, 36; marketing, 56; rural church, 11; rural credit, 35; rural economics, general, 29; rural population, 11; rural school, 8; rural sociology, general, 40; rural surveys, 16; and tenancy, 13.

At the meeting of the Land-Grant College Association in 1923, B. H. Hibbard, of the College of Agriculture of the University of Wisconsin, in a paper on the rôle of economics in the training of agricultural students, pointed out that three plans for organizing work in agricultural economics had been tried in the land-grant institutions. It had been taught (1) in a separate department in the college of agriculture, (2) in a division of the department of economics in the college of letters and sciences, and (3) in several departments dealing with production in an agricultural college. The first method, according to Professor Hibbard, is the only one which thus far has given any degree of satisfaction. The course in economics for agricultural students should include not less than seven semester units, four of which should be given to the general principles of economics and three to the application of these principles to agriculture. This course should come not later than junior year and might advantageously be preceded in sophomore year by studies in economic history, agricultural geography, and bookkeeping. Specialization in agricultural economics for those students majoring in this subject should be arranged for in junior and senior years.

This subject was also discussed by Henry C. Taylor, Chief of the Bureau of Agricultural Economics. He advocated the teaching of economic geography, agricultural history, elementary statistics and graphic methods, and farm inventories and accounts in freshman and sophomore years and the outlines of agricultural economics in junior year. These required courses should be followed by the choice of three special courses from the following list: Agricultural statistics, farm management and practice, marketing of farm products, cooperative marketing at home and abroad, agricultural finance, land problems, country-life problems.

It should be borne in mind that what the student gets out of the study of economics is not a formula that will serve as a guide to his actions in the future, but rather a method of gathering facts and analyzing problems, which method may be applied to the solution of such problems as will arise from time to time as he enters on the duties of everyday life (499).

In its division of rural social science, the Massachusetts Agricultural College in 1923–24 offered a required course in the elements of rural sociology and elective courses on the social condition of rural people, rural government, rural organization, field work in rural sociology, and rural social surveys. This was in addition to one required course in agricultural industry and resources and 14 electrive courses in various branches of rural economics.

At the New York College of Agriculture at Cornell University in 1924–25 courses were listed in about 20 different subjects under the heads of farm management, marketing, rural economy, and history of agriculture in the department of agricultural economics and farm management, and in the department of rural social organization courses are offered on the social problems of rural communities, the rural family, organization of agriculture in the United States, rural leadership, the rural community, the social psychology of rural life, the village, field work in rural society, and research in rural social organization.

In an article on the development of the work in agricultural economics and allied subjects published in Bureau of Education Bulletin 37, 1924, Doctor Taylor sums up progress in recent years as follows:

In the academic year 1909–10, 82 courses, averaging 3.3 credits, were offered in 40 of our agricultural colleges, while in the academic year 1919–20, 308 courses, averaging 3.4 credits, were offered, or an increase of 275 per cent in the number of courses offered. Instruction in farm management increased rapidly, as indicated by the fact that the number of courses offered increased from 42, averaging 3.6 credits, in 1910 to 85 courses, averaging 3.9 credits, in 1920. This shows an increase of 102 per cent in the courses offered in this subject. The courses offered in agricultural economics increased from 22, averaging 3.1 credits, to 56, averaging 2.9 credits, or an increase of 155 per cent for the period 1910 to 1920. Courses in marketing were not introduced until 1911, in which year two courses were offered. The growth in this subject has been rapid, and to-day land-grant colleges are offering 42 courses. All other courses besides farm management, agricultural economics, and marketing have increased from 18 to 125 per cent (469).

In 1910, 22 colleges employed 28 part-time instructors and 6 colleges had 11 full-time instructors in agricultural economics; in 1915, 31 colleges reported 49 part-time instructors and 14 had 46 full-time instructors; in 1921, 30 colleges reported 79 instructors and 26 colleges had 104 full-time instructors. In 1921, 70 of these instructors in 29 colleges had bachelor of science degrees; 60 instructors in 27 colleges had master of science degrees; and 41 instructors in 21 colleges had the doctor of philosophy degrees. At that time 33 land-grant colleges reported 6,908 regular, 3,109 special, 294 short-course, and 268 post-graduate students, making a total of 10,579 students engaged in work in agricultural economics, farm management, and allied subjects.

In the same publication C. J. Galpin states that from 1911 to 1922 rural sociology was admitted into 40 land-grant colleges and full-time professors of this subject were employed in 15 colleges (469).

Courses in rural sociology have thus far been mainly of undergraduate grade and have usually been for juniors and seniors. A few colleges are offering graduate courses. A considerable number of master's degrees and a few doctorates have been granted to students majoring in rural sociology.

RECENT RESEARCH WORK OF AGRICULTURAL COLLEGES

The agricultural colleges have continued to do research mainly through the experiment stations. Because of conditions growing out of the World War the growth of the stations during the past decade has been relatively slow.

In 1925 these stations had an annual income of about $10,500,000, including $1,440,000 from the Federal Government under the Hatch and Adams Acts. They employed about 2,400 trained workers, about half of whom did more or less teaching in the colleges. They issue annually about 1,000 publications freely distributed to nearly a million addresses. The contents of these publications are generally summarized in the agricultural press and form the basis of much of the extension work of the colleges. Many of them find their way abroad. Summaries of all of them are regularly published in the Experiment Station Record and sent to libraries and agricultural institutions throughout the world.

In 1924–25 the total number of projects carried on by the experiment stations was 5,538. These dealt with a great variety of problems relating to soils, field crops, horticulture, animal husbandry, plant and animal diseases, beneficial and injurious insects, noxious animals, dairying, rural engineering, farm buildings, water supply, sanitation, foods and human nutrition, etc. There were also 235 projects in the field of rural economics and sociology.

The Purnell Act of February 24, 1925, authorizes an increase of Federal funds to the experiment stations to the extent of $20,000 to each State for the fiscal year 1926 and an additional sum of $10,000 each year for four years, after which the annual sum will be $60,000 as long as this law is in force. (Fig. 23.) Appropriations under this act must be made annually by Congress:

The funds appropriated pursuant to this act shall be applied only to paying the necessary expenses of conducting investigations or making experiments bearing directly on the production, manufacture, preparation, use, distribution, and marketing of agricultural products, and including such scientific researches as have for their purpose the establishment and maintenance of a permanent and efficient agricultural industry, and such economic and sociological investigations as have for their purpose the development and improvement of the rural home and rural life, and for printing and disseminating the results of said researches.

It is expected that this act will greatly broaden and strengthen the research work of the agricultural experiment stations in the fields of rural economics and sociology and home economics, and that this will react very favorably on the resident teaching and extension work of these institutions in such lines. The history of the Purnell Act is given in the Proceedings of the Land-Grant College Association for 1925.

SHORT COURSES

The wide spread of the extension work and the great increase of secondary schools in which agriculture was taught, brought into prominence problems relating to the short-course work of the agricultural colleges, which had become very varied and complex. In 1924 the committee on college organization and policy of the Land-Grant College Association, with the approval of its executive body, asked the committee on instruction in agriculture, home economics, and mechanic arts " to study the aims, character, duration and present status, proposed development and changes of the short courses offered at the land-grant institutions " (499). It was found that 45 of these institutions were offering short courses in agriculture, as compared with 22 in home economics and 24 in mechanic arts. These courses varied in length from one day to three years. They covered a wide range, including such subjects as general agriculture, farm management, agronomy, horticulture, forestry, animal husbandry, dairying, veterinary medicine, and economic entomology; and those of median scope, such as soils, market gardening, cotton, deciduous fruits, citrus and subtropical fruits, floriculture, beef cattle, poultry, beekeeping, farm structures; or specialties, such as grain grading or judging, nut culture, ice-cream making, cotton marketing and classing, elevator

FIG. 23.—Fred S. Purnell

management, and land classification and appraisals. There were also courses for canners, herdsmen, gardeners, nurserymen, editors, and teachers.

A considerable amount of the short-course work listed under mechanic arts was in the field of agricultural engineering and the special units, such as tractor repair and operation, gas engines, blacksmithing, etc.

In general the short courses in agriculture aimed (1) to prepare persons not in school to engage in agricultural pursuits, (2) to increase the knowledge and improve the practices of persons engaged in agriculture, (3) to acquaint the students with the personnel, equipment, and other facilities of the colleges for aiding them in their vocations after they returned to their homes. Special directors of short courses were employed at a number of the land-grant institutions.

The character and variety of the short-course work are evidently being affected by present day educational movements of various kinds. There is, for example, a widespread feeling that the large investment of funds in the buildings, equipment, and faculties of the colleges is not justified unless the plant and personnel of these institutions are being used to the fullest extent. Then there is the prevalent notion that mature persons engaged in particular pursuits are greatly benefited by even a short stay at the institutions where they may receive intensive instruction or information from experts. Thus we have what are called unit courses of various kinds for doctors, teachers, butter-makers, poultrymen, fruit growers, automobile chauffeurs, metermen, plumbers, and home makers (499).

The committee felt that the colleges should make a definite effort to organize their short-course work so that it would not interfere with the proper performance of the research, long-course teaching, and extension work. They believed that the demand for short courses would continue to increase and that the present-day outlook in education favored the use of such courses. It was therefore desirable that the colleges should agree on standard definitions of short courses and employ uniform terms in stating their duration and character. To aid in this matter the committee made suggestions, as follows:

(1) A short course is a course of systematic instruction in a given subject or group of subjects of shorter duration than a 4-year college course and not leading to a degree. Obviously a course of systematic instruction can not be given in a few unrelated lectures within a period of a few days.

(2) Extension meetings, farmers' weeks, and similar meetings for a few days, having a miscellaneous program and no really systematic instruction, should not be called short courses but conferences or institutes.

(3) Short courses may be classified according to their duration as years' courses, months' courses, or weeks' courses and should be designated by their duration rather than by the general term "short course." For example, instead of announcing a short course in dairying, occupying six weeks, the college should announce a 6-weeks' course in dairying.

(4) Full consideration should be given by the colleges to whatever informational or instructional work is being done by their extension departments, by the special secondary schools, or by the ordinary high schools, and they should so limit and organize short courses as to give them a definite place in the college program without duplicating the work of other agencies (499).

Unit courses based on job analyses of special agricultural enterprises were advocated. These should be especially suited to agricultural conditions within the State where the college is located and should be planned for mature persons engaged in or expecting to engage in farming or other definite pursuit.

GENERAL STATUS OF THE AGRICULTURAL COLLEGES

Since 1915 the work of the agricultural colleges in the United States has been greatly broadened and strengthened. The organization of these institutions has also been more sharply defined so as to make the major lines of work distinct as (1) research (mainly through experiment stations), (2) resident graduate and undergraduate teaching, and (3) extension work. In all these lines the work has gone beyond that which relates to agricultural production and now includes a considerable range of subjects in rural economics and sociology.

The general character of these institutions as public agencies for the promotion of agriculture and country life has also undergone considerable modification. This is shown not only by the recent Federal and State legislation affecting them financially or otherwise but also by the closer and wider relations which they have with the Federal Government, State organizations, local communities, and great numbers of individuals in all parts of the several States.

The assumption of the duty of training teachers for the secondary schools has affected the agricultural colleges favorably in several ways. It has greatly broadened the interest of the college authorities and teachers in the problems of agricultural education and the application of pedagogical principles to the teaching of agriculture. It has opened a new vocational outlet for a considerable number of graduates from the agricultural courses of these colleges. It has given these colleges more prominence in the thought of the pupils in many high schools and brought a considerable number of them to the colleges for long or short courses. It has fundamentally affected the relation of these colleges to the public-school system of the several States and made them more fully an essential part of this system. Since the United States has only begun to develop a comprehensive system of vocational education, it may be expected that with the accelerated progress which such education will make the colleges standing at the head of the agricultural division of this system will have an increasingly important part to play in its development and maintenance.

Resident teaching in the agricultural colleges has been greatly strengthened and diversified in recent years. About $10,000,000 is now annually spent for agricultural instruction in the land-grant colleges. The courses in the various branches of agriculture have in general become more highly specialized and technical. Strong emphasis is now being placed on courses in rural engineering, rural economics, and sociology. Special attention is being paid to better organization of the curriculum, the adoption of a group system of electives, provisions to meet the needs of individual students according to their interests and capabilities, promotion of better teaching, and recognition of the importance of expert supervision of the educational work as a whole by the appointment of directors of resident teaching or similar officers.

Graduate courses for investigators, teachers, and experts in agricultural specialties have increased, particularly in the stronger colleges or universities where agriculture and related subjects are taught.

A considerable number of the graduates of the agricultural colleges engage in general farming. Scattered throughout the States, such men are often leaders of agricultural progress in their several communities. Others pursue agricultural specialties, such as breeding of improved seeds or types of livestock, orcharding, forestry, greenhouse culture of vegetables, flowers, etc. Many become administrative officers or teachers in colleges and schools or investigators in experiment stations or the United States Department of Agriculture. Others hold administrative offices in Federal and State departments of agriculture or other public services.

There are now many lines of business in which such graduates are employed. Social workers and even missionaries are being trained in our agricultural colleges. More than a hundred occupations are open to graduates of these colleges.

The agricultural colleges, through their research, teaching, and extension work, have attained a broad leadership in agricultural progress, and their influence is increasingly felt in all parts of the United States. They have in large measure made successful farming an occupation requiring not only skill, thrift, and good business ability, but also a knowledge of scientific principles and their direct and proved application to farm operations. The value of such knowledge has been more broadly demonstrated than ever before during the recent economic depression of agriculture, due to world-wide causes over which individuals had no control. In this difficult situation there have been many farmers whose knowledge of improved practices, gained directly or indirectly from our agricultural colleges, has enabled them to weather the storm and keep their business going with a measure of success unattainable by their more ignorant neighbors. This is why the farming people have held on to the extension forces of the agricultural colleges and have led the legislatures in many States to increase the personnel and equipment of these institutions for resident teaching and experimental work. Particularly have the farmers asked the colleges to strengthen their teaching and research on subjects within the field of rural economics. Appreciating the great benefits that have come to agriculture from the work of these institutions relating to agricultural production, the farming people are hopeful that when these institutions are strongly engaged in economics work they will be able to do much toward giving agriculture a sounder and more stable economic basis.

Part 7. SECONDARY EDUCATION IN AGRICULTURE, 1862–1925

DISAPPEARANCE OF AGRICULTURE FROM SECONDARY SCHOOLS, 1862–1880

When the college land grant act of 1862 was passed agriculture had almost entirely disappeared from secondary schools. After the Civil War the public high schools increased rapidly in number and attendance, but their courses of study were literary and scientific and were very largely determined by the requirements for entrance to colleges, though very many of their students did not take or complete such preparatory courses. Such academies as survived competition with the high schools made their courses conform closely with those of the public schools.

In 1876 considerable interest in manual training was aroused by the exhibit of the Russian system at the Centennial Exposition in Philadelphia. Under private auspices the establishment of manual-training schools was begun soon thereafter in New York City and St. Louis, and somewhat later in Chicago, Toledo, Cleveland, and Cincinnati. A public manual-training school was organized in Baltimore in 1884 and very soon thereafter in Philadelphia and Omaha. This movement grew rapidly after 1890 and some work in manual training was undertaken in many high schools. In 1894 the Bureau of Education received reports from 15 manual-training schools, with 3,362 students. In 1913, 1,677 schools were giving such instruction to 183,571 students of secondary grade.

When the land-grant colleges were established it was very generally supposed that they would meet the need for agricultural education. In many States they admitted students from the common schools and maintained preparatory departments. Some elementary and informational instruction in agriculture was early given in these colleges, in some cases even to preparatory students, and farm labor was required or encouraged. It has been seen, however, that as these colleges developed the tendency more and more was to confine the direct teaching of agriculture to junior and senior years and to lay the foundations for this instruction through the teaching of fundamental sciences in freshman and sophomore years, with more or less attention to their agricultural relations. The result was that very many students who had enrolled in agricultural courses in these colleges prior to 1900 left college without having received any instruction in agriculture as a distinct branch of knowledge.

It was soon apparent that of the masses of farm children only a small number would go to these colleges at all and that very few of those who did go would receive any considerable amount of agricultural instruction. The colleges might do much for agriculture by training experts and leaders and through their research and extension work, but they would have to be supplemented by lower schools in which agriculture was taught if ever the real need for agricultural education was to be supplied in any large measure.

It has been seen that economic and educational conditions in the United States during the second half of the nineteenth century were unfavorable to the development of agricultural instruction even in the land-grant colleges. It is therefore not surprising that comparatively little was done to organize such instruction in secondary schools between 1862 and 1880. During that period individuals and agricultural societies here and there urged the importance of teaching agriculture in the public schools.

BEGINNING OF A NEW MOVEMENT FOR AGRICULTURE IN SECONDARY SCHOOLS, 1881–1900

THE STORRS AGRICULTURAL SCHOOL IN CONNECTICUT

The Storrs Agricultural School was established in the town of Mansfield, Conn., in 1881. This came about from the offer made by Augustus Storrs, a native of that town, to donate a farm of 170 acres, with several buildings, for such a school. His brother Charles also offered $6,000 for equipment and improvements. The State legislature accepted these offers and passed an act establishing the school and granting it $5,000 annually for maintenance (104). An active participant in this movement was Theodore S. Gold, secretary of the State board of agriculture and former principal of the agricultural school at Cream Hill, Conn. (p. 38), which he had felt obliged to close in 1868.

The organic act stated that the Storrs school was to be " for the education of boys, whose parents are citizens of the State, in such branches of scientific knowledge as shall tend to increase their proficiency in the business of agriculture." The school was to be managed by a board of trustees, six of whom were to be chosen for a term of four years by the State senate and one by the State board of agriculture. The director of the Connecticut Agricultural Experiment Station was made a trustee ex officio, and the governor was president of the board. As secretary of the board Mr. Gold had much to do with its organization and management. S. W. Johnson was the representative of the experiment station on this board. The school was at first housed in a building on the farm, which had been constructed for a boys' boarding school and afterwards had been used for a number of years by the Soldiers' Orphans' Home.

To enter the school students must be at least 15 years old and pass examinations in English, arithmetic, geography, and American history. A 2-year course of three terms of 12 weeks each was organized, with the long vacation in the summer. The subjects taught were general and agricultural chemistry, natural philosophy, botany, zoology, geology, animal physiology, mineralogy, farm mechanics, surveying, theoretical agriculture, stock breeding, and English composition. The first year was given to the natural sciences, and agricultural science was taught in the second year. The students were expected to " acquire dexterity " on the farm and were required to labor three hours a day in the fall and five hours in the spring.

Agriculture was taught by lectures, and in agricultural chemistry the textbooks were Johnson's How Crops Grow and How Crops Feed, and Armsby's Manual of Cattle Feeding. About 1885 students began to make analyses of fertilizers, fodders, milk, etc. Elementary geometry and farm accounts were added to the course. At first instruction was given by the principal and one professor, but in 1885 a professor of agriculture and horticulture was added to the faculty. He had been farm superintendent at the State reform school for 27 years. At the Storrs school he was also farm superintendent and spent much of his time in efforts to build up the farm, which was much run down. The first herd consisted of 7 grade cows, but soon a few purebred dairy cattle were added, and in 1887 the livestock included 27 cows, 3 horses, and 7 pigs.

There was no village near by, and for several years only about 30 students could be boarded at the school. The first graduating class had six members. No degrees were granted.

In 1888 an appropriation of $10,000 was made for a laboratory and a barn, and in 1890, $50,000 was granted for a main building and a dormitory. That year one-half of the Federal appropriation under the Hatch Act was given by the State to this school for an experiment station. Field experiments were begun on the school farm, but the laboratory work was carried on at Wesleyan University, Middletown, Conn., where the director, W. O. Atwater, had his headquarters. A small office building was constructed on the farm at Storrs. The vice director of the station was located there. He was also at first associate professor of agriculture, and in 1891 became professor, the separate office of farm superintendent having been created. The senior class was employed on station work. The school course was lengthened to three years, and agricultural instruction was extended from 40 to 144 hours. In 1891 there were 63 students and 13 graduates. In 1893 this school was given the land-grant fund and became an agricultural college.

THE RHODE ISLAND AGRICULTURAL SCHOOL

Rhode Island followed the example of Connecticut by establishing a State school of agriculture, at Kingston in 1888, which was changed to the Rhode Island State College in 1892, when the benefits of the land grant act of 1862 and the Morrill Act of 1890 were transferred to it from Brown University.

THE AGRICULTURAL SCHOOL AT THE UNIVERSITY OF MINNESOTA

The organization of a secondary school of agriculture in connection with the Department of Agriculture of the University of Minnesota in 1888 was another step in the development of agricultural education which had very important results. It afforded a good example of what might be done for agriculture in a well-equipped secondary school. It thereby encouraged the organization of other schools not only in the agricultural colleges but as separate institutions in different parts of Minnesota and in other States.

The Minnesota School of Agriculture came as the final result of various efforts which the University of Minnesota had made to satisfy the demand of the farmers of the State for practical instruction in agriculture (fig. 24). On April 20, 1874, W. W. Folwell, the president, presented to the board of regents a plan for what he called a professional school of agriculture (205).

In 1875–76 a free-lecture course of 10 weeks for men engaged in farming was offered on condition that 30 persons enroll for it, and this offer was repeated for five years, but the course was never given.

Edward D. Porter became head of the agricultural department of the university in 1880, and in the winter of 1881–82 a lecture course of four weeks for farm men and women was given, which 191 attended. William H. Brewer, of the Yale Scientific School, was one of the lecturers and spoke on stock breeding. The following winter the attendance was 281 and in 1883–84 " reached the high-water mark of 1,118." At this time Juliet Corson, as lecturer on domestic science, " drew the great crowd."

Fig. 24.—Minnesota School of Agriculture, home building for boys, 1888

The first week of this farmers' course was devoted to horticulture, the second to animal husbandry, the third to dairy and sheep husbandry and dairying, and the fourth to farm hygiene, forestry, cereals, soils, and farm management.

After President Cyrus Northrop came in 1884 the lecture course was dropped, but a practical school of agriculture was held from May to November, 1885, for five students working on the experiment farm. In 1887 the attendance was 10. The president meanwhile had brought in O. C. Gregg as superintendent of farmers' institutes, which had already been conducted in the State with considerable success. The legislature in 1887 appropriated $7,500 for this work, but put it under a separate board.

Dissatisfaction at the failure of the university to do more for agricultural and industrial education reached a crisis in 1887, when the legislature appointed a committee of investigation, and there was considerable sentiment in favor of a separate agricultural college.

The board of regents then appointed an advisory board of seven farmers, and Professor Porter was instructed to consult with them regarding the establishment of a school of agriculture on the experiment farm. This was indorsed by the advisory board " as promising the best possible solution of the problem of agricultural education in Minnesota."

The plan adopted for the school was substantially that framed by David L. Kiehle, a member of the board of regents and State superintendent of public instruction. He had long been a strong advocate of manual training in the public schools. This plan, as first published in Farm, Stock, and Home in February, 1888, provided instruction following common-school training for farm boys over 14 years of age between November and April, including (1) a general business course, (2) a scientific and manual training course, and (3) a lecture course (205). In the latter the subjects were farm management, soils, plants, livestock breeding and feeding, farm hygiene, farm architecture, and the farm home. " This course should bring to the students, in familiar talks, the practical experience of men who have worked and observed intelligently in these different lines."

The organization and work of this school were greatly aided by the prior establishment of the agricultural experiment station on a farm at St. Anthony Park, between Minneapolis and St. Paul. This station, begun in 1885, became firmly established in 1888 under the Hatch Act. It had 249 acres of land, a chemical laboratory, farm house, barn, implements, livestock, water system, etc. Its staff contained a number of men trained in agriculture and related sciences who could give part of their time to teaching in the school. A building for " educational, culinary, and dormitory service " costing about $40,000 was immediately erected. The school was opened October 18, 1888, with 18 students, the number increasing during the term to 47.

There were nine teachers in the faculty, including W. W. Pendergast, principal and teacher of physics and physical geography; H. W. Brewster, mathematics; C. B. Aldrich, manual training; D. W. Sprague, penmanship; and from the experiment station, Olaf Schwartzkopff, physiology and veterinary science; Samuel B. Green, horticulture and applied botany; Otto Lugger, entomology; and D. N. Harper, agricultural chemistry.

The course of study covered two years, each consisting of two terms of 12 weeks. In the first year there was instruction in English, arithemetic, algebra, accounts, physical geography, botany, physics, woodworking, mechanical drawing, and there were lectures on farm management, farm architecture, and horticulture; in the second year there was instruction in algebra, geometry, civil government, political economy, agricultural chemistry, animal physiology, and lectures were given on grains, soils, fertilizers, livestock, dairying, horticulture, and veterinary science. To receive a certificate of graduation a student must not only complete this course but must also work in some branch of agriculture during two summers. A limited number of students had opportunity to do this practical work on the farm where the school was located. In 1889 the course was considerably changed and again in 1890–91 when a preparatory year was added.

In 1892 the course was reorganized to cover three years, and in 1902 an intermediate year of academic studies was added for students desiring admission to the college of agriculture. In 1891 a dairy building was erected. A course in dairying lasting about four weeks was offered, and a special dairy school with a term of six weeks was held especially for persons engaged in the manufacture of butter and cheese. In 1894 a summer school of four weeks' duration was opened for women, and this led to the building of a dormitory for women in 1897, when they were admitted to the school of agriculture on equal terms with the men.

The agricultural instruction in this school at first was meager, but was gradually expanded and strengthened as teachable material was accumulated and formulated and more adequate laboratory and field exercises were developed. Members of the faculty also prepared textbooks and bulletins which greatly aided the work of the school. Among these were Professor Green's books on fruit growing, vegetable gardening, and forestry, Professor Snyder's chemistry of Plant and Animal Life and Dairy Chemistry, Professor Goff's and Principal Mayne's First Principles of Agriculture, and the Exercises in Agriculture and Housekeeping for Rural Schools, edited by Professor Hays.

This school and the experiment station were so successful that the legislature from time to time appropriated generously for buildings, equipment, and current expenses. For a considerable period the schools of agriculture and dairying overshado.ved the collegiate work in agriculture, but after a time students began in goodly numbers to take the college courses in Minnesota, as in other States. Thus a great college of agriculture was gradually built up as the outcome of the definite organization of a secondary school of agriculture within the university.

The following summary will show the relative attendance in the schools and the college at intervals during 20 years beginning with 1888:

	School of Agriculture		Dairy School	College
	Men	Women		
1888–89	47			
1890–91	104		28	5
1894–95	204	59	90	9
1899–1900	327	80	73	23
1904–5	387	143	87	34
1908–9	462	192	107	188

THE ALABAMA AGRICULTURAL SCHOOLS

Alabama began the organization of secondary agricultural schools in the several congressional districts under a State act of February 28, 1889, " to establish a branch agricultural experiment station and branch agricultural school in north Alabama " (81). From two, the number of schools increased to nine through subsequent State acts, and the annual State appropriation for each school was increased from $2,500 to $4,500 in 1907. Of this sum, $750 was to be spent for experimental work under the direction of the Alabama Polytechnic

Institute. They are located at Athens, Abbeville, Albertville, Evergreen, Jackson, Sylacauga, Wetumpka, Hamilton, and Blountsville. The governing boards include the governor, superintendent of public instruction, commissioner of agriculture, and two local members for each district. All the schools are required to teach practical and scientific agriculture, which must be taken by all students over 10 years of age receiving free tuition. A normal course must also be maintained. Agricultural experiments must be made and the results published in bulletins. The schools are coeducational.

These schools proved to be a useful addition to the public-school system of Alabama. As might have been expected, there were in the early years considerable difficulties in conducting agricultural instruction in such schools, for there were practically no teachers trained for such work. However, through the employment of teachers who were either graduates of the Alabama Agricultural College or had received agricultural instruction elsewhere, the use of such elementary agricultural textbooks as were available, observation of the experiments, demonstrations, and other work on the school farms, and the labor of students in the fields and school gardens, many children were brought into contact with improved agricultural practices and received knowledge of the scientific principles underlying such practices. There was undoubtedly too much of a tendency to make these schools serve the general purposes of public schools for their districts and especially for the communities in which they were located, but even so they were doing useful work at a time when high schools were scarce in the State. The State was spending only a small sum for their support as agricultural schools, and the local communities were furnishing the land, the buildings, and much of the money for current expenses. In his message to the legislature in 1907 Governor Comer summed up the work of these schools as follows:

The nine agricultural schools located one in each of the nine congressional districts are doing a great work and should be encouraged. * * * These schools are located in different parts of the State, generally where board is cheap, and they furnish boys and girls outside of the cities not only with the most economical agricultural lessons but also with the best substitute for high schools.

He favored an increased appropriation, and the legislature responded by granting $4,500 a year to each school, with the proviso that $750 should be spent for experiments. The experiments were to be made under the " direction of the board of control and the professor of agriculture of the Alabama Polytechnic Institute." He was also to formulate the course in scientific agriculture and floriculture. An association of these schools was formed in 1907, which appointed a committee, consisting of the presidents of two schools and the director of the Alabama Agricultural Experiment Station, to prepare uniform courses of study. These included an agricultural-scientific and an agricultural-classical course, based on an elementary course of seven grades. The former course included agriculture during four years from three to five hours a week, with an hour of practical work and the sciences of physiography, physiology, botany, physics, and chemistry, together with English, mathematics, and history. In the classical course Latin during four years was substituted for part of the science and agriculture.

In 1908 these schools had substantial buildings, and their plants were valued at from $8,500 to $59,000. Five schools had from 40 to 55 acres of land, three had 80 acres, and one 163 acres. Outside of the State appropriation of $4,500, their income was from $1,757 to $6,755. Their enrollment of students was from 91 to 282 and aggregated 1,364. They graduated that year from 6 to 23 students each, a total of 86. The experimental work carried on by these schools was necessarily simple and largely demonstrational, consisting chiefly of variety and fertilizer tests, rotation of crops, and methods of cultivation.

These schools have continued operation on a comparatively modest scale. In 1919 their designation was changed by the legislature to the "State secondary agricultural schools of Alabama," and they were permitted to qualify for the teaching of vocational agriculture under the terms of the Smith-Hughes Act.

EARLY WORK OF THE OFFICE OF EXPERIMENT STATIONS RELATING TO
SECONDARY EDUCATION IN AGRICULTURE

In 1893 the Office of Experiment Stations in the United States Department of Agriculture began to take a definite interest in agricultural education below the collegiate grade, as is shown by the report of the director of the office for that year and the year 1894.

In an article on popular education for the farmer in the Yearbook of the United States Department of Agriculture for 1897 (450), after calling attention to the secondary schools of agriculture in Minnesota and Alabama, and commending the establishment of such schools, the Director of the Office of Experiment Stations said:

But it is not believed that these special agricultural high schools will fully meet the needs of our farmers for agricultural instruction of this grade. Any school so distant from the farmer's home as to necessitate long journeys and residence at the school for two or more years must necessarily be too expensive for most of the farmers' children, especially after they have reached an age when their services may be more or less utilized on the farm. What is needed is courses in agriculture in numerous schools to which farmers' children resort, near their home, to "finish" their education after they are through with the common schools.

The Office of Experiment Stations then undertook an active propaganda in different parts of the country for the introduction of agriculture into the secondary schools, through its publications, addresses at educational and farmers' meetings, correspondence and conferences with educators and others interested in this matter, and by cooperation with the Association of Agricultural Colleges, particularly through its committee on instruction in agriculture. In 1901 D. J. Crosby, a graduate of and instructor in the Michigan Agricultural College, was added to the staff of the Office of Experiment Stations as a special assistant to the director in work relating to agricultural education. The more favorable economic conditions of agriculture, the rapidly increasing attendance at the agricultural colleges, the great growth of the farmers' institutes, and other causes helped to promote the movement for secondary education in agriculture, and it made great advances during the first decade of the twentieth century.

DEVELOPMENT OF SECONDARY EDUCATION IN AGRICULTURE WITHOUT FEDERAL ENDOWMENT, 1900–1916

After 1900 the movement for secondary education in agriculture developed rapidly and broadly. It was promoted by Federal, State, county, and local agencies. Secondary instruction in agriculture was introduced into public and private colleges and schools of various kinds. Much of the work done by the agencies and institutions interested in this movement was necessarily tentative and experimental. An attempt has been made in the following pages to summarize the leading features of this movement and the early work of typical institutions.

NATIONAL AGENCIES FOR THE PROMOTION OF SECONDARY EDUCATION IN AGRICULTURE

OFFICE OF EXPERIMENT STATIONS

The Office of Experiment Stations in 1902 began to publish a section on the progress of secondary education in agriculture in its annual report, and this was continued for 10 years. In September, 1905, a department of agricultural education was established in the Experiment Station Record. Much information regarding the progress of secondary education in agriculture in this and other countries was collected by this office and published in its reports or in the Experiment Station Record. The appropriation act for the Department of Agriculture passed in 1903, for the first time gave the office specific authority for its work relating to farmers' institutes by providing $5,000 to be used—

to investigate and report upon the organization and progress of farmers' institutes in the several States and Territories and upon similar organizations in foreign countries, with special suggestions of plans and methods for making such organizations more effective for the dissemination of the results of the work of the Department of Agriculture and the agricultural experiment stations, and of improved methods of agricultural practice.

This item was amended in 1906 by inserting the words " and agricultural schools " after " farmers' institutes." The appropriation was not increased until 1908, when it was made $10,000.

Among the special publications of the Office of Experiment Stations on secondary education during the next 10 years were those on the American system of agricultural education, a secondary course in agronomy and in animal husbandry, training courses for teachers of agriculture, simple exercises illustrating some applications of chemistry to agriculture, community work in the rural high school, and home projects in secondary agriculture.

The work of the Office of Experiment Stations as a clearing house of information and advice regarding the courses, personnel, equipment, illustrative material, and literature for secondary instruction in agriculture greatly increased. Representatives of that office were active in meetings of the National Education Association, the American Association for the Advancement of Agricultural Teaching, summer schools for teachers, and other educational meetings and in holding personal conferences with school officers and teachers at schools in different States.

Cooperation with the Association of Agricultural Colleges on matters relating to secondary education, mainly through its committee on instruction in agriculture, continued to be a feature of the work of the office. Up to 1910 the proceedings of this association were published as bulletins of this office.

THE ASSOCIATION OF AGRICULTURAL COLLEGES AND EXPERIMENT STATIONS

As the movement for secondary instruction in agriculture progressed the Association of American Agricultural Colleges and Experiment Stations took an increasing interest in this subject, and its various phases were discussed at the annual conventions of the association.

In 1902 the report of the committee on instruction in agriculture contained a section on secondary courses in agriculture. The committee commended the definite organization of schools of agriculture within the colleges as emphasizing the desirability of distinguishing between collegiate and secondary instruction in agriculture.

It was believed that the special agricultural high schools in Alabama, Wisconsin, and California would, if successful, result in the establishment of similar schools throughout the Union, which would probably be under State rather than local control. But, in addition, "the teaching of agriculture should be introduced into the public high schools in or near the rural communities" (*499*).

As a practical measure it is believed that such courses may be added to those already existing in many high schools by the addition of a single teacher, who should be an agricultural college graduate, to the teaching force already supplied. The expense of maintaining this teacher and his equipment may properly be shared by the State, the village, or city maintaining the high school and the country districts from which the pupils from the farms are drawn to this school. The State may properly aid this movement by offering a stated sum annually to high schools maintaining agricultural courses (*499*).

At this time, where the teaching of agriculture in the public schools was advocated, there was insistent demand, especially from school officials, that it should be definitely shown how this could be done without disrupting existing school programs. The committee therefore undertook to show this by examples drawn to illustrate what might be done in the smaller high schools in Indiana, in the medium-sized cities of Lowell, Mass., and Des Moines, Iowa, and in the large city of Washington, D. C. Five periods a week of agriculture during four years were substituted in the Indiana course for Latin in the first two years and the elective offered in the third and fourth years. It was suggested that the work of such schools might be carried on by three teachers, one of whom should be an agricultural college graduate and might teach chemistry, botany, and zoology as well as agriculture. He might also act as principal. In the larger schools in the cities mentioned it was shown that agriculture might be introduced as an elective, to be added to the considerable number of electives already offered in these schools.

At the meeting of the association in 1905 the chairman of this committee read a paper on the relations of the agricultural colleges to the public schools. He said that the colleges should study the programs of the public schools, come into close touch with their officers and teachers, provide courses of instruction which would be attractive to school officers and teachers, and by summer schools or otherwise seek to bring such persons into direct contact with the system of education represented in these colleges.

Elementary and secondary courses in agriculture and mechanic arts in the public schools were advocated to direct students to the land-grant colleges and prepare them to enter courses in these institutions.

In 1907 the committee's syllabus of a secondary course in agronomy was published as Circular 77 of the Office of Experiment Stations.

At the meeting of the association in 1909 the chairman of the committee read a paper in which he reviewed the status of agricultural education in secondary schools and suggested ways in which such instruction could be developed in harmony with the existing educational systems of the United States. His conclusions were as follows:

> Agriculture, including horticulture and forestry, should be a regular part of public secondary education; second, the unity of our educational system should be maintained, but there should be sufficient elasticity of curriculum to meet the various needs of our people; third, the standard of the curriculum of secondary schools having agricultural courses should conform in a general way to those adopted for the general school system of the State; fourth, the standard agricultural courses, whether in the ordinary high schools or in special schools, should not be narrowly vocational, but should aim to fit the pupils for life as progressive, broad-minded, and intelligent men and women, citizens and home makers, as well as farmers and horticulturists (439).

Some disapproval of separate agricultural schools was expressed in the discussion of this paper, but the importance of such schools as finishing or vocational schools and as a means of training teachers of agriculture for the elementary schools was also brought out. The general views expressed in the paper were indorsed by formal vote of the convention, and its separate publication was requested. (See Office of Experiment Stations Circular 91.) Later in this meeting a paper was read by E. A. Burnett, dean of the Nebraska College of Agriculture, on "The Function of the Land-Grant College in Promoting Agricultural Education in Secondary Schools," in which he favored the establishment of a limited number of agricultural schools in connection with existing high schools favorably situated for serving a large country constituency. Dean Davenport, of Illinois, stated his belief that vocational agriculture should be put "within walking or riding distance" of every farm boy by creating agricultural departments in the high schools.

In 1910 the association discussed the correlation of secondary and short courses with the 4-year college course in agriculture. This discussion was introduced by a paper by D. J. Crosby, of the Office of Experiment Stations, in which he urged that in connection with secondary courses opportunities should be afforded to capable students to enter the regular college courses. He also advocated supervised home projects during the long vacation for students in schools having a 6-months term. W. M. Hays advocated secondary schools at all the agricultural colleges to aid in preparing teachers for the lower schools.

In 1911 the new committee on college organization and policy in its first report advocated the inclusion of secondary instruction by the colleges in a department of agricultural extension, but this was strongly opposed. After a long discussion of measures for Federal aid for education pending in Congress the association declared in favor of such aid for public schools of secondary grade providing education in agriculture, home economics, trades and industries, and manual training. This action was reaffirmed the following year.

In 1912 the committee on instruction in agriculture reported on the work of the agricultural colleges in training teachers of agriculture for secondary schools. An account was given of this work in the several States, and the existing situation was summed up as follows (*499*):

From the best available sources of information it appears that 40 of the agricultural colleges for white students are offering courses designed to train high school teachers of agriculture. In some cases little more than an elective or two in psychology and pedagogy is offered; in others there are summer schools; in others definitely outlined teacher-training courses, and for the most approved instruction in education, supplemented by practice teaching under expert supervision.

The committee recommended that students preparing to teach agriculture should be well grounded in the general principles of agriculture and should have not less than 20 semester hours of professional training, including special methods of teaching agriculture and practice teaching. Special provision should be made for teachers in service in secondary schools to acquire a knowledge of the science and practice of agriculture.

In 1916 this committee made a study of the relations of the agricultural colleges to the high schools in which agriculture was taught, with special reference to the problem of entrance or college credit for secondary agricultural courses. A report was made on the basis of information received from 2,200 high schools (*535*).

It appeared that 97 per cent of these schools were teaching agriculture and that 92 per cent of the agricultural colleges were offering entrance credit of from one-half to 4 units in this subject. But only one college was allowing credits for graduation for high-school agriculture and no colleges were making class sections for students who had studied agriculture in high school. The committee recommended that the colleges should train teachers of agriculture for the high schools, assist in developing suitable courses, textbooks, manuals, and equipment for high-school agriculture, and cooperate with the State departments of education in supervising high-school agriculture.

THE UNITED STATES BUREAU OF EDUCATION

The Bureau of Education has promoted the teaching of agriculture in the secondary schools by the collection and publication of statistics and other information regarding such work in this country and abroad. For a number of years it has had specialists in rural or agricultural education who have given special attention to this matter and have aided the movement through participation in educational meetings in different parts of the country, as well as by the preparation of publications. Among the bureau's publications relating to agriculture in the secondary schools are the following: Bulletin No. 1, 1908, The Training of Persons to Teach Agriculture, by L. H. Bailey; No. 6, 1912, Agricultural Education in Secondary Schools; No. 2, 1913, Training courses for Rural Teachers, by A. C. Monahan and R. H. Wright; No. 6, 1913, Agricultural Instruction in High

Schools, by C. H. Robison and F. B. Jenks; No. 14, 1913, Agricultural Instruction in Secondary Schools; No. 27, 1914, Agricultural Teaching; No. 34, 1917, Institutions in the United States giving Instruction in Agriculture, 1915–16, by A. C. Monahan and C. H. Dye; No. 38, 1917, Vocational Teachers for Secondary Schools, by Chester D. Jarvis; No. 85, 1919, Development of Agricultural Instruction in Secondary Schools, by H. P. Barrows.

NATIONAL EDUCATION ASSOCIATION

At the meeting of the National Education Association in Boston, Mass., in 1903 a committee was appointed to investigate and report as to what should be undertaken in the field of industrial education in schools in rural communities. This committee included L. D. Harvey, of Wisconsin; L. H. Bailey, of New York; Alfred Bayliss, of Illinois; W. T. Carrington, of Missouri; and W. M. Hays, Assistant Secretary of Agriculture. This committee made an extended report to the association at Asbury Park, N. J., July 3, 1905. (See Experiment Station Record, vol. 17, p. 196.) Their general conclusions were as follows: In existing 1-room district schools little result can be expected from attempts to teach nature study, elementary agriculture, and handwork, and it would be unwise to make instruction in these subjects mandatory. Much more in these lines might come from such instruction in consolidated schools and high schools. The agricultural colleges should actively engage in putting available knowledge in the field of industrial education into available form for use in elementary and secondary schools. The people in rural communities should be shown the value of industrial education and the courses of study in rural schools should be framed with reference to meeting the needs of rural children. Boys' and girls' clubs, reading courses, and farmers' institutes should be promoted. Special opportunities and inducements should be offered to teachers to prepare themselves for giving instruction in industrial subjects. An articulated series of schools from the elementary school through the college should be organized for rural people. A similar committee presented a report in 1907.

From this time the association took a more active interest in agricultural education, and at Los Angeles in July, 1907, the formation of a department of rural and agricultural education was authorized. This was organized in February, 1908, at the Washington meeting of the department of superintendence, with E. C. Bishop, of Lincoln, Nebr., as president, and D. B. Johnson, of Rockhill, S. C., as vice president. At this meeting, which was attended by nearly 1,600 persons from every State and Territory, except Arizona, Nevada, and Porto Rico, a resolution was adopted indorsing "the great value of the study of agricultural subjects in the schools of the rural districts." W. M. Hays, Assistant Secretary of Agriculture, gave the principal address at the first evening session, his subject being Agricultural Industries and Home Economics in the Public Schools. At a round table on agricultural education the educational work of the United States Department of Agriculture was outlined broadly by the writer, and the training of teachers of agriculture was discussed by E. E. Brown, United States Commissioner of Education; J. R. Kirk, president of the State Normal School at Kirksville, Mo.; and K. L. Butterfield, president of the Massachusetts Agricultural College. D. J. Crosby, of the Office of Experiment Stations, read a paper on Cooperation between the United States Department of Agriculture and State School Authorities to Promote Agricultural Education.

The convention of the association at Cleveland, Ohio, June 29 to July 3, 1908, gave unusual attention to vocational education, and at the meeting in Denver in July, 1909, much attention was given to agricultural education. Great interest centered in the discussion regarding special agricultural schools. Dean Davenport, of Illinois, opposed their establishment on the ground that their courses must of necessity be narrow and that the tendency of such schools would be to " peasantize " the farmers. He strongly urged the teaching of agriculture in the local high schools. D. J. Crosby presented the view of the Office of Experiment Stations that agriculture should be taught in both the high schools and a limited number of special schools. The latter would be especially for mature youths who had decided to follow agricultural pursuits and would have the advantage of greater breadth and thoroughness of agricultural instruction, aided by equipment of laboratories, animals, machinery, etc., superior to that of the ordinary high schools.

By this time the association had come to consider agricultural education as forming a permanent part of our public-school system, and regular provision was made for the discussion of its various phases at succeeding meetings.

THE NATIONAL SOCIETY FOR THE SCIENTIFIC STUDY OF EDUCATION

The National Society for the Scientific Study of Education, composed of professors of education and others interested in the study of education, holds annual meetings in connection with the convention of the department of superintendence of the National Education Association. Since 1902 it has published yearbooks. One part of the yearbook for 1912 was devoted to papers on agricultural education in secondary schools, prepared under direction of D. J. Crosby, of the Office of Experiment Stations.

THE NATIONAL COMMITTEE ON AGRICULTURAL EDUCATION

The national committee on agricultural education, organized in 1904 by persons interested in the teaching of agriculture in the public schools, held meetings for several years in connection with the National Education Association, at which matters relating to secondary education were discussed. It was greatly interested in the effort to create a department of rural and agricultural education in the National Education Association. When that department was organized in 1908 this committee went out of existence.

SECONDARY INSTRUCTION IN AGRICULTURAL COLLEGES

The general history of the development of secondary instruction in agriculture in the agricultural colleges has already been described. (See particularly pp. 273 and 324.) This instruction has been organized in two general forms, (1) as a distinct school of agriculture within the college, or (2) as short courses of various lengths and for different purposes. The short courses, covering a year or more, are to a considerable extent of the same general character as the regular courses in the schools, but the schools as well as college departments also offer special courses covering shorter periods. In 1915–16 the Bureau of Education listed 24 land-grant institutions as maintaining schools or secondary courses of agriculture covering from one to four years. Schools were maintained in 11 States, as follows: California, Colorado, Connecticut, Idaho, Kansas, Minnesota, Montana, Nebraska, North Dakota, South Dakota, and Washington. One-year, 2-year, industrial or vocational courses were maintained in 13 States: Iowa, Michigan, Mississippi, New Hampshire, New Mexico, North Carolina, Oregon, Pennsylvania, Rhode Island, South Carolina, Texas, Utah, and Virginia. The schools were—

taught in large part by members of the regular agricultural college faculty and the college recitation rooms, lecture rooms, laboratories, and equipment are all used. There is little difference in the organization of these so-called "schools of agriculture" and in the "1-year," "2-year," "industrial," and "vocational" courses in agriculture in other colleges (*471*).

In three States additional schools were maintained away from the college, though under its direction. The Colorado college had one at Fort Lewis, the Nebraska College one at Curtis, and the Minnesota college two, at Crookston and Morris. The school at Davis, under the University of California, served the double purpose of a secondary school and an institution giving college education in some agricultural subjects to members of classes who did most of their work at the College of Agriculture at Berkeley.

The status of the short courses in 1924 has been described in a previous chapter. (See p. 317.)

As the number of secondary courses in agriculture in special schools and the high schools increased and it became evident that such instruction would become a permanent part of our public-school system, the problem of college credit for such courses arose. In 1905 the council of the University of Missouri initiated the movement for giving credit for high-school agriculture on the entrance requirements for college. One unit was allowed for a year's work in agriculture in the high school.

About the same time the regents of the University of the State of New York, who provided uniform examinations for all the high schools of the State, decided to allow credits for nature study and agriculture provided the courses in these subjects showed educational values comparable with those of the other subjects recognized in their examinations. To meet this situation the College of Agriculture at Cornell University, at the request of the New York State Department of Education, prepared a typical syllabus for a high-school course in agriculture.

INSTRUCTION IN AGRICULTURE IN NORMAL SCHOOLS

Early in the twentieth century normal schools in a number of States began to teach agriculture. This was closely connected with the movement for the introduction of nature study and elementary agriculture into the rural schools, which will be described in a later chapter. In Wisconsin the county training schools for teachers in Dunn and Marathon Counties were combined with the schools established in 1902 in which agriculture was taught. Soon thereafter county teacher-training schools in Michigan began the teaching of agriculture. About the same time the State Normal and Industrial College for Women, at Rockhill, S. C., began instruction in agriculture in connection with school-garden work.

In Missouri the State Normal School at Kirksville in 1900–1901 began to give a 1-year course in agriculture under the active leadership of the principal of the school, John R. Kirk, who was greatly interested in promoting agricultural education. It was the first attempt to give a systematic course in agriculture at a normal school in the United States. This resulted in 1905 in the publication of a manual and textbook of elementary agriculture entitled "Agriculture Through the Laboratory and School Garden," by Miss C. R. Jackson and Mrs. L. S. Dougherty, instructors in that school. This book shows that the course in agriculture there treated of soils, leguminous plants, propagation and improvement of plants, pruning, enemies of plants, rotation of crops, principles of feeding, milk and its care, and ornamentation of school and home grounds. Suggestions for laboratory exercises and field work and numerous references to the literature of the subject were prominent features of this book.

About the same time the normal school at Cape Girardeau began a 1-year course, which included one term each of soils and soil management, plant culture and horticultural practice, and home dairying and landscape gardening. A little later the normal school at Warrensburg undertook similar work. The courses in agriculture in these Missouri schoools were afterwards further developed and covered a longer period.

In Georgia the State normal schools at Athens and Milledgeville early began to develop courses in agriculture. In 1906–7 at Athens this subject was taught throughout the diploma course of three years and was one of the subjects in the short review course. In the senior year students recited one double period a week on elementary agriculture, which included a review of previous work and a study of methods. The school had a 20-acre farm which furnished food for the students and was also utilized as a laboratory for the classes in agriculture. Students did practical work with different varieties of plants and fertilizers, budding, grafting, spraying, growing of plants in pots, etc. They studied rural-life problems, made detailed studies of a few staple crops in the South, and had some instruction regarding livestock and truck farming. At Milledgeville agriculture was a required subject in the freshman year and was followed in the junior and senior years by special courses on plants, animals, climate, weather, soils, etc.

In the Alabama State Normal School at Jacksonville agriculture was taught in 1906–7 in the first and second years and horticulture in the fourth year, with practical exercises in pruning, grafting, etc. The Colorado State Normal School at Greeley about this time required agriculture four hours a week throughout the eleventh grade of the high-school course and the ninth grade of the normal-school course and offered it as an elective in the twelfth grade of the high-school course. It was taught by an associate professor of nature study, school gardening, and elementary agriculture.

In 1907 the Office of Experiment Stations reported that 64 of the 182 State normal schools in the United States were teaching agriculture (*439*).

Of these, 4 are in Alabama, 3 in California, 1 in Colorado, 2 in Connecticut, 2 in Georgia, 3 in Illinois, 1 in Iowa, 1 in Kansas, 1 in Louisiana, 3 in Maine, 3 in Michigan, 5 in Missouri, 1 in Montana, 3 in Nebraska, 1 in North Carolina, 2 in North Dakota, 1 in Ohio, 3 in Oklahoma, 1 in Oregon, 1 in South Carolina, 1 in South Dakota, 1 in Texas, 2 in Utah, 2 in Virginia, 3 in Washington, 6 in West Virginia, and 7 in Wisconsin.

The instruction in agriculture in 13 of these institutions is confined to the textbook, in 35 the textbook work is supplemented by laboratory exercises, school garden work, or other practicums, while in the remaining 16 schools the nature of the instruction is uncertain, though it is likely that fully half of these provide practice work.

Fully 70 per cent of the teachers of agriculture in normal schools were trained for other lines of work, and of the remaining 30 per cent nearly one-half are burdened with other science work.

In some of the normal schools agriculture was taught by teachers of agriculture, in others by teachers of science, and in the remaining schools by other teachers—principals, teachers of pedagogy, economics, and other subjects.

Oklahoma in the general law of May 20, 1908, for a system of agricultural education, provided $2,500 annually for a department of agricultural and industrial education in each of the State normal schools. The same year Texas appropriated $2,000 a year for two years to each of its three State normal schools for departments of agriculture, manual training, and domestic science, and also made provision for teachers' courses in elementary agriculture in the summer sessions at these schools.

In 1910 the Massachusetts State Normal School at North Adams, with the cooperation of the agricultural college, undertook special work with reference to rural schools, which was extended to cover three years of instruction on problems relating to farm crops, horticulture, poultry, and dairying.

In New York, after the passage of a law giving State aid to schools organizing departments of agriculture, home economics, and manual training, the State Normal and Training School at Cortland in 1911 offered 2-year and 1-year courses for men with instruction in agriculture and allied sciences, psychology, and education.

The normal schools, as well as the agricultural colleges, in a number of States offered short summer or winter courses in agricultural subjects, with special reference to the needs of teachers in service. A unique summer school of this kind, apart from the normal schools, was held at Cape May, N. J., August 6–31, 1908, under direction of H. O. Sampson, of the Office of Experiment Stations. The instruction was carried on by lectures, laboratory demonstrations, and field trips. Special effort was made to show how elementary instruction in agriculture could be effectively given without expensive apparatus and with the use of a school garden and of livestock on neighboring farms.

The number of normal schools in which agriculture was taught increased rapidly. In 1910 some instruction in agriculture was given in 156 State and county normal schools. This movement was thereafter affected by the increasing attention to teacher training in the agricultural colleges, the introduction of agriculture in numerous high schools, and the difficulties attending efforts to introduce this subject in the rural elementary schools. It became more difficult for normal schools to offer acceptable courses in agriculture, as distinguished from nature study, unless they had teachers well trained in agriculture. Some normal schools therefore dropped agriculture, while in others the courses in that subject were made more systematic and stronger.

For the year 1915–16 the Bureau of Education reported that 124 public normal schools were teaching agriculture, not including 27 county training schools in Wisconsin. These schools were located in 37 States and offered instruction in agriculture ranging from 20 to 1,512 recitation hours. In 49 schools from 20 to 190 hours of agriculture were required of all students.

In 1922–23 teacher-training courses were given in high schools in about half the States. Rural sociology was a required study in 12 States and rural economics in 1; industrial art, including agriculture, in 13 States; and nature study in 13 States.

STATE AGRICULTURAL SCHOOLS

Under an act of March 8, 1901, the California Polytechnic School at San Luis Obispo was opened in 1903, with agriculture, domestic science, and mechanic arts as its main lines of instruction. Two substantial buildings were erected on a farm of 280 acres, and Leroy Anderson, who had been an instructor in the college of agriculture of the University of California, was made its director.

A joint meeting of the California State Teachers' Association and the State Farmers' Institute held at Berkeley December 25–29, 1905, was attended by over 7,000 persons. (Experiment Station Record, vol. 17, p. 521.)

The claims of agricultural education to a place in the public school system in secondary and elementary schools, as well as in the colleges, were elaborately and earnestly presented and discussed by a considerable number of speakers. More significant even was the general atmosphere of sympathy with the idea that the industrial element must in one form or another become a permanent and pervasive constituent of our public school system.

Governor Pardee in an earnest and thoughtful address showed that there was so little in the school curricula to aid children in their life work that great numbers of them, and especially the boys, were leaving school at so early an age that the schools were making little impression on their minds or characters. The problems of agricultural education were discussed by a number of speakers, including Governor Pardee, representatives of the University of California, and the Director of the Office of Experiment Stations. The need of supplementing the work of the college of agriculture of the university by the teaching of agriculture in the high schools and in a small number of special secondary schools was clearly pointed out. The press of the State gave much space to this meeting and particularly to its agricultural features. It was an important factor in bringing about increased attention to agriculture in high schools and in securing the establishment of the agricultural school at Davis in connection with the college of agriculture of the University of California.

In 1907 the legislature appropriated $132,000 for the equipment of a farm there and the erection of buildings. A dairy building, livestock pavilion, barn, workshops, and two cottages were soon erected, and a short course was begun in January, 1908. Leroy Anderson was transferred from the Polytechnic School at San Luis Obispo to be professor of practical agriculture in the University of California and director of the farm school at Davis. The school was developed partly as a secondary vocational school to meet the needs of mature farm boys who were not prepared to enter the college of agriculture and partly to provide practical instruction for the members of the college classes in agriculture who could not get such instruction at Berkeley because the college of agriculture then had no farm.

In Minnesota an act was passed in 1905 creating a school of agriculture at Crookston and putting it under the direction of the board of regents of the State university. An appropriation of $15,000 was made for the construction and equipment of a school building to be located on the farm of 476 acres belonging to the branch experiment station which has been maintained there since 1895. The State also gave this school an initial appropriation of $4,000 annually for maintenance. In 1908 a dormitory costing about $43,000 and a building containing a creamery and blacksmith and carpenter shops, costing about $15,000, were erected. In 1911 a science hall costing $40,000, and later other substantial buildings were added. This school prospered, and in recent years has had 500 students.

In 1910 a similar school was located at Morris, which in 1924 had 10 brick and stone educational buildings and 10 farm buildings. These two schools are coeducational, are conducted on the same general plan as the school at the agricultural college, and are in effect branches of that institution. Their school year covers six months, from October to April.

Georgia in 1906 under the leadership of Gov. Joseph M. Terrell undertook the establishment of industrial and agricultural schools in each of the 11 congressional districts of that State. The legislature passed an act under which the governor was authorized to establish such schools and cause them to be maintained. They were to be branches of the State college of agriculture and under the general supervision of the board of trustees of the University of Georgia, but each school was to have a local board of trustees appointed by the governor for a term of six years and consisting of one member from each county in its district. These boards were to cooperate with the governor and the faculty of the State college of agriculture in deciding upon courses of study and lines of farm work to be carried on. Each school was to receive for maintenance an equal share approximately of the inspection fees from fertilizers, oils, etc., collected by the State department of agriculture, not otherwise appropriated, amounting as then estimated to about $6,000 a year. The different localities in which the schools were located must furnish not less than 200 acres of land and the necessary equipment of buildings, livestock, machinery, farm implements, etc.

The course of study in said schools shall be confined to the elementary branches of an English education, and practical treatises or lectures on agriculture in all its branches, and the mechanic arts and such other studies as will enable students completing the course to enter the freshman class of the State College of Agriculture on certificate of the principal (*109*).

The faculty was to consist of a principal, "who shall be an intelligent farmer," a superintendent and instructor in farm work, an intelligent mechanic, a "practical instructor in care of stock and dairying," an instructor in English, and such other instructors and assistants as funds would permit. "It shall be the duty of said instructors in said schools to cooperate in conducting farmers' institutes and farm and stock demonstrations."

After the first temporary buildings were erected "all work on, in, and about said schools, or on or in the barns and shops connected with said schools, whether it be farming, building, care of stock, or work of whatever kind, shall be performed exclusively by the students of said schools." One-half of the receipts from the sale of the products of the farm or shop must be used to pay the students, not to exceed $100 for each student in a school year. Tuition was to be free.

The trustees of the university decided that the schools should be coeducational, the minimum age for entrance to be 14 years for boys and 13 for girls, and that the course should cover four years of 40 weeks each. Manual or laboratory work was to occupy three hours daily. The girls were to have instruction and work in home economics. About one-fourth of the students were to be required to stay on the school farm during the summer vacation and work for pay.

So popular was the movement to establish these schools that gifts from private sources in the several districts aggregated in value over $800,000. They included from 240 to 350 acres of land for each school, valued at from $5,000 to $22,000, cash donations of from $25,000 to $60,000, 10 years of free telephone and water service in more than half the districts, and installation of sewerage systems in several districts.

At the request of the governor the Secretary of Agriculture detailed W. G. Smith, of the Bureau of Soils, to aid in the selection of the school farms, and D. J. Crosby, of the Office of Experiment Stations, to assist in formulating the course of study. The latter and Joseph S. Stewart, professor of secondary education in the University of Georgia, prepared a tentative course, which was examined by a committee of the board of trustees, submitted to professors of agriculture in a number of States, and with some changes, especially the elimination of optional foreign languages, was adopted June 15, 1907. This course included class and practice work in agriculture and English during four years, together with arithmetic, United States history, penmanship, spelling, and geography in first year; algebra, ancient history, horticulture and botany, penmanship, and spelling, or an optional study in second year; algebra, rural law, and farm accounts, elementary and agricultural physics, English history, commercial geography, or a science in third year; geometry, civics, farm economics, elementary and agricultural chemistry, modern history, or a science in fourth year; 79½ hours were given to classroom and practice work in agriculture and 50½ hours (or 76 periods of 40 minutes) to the other subjects.

The schools were located at Statesboro, Tifton, Americus, Carrollton, Monroe, Barnesville, Powder Springs, Madison, Clarkesville, Granite Hill, and Douglas. All of them were in operation in 1908 and during that school year enrolled 1,001 students. The academic buildings had six rooms, chemical, agricultural, and biological laboratories, and an auditorium with 600 seats. Barns, stables, dairies, laundries, etc., were erected by student labor at several of the schools.

In 1911 the funds derived from the fertilizer tax were withdrawn from these schools, and they were given an annual appropriation from the State treasury. In 1915–16 this amounted to $10,000 for each school. That year they each had 4 or 5 men teachers and from 2 to 6 women teachers. The students numbered from 45 to 145 boys and from 12 to 75 girls. For a number of years these schools encountered many difficulties, owing to the experimental stage of vocational education and the opposition or indifference of school authorities and people generally to such education. But their courses of study were gradually improved and standardized, and they became high schools whose graduates were accredited for college entrance, particularly to the college of agriculture of the University of Georgia. After the passage of the Smith-Hughes Vocational Education Act in 1917 these schools secured an allotment of funds provided under that act.

New York established its first State school of agriculture in 1906 and located it at St. Lawrence University at Canton (*439*). This university was established in 1856 as a denominational institution and had developed a college of arts and sciences and schools of theology and law.

The school of agriculture was intended to meet the needs of young people who had not taken the regular high-school courses and thus prepared themselves to enter a college of agriculture. It was expected that this new school would be strictly vocational. Agriculture, mechanic arts, and home economics would be taught, together with the elements of underlying sciences and a few academic subjects. An appropriation of $80,000 for buildings and equipment and $12,000 for maintenance was made at first. A main school building and a dairy building were erected, and the school was opened in 1907. A farm of 63 acres was immediately used, and this was changed for a farm of 100 acres in 1910. The early faculty consisted of a dean and teacher of animal husbandry and dairying and teachers of farm engineering and manual training, domestic science, chemistry and physics, and academic subjects, with assistants in cheese and butter making, poultry, veterinary science, and some other subjects. There was also a farm superintendent. The agricultural course of two years included agronomy, animal husbandry, dairying, poultry, veterinary science, farm engineering, surveying, agricultural chemistry, physics, manual training (mechanical drawing, woodworking, and forge work), agricultural arithmetic, farm accounts, English, civics, political economy, commercial and parliamentary law. Students must be at least 16 years old, and there were no entrance requirements. A class of six members was graduated in 1909. Attendance at this school grew, and it was found necessary to make a distinction between those students who had had only common-school education and those who had taken at least a part of a high-school course. For the former a regular course of three years was offered, while the latter might so arrange their studies as to graduate in two years. During the second and third years agricultural students might specialize to a certain extent in animal husbandry, poultry, dairying, or horticulture.

In 1908 two other New York State schools of agriculture were established. One of these was located at Alfred University, Alfred, and the other by itself at Morrisville (*439*).

Alfred University had grown out of a small school organized in 1836, which in 1843 received a charter as Alfred Academy and Teachers' Seminary. In 1857 it was made a university and added an undergraduate college to the academy. The New York State School of Clay Working and Ceramics was established on land adjacent to the university and is managed by its trustees.

The school of agriculture was given a board of managers appointed by the university trustees. R. A. Pearson, State commissioner of agriculture; L. H. Bailey, director of the State College of Agriculture; and F. N. Godfrey, master of the State Grange, were members of the first board of managers. The initial appropriation provided $75,000 for buildings, farm, and equipment and $5,000 for maintenance, to which were added in 1909, $40,000 for a dairy building, greenhouse, and other equipment, and $10,000 annually for maintenance. The main building was a 4-story structure of brick and stone containing 10 laboratories, a classroom, an assembly room, and a library. The farm consisted of 230 acres, a large barn, and 50 cattle, and there was a dormitory for 20 boys.

The faculty included the president of the university, who was also teacher of rural sociology and ethics; O. S. Morgan, director and teacher of horticulture and agronomy; and teachers of animal husbandry, domestic science and arts, drafting and shopwork, chemistry and physics, botany and zoology, and farm mathematics; and a farm superintendent. The regular course occupied three years, but there were also special courses and a farmers' week. Students in the university were permitted to take some studies in this school.

A novel feature of its 3-year course was its arrangement under three heads, viz, for boys, for boys and girls, and for girls. The work under the first and third headings was almost evenly balanced in time units, and among the technical studies common to boys and girls were general agriculture, general and agricultural botany, farm law and accounts, rural sociology, butter, cheese, poultry, plant diseases, general and landscape gardening, and insect pests. Besides English, arithmetic, history, and hygiene, instruction was given in physical culture, music, parliamentary practice, and social life.

The school opened October 18, 1909, and had two terms of 12 weeks each. Thirty-six boys and 10 girls attended the first year. In 1912–13 there were 173 boys and girls in the school, and, in addition, 46 students came from the college and academy.

The school at Morrisville opened October 26, 1910. The supervisors of Madison County were authorized to transfer county-seat buildings at Morrisville for use of the school, which was given $20,000 for repairs and the purchase of a farm of about 200 acres. In 1910 the State gave $59,275 for buildings, equipment, teachers' salaries, and maintenance. The school thus acquired three substantial buildings, one of which was used for shops and drafting. It was managed by a board of six trustees appointed by the governor, together with the commissioner of agriculture and the director of the State College of Agriculture, as members ex officio. The first course covered two years, and in 1911–12 was attended by 26 boys and 6 girls.

A State act of 1910 authorized the three agricultural schools then established to give courses for the training of teachers of agriculture, mechanic arts, and home making. If they gave such courses they were to receive the same State aid as was given to high schools under this law.

Additional State schools of agriculture were afterwards established at Cobleskill (1916), Delhi (1914), and Farmingdale (1916). The latter is on Long Island, about 30 miles from New York City. It has been given larger funds and has a more elaborate plant. Special efforts have been made to draw students from the city, and a considerable number of these have been children of foreign-born parents who in their native countries lived on the land.

The first constitution of Oklahoma required the teaching of the "elements of agriculture, horticulture, stock feeding, and domestic science in the common schools." An act of May 20, 1908, passed by the first State legislature, provided for an articulated system of instruction in the subjects mentioned and in forestry, roadmaking, and economics, extending from the agricultural college to the common schools (*439*). The Agricultural and Mechanical College was required to assist in promoting the teaching of agricultural and industrial subjects in the lower schools; departments of agricultural and industrial education were to be established in the State normal schools, and agricultural schools of secondary grade were to be organized in each judicial district. The courses in these schools were to include not only agricultural and industrial subjects, but also "the common-school branches, languages, manual training, manufactures, the sciences, and other necessary studies." At least two of these schools were to be established in 1908–9 and two each year thereafter. Each school must provide not less than 80 acres of land for experimental purposes, without expense to the State. The State superintendent of education, president of the State board of agriculture, and the president of the Agricultural and Mechanical College were constituted a commission of agricultural and industrial education to prepare detailed courses of study for these schools and to articulate these courses so that their graduates could enter the Agricultural and Mechanical College without further examination.

There was also to be established at the agricultural college a chair of agriculture for schools, whose occupant was to visit the schools in which agriculture was taught and give advice in this way and through correspondence and publications on all matters relating to the teaching of agriculture and allied subjects. Under this law, schools were located at Warner, Tishomingo, Broken Arrow, Lawton, and Helena. The first year each had a State appropriation of $20,000 for buildings and $12,000 for maintenance. A sixth school, known as the Panhandle Agricultural Institute, was established at Goodwell to serve part of a district and had $12,000 for buildings and $5,000 for maintenance. One-fourth of the maintenance for each school was to be spent for experiments.

In Arkansas the movement for agricultural schools began in 1906, when the Washington County Farmers' Union passed a resolution indorsing the establishment of special agricultural schools (*83*). A bill for one school was passed by the legislature in 1907, but was vetoed by the governor. On April 1, 1909, a law was approved for four State agricultural schools in districts of from 17 to 20 counties. The management of each school was assigned to a district board of five persons, "intelligent farmers," appointed by the governor for a term of 10 years after the initial appointments which were from 2 to 10 years, so that there would be one vacancy to be filled every two years. The minimum age of admission of students was fixed at 15 years.

This act carried an appropriation of $40,000 for each school. The communities in which the schools were located contributed generously toward lands, buildings, and maintenance. Agriculture and horti-culture, home economics, natural sciences, and academic subjects such as are usually taught in high schools, were included in their courses. The regular courses covered four years of secondary work, but pro-vision was also made for preparatory and short courses.

The schools were opened for students during 1910 and 1911. Each school had in 1912 from 200 to 500 acres of land and from three to six substantial brick buildings, including a main building (with classrooms and laboratories), dormitories for boys and for girls, a dining hall, etc. The faculties consisted of a principal and from 5 to 10 teachers. The teachers of different branches of agriculture were from the land-grant colleges in Alabama, Arkansas, Illinois, Iowa, Kansas, South Carolina, and Texas.

Various field crops, fruits, and vegetables were grown on the farms, where the students did much of the labor and were paid from 10 to 15 cents per hour. In some cases they also assisted in the construc-tion of buildings.

These schools developed strongly as vocational institutions. Their agricultural equipment of livestock, farm machinery, etc., increased, and their agricultural courses were strengthened. In 1915–16 the number of boys in the secondary agricultural classes in the several schools was as follows: Jonesboro, 67; Russellville, 98; Magnolia, 42; Monticello, 78.

The Nebraska Legislature in 1910 appropriated $100,000 for an agricultural school to be located at Curtis on a 20-acre campus within the city limits. It also had for demonstration and other purposes a 413-acre farm. It was developed under the direction of the Uni-versity of Nebraska and was considered a branch of its College of Agriculture.

In 1910 the Vermont Legislature passed a bill discontinuing the State Normal School at Randolph and transferring its buildings and other property to a new State school of agriculture, which was also given $20,000 for buildings, repairs, and equipment and $10,000 an-nually for maintenance. The course covered two years. In 1915–16 this school had 6 teachers and 78 boy students.

Colorado in 1911 provided for a school of agriculture and me-chanic arts at the Fort Lewis School, formerly a United States Indian school. This school was to be in charge of the State board of agriculture and thus was brought into connection with the State agri-cultural college at Fort Collins, which was also managed by this board. It was to receive a State fund of $75,000 during the biennium, not less than half of which was to be expended for equipment. In 1915–16 this school had a plant valued at $200,000, received $30,000 from the State, spent for maintenance $17,644, had 3 men and 2 women as teachers and 27 boys and 10 girls as students.

COUNTY AGRICULTURAL SCHOOLS

In Wisconsin under the leadership of L. D. Harvey, State superintendent of education, who had prepared a report on instruction in manual training and agriculture in other countries and States, a State act for county schools of agriculture and domestic science was passed in 1901 (439).

This act authorized county boards to establish schools of agriculture and domestic economy in which were to be taught the elements of agriculture, farm accounts, manual training, domestic economy, and other subjects. Each such school was to have at least 3 acres of land suitable for experiments and demonstrations. Completion of the course of study in the common schools was required for entrance to the county schools, but winter classes for "students of advanced age" were to be organized whenever there was sufficient demand for them. The State superintendent of education, with the advice of the dean of the State College of Agriculture, was to prescribe the course of study and determine the qualifications of teachers for these schools, which were to be managed by county boards. Not more than half the amount expended for instruction was to be paid by the State, which practically fixed a maximum allowance of $2,500 for each of the two schools first established. Two counties might unite in the establishment and conduct of a single school.

Marathon and Dunn Counties, which had been first to have county teacher-training schools under an act of 1899, were also first in organizing schools of agriculture and domestic economy in 1902. Such schools were combined with the county normal schools at Wausau and Menomonie. A similar school was opened at Winneconne, November 4, 1907, with K. L. Hatch, who had been superintendent of schools at Waterloo, as principal and teacher. The agricultural school interchanged classes with the teacher-training school when located in the same building.

In Minnesota a State act of 1905 gave the counties local option regarding the establishment of county schools of agriculture and domestic economy if the people took interest enough in the matter to vote upon it. Each school was to have not less than 10 acres of land for experiments and demonstrations. Such schools were put under the control of the State superintendent of education.

Kansas had had for several years a general law permitting the establishment of county high schools. One of these schools was established in Norton County and in 1905 substituted an agricultural course for its general science course and employed a graduate of the Kansas Agricultural College to teach agriculture and the natural sciences.

The Michigan Legislature in 1907 passed an act authorizing the establishment of county agricultural schools under the control of county boards of five members, including the county commissioner of schools and four members appointed by the board of supervisors.

These schools were to have a 2-year course, including agriculture, farm accounts, manual training, home economics, and other related subjects, and were to have at least 10 acres of land. General supervision of these schools was committed to the State superintendent of education, with the advice of the president of the State agricultural college. Their principals were to be graduates of State agricultural colleges. The first school under this law was opened at Menominee November 18, 1907, with J. F. Wojta, formerly connected with the Minnesota School of Agriculture, as principal. Recently this has been discontinued as a county school.

A Mississippi law, passed in 1908, permitted counties to establish agricultural high schools for which a tax not to exceed 2 mills might be levied. When a school is located and has school and dormitory buildings to accommodate at least 40 pupils in its high-school department, the State will give it $1,000, on the approval of the State superintendent of education. Within a year 15 counties had established schools under this law, the first being at Mashulaville, in Noxubee County, supported by a tax of 1 mill.

In North Carolina a law of March 3, 1911, provided for county farm-life schools. These schools were to be outside of any city or town of more than 1,000 inhabitants and not within 2 miles of any city or town of more than 5,000 inhabitants. The county, township, or school district, or all these combined, were to provide at least $2,500 a year for maintenance, a school building, dormitories for not less than 25 boys and girls, a barn, a dairy building with equipment, and a farm of not less than 25 acres of good land. The teachers had to have high-school teachers' certificates on all required subjects except Latin, Greek, and modern languages. Men teachers were to have certificates from the State board of examiners and the president of the North Carolina College of Agriculture and Mechanic Arts attesting to satisfactory qualifications for their special work. The women teachers were to have similar certificates from the State board and the president of the State Normal and Industrial College. Provision was to be made for regular scondary courses in agriculture and home economics and also for extension work and short courses for adult students, both men and women. One school in each county meeting these requirements might receive a State fund of $2,500 annually for maintenance but not more than 10 schools could be established in any one year. In 1915–16 the Bureau of Education reported 18 such schools, with an attendance of from 6 to 25 boys.

In general, the county has proved to be too small a unit for the adequate maintenance of a special agricultural school.

STATE-AIDED LOCAL HIGH SCHOOLS TEACHING AGRICULTURE

In addition to appropriations for State, district, or county agricultural schools, certain States undertook to provide funds for local high schools in which agriculture was taught.

Virginia in 1906 undertook the encouragement of the establishment of high schools in rural communities with a State appropriation of $50,000 annually. This was doubled in 1908, and in addition $15,000 was appropriated for county teacher-training courses in certain high schools. The same legislature also gave $20,000 to be divided equally among 10 high schools, one in each congressional district, for the teaching of agriculture and home economics. Manassas offered $25,000 and 15 acres of land and was the first town to receive the State appropriation. Appomattox came second with $5,000 by private subscription and a promise to erect a $10,000 building and provide all the land desired for the school. Schools at Burkeville, Chester, Courtland, Elk Creek, Hampton, Lebanon, and Middletown also received a share of this appropriation. In 1910 the State appropriation for this work was increased to $25,000. To promote the development of the agricultural work of these schools The Virginia Association of Agricultural Schools was formed November 24, 1909, with the director of the Virginia Agricultural Experiment Station as secretary-treasurer.

In 1908 Texas appropriated $32,000 to provide a fund from which the State board of education was to duplicate amounts, not less than $500 nor more than $2,000, that might be appropriated by the trustees of any common-school district or independent-school district to the establishing, equipping, and maintaining of departments of instruction in agriculture, including courses in manual training and domestic economy, "subsidiary to agriculture." The school boards were to provide laboratories for instruction in botany, zoology, and other sciences related to agriculture and land for the production of farm and garden plants and employ a teacher trained in agriculture and allied branches. This measure was intended primarily to stimulate the establishment of agricultural courses in the public schools, and it was therefore provided that State aid should not be given more than twice to the same school.

About this time the Legislature of Louisiana passed a law for the encouragement of agricultural teaching in high schools and voted $500 to each school maintaining a course approved by the State board of education. This was afterwards modified so that such schools were divided into two types. Schools of type 1 had to have from 5 to 10 acres of land for practical agricultural instruction and were granted annually $1,200 of State money; those of type 2 must provide practical instruction through home projects and were granted $400. In 1915–16 there were 42 schools of type 1 and 28 of type 2.

In Minnesota the Putnam Act in 1909 provided not to exceed $2,500 for each of 10 high or consolidated rural schools which maintained agricultural and industrial departments, with teachers trained in agriculture, manual training, and domestic science and not less than 5 acres of land. Not to exceed 10 schools might be added to the list during each biennium. This act was amended in 1911 to permit 30 schools to receive this State fund. There was also passed the Benson-Lee Act giving $1,000 annually to each of 50 high schools or graded schools maintaining a course in agriculture and a course in home economics or manual training. The State high-school board, which was charged with the administration of this act, required that a trained agricultural teacher should be employed and given not less than a continuous half day for agricultural work, with a room exclusively for his use. Two satisfactory daily periods in an agricultural subject would count as a credit. The agricultural instruction must include textbook and laboratory work, special work of local interest, a winter short course, and cooperation in farmers' institutes. Under these acts 129 schools had agricultural courses in 1915–16.

In Maine a law enacted in 1909 provided that any incorporated academy maintaining a course in manual training, domestic science, or agriculture approved by the State superintendent of schools might receive annually from the State a sum equal to that expended for such instruction, up to $250 for each course. This act was amended in 1911 to make it apply to high schools as well as academies and to allow reimbursement for two-thirds of the expenditures for such instruction up to $500 annually.

Maryland in 1910 provided State aid for agriculture, home economics, manual training, and business courses in two classes of high schools. Schools with at least 80 high-school pupils and a 4-year course would receive $400 toward the salary of each of two special teachers, and schools with at least 35 high-school pupils and a 3-year course would receive $400 toward the salary of one special teacher. Nine high schools giving instruction in agriculture received State aid in 1911.

The New York education law of 1909 as amended in 1910 provided that schools of agriculture, mechanic arts, and home making might be established in cities or in union free school districts (*318*). These schools were for " pupils who have completed the elementary school course, or have attained the age of 14, or who have met such other requirements as the local school authorities may have prescribed." The commissioner of education was authorized to grant $500 annually to such schools maintained for 38 weeks, employing one full-time teacher, having an enrollment of at least 25 pupils, and maintaining a course approved by him, and $200 for each additional teacher similarly employed, or pro rata amounts to schools having a shorter term. This act was afterwards amended to allow two-thirds of the salary of the special teachers to be paid by the State. The State education department committed the administration of this law to its division of trades schools, and it was ruled that departments or courses as well as separate schools might be given State aid under this law. F. W. Howe, formerly connected with the Office of Experiment Stations, was appointed supervisor of agricultural education.

In 1913 the law was amended to permit the organization of part-time, continuation, or evening vocational schools, to reduce the necessary school year to 36 weeks and the enrollment to 15 pupils, to permit the employment of vocational teachers for 12 months, and to increase the maximum State allowance to each teacher to $1,000 a year. That year the State supervision was committed to a division of vocational schools, in which L. S. Hawkins was the specialist in agricultural education (*318*). Suggested 4-year courses in agriculture for intermediate and high schools were outlined, and "there must be provision for two weekly laboratory exercises of 90 minutes each in each class taught by the agriculture teacher." A definite plan for home-project work was published, and it was announced that "no credit is to be given for any subject in agriculture until a satisfactory project for that year has been carried out by the pupil seeking such credit." Additional regents' credit might be given for a project of sufficient importance when this is "summed up in a carefully written thesis which presents a complete discussion of the problem or experiment undertaken, the scientific facts and principles involved, and the practical results accomplished." When the teacher was employed during the summer, part of his work was to be the supervision of home projects of pupils or of boys or young men not in school. In 1915–16 there were 68 State-aided vocational agricultural departments in public high schools in New York.

Massachusetts in 1911 made it possible for a vocational agricultural school to be established in any existing high school by a town or group of towns. Such school approved by the State board of education would receive two-thirds of the salary of the teacher of agriculture. In 1915–16 there were 14 schools receiving State aid for instruction in agriculture.

In North Dakota in 1911 a law was passed providing that any high, graded, or consolidated school having an agricultural department might receive State aid to the extent of $2,500, provided, however, that the number of schools the first year be limited to five and that not more than five were to be added each two years. To receive State aid the school must employ trained instructors in agriculture, manual training, and domestic science and have within 1 mile of the school building not less than 10 acres of land for a school garden and field demonstrations.

In Pennsylvania the new school code of 1911 provided that agriculture shall be taught in township high schools and that a portion of the State school fund may be used "to promote education in conservation, forestry, and agricultural and industrial pursuits." L. H. Dennis was appointed expert assistant in agricultural education in the State department of education to supervise the introduction of agriculture into the township high schools. Under a State act of May 1, 1913, two-thirds of the amount paid for instruction in agriculture might be received by a high school from State funds. In 1915–16 there were 18 schools receiving State aid for teaching agriculture.

In Utah in 1911 the State board of education provided that every accredited high school must teach agriculture in order to participate in the maintenance fund provided for such schools. In 1915–16 there were 14 high schools in Utah in which agriculture was taught.

In Wisconsin a State law of 1911 provided for State aid of $250 for each department of manual training, domestic science, or agriculture established in connection with any free high school. In 1915–16 agriculture was taught in 79 high schools in Wisconsin.

The Michigan Agricultural College, which established a department of agricultural education in 1908, with W. H. French, formerly deputy superintendent of public instruction, in charge, actively promoted the teaching of agriculture in the high schools in the State. As a result such instruction was soon offered in a number of schools which were able to obtain qualified teachers. In 1912 a State commission on industrial and agricultural education recommended the introduction of agriculture into the high schools, with State supervision and financial aid. This was not done, but in 1915–16 there were 55 high schools teaching agriculture under the supervision of the State agricultural college.

AGRICULTURE IN PUBLIC HIGH SCHOOLS WITHOUT STATE AID

About the beginning of the twentieth century local high schools began to introduce instruction in agriculture, and by 1915 the number of such schools was large. Brief accounts of a few of these schools are given here to illustrate early types of agricultural work in the high schools which did not receive State aid.

In 1902 the city of Elyria, Ohio, appointed Lyman Carrier, a graduate of the Michigan Agricultural College, as teacher of sciences in the public high school and arranged an elective course with agriculture in the third and fourth years.

The high school at Waterford, Pa., which was established in 1800 and had a stone building erected in 1822, organized an agricultural course in 1905 in addition to those in language and science (*439*). The school was fortunate in getting as teacher of agriculture H. O. Sampson, a graduate of the Iowa Agricultural College, who was able to arouse much interest among the students and the neighboring farmers. The course was planned to cover five hours a week for four years. The first year was devoted to a study of the life and uses of plants, the second year to field, orchard, and garden crops, the third year to animal husbandry, dairying, and soil physics, and the fourth year to the chemistry of soils, plants, and animals. Instruction was given through textbooks and lectures (some of which were before the whole school), with agricultural books, bulletins, and papers for reference. Much was made of laboratory work and outdoor practicums. The pupils made much of their own apparatus. The school had no land or livestock but used neighboring farms for observation and stock judging. Farmers often brought animals to the vicinity of the schoolhouse to be studied by the agricultural pupils. Mr. Sampson soon left this school to take up work in the Bureau of Soils at Washington, but his successor continued the course with marked success, and was able to report in 1907 that 95 per cent of the boys at the school were in that course. A Babcock tester had been added to the laboratory equipment and was used by the students for testing milk sent in by their parents and others. Through the good relations of the teacher with the students and their parents the school was "sharing with church and grange in providing a meeting place for town and country on a ground of common interest."

About this time the school board of Cecil County, Md., at the request of people in the northern part of that county decided to establish a high school at Calvert and to give the course of study an agricultural trend (*439*). The board applied to the Maryland Agricultural College and the United States Department of Agriculture for aid in organizing the school. (Mr. Sampson was furloughed to be its principal and teacher of agriculture.) The school was opened November 5, 1906, in a rented 2-room building, with about 9 acres of land adjacent to it. A 4-year course was prepared with the cooperation of the county board and the Office of Experiment Stations. It included English, Latin, arithmetic, algebra, geometry, history, drawing, farm bookkeeping, and farm surveying, together with four years of agriculture combined with physical geography and the elements of physics, chemistry, and botany. There were also laboratory and field exercises. The principal was very active in bringing the school to the attention of the community. The pupils participated in educational meetings, contributed articles to the county papers, took part in a farmers' institute and corn-judging contest, helped to renovate and spray an old orchard, and made observation trips to farms. The principal visited the elementary schools within a radius of 5 miles from Calvert and interested the teachers and pupils in nature study and elementary agriculture. In the spring months he conducted a night school for the boys who had to leave the day school to assist in farm work.

The Farragut School at Concord, Tenn., was reorganized about 1907 to make it serve the community more fully. It had then a new brick building and 12 acres of land about 1½ miles from a small village. This housed both elementary and high-school departments, with a laboratory and home economics and manual training rooms. Six acres were used for demonstrations and for growing food for livestock. Three courses, Latin, English, and agriculture, manual training, and home economics, were offered. In the latter, besides the sciences and academic subjects common in high-school courses, instruction was given in agriculture, manual training, or home economics during the first two years, and in the third and fourth years the student might continue the study of agriculture or take more physics and chemistry. Evening meetings for social and educational purposes held at the school brought it into closer touch with the people of the community.

The high school at Fairfield, Nebr., in 1911 made visits to farms adjacent to the town a prominent feature of its agricultural instruction. The farmer visited, if he were in the livestock business, talked to the class on the history and merits of his favorite breed. Before going to the farm the students got all available information on this subject from textbooks and teachers. The practical talk and demonstration closed the instruction on this matter. A local expert judge of cattle was employed to accompany the class to the farm.

The high school at Coin, Iowa, offered four years of agriculture as an elective in 1910 (*439*). Agriculture was taught by the school superintendent, who had arranged the nature study in the grades so as to make a good preparation for agriculture in the high school. The instruction covered soils, crops, and silos in the first year; plant propagation, fruit growing, drainage, fertilizers, and maintenance of soil fertility in the second year; animal husbandry and dairying in the third year; farm buildings, sanitation, water supply, ornamentation of home surroundings, farm mechanics and machinery, roads, bee keeping, farm forestry, and the elements of farm accounting, marketing, and farm economics in the fourth year.

The consolidated school in Magnolia Township, Putnam County, Ill., had a high-school department, in which agriculture, manual training, and home economics occupied a prominent place in 1908. This school was located out in the country, 2 miles from the small village of McNabb and was housed in a $12,000 brick building on a tract of 24 acres of timber pasture donated by John Swaney, a farmer in moderate circumstances. An abandoned schoolhouse nearby was fitted up for a teachers' home. In the seventh and eighth grades three 20-minute periods a week were given to elementary agriculture, and in the eighth grade there was also bench work. The high-school course contained agriculture during the four years as an elective instead of Latin or home economics, together with physiology, zoology (including entomology), botany, chemistry, physics, and the academic subjects usually found in a standard course. In agriculture, agronomy and horticulture were taught in the first year, swine husbandry in the second year, soil physics and feeding and judging livestock in the third year, and soil fertility as related to systems of farming in the fourth year. Besides the classroom instruction there were laboratory, shop, and field exercises and observation trips to a near-by branch experiment station and to farms. The principal taught agriculture, manual training, science, and some mathematics.

The Agricultural High School of Baltimore County at Sparks Station, Md., was opened in 1909, with B. H. Crocheron, a graduate of Cornell University, as principal and teacher of agriculture (*439*). This school was formed by the consolidation of four schools and was supported by county funds and local contributions. The pupils came by train, by private conveyance, or in school wagons. The first year there were 50 pupils in the high school and considerably more in the grades. The high-school course included the usual academic subjects, except foreign languages, which were replaced by agriculture, home economics, and manual training. The school had 7 acres of land and a new granite building containing five classrooms, three laboratories, and a farm-machinery room. During the summer the high-school boys were required to conduct what are now called home projects, under direction of the principal. The school tested seeds and milk for farmers.

The initial success of the school was very largely due to the interest aroused in the county by the preliminary activities of Mr. Crocheron. Before the opening of the school he moved about in the county getting acquainted with the people, attending their agricultural meetings, teachers' institutes, etc. The men's agricultural club and the women's home-interest club were made responsible for the public meeting when the school building was dedicated. After school opened a series of monthly meetings for rural teachers were held there, at which lessons in school methods, administration, and agriculture were given. The principal also contributed lessons in elementary agriculture to a local publication, which was sent free by the school authorities to every teacher in the county.

For adult farmers a course of 10 weekly lectures was given, with an average attendance of 125 men and women. At the end of the series of lectures a 2-day corn congress was held, with exhibits, demonstrations, and addresses on corn growing and cooking. Twenty rural schools held preliminary corn shows and sent their best exhibits to the congress.

For the farmers' wives monthly meetings were held on Saturday afternoons, the school wagons being used to transport them. There was an average attendance of 85 women, divided into four groups which studied home economics, carpentry, home crafts, or modern literature. A literary society was organized for young people not in school, with spelling bees, debates, etc.

The number of high schools in which some agriculture was taught increased very rapidly after about 1905. Instruction in agriculture or in its relations to botany, chemistry, or zoology was given in about 400 high schools in 1900 and in about 2,000 schools in 1912. This latter number had doubled by 1915.

This work was usually done by a single teacher in each school. Comparatively few of these teachers were well trained in agriculture. Most of them had been employed primarily to teach science or some other subject. A number of textbooks on agricultural subjects, prepared with special reference to their use in secondary and elementary schools, were available prior to 1915. There were also Federal and State bulletins giving outlines of courses in agriculture for secondary schools and instructions for teaching this subject. Textbooks and manuals prepared for college students and informational bulletins of the United States Department of Agriculture and the State experiment stations were abundant. Short courses at the agricultural colleges were open to teachers, especially during the summer. Some high-school teachers, especially those trained in the sciences, who were thoroughly interested in teaching agriculture and made the best of their opportunities for acquiring knowledge of this subject, taught it with great success. But in very many cases the instruction in agriculture in the ordinary high schools during this period was textbook work, and often it was merely a small supplement to the instruction in one or two natural sciences.

AGRICULTURE IN PRIVATE SECONDARY SCHOOLS

Secondary schools on a private foundation early began to introduce the teaching of agriculture. Among these was the National Farm School at Doylestown, Pa., established in 1896, with special reference to the training of city boys. This school was so successful that in 1901 the State gave it an appropriation of $2,500 annually for two years, which was afterwards increased. Its equipment included a farm of 122 acres, a main building, barn, greenhouses, and livestock. The course covered four years. The science and practice of agriculture were taught, together with English, mathematics, and natural science, and the boys did much of the labor on the farm.

The Agricultural and Technical Institute at Winona Lake, Ind., founded in 1902, introduced agriculture, a graduate of Purdue University teaching that subject. In 1906 this institution was reorganized as an agricultural school, with a 2-year course, given in three departments, (1) agriculture and chemistry, (2) dairying and animal husbandry, and (3) horticulture and forestry.

The Mount Hermon School, near Northfield, Mass., founded by D. L. Moody, established in 1903 an agricultural department and put at its head Harry Hayward, assistant chief of the Dairy Division of the United States Department of Agriculture and a graduate of that school.

Smith's Agricultural School and Northampton School of Technology, at Northampton, Mass., resulted from provisions in the will of Oliver Smith in 1844. Those relating to an agricultural school did not make the fund for this purpose available before December 22, 1905, at which time it amounted to $310,000.

This school has two large brick buildings, a farm house, a barn, and a farm of 93 acres, but no dormitories. It is open to boys and girls. For admission preference is given to those students who have completed elementary courses, but others may be admitted on trial. The academic subjects taught are English, general mathematics, general history of industry, United States history, citizenship, economics of production, exchange and distribution, first aid, personal hygiene and social problems. Approximately half of each pupil's time is spent in shops, laboratories, workrooms, and outside productive work; the other half is spent in class room study. Agricultural subjects are taught by the director, the head of the agricultural department, and the farm superintendent. The agricultural course occupies four years of 32 weeks. The school opened with departments of agriculture, household arts, and trades. The latter has since been divided into departments of carpentry, sheet metal, silk textiles, and automobiles.

The Illinois College at Jacksonville, Ill., began secondary work in agriculture in 1908 as the result of a bequest of $20,000 for this purpose by Mrs. Phoebe G. Strawn. Courses were offered in soil fertility and fertilizers, soil physics, agricultural botany, and agricultural zoology. This work was supplemented with occasional lectures by agricultural experts. The first lecture was given by Dean Davenport, of the University of Illinois.

In Vermont in 1910 a secondary school of agriculture was opened at Lyndonville. This resulted from donations by Theodore N. Vail, president of the American Telephone & Telegraph Co., who provided a small farm with its buildings and funds for the agricultural instruction. He also permitted the students of this school to utilize his large estate on the hills near Lyndonville for observation and judging of his dairy herd, studies in farm forestry, etc. A 2-year course in scientific and practical agriculture was offered, with special reference to Vermont conditions. This course extended over nine months in each year and was open to residents of the State eligible for admission to an approved high school. Students might pay their expenses in cash or by working on the school farm throughout the year.

From 1908, when the Office of Experiment Stations reported that there were 16 private colleges and schools teaching agriculture, the introduction of this subject into private schools proceeded rapidly. In 1915–16 the Bureau of Education reported that some instruction in agriculture was given in 12 private agricultural secondary schools and 149 private secondary schools in 37 States.

GENERAL STATUS OF SECONDARY EDUCATION IN AGRICULTURE IN 1916

During the 25 years beginning about 1890 there was a new and rapidly growing movement for the establishment of schools and courses in agriculture of secondary grade in a great variety of institutions. When the United States Bureau of Education made a survey of the status of this movement for the school year 1915–16 it found that secondary instruction in agriculture was given in the following classes of institutions:

1. Secondary schools of agriculture at State agricultural colleges_____ 28
2. Public normal schools (not including 27 county teacher-training schools
   in Wisconsin)_____ 124
3. Special agricultural schools receiving State aid_____ 74
4. Vocational agricultural departments in public high schools under State
   supervision_____ 421
5. Public high schools not State aided_____ 2, 760
6. Private agricultural secondary schools_____ 12
7. Private secondary schools (not special)_____ 149
8. Secondary and higher schools for negroes_____ 107

Total_____ 3, 675

The statistics for number of students pursuing agricultural courses were incomplete. At the secondary schools in the agricultural colleges there were 3,958 students; in the State-aided special schools, 6,643; in the public high schools, 60,925; and in the private schools (not special), 2,001. It thus appears that more than 73,000 students in secondary schools in the United States received more or less instruction in agriculture during that year. The movement had, however, far outrun the ability of the colleges and normal schools to supply an adequate number of teachers trained in agriculture. Under such conditions the inevitable result was that agricultural instruction in many schools became merely cultural or informational and involved mainly textbook work. On the other hand in a limited number of schools the agricultural instruction became more vocational, better-trained teachers were employed, and laboratory and practice work at the schools or on home farms was required.

During this period manual training and home economics had been introduced into many of the schools where agriculture was taught and also into many other secondary schools throughout the United States. But the instruction in these subjects had also not had the distinct vocational results which had been anticipated. Hence a demand arose for a more definite type of industrial education for students coming out of the elementary schools. Propaganda to secure State and Federal aid for vocational education increased in intensity and extent. The movement for secondary agricultural education became involved in the broader movement for education relating to all the industries.

DEVELOPMENT OF SECONDARY EDUCATION IN AGRICULTURE WITH FEDERAL AID, 1917–1925

The Smith-Hughes Vocational Education Act was approved by President Wilson February 23, 1917. It is permanent legislation and carries annually large amounts of Federal funds for instruction in agriculture, home economics, and trades and industries to persons over 14 years of age. This act and the Smith-Lever Agricultural Extension Act passed in 1914 were the outcome of an active movement for vocational education below college grade carried on for more than a decade by agricultural and industrial forces, especially as represented by the Association of American Agricultural Colleges and Experiment Stations and the National Society for Industrial Education. The activities of the forces seeking Federal aid for vocational education were more or less interrelated. Therefore to understand the full significance of the movement it is necessary to consider its industrial as well as its agricultural features.

RISE OF THE MOVEMENT FOR INDUSTRIAL EDUCATION

During the nineteenth century there were in a few places in the United States efforts to provide distinctly vocational training of elementary or secondary grade. Such, for example, were the Girard College in Philadelphia (1848), the mechanics institutes in New York City (1820), Cincinnati (1828), Richmond, Va. (1854), and Rochester, N. Y. (1856); the Miller School in Albemarle County, Va. (1878), the institutes for negroes at Hampton, Va. (1868), and

Tuskegee, Ala. (1880); the evening classes of the Franklin Institute in Philadelphia (1824), the Cooper Union in New York City (1859), the industrial school in Boston (1848), and the trade school in Lowell, Mass. (1872).

Manual training in city high schools after 1880 had some vocational features but was mainly of general educational value. Meanwhile the apprenticeship system as a preparation for industrial work was passing away. Increasing numbers of boys and girls were leaving the high schools without preparation for any industry. Many of these youths were drifting into the " blind alley " occupations or into criminality. The great corporations which employed many workers in mechanic arts were seeking substitutes for the apprenticeship system. From 1904 the National Association of Manufacturers had a committee on industrial education, which repeatedly urged the establishment of trade schools. The National Metal Trades Association discussed this subject in 1910 and contributed $1,000 to the National Society for the Promotion of Industrial Education. A convention of persons interested in trade schools was held at Indianapolis in 1907. The labor unions, which at first had opposed industrial schools for fear they would turn out too many trained workers for different trades, were beginning to realize the importance and desirability of a carefully guarded public system of vocational education of secondary grade. In 1907 the American Federation of Labor adopted a resolution favoring industrial and technical education and the following year created a committee, which reported in favor of such education under public control and with Federal aid. Educators, publicists, and industrial leaders were awakening to the importance of training American youth for industrial pursuits and were watching with increasing interest the efforts of European countries, especially Germany, to maintain an adequate supply of skilled workers in industries with the aid of vocational schools. The National Education Association began the discussion of industrial education in 1900, which was continued at succeeding meetings, especially through the work and reports of committees. In 1908 this association approved trade schools, industrial schools and evening continuation schools and in 1912 created a committee of educators, employers, employees, and social workers to study the needs of adolescents for vocational guidance and education.

THE MASSACHUSETTS COMMISSION ON INDUSTRIAL AND TECHNICAL EDUCATION

The Massachusetts Legislature by an act of May 24, 1905, provided for a commission on industrial and technical education (*179*), consisting of nine persons " representing the manufacturing, agricultural, educational, and labor interests " to " investigate the needs for education in the different grades of skill and responsibility in the various industries in the Commonwealth. They shall investigate how far the needs are met by existing institutions and shall consider what new forms of educational effort may be advisable," taking into account " similar educational work done by other States, by the United States Government, and by foreign governments." This commission of eight men and one woman, with Carroll D. Wright as chairman, made its report in April, 1906. They had studied the problems of industrial education as related to both the children and the industries. They found a general and theoretical interest among educators and students of social phenomena and " a practical and specific interest among manufacturers and wage earners because of a personal need."

Children going into industrial pursuits from the elementary schools wasted three or four years before attaining productive efficiency, and even if they completed a high-school course they lacked manual skill and " industrial intelligence."

The commission recommended that instruction and practice in the elements of productive industry, including agriculture and the mechanic and domestic arts, should be given in the elementary schools for both cultural and industrial purposes, that in the high schools " instruction in mathematics, the sciences, and drawing shall show the application and use of these subjects in industrial life " and elective industrial courses in the principles of agriculture and the domestic and mechanic arts should be provided, and that evening and part-time industrial courses should also be established.

To carry out this plan a State commission on industrial education was proposed, and to aid in the establishment of industrial schools and classes the State was asked to pay annually from one-fifth to one-half of their cost proportionate to the amount expended from local taxes for these purposes. An act embodying these proposals was passed in 1906, but in 1909 charge of industrial education was given to the reorganized State board of education, under which were a commissioner of education and two deputy commissioners, one of whom must be especially qualified to deal with industrial education.

THE NATIONAL SOCIETY FOR THE PROMOTION OF INDUSTRIAL EDUCATION

The first report of the Massachusetts Commission on Industrial Education created widespread interest in this subject. Soon after its publication James P. Haney, director of manual training in the public schools of New York City, and Charles R. Richards, director of the department of manual training in Teachers College of Columbia University, " came to the conclusion that the time had come to secure united action concerning industrial education." They brought together 11 other men in New York June 9, 1906, and this company appointed a committee on organization. As a result of their efforts about 250 persons met at Cooper Union November 16, 1906, and formed the National Society for the Promotion of Industrial Education (52). New York, Chicago, Boston, Philadelphia, Milwaukee, Cincinnati, Raleigh, and other cities were represented at this meeting. Henry S. Pritchett, then president of the Massachusetts Institute of Technology, was elected president of the society, and Professor Richards was made secretary. Among the members of its first board of managers were Doctor Haney, Frank A. Vanderlip, Jane Addams, James P. Munroe, S. B. Donnelly (secretary of the general arbitration board of the New York building trades), Mrs. M. M. Kehew (a member of the Massachusetts Commission on Industrial Education), and Frederick P. Fish (president of the American Telephone

& Telegraph Co.). Educators, manufacturers, mechanics, business men, and persons of other occupations were members of the society. The constitution stated that—

the objects of this society shall be to bring to public attention the importance of industrial education as a factor in the industrial development of the United States; to provide opportunities for the study and discussion of the various phases of the problem; to make available the results of experience in the field of industrial education, both in this country and abroad, and to promote the establishment of institutions for industrial training.

The society immediately began to issue bulletins containing information regarding its organization and work and matters relating to the progress of industrial education. It soon gained the favorable attention of President Roosevelt, who sent to Doctor Pritchett on May 24, 1907, an extract from an address he was about to make at the fiftieth anniversary of the founding of the Michigan Agricultural College (194). In this address the President said:

For at least a generation we have been waking to the knowledge that there must be additional education beyond that provided in the public school as it is managed to-day. Our school system has hitherto been well-nigh wholly lacking on the side of industrial training, of the training that fits a man for the shop and the farm. This is a most serious lack, for no one can look at the peoples of mankind as they stand at present without realizing that industrial training is one of the most potent factors in national development. We of the United States must develop a system under which each individual citizen shall be trained so as to be effective individually as an economic unit, and fit to be organized with his fellows so that he and they can work in efficient fashion together. This question is vital to our future progress and public attention should be focused upon it. Surely it is eminently in accord with the principles of our democratic life that we should furnish the highest average industrial training for the ordinary skilled workman. * * * Surely this means that there must be some systematic method provided for training young men in the trades, and that this must be coordinated with our public school system.

The first annual meeting of the society was held at Chicago in January, 1908, at which time Henry Wallace, of Iowa, editor of Wallaces' Farmer, spoke on the training of farm boys. But the society made its first real contact with the movement for secondary education in agriculture when it held its second annual meeting at Atlanta, Ga., in November, 1908. There Hoke Smith, then Governor of Georgia, called attention to the 11 district agricultural schools being established in that State, and Charles R. Davis, Member of Congress from Minnesota, spoke on his bill for Federal aid to agricultural and industrial education in secondary schools. This bill had been introduced first in the second session of the Fifty-ninth Congress and in modified form in the first session of the Sixtieth Congress (1907). It practically was intended to extend Federal aid to agricultural high schools of the Minnesota type, with branch experiment stations, and to normal schools giving instruction in agriculture, home economics, and mechanic arts.

W. M. Hays, who had been active in the movement for agricultural schools in Minnesota, and had been in close touch with Mr. Davis in the formulation of his bill for Federal aid to secondary schools, attended the meeting of the society at Milwaukee in December, 1909, in his capacity as Assistant Secretary of Agriculture, and spoke on vocational education and legislation. While he did not mention the Davis bill, it was understood that he was an active advocate of that measure.

The society at this time was giving much attention to the promotion of State legislation for industrial education. It cooperated in 1910 with the American Association for Labor Legislation in the preparation of a bulletin giving a summary of legislation in the United States relative to industrial education in public elementary and secondary schools, prepared by Edward C. Elliott, professor of education in the University of Wisconsin, and a critical and comparative comment on this legislation, by C. A. Prosser, deputy commissioner of education in Massachusetts. This showed that 29 States had legislated for practical education in agriculture, home economics, trades and industries, or manual training in secondary schools supported and controlled by the public, wherein tuition was free and open to all able to meet their entrance requirements.

Current discussion and legislation regarding vocational education showed such a confusion of terminology that Doctor Prosser, with the aid of David Snedden, undertook in this bulletin to give definitions of some of the terms commonly used in describing its various forms. Vocational education was defined as that whose controlling purpose is to fit for a calling or vocation. It may be divided into five forms, professional, commercial, industrial, agricultural, and household.

The Society for Industrial Education was at this time in close touch with the American Federation of Labor, and John Mitchell, then second vice president of the federation, was on the board of managers of the society. At its meeting in Boston, in 1910 Charles H. Winslow, as a representative of the federation, in a paper on " Labor's Demands on Industrial Education," maintained that " all industrial education should be a public function and provided for by public funds," and that " emphasis must be placed on education rather than on product," for " we must not develop a one-sided education with the single aim of turning out a mechanic at the possible sacrifice of the citizen of to-morrow."

Meanwhile the Association of Agricultural Colleges had moved in support of Federal aid for agricultural extension work under direction of these colleges. In 1909 its committee on extension work outlined a plan for a Federal appropriation for this purpose, and on December 15, 1909, a bill embodying this plan was introduced in the House of Representatives by Mr. McLaughlin, of Michigan. Early in 1910 Senator Dolliver, of Iowa, introduced two bills, one for extension work and the other for vocational education in secondary schools. These were combined by the Senate Committee on Agriculture and Forestry, of which Mr. Dolliver was chairman, and on June 2, 1910, he reported a bill (S. 8809, 61st Cong., 2d sess.) " to cooperate with the States in encouraging instruction in agriculture, the trades and industries, and home economics in secondary schools; in maintaining extension departments in State colleges, and in preparing teachers for these vocational subjects in State normal schools and to appropriate money and regulate its expenditure."

Senator Dolliver died October 15, 1910, and Senator Carroll S. Page, of Vermont, on March 3, 1911, introduced a similar bill. This was amended at different times by Senator Page and as Senate bill 3 was debated in 1912 and 1913. (See p. 364.)

The Society for Industrial Education at its annual meeting at Cincinnati, Ohio, November 2–4, 1911, received a report from its committee on national legislation, by Doctor Snedden, which dealt at some length with the Page bill. This report stated that the society "hitherto has not given very serious consideration to this measure," but the committee thought that the objects contemplated by the Page bill were on the whole worthy of the encouragement of the society, though in details the bill needed amendment. A substitute bill was therefore presented for the consideration of the society. This was a simpler measure leaving out appropriations for extension work and branch experiment stations and specific reference to normal schools in the provisions for training teachers, and providing for a single administrative agency in Washington and in each State and a system of reimbursement in the expenditure of the Federal funds, which were to be allotted to the States on the single basis of population. Details of the organization of the schools for vocational education were to be left to the local school authorities. The society was by this time willing to take a more active part in support of Federal appropriations for secondary vocational education. In the published proceedings of the Cincinnati meeting the secretary comments on the broader and more constructive aims of the society and includes among them " to aid in bringing about national legislation in favor of industrial education, of such a character as to insure wise and efficient administration of funds for the purpose intended." The society had grown to be a strong organization with over 1,300 members, many of whom had great influence in the industrial world; it had financial assistance outside of the dues paid by its members, and maintained a salaried secretary who spread its influence widely by correspondence, addresses before various organizations, the distribution of publications, etc.

At the meeting of the society at Philadelphia, December 5–7, 1912, Senator Page made a statement regarding the history of his bill and gave special credit to Doctor Snedden and Doctor Prosser for their assistance in perfecting the bill. Speaking on this subject from the standpoint of the manufacturer, James P. Munroe, of Boston, strongly favored the Page-Wilson bill and offered resolutions asking the Senate " to give immediate and favorable consideration " to this bill. These resolutions were passed unanimously by a rising vote.

On April 1, 1912, Doctor Prosser became secretary of the society and began a very active propaganda in its interests, including especially the advocacy of Federal aid for vocational education. This is shown in his first report in Bulletin 16 of the society.

When it appeared that Congress would not pass the Page bill the National Society for Industrial Education undertook to secure the appointment of a commission on national aid for vocational education. On April 7, 1913, Senator Hoke Smith introduced a joint resolution creating such a commission. After this resolution had passed the Senate and was pending in the house the society voted to push its enactment and " to aid this commission in recommending and securing legislation providing national grants for the work which shall be based on sound principles of government and of administration." This resolution passed both Houses and was approved by President Wilson January 20, 1914. It provided for a commission of nine persons to be appointed by the President. The appointments made included the secretary and four other members of the society. In this way the society was very influential in determining the character and form of the Federal legislation to aid vocational education. The commission framed a bill which included Federal aid to secondary education in agriculture, home economics, and trades and industries. The society at its meeting in Richmond, Va., in December, 1914, resolved that as an organization, and through the action of its individual members, it—

should press forward as rapidly as possible, having due regard to the soundness and permanency of the several steps, toward the securing of Federal aid, under wise restrictions, for the promotion of industrial, as well as agricultural and household arts education in the several States.

Two years more were required before the legislation sought was obtained through the passage of the Smith-Hughes Vocational Education Act. The influence of the society was then further shown by the appointment of James P. Munroe as the member of the Federal Board for Vocational Education to represent trades and industries and of Doctor Prosser as director of the administrative organization created by the board. Since that time the society has been active in promoting the general interests of vocational education, especially in its industrial phases, through its annual meetings and publications. The broader aspects of its work were indicated in 1918 by the change of its name to Society for Vocational Education.

THE BILLS IN CONGRESS FOR FEDERAL AID TO VOCATIONAL EDUCATION PRIOR TO 1914

In Congress the movement which resulted in the Smith-Hughes Vocational Education Act may be said to have begun on February 21, 1906, when Ernest M. Pollard, of Nebraska, introduced in the House of Representatives a bill to grant Federal aid to normal schools. A similar bill was introduced in the Senate the next day by Elmer J. Burkett, of Nebraska. This bill had been drafted by the president of the State normal school, the State superintendent of public instruction, and the attorney general of Nebraska because that State had no institution for training teachers of agriculture, though a law passed in 1901 required examinations in this subject for certain grades of teachers' certificates. Under this bill Federal funds were to be given to the States for training teachers of agriculture, manual training, domestic science, and related subjects. The initial appropriation was to be $500,000, and this was to be increased annually by $100,000 until it reached a maximum of $1,000,000. One half of the appropriation was to be equally divided among the States and the other half was to be allotted to the normal schools in proportion to the length of their term and the number of their students. The Secretary of the Interior was to administer the act. This bill was before the Fifty-ninth, Sixtieth, and Sixty-first Congresses. It had considerable support throughout the country, including the indorsement of the department of superintendence of the National Education Association. A somewhat similar bill was introduced in the Sixtieth Congress by

Senator McCreary, of Kentucky. The Burkett-Pollard bill is supposed to have had some influence on the insertion in the Nelson amendment to the agricultural appropriation act of 1907 of the proviso that the Federal funds granted to the land-grant colleges under that act might be spent for the training of teachers of "the elements of agriculture and the mechanic arts."

At the time that Georgia was greatly interested in the establishment of agricultural schools, Leonidas Livingston, of that State, at the suggestion of Governor Terrell, on December 18, 1906, introduced in the House of Representatives a bill to grant annually $10,000 of Federal funds to such schools in each congressional district throughout the United States. The same bill was introduced in the Senate by Alexander Clay, of Georgia, January 21, 1907. This was followed a few weeks later by a bill introduced by Representative William Adamson, of Georgia, to appropriate $2,500 annually to each branch agricultural experiment station established in congressional districts in any State or Territory.

On January 22, 1907, Representative Charles R. Davis, of Minnesota, a member of the Committee on Agriculture, introduced his first bill for Federal aid for vocational education. This proposed to give annually 10 cents per capita of population for the teaching of agriculture and home economics in secondary agricultural schools in districts of not less than 10 counties, and for the teaching of mechanic arts and home economics in urban schools, and $2,500 to each branch experiment station connected with an agricultural school. The Secretary of Agriculture was to administer the act.

In the Sixtieth Congress Mr. Davis, though no longer on the Committee on Agriculture, actively supported his bill. The friends of the normal schools secured the favorable influence of President Roosevelt and as a result the Davis bill was amended to include an appropriation of 1 cent per capita of population for the teaching of agriculture, home economics, and mechanic arts in public normal schools. The bill gained a large and increasing measure of support. It was indorsed by the National Grange, the Farmers' National Congress, the National League for Industrial Education, and the Southern Education Association. W. M. Hays was closely associated with Mr. Davis in framing and supporting this bill. It was, however, strongly opposed by educators and others who feared that it would create a system of vocational education apart from the general public-school system. This opposition was voiced, for example, by Elmer E. Brown, then commissioner of education, and Eugene Davenport, dean of the Illinois College of Agriculture. In an effort to allay opposition, the bill was amended so as to give the administration of the act to the Secretary of the Interior, in cooperation with the Secretaries of Agriculture and Commerce and Labor. But this was not very satisfactory.

The American Federation of Labor now began to take more active interest in this matter and through its committee on industrial education somewhat revised the Davis bill and gave it to Senator Dolliver, of Iowa, who introduced it in the Senate January 5, 1910. Soon afterwards Mr. Davis introduced it in the House. In the Dolliver-Davis bill lump sums to be distributed to the States were appropriated.

With this bill Senator, Dolliver also introduced the agricultural extension bill which Mr. McLaughlin had introduced in the House. Both bills went to the Senate Committee on Agriculture and Forestry, of which Mr. Dolliver was chairman. That committee decided to combine these bills and on June 22, 1910, reported the combined bill favorably. In this new bill the administration was given to the Secretary of the Interior. It was now hoped that all the forces which had been interested in the previous bills would unite in support of this combined bill. But this did not occur, and new forms of opposition arose. The Association of American Agricultural Colleges and Experiment Stations decided to give its active support to the McLaughlin extension bill. The National Society for Industrial Education (Bulletin 15) declined to indorse the Dolliver bill, but instead gave out a statement calling for clearer definition of the purposes of such legislation, limitation of Federal funds, State offset, use of funds for vocational education, State supervision, etc.

The friends of the Dolliver bill therefore decided not to press that measure in the Sixty-first Congress but to prepare for an active campaign in the Sixty-second Congress. Senator Dolliver died in October, 1910. Senator Carroll S. Page, of Vermont, a member of the Senate Committee on Agriculture and Forestry, on the closing day of the Sixty-first Congress introduced a somewhat modified form of the Dolliver bill.

THE PAGE BILL

The original bill by Senator Page was introduced March 3, 1911 (S. 10905, 61st Cong. 3d sess.), and was referred to the Committee on Agriculture and Forestry. It proposed appropriations (1) of $5,000,000 annually for instruction in the trades and industries, home economics, and agriculture in public schools of secondary grade in the States, Territories, and District of Columbia; (2) $4,000,000 annually for instruction in agriculture and home economics in State district agricultural schools of secondary grade; (3) $1,000,000 annually for branch agricultural experiment stations at the agricultural high schools; (4) $500,000 annually, with additional amounts increasing by $200,000 for five years, for extension departments of agriculture, trades and industries, home economics, and rural affairs, at the land-grant colleges, or State departments of agriculture, provided the States appropriated sums equal to the additional amounts; and (5) $1,000,000 annually for instruction in agriculture, trades and industries, and home economics at State and Territorial normal schools. In States where separate schools and colleges are maintained for negroes there must be a division of the funds for instruction in proportion to the population of the two races. The districts for State agricultural schools and branch experiment stations must include from 5 to 15 counties. Short, continuation, and evening courses must be provided for persons not able to take the regular courses. The Secretary of the Interior, with the assistance of the Secretaries of Agriculture and of Commerce and Labor, was charged with the administration of this law.

In a different form this bill was again introduced in the Senate April 6, 1911 (Senate 3), and in the House by William B. Wilson, of Pennsylvania, who had been for eight years secretary of the United

Mine Workers of America. In the Senate it was reported with amendments by the Committee on Agriculture and Forestry February 26, 1912. Senator Page made his principal speech on his bill in the Senate June 5, 1912 (411). It had by this time grown from 12 to 36 sections. An appropriation of $480,000 annually to the State colleges of agriculture and mechanic arts for the preparation of teachers had been added. The Secretary of Agriculture alone was to administer the funds granted for extension departments and branch experiment stations. The States must provide a board for vocational education, which might be the board for education in general, to control the funds given for vocational instruction and teacher-training. The total annual Federal appropriations were to increase from $2,077,000 in 1913 to $14,752,000 in 1921.

Senator Page stated that in connection with a meeting of the Southern Commercial Congress in Washington in December, 1911, a large number of educators from all parts of the country, including the executive committee of the Association of Agricultural Colleges, had held a conference on this bill and that it had been revised by a subcommittee and then indorsed by the conference.

The bill was then withdrawn by unanimous consent, and a substitute bill was reported June 14, 1912, which carried lump sums to each State for vocational education and teacher training but no appropriation for branch experiment stations. This substitute bill, drafted by the secretary of the National Society for the Promotion of Industrial Education, representatives of the American Federation of Labor, and W. M. Hays, had been introduced in the House April 20, 1912, and discussed there in hearings before the Committee on Agriculture.

Meanwhile Senator Hoke Smith, of Georgia, and Representative A. F. Lever, of South Carolina, had introduced an agricultural extension bill, which was passed by the House of Representatives August 23, 1912. The Senate substituted the Page bill with additional amendments January 27, 1913. The conference committee of the two Houses could not agree, and the Sixty-second Congress ended without final action on these measures.

The Page bill was introduced again in the Sixty-third Congress April 7, 1913, but it was increasingly apparent that Congress would not pass this bill, especially since there was strong opposition to the uniting of appropriations for agricultural extension work and vocational education in a single bill. The proposition to create a commission to study the situation with regard to vocational education and report recommendations which might aid in the solution of the problem of Federal aid for such education was therefore received with favor in Congress, and the resolution for this purpose (see p. 361) was practically substituted for the Page bill.

THE COMMISSION ON NATIONAL AID TO VOCATIONAL EDUCATION

The law under which the commission on national aid to vocational education was created simply made it its duty " to consider the subject of national aid for vocational education and report their findings and recommendations " (412). Its members, appointed by the President, were Hoke Smith, of Georgia, and Carroll S. Page, of

Vermont, from the Senate; D. M. Hughes, of Georgia, and S. D. Fess, of Ohio, from the House of Representatives; John A. Lapp, director of the Indiana Bureau of Legislative Information, who had been secretary of the Indiana Commission on Industrial and Agricultural Education; Florence Marshall, director of the Manhattan Trade School; Agnes Nestor, president of the International Glove Workers Union and member of the committee on industrial education of the American Federation of Labor; Charles A. Prosser, secretary of the National Society for the Promotion of Industrial Education; and Charles H. Winslow, of the Bureau of Labor Statistics, who had been a member of the Massachusetts Commission on Industrial Education. It will be observed that the commission had no members from organizations specially interested in agricultural education. Senator Smith was elected chairman and Ernest A. Wreidt, director of the Public Education Association of New York City, was made its secretary.

The commission was not called together until April 2, 1914, and under the law was required to make its report not later than June 1, 1914. The enactment of the Smith-Lever Extension Act on May 8, 1914, enabled the commission to confine its investigation to the field of secondary-school education. It studied the extent of the need of vocational education in the United States, the need of national grants for such education, what kinds or forms of vocational education should be stimulated by national grants, how far the Federal Government could aid through expert knowledge and to what extent Federal grants should be made and under what conditions. It therefore dealt with national grants (1) to Federal agencies for information and advice, and (2) to the States. To gain information under the first head, hearings and conferences with department officials at Washington were held; under the second head, in addition to hearings, a questionnaire was sent to State, city, and county superintendents of public instruction and to national organizations of labor and to representative employees. The literature of the subject was also collated and studied as far as possible.

At the hearings before the commission, the Secretary of Agriculture was represented by the writer, Director of the Office of Experiment Stations, who explained what the Department of Agriculture was doing for the promotion of agricultural education and extension work. At another time the writer, in his capacity that year as president of the Association of American Agricultural Colleges and Experiment Stations, explained the work of these institutions relating to secondary education and the declarations of the association in favor of a system of public secondary education in agriculture, including special agricultural schools and the teaching of agriculture in the local high schools.

The standard agricultural courses whether in the ordinary high schools or in special schools, should not be narrowly vocational but should aim to fit the pupils for life as progressive, broad-minded and intelligent men and women, as well as good farmers and horticulturists. The standard courses in agricultural secondary schools, should be so organized as to form a natural and proper preparation for entrance to agricultural colleges (412).

The association had declared in 1911 (and reaffirmed this declaration in 1912) that it favored.

Federal aid for public schools of secondary grade, providing secondary education in agriculture, home economics, the trades and industries, including manual training, and for the education and professional training of teachers for these schools in the several States, as may be determined by the legislature.

This was confirmed by W. O. Thompson, president of Ohio State University, chairman of the executive committee of the association, in a written statement to the commission. Dean Davenport, of the College of Agriculture of the University of Illinois, also wrote to the commission his views regarding the use of the high schools, rather than special schools, for secondary vocational education, and in another statement emphasized the " great need for national grants for vocational education, leaving the States free to determine the character and extent of the use of such funds, but requiring them to devote at least an equal amount to the same general purpose." The Federal departments could be helpful by furnishing information and advice. P. P. Claxton, United States Commissioner of Education, presented a list of the publications of the Bureau of Education on education in agriculture, home economics and the industries, and emphasized his interest in the practical education of the rural people.

As the result of their intensive investigation the commission concluded that the kind of vocational education most urgently demanded was that which would prepare workers for the more common occupations in every part of the United States having for their purpose to conserve and develop our resources; promote a more productive and prosperous agriculture; prevent waste of labor; supplement apprenticeship; increase wage-earning power; meet the demand for trained workmen; and offset the increased cost of living. National grants to the States were needed, especially for agricultural, trade, and industrial education, partly for the preparation of efficient teachers and partly for the payment of a portion of the salaries of teachers in service. Such grants were justified by the urgency of the demand for the training of workers, by the interstate and national character of the problem, by precedents in Federal legislation, and by the successful results of previous grants for education. National appropriations to Federal agencies should be " for studies, investigations, and reports furthering the efforts of the States to place the work of their vocational schools on a scientific and business-like basis."

On this general basis the commission elaborated its report, and submitted the draft of a bill to provide for the promotion of vocational education through the cooperation of the Federal Government with the States. The recommendations of the commission, as embodied in this bill, are summarized in their report as follows:

1. That national grants be given to the States for the purpose of stimulating vocational education in agriculture and in the trades and industries.
2. That grants be given in two forms:
    (a) for the training of teachers of agricultural, trade and industrial and home economics subjects.
    (b) For the paying of part of the salaries of teachers, supervisors, and directors of agricultural subjects and of teachers of trade and industrial subjects.
3. That appropriations be made to a Federal board for making studies and investigations which shall be of use in vocational schools (412).

The amounts of grants were to be stated separately for the several purposes as was finally done in the Smith-Hughes Act.

The schools to be aided were to be public schools in which the instruction would be of less than college grade, designed " to prepare boys and girls over 14 years of age for useful or profitable employment in agriculture and in the trades and industries "; part-time and evening schools should be provided.

For administering this law the States were to provide State boards with which the National Government could deal and there should be a Federal board, consisting of the Postmaster General, Secretaries of the Interior, Agriculture, Commerce, and Labor, with the Commissioner of Education as its executive officer.

The Federal law would " set up conditions safeguarding the proper expenditure of the money," and the States were to provide for " the proper custody and disbursement of the Federal grants."

The report of the commission was printed and widely circulated, but it was not thought best to attempt to secure the passage of the bill at the short session of the Sixty-third Congress, beginning in December, 1914.

President Wilson, in his message to Congress December 7, 1915, strongly favored Federal aid to industrial and vocational education as a means of making " the industries and resources of the country available and ready for mobilization."

The bill of the commission was introduced in the Senate by Hoke Smith December 7, and in the House of Representatives by D. M. Hughes, December 19, 1915. (Fig. 25.)

It was reported favorably in the Senate January 31, 1916, and in the House February 10, 1916. Amendments adopted in the Senate required the Federal board to select a director, four specialists, and an advisory council of seven persons representing various interests, and to permit the board to have departments of the Government make studies and investigations for it. The bill passed the Senate unanimously July 31, 1916. In the House Mr. Hughes as chairman of the Committee on Education explained the measure, but the minority leader, Mr. Mann, of Illinois, asked that the bill be held until the short session, and it went over. When Congress met in December, 1916, President Wilson in his message said:

[This measure] is of vital importance to the country because it concerns a matter too long neglected, upon which the thorough industrial preparation of the country for the critical years of economic development immediately ahead of us in very large measure depend. It contains plans which affect all interests and all parts of the country, and I am sure there is no legislation now pending before the Congress whose passage the country awaits with more thoughtful approval or greater impatience to see a great and admirable thing set in the way of being done.

The House bill differed from the Senate bill by the substitution for the Federal Board with five Cabinet officers of a board comprised of the Commissioner of Education and four associate members, no more than two of whom were to be of any one political party, to be appointed by the President and each to have a salary of $5,000 a year. Meanwhile there had arisen much sentiment in favor of a board containing representatives of different vocational lines. This was urged by the National Society for Industrial Education, the United States Chamber of Commerce, the American Federation of Labor, and other organizations. There was also strong opposition to a board in which the Commissioner of Education would be the executive officer, for it was feared that this would result in defeating the distinct development of a system of real vocational education. On the other hand there were many people, including a large number of educators, who did not favor an organization of vocational education entirely separate from the general public-school system. For a long

FIG. 25.—D. M. Hughes

time the problem of unified or separate control of vocational education had been debated in the National Education Association, the National Society for Industrial Education, and elsewhere.

When the bill was discussed in the House an amendment offered by Mr. Lenroot, of Wisconsin, was adopted, which made the four appointed members representatives of manufactures, commerce, labor and agriculture, respectively, and provided that the board should annually elect one of its members chairman.

When the bill went to conference it was understood that President Wilson was opposed to a board entirely separate from the executive departments.

The final result was a compromise by which the Federal board was made to consist of the secretaries of Agriculture, Commerce, and Labor, the Commissioner of Education, and representatives of manufactures and commerce, agriculture, and labor. This board, therefore, was put in control of representatives of the industries, including agriculture, but the public-school system was represented by the Commissioner of Education as a member of the board. In the States under this act the control of the funds for vocational education might be in a separate board of vocational education or in the general board or department of education as each State might determine.

The friends of home economics education were not satisfied with the provisions for that subject in the commission's bill, which were confined to the preparation of teachers. They therefore secured the addition of home economics to those sections of the bill which deal with the payment of the salaries of teachers in service, though not more than 20 per cent of the annual appropriation can be spent for the teaching of this subject.

Those who were opposed to the use of Federal funds by sectarian or private institutions obtained an amendment specifically stating that no portion of any moneys appropriated under this act shall be applied directly or indirectly " for the support of any religious or privately owned or conducted school or college." The bill passed the House January 9, 1917, and was sent to conference. The agreement reached by the conferees was adopted by both Houses, and the bill became a law through its approval by President Wilson February 23, 1917.

THE SMITH-HUGHES VOCATIONAL EDUCATION ACT

The passage of the Smith-Hughes Vocational Education Act practically created a system of vocational education of broad scope as a permanent part of the public-school organization throughout the United States. It provided funds for the immediate extension of the efforts of the States in this direction and by a gradual increase of the Federal aid helped to put this system on a sound and substantial footing within a few years. It would then remain for the States and local communities, with or without additional Federal assistance, to increase the strength and scope of vocational education to meet the development of the various local vocations.

The act also exemplified a new phase of Federal cooperation with the States in educational work. In the Morrill Land Grant Act of 1862 the Federal Government gave lands to the States for colleges without requiring them to account for the use of these lands. Later the Government gave money to the land-grant colleges for experiment stations and for instruction, with limited but increasing requirements for Federal supervision. In the Smith-Lever Extension Act the extreme limit of Federal union with the States in an educational enterprise was reached. This act required cooperation between the Federal Department of Agriculture and the States as represented by the land-grant colleges, in providing funds and in planning and conducting extension work in agriculture and home economics. The plans adopted under this act have set up in the several States an organization representing both the State and the Federal Government. The work in each State is in charge of a director, who is a joint representative of the State agricultural college and the United States Department of Agriculture. He has the franking privilege, and his salary comes from Federal and State sources. In the counties the agents generally receive part of their salary from direct individual schools receiving the benefits of this act. The Federal commissions and the franking privilege. Officers of the department participate in the extension work in the State, and all the extension work of the department in the States is subject to the administration of the extension directors.

In the Smith-Hughes Vocational Education Act a more limited cooperation between the Federal Government and the States is provided for. In each State there is a board of vocational education, and the Federal board deals only with this State board and not with individual schools receiving the benefits of this act. The Federal funds are expended in accordance with plans submitted by the State boards and approved by the Federal board. The Federal authorities inspect the work and the expenditures in each State so far as to determine whether they come within the provisions of the law and entitle the State to reimbursement from the Federal funds. Beyond this the Federal board has only advisory functions and aids the work in the States by furnishing information through publications or otherwise and by conferring with State officials in charge of different lines of work.

SECONDARY AGRICULTURAL EDUCATION UNDER THE SMITH-HUGHES ACT, 1917–1925

THE FEDERAL BOARD FOR VOCATIONAL EDUCATION

On July 17, 1917, President Wilson, by and with the advice and consent of the Senate, appointed the following members of the Federal Board for Vocational Education: For one year, as representative of manufactures and commerce, James P. Munroe, of Massachusetts, a graduate of the Massachusetts Institute of Technology and secretary of its faculty for several years, and a prominent worker for many years in the movement for industrial education; for two years, as representative of agriculture, Charles A. Greathouse, of Indiana, who had been State superintendent of public instruction; for three years, as representative of labor, Arthur E. Holder, a machinist, who had been deputy commissioner of the Iowa Bureau of Labor and had represented the American Federation of Labor in national legislative matters. The ex-officio members were D. F. Houston, Secretary of Agriculture; W. C. Redfield, Secretary of Commerce; W. B. Wilson, Secretary of Labor; and P. P. Claxton, Commissioner of Education. The first meeting of the board was held in the office of the Secretary of Agriculture, July 21, 1917. Secretary Houston was elected chairman, Mr. Munroe vice chairman, and Commissioner

Claxton secretary. The board appointed Charles A. Prosser director of its administrative staff, with the following assistant directors: Agriculture, Layton S. Hawkins, of the New York State Department of Education; industrial education, Lewis H. Carris, of the New Jersey State Department of Education; home economics, Josephine L. Berry, head of the home economics division of the Department of Agriculture of the University of Minnesota; research, Charles H. Winslow, director of vocational research, Indianapolis. Cheesman A. Herrick, president of Girard College, Philadelphia, was appointed temporary agent for commercial education.

For administration and inspection the country was divided into five sections: North Atlantic, Southern, North Central, West Central, and Pacific. Headquarters for agents of the board were established in New York City, Atlanta, Ga., Indianapolis, Ind., Kansas City, Mo., and San Francisco, Calif. From August 17 to 28, 1917, the board held conferences with representatives of the boards charged with the State administration of the Smith-Hughes Act at which " the purpose of the law was discussed with particular reference to the general principles upon which it is based and the methods by which these principles should be taught into practice." The first bulletin of the board was issued in November, 1917, and was entitled " The Smith-Hughes Act: Policies of Federal Board for Vocational Education," (497).

Among the policies announced at this time were the following:

The Federal board believes that the following fundamental principles should govern the appropriations from the National Government to the States for vocational education. The money is designed:

(1) To stimulate the States to undertake a new and needed form of service—that for vocational education—which the National Government believes necessary to the public welfare.

(2) To equalize, in part at least, the inequalities of burden among the States in carrying on this service.

(3) To purchase for the National Government a reasonable degree of participation in the carrying on of this work in which the National Government is so deeply concerned.

(4) To establish standards of efficiency in vocational education and to set up minimums below which work in vocational education for which reimbursement from Federal moneys is desired can not be allowed to fall.

The Smith-Hughes Act does not provide for the education of " backward, deficient, incorrigible or otherwise subnormal individuals, but only for thorough vocational instruction to healthy, normal individuals."

The Federal board and its representatives will deal with the State boards for vocational education and not with individual schools.

By January 1, 1918, each of the 48 States had through legislative enactment or the governor accepted the provisions of the Smith-Hughes Act, had submitted plans which met with the approval of the Federal board, and had been certified to the Secretary of the Treasury for the allotment for the fiscal year ended June 30, 1918. In 14 States a special board for vocational education was created or utilized; in 32 States the general State board of education was designated to administer the Smith-Hughes fund; in Minnesota the State high-school board was utilized; and in Colorado, which did not have a State board of education, the State board of agriculture had the administration of vocational education added to its duties as a supervisory board for the State land-grant college.

Meanwhile the United States had entered the World War, and the War Department and the Shipping Board had called on the Federal Board for Vocational Education to aid in training conscripted men for the vocations required for military purposes or for shipbuilding. The problem of training disabled soldiers and sailors was also being considered in cooperation with other branches of the Government. This led to the vocational rehabilitation act of June 27, 1918, under which the administration of this work was committed to this board and formed a large, difficult, and rapidly increasing feature of its work until it was transferred to the Veterans' Bureau on August 9, 1921.

The rehabilitation work was distributed among schools and colleges in the several States. It included instruction in many occupations, among which were many branches of agriculture.

Conditions growing out of the war intensified the interest of the people of the United States in vocational education, but also brought about unusual difficulties which for a considerable period prevented its most orderly and satisfactory development.

AGRICULTURAL WORK OF THE FEDERAL BOARD

The assistant director for agriculture, L. S. Hawkins, came into this work after several years' experience as a specialist in agricultural education in the State department of education in New York, which had developed under State laws both special agricultural schools and departments of agriculture in a considerable number of high schools. He had also received part of his education in the State normal school at Cortland, N. Y., and had been head of the department of science and agriculture in that school. He was thus familiar with administrative problems relating to State supervision of agricultural education and to the organization, equipment, and curriculum for secondary instruction in agriculture.

Charles H. Lane became a member of the agricultural staff of the Federal board by transfer from the Office of Experiment Stations of the Department of Agriculture, where for several years he had had charge of its work relating to agricultural education. He was therefore thoroughly familiar with the status of teacher training in agriculture and agricultural instruction in secondary schools throughout the country. Another member of this first staff was William G. Hummel, a graduate in agriculture at the universities of Illinois and California, who had taught agriculture in high schools in California and had been for seven years teacher of agricultural education in the University of California.

The board immediately undertook investigations on the organization of secondary schools in agriculture, including courses of study and supervision; materials and methods in secondary-school agriculture; and supervised practical work in agriculture, including the home-project method of instruction. The results of this work have been published in a series of bulletins.

Cooperation was carried on with the Department of Agriculture, through its division of agricultural instruction, on the subject matter of secondary instruction in agriculture. Outlined lessons on plant and animal production were prepared in this division by E. H. Shinn and unit courses in poultry and swine husbandry by C. H. Schopmeyer. These led to attempts to make job analyses of various agricultural enterprises. With the cooperation of specialists in the department and members of the staff of the Federal board, Mr. Schopmeyer prepared bulletins containing analyses of potato growing, poultry husbandry, and the management of a farm business, and F. A. Merrill prepared job-lesson units for selected truck and fruit crops adapted to southern conditions.

Much information regarding the development of agricultural education under the Smith-Hughes Act is contained in the annual reports of the Federal board (*481*), and its Yearbook of 1923 gave in considerable detail a description of outstanding developments and summary of progress by States.

Through its publications and participation in conferences with State supervisors and school officials and teachers the board has done much to determine and improve the standards for secondary education in agriculture in the United States. Its careful and impartial examination of the plans submitted by the State boards and its inspection of the accounts and work in the several States have also contributed toward firmly establishing a good system of vocational education in agriculture.

RELATION OF VOCATIONAL INSTRUCTION IN AGRICULTURE TO EXTENSION WORK

As the number of schools receiving the benefits of the Smith-Hughes Act increased, the teachers of agriculture in these schools came frequently into contact with the extension agents operating under the Smith-Lever Act. On their own initiative or by request of the people in the vicinity of the school, Smith-Hughes teachers in a number of places undertook extension work among the farmers. In some cases the number of students taking agriculture in the school was small, while the salary of the teacher was relatively large. This made vocational education in agriculture expensive, and the community therefore felt that it was entitled to services from this teacher outside of school. School officials and teachers sometimes raised the academic question whether extension work in agriculture, particularly boys' and girls' club work, did not really belong to the public schools, rather than to the agricultural colleges. This situation was aggravated in some cases by the extravagant claims of extension agents regarding the scope of their work, particularly with young people. While there was much friendly cooperation between teachers and extension agents, personal jealousies and antagonism made discord in various places.

This matter was brought to the attention of the Federal board and the Department of Agriculture and seemed to them to be of sufficient importance to call for a declaration of their policy regarding it. Therefore on February 21, 1918, they agreed on a " memorandum on instruction in vocational schools and extension work in agriculture " (see report of Federal board, 1919, p. 42), which after setting forth the general nature of the work called for under the

Smith-Hughes and Smith-Lever Acts dealt with the relationship of the two lines of work, as follows:

In many counties of the various States there will be the cooperative agricultural extension system conducted by the State agricultural college in cooperation with the United States Department of Agriculture and the county under the provisions of the Smith-Lever Extension Act and under other Federal and State legislation. There will also be vocational agricultural instruction carried on by the State board for vocational education in cooperation with the Federal Board for Vocational Education and the county or the local school district under the provisions of the Smith-Hughes Act. Both the extension service and the vocational instruction will deal with both adults and children.

In each State there is a State director of agricultural extension service and an executive officer of the State board for vocational education. It is suggested that these two officials determine upon a plan of cooperation for the State based upon the following general policies or principles.

(1) It is to be understood that all agricultural extension work should be administered by those in charge of extension activities in the State and that all vocational education in agriculture should be administered by those in charge of the vocational schools of the State.

(2) That all extension work with adults done by teachers in vocational schools be in accordance with the plans of the extension system for the State, and in cooperation with the agent who is in charge of the administration of the extension work in the county.

(3) That in counties having vocational schools of agriculture the extension service will conduct its extension work in agriculture with children chiefly through the organization of clubs for the carrying on of definite pieces of work for the improvement of agricultural practice. The practical agricultural work of the schools will chiefly consist of home project work by the students as a part of the systematic practical instruction provided for in the Smith-Hughes Act. It is advised that in such counties a cooperative agreement be made between the extension authorities and the school authorities whereby it will be arranged for the teachers of agriculture to take part in the extension activities with the children within the territory of the school and that such territory be set forth in the agreement.

(4) That in every case care be taken to see that work which is supported by Federal funds under any of the aforementioned acts will not in any way duplicate or overlap work being carried on in that same community when that work is supported in any part from another Federal fund (481).

This statement helped to bring about more or less satisfactory agreements between the vocational education and extension forces in a number of States, and there was also a general tendency toward improved relationships as the work of the two agencies progressed. But there remained sufficient unrest regarding various phases of this problem to bring about other formal attempts at its solution.

At their annual meetings in 1920, both the agricultural section of the National Society for Vocational Education and the department of rural education of the National Education Association independently voted to create committees on this subject, but later the committee appointed by the former society was asked to serve also as the committee of the latter organization. Its report in February, 1921, was accepted as a progress report, and the Association of Land-Grant Colleges was invited to join with the other two organizations through a joint committee. Later a committee of the Association for the Advancement of Agricultural Teaching was invited to sit with this joint committee. There were 14 persons, representing the four organizations, who joined in the final report, adopted May 9 and 10, 1921. (Proceedings of Association of Land-Grant Colleges, 1921, p. 232.) A. R. Mann, dean of the New York College of Agriculture, was chairman of the joint committee. Their report was based on the memorandum of the Department of Agriculture and Federal Board for Vocational Education cited above and "in the light of subsequent experience" offered "explanations and interpretations of the foregoing memorandum as tending to facilitate sound and harmonious adjustments with the States."

After briefly describing extension work and public-school education in agriculture and home economics, the committee proposed a basis for agreements in related lines of work.

It is recognized that the functions, obligations, and responsibilities of the parties to the agreement, as defined by law, may be similar, with the possibility of overlapping, as in the fields of (1) the junior project work of the schools and the junior extension (boys' and girls' club) work of the college both in agriculture and home economics, (2) the part-time and evening homemaking courses of the State board for vocational education and the home economics extension work of the college, and (3) the short-unit courses in agriculture and home economics, in the public schools, and the extension classes conducted by the land-grant colleges. In a spirit of fairness to both groups of interest, this report seeks to present a basis for clear differentiation of the functions of the respective agencies in these closely related tasks. It is proposed that the work in these related fields shall be made a matter of cooperative agreement in the several States. Such cooperative agreement should recognize the following facts and principles:

(1) It is the function, duty, and responsibility of the public school to provide education for all children, and to provide such adult education as is authorized by law.

(2) Under the law, it is the function and duty of the land-grant college of agriculture to maintain extension service. The theory underlying extension service is that it is, first to provide supplemental education for persons engaged in agriculture and home-making, and, second, to enable the college and the Federal Department of Agriculture to bring their advances in knowledge to farmers and their families who can make the applications. Furthermore, by virtue of its staff of technical specialists and its responsibility for training vocational teachers, the land-grant college is in a position to furnish technical information and advice in the fields of agriculture and home economics to vocational work in the schools.

(3) It is clearly recognized and affirmed that the college of agriculture is the source and authority, in the State, in technical subject matter in agriculture and home economics. The principle should be clearly observed that neither the State nor any lesser administrative unit charged with the supervision of vocational education, should employ any itinerant subject-matter specialists for the purpose of giving technical instruction in any phase of agriculture or home economics. In so far as the vocational schools may have need for the assistance of technical specialists other than the regular vocational teacher or teachers in the local schools, they should look to the college of agriculture to supply such specialists. If, by reason of limitation of funds, the college is unable to meet all demands for aid on technical matters, the remedy is to be found in strengthening the resources of the college to fully meet the requirements, and not in establishing subject-matter specialists as part of the State vocational system.

(4) There are three types of situation to be considered: (a) Where agricultural and home economics education is fully developed by the local schools, (b) where such education has not yet been undertaken by the local schools, (c) where such education is in process of development by the local schools.

(a) Where the school provides a comprehensive program of agricultural and home economics education which meets the needs of children and adults, through systematic instruction and supervised practice, the extension forces of the land-grant colleges shall not duplicate such work of the schools, but shall rather cooperate with the schools by providing, on request, subject matter, special lectures, conferences, and other similar services. This shall not be interpreted to limit the freedom of the extension forces to prosecute their extension work through local organizations of farmers.

(b) Where the school does not provide such a program of instruction in agriculture and home economics, the extension service of the college should organize extension work.— In such localities, the school should give its fullest support and cooperation to the extension workers.

(c) It is recognized that, in some places, schools will be in the process of developing such educational programs. In these cases, the following principles should apply: Extension workers should confine their work with children to those whom the school does not enroll in systematic vocational or prevocational project work, including supervised home practice: unless requested or authorized by school authorities to enroll them. The school should organize its work with adults to provide systematic vocational instructions defined herein. The school should offer its facilities to the junior extension worker wherever the school has not, in reasonable operation, vocational or prevocational project work accompanied by supervised home practice.

(5) Before undertaking junior extension work in any county, the extension division should submit in writing to the county superintendent of schools, the plans proposed for junior extension in that county, and should endeavor to arrange for a basis of understanding and cooperation. Copies of plans, when agreed upon, should be filed with the State department of education for consideration, before being put into operation.

(6) The State department of education should look to the land-grant college to furnish technical subject matter in agriculture and home economics in the form of outlines, leaflets, and bulletins for use in the public schools. It is understood, however, that no such material in agriculture and home economics should be used in the schools until approved by the State department of education.

The committee also recognized that—

The highest service in this great field will spring from a spirit of copartnership, or mutual respect, and from intimate association on a clearly defined basis, with the single purpose of serving the complete vocational needs of the communities. When both of the agencies shall have been fully developed on a carefully adjusted basis, there will be large place for them both in every community (499).

At present both agencies are far from filling their respective fields. In its report for 1924 the Federal board made the following statement:

Approximate number eligible for training and number and per cent reached

	Total	In classes of vocational agriculture	Per cent reached
Farm boys in school	978, 371	66, 485	6. 79
Farm boys out of school (14–20 years)	1, 202, 135	3, 294	0. 27
Men on farms (over 20 years)	8, 309, 538	15, 560	0. 18

That year about half a million boys and girls were enrolled in the extension clubs.

WORK IN THE STATES UNDER THE SMITH-HUGHES ACT

During the first year after the passage of the Smith-Hughes Act 40 States began or further developed the training of teachers of agriculture and organized vocational agricultural instruction in schools. Within the next five years all the States were engaged in both these lines of work.

In general, the land-grant colleges for whites and negroes received Federal aid for teacher training, since they alone had sufficient agricultural equipment and personnel to enable them to give satisfactory training for teachers of agriculture in secondary schools.

The number of instructors of teacher-training courses in agriculture was 222 in 1919 and 241 in 1924. That year the number ranged from 1 in Arizona, Delaware, Louisiana, Maine, Nevada, and New Mexico to 10 in Colorado, 11 in New York, 15 in Massachusetts, 18 in Illinois, and 22 in California. In teacher-training courses there were 1,289 men and 45 women in 1919 and 4,692 men and 55 women in 1924, when the number in the several States ranged from 4 in Nevada to 869 in Iowa. There were from 1 to 5 women students in 7 States and 35 in California. In 1918, $121,140.44 (including $56,642.27 of Federal money, $53,023.21 of State money, and $11,578.32 of local money) was spent for teacher training in the 48 States, and $756,354.08 (including $342,307.91 of Federal money, $313,980.80 of State money, and $100,015.37 of local money) in 1924.

Teacher training—The effect of the Smith-Hughes Act on the teacher-training work in agriculture of the institutions receiving the benefits of this act was immediately to enlarge and strengthen their work in this direction, especially with reference to the problems of secondary education. The training became more distinctly vocational in the sense that it had more definite relation to farm practice. There has been a growing realization that farm boys and girls should not only be taught and led to practice the best modes of farm operation but should also be instructed in the scientific, economic, and social aspects of agriculture and country life. Teachers of agriculture should, therefore, have a broad training in the principles and methods of education and their applications to agricultural teaching, and in science, economics, and sociology, as well as in the science and practice of agriculture. This really calls for more than an undergraduate course for the prospective teacher of agriculture, and yet under present conditions the great majority of students in the teacher-training courses are not able to go beyond the 4-year course for the bachelor's degree. One special difficulty relates to practice teaching as a part of the course. There is also a fundamental difficulty in that the teaching of agriculture has not been well organized on the basis of the problem method, and yet the home-project work called for under the Smith-Hughes Act makes it essential that agricultural instruction in the secondary schools should very largely be based on the practical projects of the students. It is therefore not surprising that the different States have attempted to solve the practical problems involved in the organization and conduct of their teacher-training work in agriculture in various ways, and it can not yet be said that such training is standardized. Practically all the States require a 4-year course in agriculture and from 9 to 20 hours of professional work in education. In a few States there is definite encouragement of at least a year of graduate work. Supervised practice teaching is generally required, either in the community where the college is located or in selected high schools outside.

There has been a growing realization that the duty of the teacher-training institution is not finished when the student graduates, but that it extends to the giving of assistance to the teacher in service. This is partly accomplished by summer sessions at the college but also in other ways. A few institutions have a regular system of what is known as itinerant teacher training. This is described in the report of the Federal Board for Vocational Education for 1924 as follows:

It ordinarily means individual instruction of the teacher at the school he serves by a competent person whose duty it is to carry on such work where needed. It implies going here, there, and everywhere in a State where a teacher is not doing the desired kind of work, and staying with him, or going back to him until he gains enough additional knowledge and skill to meet his problems more efficiently. The third effective means for the professional improvement of agricultural teachers in service is the State and sectional meetings of agricultural teachers for conference, demonstration, and practice.

State supervision.—Before the passage of the Smith-Hughes Act only Massachusetts, New York, Pennsylvania, Indiana, and Wisconsin had provided adequate supervision of agricultural education conducted with the aid of State funds.

The instruction in agriculture in the other 34 States granting aid for agriculture in high schools was supervised by deputy commissioners of education, professors of secondary education, high-school inspectors, and professors of agricultural education connected with land-grant colleges.

At the beginning of the 5-year period of the administration of the Federal vocational education act some States made temporary arrangements in securing supervision and inspection of instructors through competent persons detailed from State institutions or through the use of persons already in the employ of the State board in some other capacity. (Federal Board Report 1922, p. 37.)

In 1922 there were 42 full-time and 27 part-time supervisors.

In general, supervision has been conducted by personal conferences of the supervisor with the teachers, special preparation of material in the way of outlines for directed or supervised practice in agriculture, bulletins covering the main points in the administration of vocational agricultural education in the State, blanks for reports from the schools to the State board; through community surveys to determine how best to adapt the vocational agricultural instruction to the needs of the vocational pupils in the State, and through State-wide, regional, and sectional conferences. (Federal Board Report 1920, p. 79.)

Attention was often given to promotional work, improvement of the content of the course of study, methods of instruction, supervised practice, part-time instruction, and improvement of the system of reports and records. Because there have been many inexperienced teachers and the force has been rapidly changing, much attention has had to be given to the solution of specific problems arising in connection with the work in different localities. Successful experience in teaching agriculture has therefore been of great advantage in the case of supervisors.

Agricultural instruction in the schools.—Even before the passage of the Smith-Hughes Act it was evident that most of the secondary instruction in agriculture would be given in the local high schools. This plan for such instruction was greatly helped by the provision in that act for practical farm work during six months. While the special agricultural schools have much more extensive equipment of buildings, farms, animals, machinery, etc., and a larger agricultural faculty, they can not provide any large amount of practical work on the school farms in case they have many students. From the beginning of the operation of the Smith-Hughes Act the number of schools in which departments of vocational agriculture were established was very much greater than that of the special schools receiving Federal aid. There are only about 170 special agricultural schools in the United States, but in 1918 according to the records of the Federal Board for Vocational Education, 609 schools received Smith-Hughes funds and this number steadily increased until in 1923 there were 2,673. These schools ranged from small institutions in the open country to large high schools in villages or cities. Most of the schools employ only one teacher of agriculture. The total number of these teachers in 1923 was 3,012. Their departments of agriculture—

are in the nature of part-time schools of the occupational extension type, the instruction being designed to supplement the employment of the pupil on the home farm. In order that these schools may really carry out this type of instruction it has been found necessary to limit the attendance upon vocational agricultural classes to pupils who are actually engaged in some form of farm work. In most cases these schools or departments offer two, three, or four year courses for 36 weeks in the year with half of the pupils' time given to non-vocational high-school subjects. The work in vocational agriculture is usually accepted as a part of the high-school course, thus enabling the pupils completing the vocational agricultural work to secure not only the agricultural certificate but also the diploma granted by the school. The group reached by this instruction is usually composed of pupils who would ordinarily be enrolled in other high-school courses. (Federal Board Report, 1919, p. 37.)

Short winter courses and evening courses for persons out of school are increasing in number. The agricultural instruction increasingly deals with the agricultural needs of the local communities. The science work in the Smith-Hughes school is being more definitely related to agriculture and home economics.

With few exceptions the State plans provide as the qualifications of teachers of vocational agriculture graduation from a 4-year college course planned for the training of teachers of vocational agriculture and at least two years of practical farm experience. (Federal Board Report, 1919, p. 39.)

In 1922 the Federal board reported that—

The methods of adaptation of instruction to local conditions commonly used are: The survey of farm enterprises of the community, the organization of courses on the basis of farm enterprise, the formulation of courses of study by the local teacher, which courses are later approved or modified by the State supervisor.

The results of this adaptation are: Increased interest on the part of pupils in the work studied; vocational education in agriculture which actually functions in the community and which, as a result, elicits the support of farmers; and, on the whole, more thoroughgoing and efficient work done by the teachers.

The importance of the supervised farm practice as an essential feature of secondary instruction in agriculture with a vocational aim has been more fully recognized as the work under the Smith-Hughes Act has progressed. The home project is required equally in connection with all-day, part-time, and evening instruction. But there is an increasing demand to go beyond the formal requirements of the Smith-Hughes Act as regards farm practice. Students are required or requested to undertake farm work outside the assigned home project in order to develop skill in particular directions. Group or class projects have increased in number. The financial returns of supervised farm practice have greatly increased. For the fiscal year 1921–22 the labor income of vocational pupils in the all-day white schools amounted to $2,953,566.

In 1922–23 the 57,099 students enrolled in project work used 134,904 acres of land, 72,741 animals, and 691,808 birds. The previous year 79 per cent of those enrolled completed their projects, with a total labor income of $3,573,321.50 or about $96 per student.

Most of the instruction given under the Smith-Hughes Act has been through all-day courses given to children regularly attending school. But young people out of school and employed on farms as laborers or tenants may come back for part-time or short courses and more mature men and women who are farm tenants or owners may come to evening classes. The part-time courses cover from two weeks to three months and from four to eight hours per day. The instruction outside of the regular courses is often given through short-unit courses dealing with particular farm enterprises, such as potato growing, milk production, poultry husbandry, etc.

In 1924 there were 62,912 boys and 2,446 girls studying agriculture in all-day schools, 2,143 boys in part-time classes, 3,063 boys and 193 girls in short-unit courses, and 13,248 men and 1,979 women in evening classes. In all there were 85,984 persons receiving instruction in agriculture under the Smith-Hughes Act, as compared with 15,453 in 1918.

Special efforts have been made to develop instruction in vocational agriculture for negroes in the Southern States. It has been impracticable to get an adequate supply of well-trained teachers, but their number is increasing. Teacher training is done in the land-grant colleges for negroes and at Hampton and Tuskegee Institutes. Thirteen States have employed a negro teacher trainer, who visits the vocational agricultural departments of negro schools and assists in the improvement of teachers in service.

The white supervisors also have actively promoted the negro work. In 1922–23 there were 202 departments of vocational agriculture in negro schools, with an enrollment of 4,880. There were also nine part-time schools with 201 students and 18 evening classes with 813 students. In the project work 5,656 students were enrolled. In 1921–22, 78 per cent of the negro students completed their projects, the labor income being $332,457.21. Since very few negro farm boys enter high schools it has been necessary to carry the vocational agricultural instruction into the grades, and the schools for this purpose have been carefully selected.

The most successful work of this kind has been done with pupils whose parents are landowners. It is very difficult to reach the renters on the large plantations.

The influence of the Smith-Hughes work has gone beyond the schools receiving funds under that act. Incomplete statistics published by the Federal board in 1924 showed that in 13 States there were 227 schools with 197 teachers and 3,656 students in courses of vocational agriculture. Ninety of these schools were receiving State aid.

The amount of Federal funds available for vocational education in agriculture in secondary schools increased from $547,027.79 in 1918 to $2,036,502.12 in 1924. There was a further increase to $2,526,826.66 in 1925 and the maximum of $3,021,887.39 was reached in 1926. In 1918, 50 per cent of the available amount was expended in the States and 94.9 per cent in 1923. That year the Federal funds were used as follows: For supervisors, $31,612.67; evening schools, $38,504.07; part-time classes, $22,753.08; short-unit courses, $21,909.35; all-day schools, $1,554,919.58. The total cost of agricultural instruction in 1923 was $4,647,042.04, of which $1,669,-698.75 was Federal money, $1,108,461.22 was State money, and $1,868,882.07 was local money.

The results of five years' work of the schools receiving the benefits of the Smith-Hughes Act are summed up by Professor Myers in the report on his study of the effectiveness of vocational education in agriculture (490). Reports from 722 schools in 35 States showed 8,340 persons out of school who had had one or more years of instruction in vocational agriculture. On the average these persons had spent 2.7 years in high school, during which time they had been in agricultural classes 1.7 years. Fifteen and seven-tenths per cent of them had had 3 or 4 years of agricultural instruction, and of these 80 per cent had graduated. Of the total number of students, 50.4 per cent had graduated and 22 per cent had been to college. Of those who went to college 36.5 per cent went to agricultural colleges. Four thousand four hundred and eighty-eight, or 54 per cent, of the total number were engaged in farming, though 13.6 per cent of the farmers had followed other pursuits for a time. Of the total number 5 per cent were in occupations related to agriculture, 8 per cent had gone to agricultural colleges, 14 per cent to nonagricultural colleges, 10 per cent were in nonagricultural occupations, and 9 per cent were not accounted for; 311 had become teachers in rural schools. Of the farmers, 10 per cent were owners, 6 per cent managers, 7 per cent renters, 48 per cent partners, and 29 per cent laborers.

Part 8. AGRICULTURE IN THE ELEMENTARY SCHOOLS

During the past 25 years there has been a definite and widespread movement for the teaching of agriculture in the public elementary schools in the United States. The desire for this has been expressed at different times from the beginning of'the movement for agricultural education in this country. After the establishment of the agricultural colleges the National Grange in 1878 passed a resolution favoring such teaching. The public school system, especially in the rural districts, was not in condition to attempt this work at that time. Preparatory efforts to improve the curriculum of the elementary schools were, however, under way. Out of them came definite and feasible plans for elementary instruction in agriculture. These earlier movements may be grouped under the heads (1) object teaching, (2) nature study, and (3) school gardens.

OBJECT TEACHING

The basing of elementary instruction on objects rather than on books had been taught and exemplified by Pestalozzi and his followers. Joseph Neef had used this method in his private schools in this country from 1809 to 1825. The first definite object teaching in connection with a public school in the United States was at the State Normal School at Westfield, Mass., about 1845, under the influence of Horace Mann. It was taken up very actively at the normal school in Oswego, N. Y., about 1860, by E. A. Sheldon and after 1875 was developed there in connection with the teaching of elementary science. William T. Harris introduced it in the St. Louis schools during his superintendency there between 1867 and 1880.

Great impetus was given to this movement through the wide publicity caused by the radical reorganization of the elementary instruction in the schools of Quincy, Mass. Charles Francis Adams was a member of the school committee of that town. Becoming greatly dissatisfied with the results of elementary instruction according to the conventional plan, he succeeded in bringing in Francis W. Parker as school superintendent. From 1876 to 1880 Colonel Parker based the elementary curriculum in the Quincy schools on object teaching. His great energy and enthusiasm inspired the teachers under him. The pupils worked with a great variety of objects in and out of the school, did modeling in sand, and visited the fields and woods to gather plants and other things. The study of language, geography, etc., was correlated with the object study. After this Colonel Parker carried this method into the schools of Boston as a supervisor and in 1883 began a 16-year term as principal of the Cook County (Chicago) Normal School in Illinois, whence his influence was widespread.

Object teaching did much to arouse the interest of pupils in the elementary grades, but as pursued by the ordinary teacher, was too much a disconnected study of a variety of objects and had comparatively little educational value.

NATURE STUDY

Meanwhile the teaching of science was getting into the public-school system, and under the influence of Agassiz particularly was taking on certain phases of object teaching. Such teaching was done at first in the normal schools and high schools, but before long efforts were made to adapt it to the simpler instruction required in the elementary schools. H. H. Straight, who had studied under Agassiz, became a teacher in the Oswego Normal School in 1876, where he developed a plan for more systematic object teaching as elementary instruction in science and carried this over to the Cook County Normal School in 1883.

W. S. Jackman brought an improved plan for such work from Pittsburgh, Pa., to this school in 1889. He had children go out into the fields and woods and study natural objects and phenomena according to what they found there season by season. Beginning with 1890 he published "outlines in elementary science" in bimonthly pamphlets and put them into book form in 1891. Meanwhile Arthur C. Boyden had been teaching similarly at the normal school at Bridgewater, Mass., and in 1889 as a member of a committee of the Plymouth County Teachers' Association made an outline for the study of trees, which was sent to every school in the county and afterwards was presented at teachers' institutes throughout the State. For several years exhibits of the results of such instruction were made in cities. From 1889 to 1901 he taught on this plan at a summer school at Cottage City, Mass.

Frank Owen Payne independently began such work at Corry, Pa., in 1884, and lectured on this subject in Minnesota and New Jersey. About 1889 he used the term nature study for such instruction, and this soon came into general use to designate this elementary teaching. For a time teachers of science in higher schools thought their work should be called nature study, but with the specialization of science teaching this designation of the high school and college teaching of sciences disappeared. Nature study has since been defined as "primarily the simple observational study of common natural objects and processes for the sake of personal acquaintance with the things which appeal to human interest directly and independently of relations to organized science."

Nature study soon came into contact with the movement for the improvement of agriculture. At a conference on agricultural conditions in the State of New York in 1893 George T. Powell made a plea for interesting children in nature study as a first step toward instructing them in agriculture. This resulted immediately in an experimental test of this plan in the schools of Westchester County. S. F. Nixon, chairman of the ways and means committee of the New York Assembly, met with the committee which had this matter in charge. In 1894 Mr. Nixon secured the passage of a bill for the promotion of horticulture in western New York as suggested by

John W. Spencer and L. H. Bailey, then professor of horticulture at Cornell University. (See p. 275.) The work under this extension act included promotion of nature study in the schools by Bailey and others. He and his associates went out to the teachers' institutes and a large number of schools throughout the State, explained their work and publications, and demonstrated to teachers how nature study might be taught.

Mr. Spencer, as chief assistant in this work, called for nature-study leaflets in 1896 and afterwards originated the junior naturalists clubs. The first leaflet, by Professor Bailey, was entitled " How a Squash Plant Gets Out of the Soil," and was intended for use by teachers (*251*). The second was on " How a Candle Burns "; the third on " Four Apple Twigs "; the fifth on " Some Tent-makers " (i. e., the apple-tree tent caterpillar) ; and the seventh on " Hints on Making Collections of Insects."

The clubs were for the most part informal groups of children enrolled in the schools and led by their teachers to make observations of natural objects and phenomena in the region about them, read about these things and write letters to " Uncle John " (Spencer) about what they had seen and handled. Through these letters they were brought into touch with the agricultural colleges and sometimes stimulated to continue their school life further than they would otherwise have done. When desired the clubs were given a charter and provided with badges or buttons. The publications connected with this work were attractively printed and illustrated. Those for the children were quite simple. The clubs grew rapidly, and within a few years as many as 25,000 children in New York, and to a limited extent in other States and a few foreign countries, were enrolled in them.

Mrs. Mary Rogers Miller started the home nature-study course with leaflets for teachers, and Mrs. Anna Botsford Comstock succeeded her in this work in 1903. Mrs. Comstock's book of 938 pages, entitled " Handbook of Nature-Study," was based on the leaflets issued up to 1911. Promotion of nature study with an agricultural trend was taken up by a number of the other land-grant colleges.

As the result of influences emanating from the sources mentioned and many others nature study spread out widely within a few years, but mainly in the city and village schools, where there were teachers who had had some training in science. A considerable literature of the subject appeared. Among the books was one by L. H. Bailey, entitled " The Nature-Study Idea," which was published in 1903. The Nature-Study Review was established in 1905 and the American Nature-Study Society in 1908.

Nature study made a permanent impression on the elementary-school curriculum and in various forms has been continued to the present time. Somewhat independently at first, but later in close connection with nature study, the school-garden movement was developed in this country.

THE SCHOOL-GARDEN MOVEMENT

In the first half of the nineteenth century several German States introduced gardening into rural schools and somewhat later into city schools. Before the end of the century this movement had spread to other European countries. In Germany the garden at the village school was intended primarily for the teacher as a source of vegetables and fruits for his table. But teachers interested in nature study made it also a means of promoting that work. It furnished a field and materials for observations by the pupils, and by their participation in the work of planting and caring for the garden they obtained useful practical knowledge and experience. Such a garden at Alfter, in the Rhine Province, was visited by C. B. Smith and described by him in Circular 42 of the Office of Experiment Stations in 1899.

As early as 1856 General Armstrong, who afterwards founded Hampton Institute, introduced vegetable growing in some schools in Hawaii. This became a part of the school work in that Territory, and in 1898 a department of nature study and agriculture was organized in the normal school at Honolulu, with garden and field work.

In the report prepared by D. J. Crosby, of the Office of Experiment Stations, for the American Park and Outdoor Art Association in 1903 (*422*), two phases of this movement are described, (1) a somewhat restricted attempt to improve school grounds by planting trees, shrubs, and flowers, and (2) the more general planting of school gardens. Beginning about 1900, improvement of school grounds was undertaken, sometimes with the aid of voluntary associations, in Rochester, N. Y., Cleveland, Ohio, Washington, D. C., Detroit, Mich., and other cities. In New York the junior naturalists clubs were used to promote such work. A garden confined to native wild flowers and ferns was begun in connection with the George Putnam Grammar School in Boston, Mass., in 1891, and after 10 years was used for growing vegetables. The Vineyard Street Grammar School in Providence, R. I., began the planting of ferns and violets in 1892. By 1903 school gardens were in use in a considerable number of places in Massachusetts, Connecticut, Maine, Rhode Island, Vermont, New York, New Jersey, District of Columbia, Virginia, Kentucky, Alabama, Ohio, Illinois, Indiana, Michigan, Minnesota, Nebraska, Missouri, California, Colorado, and Utah. A few examples will serve to show the general character of the work at that time.

At the school of horticulture at Hartford, Conn., there were 166 gardens apportioned as follows: For teachers, 24 gardens, each 10 by 30 feet; for boys and girls, 125 gardens, each 10 by 25 feet, for first-year pupils; 16 gardens, each 10 by 30 feet, for second-year pupils; and 1 garden, 10 by 40 feet, for a third-year pupil. The pupils were drawn largely from the city schools and had one hour a week in the gardens. The second-year pupils also had root grafting and greenhouse work, including the preparation of soil, potting, repotting, and pricking out plants, and were later instructed in budding, spading, etc. Each city school was given six free scholarships. First-year pupils not receiving scholarships were charged $5 tuition. The director of this school was H. D. Hemenway, a graduate of the Massachusetts Agricultural College and the author of " How to Make School Gardens " (1903).

In New York City Mrs. Henry Parsons, a member of the school board, secured permission in 1902 to fence an area 114 by 84 feet in De Witt Clinton Park, at Fifty-second Street and Eleventh Avenue, to give some of the children in the vicinity useful and wholesome employment. A tent was put up, which contained blackboards and seats, and later a flagpole was raised. The children came in squads of 25, each wearing a tag numbered to correspond with the number of his 3 by 6 foot garden.

At first the children were given the choice of being farmers or policemen, and quite a good many thought they would like to be policemen, but after the third day the police force had all deserted to the farm (*422*).

School gardening made a permanent impress on the public-school system of New York City. In 1925 the School Garden Association of New York found 142 gardens in use by elementary schools in that city, 117 at the schools, 17 in city parks, and 8 in vacant lots.

At the Hampton Institute in Virginia the Whittier School for negro children had 200 plats, varying in size from 4 by 6 to 11 by 15 feet. Each plat was worked by two pupils, and all of the work was done under the supervision of a man in general charge of the gardens. Every child in the school, from the kindergarten to the seventh grade, was required to work in the gardens two recitation periods a week. The work was conducted on pedagogical principles, and so correlated with the other school exercises as to make it truly educational. It was also arranged in such a way that pupils finishing at the Whittier School were fully prepared to take up the agricultural work in the institute.

At Cleveland, Ohio, the Home Gardening Association promoted gardening by children and adults, and originated the method of encouraging the work by selling penny packages of seeds. Lessons were given at the schools on the planting and care of the gardens. Exhibits were held in the fall with prizes of money or bulbs. The money was devoted to improving school grounds. In 1905 a curator of school gardens was appointed to have charge of the planting and improvement of school gardens and grounds throughout the city. The work at Cleveland continued to grow, and in 1908 there were gardens for defective and delinquent children as well as for normal children. A kitchen garden was maintained in connection with a cooking school. While this work was supported with school funds it was not a part of the school curriculum, but entirely voluntary, and done outside of school hours.

The normal schools at Hyannis and Framingham, Mass., had incorporated school-garden work in their practice schools. At Hyannis the garden work was the basis for numerous exercises in connection with the mathematics, bookkeeping, business training, drawing, and language work of the school. The children wrote letters to the seedsmen from whom they purchased seeds, sold their produce, deposited money in the bank, made purchases, and paid for them with checks drawn on their account.

Normal schools at Johnson, Vt., Los Angeles, Calif., and Salt Lake City, Utah, had made garden work a feature of their practice school for several years.

In Washington, D. C., only home gardening by the normal-school students was attempted at first, but afterwards the Department of Agriculture provided a small greenhouse and workroom, where these students met once a week for instruction and practice. Then the children in 12 practice schools were given seeds for home planting and were put under instruction in gardening by the normal students. A class of 30 boys and girls had a garden on the department grounds.

In 1905 the work in Washington and a number of other cities was described in Bulletin 160 of the Office of Experiment Stations, by B. T. Galloway and Susan B. Sipe, and a farmers' bulletin on the school garden, by L. C. Corbett, horticulturist of the Bureau of Plant Industry, was published.

In 1906 the Bureau of Plant Industry reported that it had distributed 377,540 packets of vegetable and flower seeds to every State and Territory except Nevada and Wyoming. "It can safely be said that more than a thousand teachers of schools in various parts of the country are interested in this work."

In 1908 the Office of Experiment Stations reported that school gardens had not been generally successful in connection with rural schools, except where combined with home gardens and boys' and girls' clubs.

The school-garden movement continued to grow and to get a larger measure of public support. At the San Francisco meeting of the National Education Association in 1911 the School Garden Association of America was organized, with V. E. Kilpatrick, of New York, as president, and D. J. Crosby, of the Office of Experiment Stations, as secretary. A joint meeting of this new organization with the American Nature-Study Society and the department of rural and agricultural education of the parent society was held, thus emphasizing the union of the forces in an effort to improve the curriculum of the elementary schools.

This association continued to promote gardening in connection with the schools until after the World War, when its place was taken by the Council of Nature Study and School Gardening, which meets annually in connection with the winter meeting of the department of superintendence of the National Education Association.

Experience showed that only the children in the first few grades were interested in the growing of plants in the little plats usually found in the school gardens. After that a community garden or home garden served to prolong the interest, but these were difficult for the schools to manage without special provisions for supervision of the outside work. The development of the boys' and girls' clubs as a part of the agricultural extension system under the Smith-Lever Act drew the attention of the rural schools away from the school gardens, in which they had never been largely interested.

On the other hand, the smaller cities in large numbers took up this work. In 1915 the Bureau of Education considered the garden movement of sufficient importance to warrant the establishment of a division of school and home gardening, and this was put in charge of J. L. Randall. Reports were received in 1916 from 1,220 city superintendents who were encouraging some form of school-directed gardening. The public appropriations for this work in 20 cities ranged from $1,000 to $19,893, in 12 cities from $500 to $1,000, and in 108 cities were less than $500. Many other agencies were promoting the work, and 220 cities had funds from private sources.

Home-garden work through the schools, particularly in the cities, was greatly stimulated during the World War when there was widespread and increasing interest in supplementing the ordinary production of food by resorting to unusual means. To aid this enterprise the Bureau of Education secured from President Wilson's national security and defense fund in 1918 $50,000, to which $200,000 was afterwards added. This money was used to organize the United States School Garden Army, with J. H. Francis as director. This army had officers with military titles, and the members received badges. The country was divided into five districts with Federal supervisors. Leaflets and other publications describing and stimulating the work were published and widely distributed. The bureau reported that on July 10, 1918, 1,500,000 boys and girls were enrolled in this army. This undoubtedly included many children who had already been organized for similar work by the extension agents of the Department of Agriculture and the State agricultural colleges and other agencies. The reaction which occurred after the abnormal pressure for war work ceased greatly diminished the strength of the school-garden movement throughout the country. It then became largely a matter of local interest as fostered by agencies outside the school or by individual superintendents or teachers. It was more closely identified with nature study as carried on in the lower grades, and there was a fuller realization that it had a cultural rather than even a prevocational value. The interest aroused among educators in nature study and school gardening and the results of experience and investigation with reference to the educational and practical problems involved in such work had important effects on the movement for the more definite teaching of agriculture in the elementary schools.

ELEMENTARY INSTRUCTION IN AGRICULTURE

The great awakening of public interest in the teaching of agriculture in the colleges which occurred about 1900 led to an active demand that this subject be taught in the elementary as well as in the secondary schools. Teachers here and there, particularly in schools where the grades were combined with the higher departments, undertook the teaching of agriculture to the younger children. In this effort there were many failures but some notable successes. The farming population, especially as represented by their organizations, without realizing the great difficulties attending the general introduction of a subject like agriculture into the rural schools, moved the legislatures to pass laws permitting or requiring the teaching of agriculture in the rural or all elementary schools of the State. The spread of the nature-study and school-garden movements intensified the desire of the farmers and the other friends of rural education to have instruction more definitely related to agriculture in the rural elementary schools which were the only educational institutions attended by the great mass of farm boys.

About the same time the consolidation of rural schools became a matter of widespread discussion, and the laws permitting such consolidation, which had been passed in the New England States, New York, Pennsylvania, and Ohio, began to have a decided effect. Successful consolidation of a number of schools in these States soon led to similar movements in New Jersey, Iowa, Minnesota, Michigan, Nebraska, and Wisconsin. Obviously there was a better chance for the successful teaching of agriculture in such schools and examples of this soon began to appear.

REPORT OF COMMITTEE ON INSTRUCTION IN AGRICULTURE OF THE
AGRICULTURAL COLLEGE ASSOCIATION

Some normal schools began to teach agriculture, and some agricultural colleges made special provisions for instructing teachers in short courses or summer schools.

The movement for the teaching of agriculture in the elementary schools attracted the attention of the Association of Agricultural Colleges, and at its meeting at Washington in 1903 it was suggested that its committee on instruction in agriculture make a report on this matter. This was done in 1904, when a report was presented on " the teaching of agriculture in the rural common schools " (*499*).

The committee found that nature study having an agricultural trend was about all that had been attempted in the way of teaching agriculture in the rural schools until quite recently, when State superintendents of public instruction, the officers of some of the agricultural colleges, the National Education Association, the American Civic Association, as well as a number of other organizations and numerous individuals in various official positions had interested themselves in the introduction of elementary agriculture and gardening into the rural schools.

Outline courses in agriculture had been prepared in a number of States. In Illinois the course, prepared by Dean Davenport of the college of agriculture, was arranged by months, with suggestions for practicums, observations, readings, and correlation of agriculture with other school work.

In Missouri a course entitled "Elements of Agriculture for the Public Schools " was prepared by the State superintendent of schools and published by the State board of agriculture. In Indiana the State manual for the elementary schools in 1904–5 included courses in nature study and agriculture. The Department of Agriculture of the University of Minnesota prepared a bulletin on rural-school agriculture for the use of the teachers in that State. The agricultural colleges in a number of States were promoting this movement through summer schools and special publications for teachers. A great impetus was given to the movement by the improvement of textbooks and works of reference. Indirectly this brought about legislation requiring the teaching of agriculture in all the rural schools in a number of States. State adoption of textbooks in agriculture had been made in Alabama, Georgia, Louisiana, North Carolina, and Tennessee. Every city and county in Virginia, a majority of the counties in Maryland, about 15 counties in California, and a number of counties in Florida had also adopted such textbooks.

The obstacles to the general introduction of agriculture into the rural schools were pointed out by the committee. These included the conservatism or apathy of State, county, and local school officers and of members of agricultural college faculties in many States; lack of trained and experienced teachers; and shortness of school terms. Consolidation of schools would help, but special effort must be made to provide competent teachers. Nature study would give the pupils an excellent preparation for the more formal study of agriculture in the sixth or seventh grade. On the average not less than one hour per week during two years would be required to make the course effective. "A well-arranged and up-to-date textbook, with illustrations and suggestions for practical exercises, should be adopted as a basis for this study."

Excursions to neighboring farms, visits to county fairs, exhibits by pupils of these fairs, farmers' institutes, and other meetings were advocated. Classroom instruction should be supplemented by simple experiments with plants and animals at school and at home. Every effort should be made to connect the instruction with the pupil's home life.

Illustrative material should be supplied consisting of charts, pictures, collections of specimens (largely made by the pupils), and boxes, cans, plates, and other inexpensive material which can be used in making apparatus for conducting experiments. There should also be a few standard reference books on the different divisions of agriculture and the publications of the State experiment stations and the United States Department of Agriculture.

The committee then presented a syllabus of an elementary course in agriculture, which included the plant and its environment, farm crops, fruits, types and breeds of domestic animals and their care and management, the dairy cow, composition, handling and uses of milk, farm plans and structures, farm machinery, marketing, and farm accounts.

OFFICE OF EXPERIMENT STATIONS SYLLABUS ON NATURE STUDY AND ELEMENTARY AGRICULTURE

This report was followed up through the office of Experiment Stations by the preparation by the writer and D. J. Crosby in 1905 of a suggestive course of nature study and elementary agriculture for the schools of California. (Office of Experiment Stations Report 1906, p. 281.) This was done at the request of a committee appointed at a meeting of the State Teachers' Association with the State farmers' institute. The following is a synopsis of this course, arranged for three groups of children:

Nature study and agriculture, by groups

Group	Character of instruction	Garden
I. Nature study, children 6 to 8 years old.	Observation: Observe wild and cultivated plants, trees, insects, and wild and domestic animals in environment at home and near school.	School garden: Plant and grow some of the common hardy vegetables, such as radishes, lettuce, beets, and carrots; and one or two quick-growing flowers, such as dwarf nasturtiums.
II. Nature study, children 9 to 11 years old.	Observation and comparison: Observe weather, soils, wild and cultivated plants, trees, insects, and wild and domestic animals in environment of school district and vicinity; compare habits of plants and animals in order to become familiar with their different modes of living, their struggles for existence, and their uses to man.	School garden: Plant and grow typical economic plants of the region, giving some attention to different varieties, and to the relation of crops to different conditions of soil, weather, treatment, etc.
III. Agriculture, children 12 to 14 years old.	Observation, comparison, and judgment: Study objects as above, within and beyond horizon of children's observation; introduce textbooks and reference books on elementary agriculture as sources of information concerning objects beyond the limits of personal observation; illustrate processes by simple experiments; study different types of plants and animals; visit typical farms; teach sources and uses of agricultural literature—books, bulletins, and farm journals.	School and home gardens: Plant and grow different varieties of crops— e. g., wheat, barley, sugar beets, potatoes; introduce exercises in pruning, grafting, making cuttings. Encourage pupils to grow crops, poultry, and farm animals at home, keeping account of labor, fertilizers, feed, gross and net returns, and have them experiment on different methods of planting, cultivating, harvesting, and preparing for market.

In 1905 the committee of five made a report to the National Education Association in which they recommended that agriculture be taught in the last three years of the common school but that the teachers of the 1-room rural school should not be positively required to do this because generally they are not prepared to teach this subject and the school term is often too short to permit an additional study.

By this time laws permitting or encouraging the teaching of agriculture in the rural schools had been passed in Alabama, Florida, Georgia, Illinois, Louisiana, Maryland, Michigan, Missouri, North Carolina, and Wisconsin. Within the next five years 13 States had passed mandatory laws on this subject. It was encouraged by State and county school officers and taught in some of the rural schools of 31 other States and Territories. In 1915 the teaching of agriculture in public rural elementary schools was required in 22 States.

TEXTBOOKS OF ELEMENTARY AGRICULTURE

Soon after 1900 a new type of textbooks of elementary agriculture began to be published. These combined statements of facts about the plants, animals, implements, etc., used in farming and horticulture with simple explanations of principles underlying the practice of agriculture and the results of experiments relating to agriculture. An early book of this type, first issued in 1903, was entitled " Agriculture for Beginners," by C. W. Burkett, F. L. Stevens, and D. H. Hill, professors of agriculture, biology, and English in the North Carolina College of Agriculture and Mechanic Arts. The subject was treated in logical order, but teachers were asked to " feel free to teach each topic in the season best suited to its study." Many definite suggestions for observations and simple experiments were made.

Lead the pupils out into the field, make simple experiments before them, and have them also perform experiments. Let them learn directly from nature. * * * In many cases it will be best to perform the experimental or observational work first, and turn to the text later to amplify the pupil's knowledge.

The book was attractively printed and had over 200 illustrations.

Without doubt the publication of such textbooks greatly promoted the definite teaching of agriculture in the rural schools. As a rule the teachers in these schools had neither the training nor the time to prepare lessons and practicums themselves but could often use the books and follow some of the practical suggestions made in them. There was, of course, the inevitable tendency for many teachers simply to hear recitations based on the text, and this has been largely the kind of instruction in agriculture given in rural schools up to the present time. Some of the States adopted a particular textbook of agriculture for use in all the elementary schools attempting to teach this subject.

While the movement for the teaching of agriculture in the rural elementary schools continued to grow and there was an increasing number of instances where this was done successfully, particularly in the consolidated schools, it was soon apparent that provision must be made for more informal instruction suited to the actual conditions in most rural schools. In 1909 the Office of Experiment Stations reported that such instruction through boys' and girls' clubs, judging contests, excursions, and boys' encampments was rapidly extending in all parts of the country.

BOYS' AND GIRLS' CLUBS

The boys' agricultural clubs grew out of an attempt to arouse interest in farmers' institutes in Macoupin County, Ill. When the adult farmers did not respond to special efforts to get them to attend institutes, W. B. Otwell, as president of the county institute, distributed carefully selected corn to 500 boys, who grew it and made an exhibit for prizes at the next institute in 1900. This was so successful that the next year 1,500 farmer boys entered the contest. There was then no difficulty in getting a large attendance of boys and adults at the county institute. When Mr. Otwell was put in charge of the Illinois agricultural exhibit at the St. Louis Exposition in 1904 he got 8,000 boys in the State to grow corn for prizes and 1,250 exhibits of their work received awards there. This kind of work was taken up more or less directly under the auspices of the State college of agriculture, the Illinois Farmers' Institute, and the county institute secretaries, and county superintendents of schools in a number of counties in Illinois. In February, 1902, O. J. Kern, who was actively promoting the improvement of the rural schools in Winnebago County, organized a " farmer boys' experiment club," in cooperation with the agricultural college. Seeds of sugar beets were furnished by the college and seeds of corn by the State Farmers' Institute. The club began with 37 members, and in November 1903 there were 405. Excursions were made to the colleges in Illinois, Iowa, and Wisconsin by the boys and their parents. The boys tested the seed, made observations on the growth of the plants, determined the percentage of smut in fields of oats, etc. Meetings of the club were held at various farms, a half-day was given them at the county farmers' institute, and monthly lectures by college officers and others were provided at the county seat during the fall and winter. Similar clubs were organized in a number of other counties in Illinois and in 1904 the State superintendent of farmers' institutes estimated that not less than 2,000 boys were in the clubs in that State. Local clubs were formed, usually by townships, and united in a county association.

In Ohio A. B. Graham, as superintendent of schools at Springfield, began to organize boys' clubs in 1902 and in 1905, when he was made superintendent of extension work at Ohio State University, 3,000 pupils in the rural schools were members of these clubs. About this time clubs were organized in Texas in connection with the Texas Farmers' Congress. In Iowa the first club was organized in 1904 at Sigourney, Keokuk County, by the county superintendent of schools. As a special feature each of the 147 school districts in Keokuk County held a school fair in the fall of 1904, where the boys exhibited the fruits, vegetables, and farm crops which they had grown. The best and second-best articles of each class were then shown at the 16 township fairs, and the three prize articles of the several kinds from each township fair were exhibited at a county school fair. This county fair exhibit contained more than 3,000 articles. In connection with each fair there was a program of talks, papers, recitations, and music. At the county fair there were a corn-judging school, a debate, and a composition contest. A small admission fee at the fairs paid all expenses.

In 1907 a boys' club was organized in Holmes County, Miss., by W. H. Smith, a school superintendent. The following year clubs began to be organized in connection with the farmers' cooperative demonstration work in the Southern States under Seaman A. Knapp. The clubs were formed on the basis of each boy's growing an acre of corn or other crop. In 1909 there were more than 10,000 boys enrolled in the competitive corn contests, and in 1910 over 46,000 boys were connected with the clubs. These clubs spread rapidly and ultimately became a prominent feature of the cooperative extension work under the Smith-Lever Act. School teachers and officers in many places cooperated from the beginning in the organization and work of these clubs.

Clubs for girls paralleled those for boys under various auspices. The girls' clubs dealt with gardening, canning, and household arts. In 1909 the Office of Experiment Stations reported that club work for boys and girls was organized in at least 395 counties in 29 States, the membership totaling more than 150,000.

STATE COURSES IN ELEMENTARY AGRICULTURE

About 1905 the State superintendent of public schools in Wisconsin issued a manual for the common schools of that State which contained an outline course in elementary agriculture, and a similar course for the schools of South Dakota was published. The New York State education department issued a course of study and syllabus for elementary schools which contained an outline for nature study in the first six years of the elementary course and agriculture in the remaining two years. This was further elaborated in 1909, when it was presented as the study of birds, animals, and plants. The nature study and agricultural features were combined throughout this course. Much of the course was based on the study of the hen, the cow, and the pea as interesting living things in nature and as having agricultural value.

The report of the office of Experiment Stations for 1910 states that—

In Massachusetts a committee of five appointed by the conference on agricultural science at the Massachusetts Agricultural College in 1908 prepared and the agricultural college published a course in elementary agriculture which consisted of a series of practical exercises, for each of which appropriate materials and directions were suggested.

In 1919 the State superintendent of public instruction in Missouri undertook to meet the difficulty arising from the great variety of work which the rural teacher has to do in the school by trying a rotation plan of teaching elementary agriculture. He selected 15 counties for this experiment. The work was for boys and girls and included not only subjects directly pertaining to farming but also those relating to the life and welfare of children and adults, such as health, sanitation, home conveniences, social conditions, and community interests. The course covered four years. Each year there was in each school only one agricultural class made up of children in grades 5 to 8. The teachers were aided by a preliminary week of intensive training and by weekly conferences for practice under direction of the county superintendent (465).

In an analytical survey of State courses of study for rural elementary schools by C. M. Reinoehl, of the University of Arkansas, made in 1922 and published by the Bureau of Education (474), it appeared that all the States except California, Florida, Arkansas, and Rhode Island had issued such courses. The 35 State publications containing the most complete and detailed outlines were used in this survey. Agriculture has been given a prominent place in those State courses.

The materials have to do with plant culture (47 per cent), animal husbandry (20 per cent), farm management and improvement (27 per cent), and plans and methods of teaching (6 per cent). Facts about farm work are emphasized.

The most common method of teaching agriculture is the textbook method. Teachers ,have been encouraged in the use of this method by the type of outlines in some States. There are few method topics. The project and the problem methods are coming into use (474).

The development of the home project in connection with the secondary schools and the extension clubs has had an increasing influence on the teaching of agriculture in the elementary grades, particularly in the consolidated schools. Many of the children from 12 to 15 years old have been in the clubs and thus have been encouraged to study agriculture in the school as an aid to their club work. The development of the vocational instruction in agriculture under the Smith-Hughes Act has also stimulated more interest in the elementary instruction on the part of school officers and teachers. The Federal and State officers in charge of the Smith-Hughes work are increasingly impressed with the desirability of encouraging the elementary instruction on a prevocational basis.

The division of agricultural instruction, in the Office of Experiment Stations and later in the States Relations Service, aided in various ways the movement for the introduction of agriculture into the elementary schools. In cooperation with the State agricultural colleges and State departments of education it prepared outline courses of agriculture for elementary schools in Maryland, Ohio, North Carolina, and Arkansas. Lessons on corn, potatoes, dairying, and gardening were also issued. Leaflets were prepared showing how teachers could use the farmers' bulletins in their school work. Classified lists of department publications and suggestions for illustrative material and sets of lantern slides on agricultural subjects have been distributed.

Along with the movement for the teaching of agriculture in public elementary schools there was similar teaching in special or private schools. Among the early schools of this kind were the Thompson's Island Farm School, near Boston, the Baron de Hirsch Agricultural and Industrial School, at Woodbine, N. J., the School of Horticulture, at Hartford, Conn., the School of the Youths' Directory of San Francisco, at Rutherford, Calif., and schools for negroes at Hampton, Va., Tuskegee, Ala., Atlanta, Ga., Manassas, Va., Enfield, N. C., and elsewhere.

STATUS OF ELEMENTARY AGRICULTURE IN RURAL SCHOOLS

The recent status of elementary agriculture in the rural schools of the United States has been shown in the report of a committee, of which E. H. Shinn was chairman, presented to the American Association for the Advancement of Agricultural Teaching on November

12, 1923 (*62*). This report was based on replies to a questionnaire from State superintendents of education, supervisors of rural schools, presidents of State normal schools, State supervisors of agricultural education, and heads of teacher-training divisions in the land-grant colleges. The findings of the committee are summarized as follows:

(1) On the basis of the returns it appears that about 28 of the States require by legislative acts that elementary agriculture be taught in the rural schools. A few other States have special rural aid laws, etc., looking to the betterment of rural schools.

(2) Thirty-five of the 48 States report that the State departments of education are sympathetic and are encouraging better rural school education while a few replies say that nothing particular is being done in this direction. Examples of well organized programs on the part of State departments of education for improving agriculture and nature-study in rural schools are rare.

(3) In about two-thirds of the States the returns show that courses are offered in elementary agriculture for rural teachers. The other replies say that very little or no teacher-training work is offered. A number of returns say that there is no demand for training of this kind. As a rule the courses are offered in normal schools or teachers' colleges, high schools, and special agricultural schools.

(4) Returns from only 20 States indicate that the teaching of agriculture and nature-study in rural schools has been effective.

(5) The type of school in which the work has functioned best, according to the returns, is the consolidated rural school. A few returns say that the work has functioned best in no particular type of school, that it is the teacher rather than the school that counts most.

(6) Returns from more than half of the States say that agriculture and nature-study when properly taught have vitalized other school subjects.

(7) In reference to problems and difficulties, about five-sixths of the returns say that lack of competent teachers for the work is the great problem.

(8) Returns from about half of the States regarding suggested solutions say that better trained teachers is the greatest need. Various other suggestions are offered, such as consolidation, supervision, better organized courses, higher standard for teachers, and establishment of departments of rural education, etc.

BIBLIOGRAPHY

The bibliography herewith includes only such works as have contributed in some way to the preparation of this general history of agricultural education in the United States. For collateral information only a few standard works were used. To a very limited extent have State and local reports and other documents been cited. There is a vast bibliography of agricultural education in State and local reports and bulletins, and in magazines, agricultural and other papers, textbooks, etc., to which no reference is made here.

GENERAL

1. Andrews, B. F. The land grant of 1862 and the land-grant colleges. 63 p. Washington, 1918. (U. S. Bur. Educ. Bul. 13, 1918.)
2. Atkeson, T. C. Semicentennial history of the Patrons of Husbandry. 364 p. illus. New York, 1916.
3. Bailey, L. H. Cyclopedia of American agriculture. v. 4. 650 p. New York, 1909.
4. Bailey, L. H. The nature-study idea, being an interpretation of the new school movement to put the child in sympathy with nature. 159 p. New York, 1903. 2d ed. 1909. 3d ed. rev. 246 p. New York, 1909.
5. Beginnings of education in agriculture and home economics. Journal of home economics, v. 2 (1910), p. 29–31.
6. Bath and West of England Society. Journal. v. 1. 282 p. London, 1853.
7. Bevier, Isabel. Home economics in education. 226 p. Philadelphia [1924].
8. Bishop, E. C. The present status of agricultural education in public schools. (In Proc. Nat. Educ. Assoc., v. 47 (1909), p. 976–982.
9. Blackmar, F. W. The history of Federal and State aid to higher education in the United States. 343 p. Washington, 1890. (U. S. Bur. Educ. Circ. Inform. (1890), no. 1.)
10. Blauch, L. E. Federal cooperation in vocational education. The evolution of the Smith-Lever and the Smith-Hughes Acts. Ms. in Univ. of Chicago. 1923. 375 p. (Also copy in Bur. Educ.) Contains extensive bibliography. A thesis for the degree of doctor of philosophy.
11. Bogart, E. L. Economic history of the United States. 2d ed. 597 p. illus., New York, 1914.
12. Brewer, W. H. Manuscript of statement on the intent of the land grant act of 1862. (Copy in Div. of Agr. Instr., U. S. Dept. Agric.)
13. Brown, E. E. The making of our middle schools; an account of the development of secondary education in the United States. 547 p. New York, 1903.
14. Browne, C. A. A sketch of agricultural chemistry in America from 1663 to 1863. Manuscript in Bur. Chem. 16 p. (Abstract in Science, n. s. v. 60, p. 87. July 25, 1924.)
15. Browne, C. A. The life and chemical services of Fredrick Accum. 58 p. Portrait. (From Jour. of Chem. Education of Am. Chem. Soc. 1925.)
16. Buck, S. J. The Granger movement; a study of agricultural organization and its political, economic, and social manifestations, 1870–1880. 384 p. Cambridge, Mass., 1913. (Harvard historical ser., v. 19.)
17. Butterfield, K. L. Chapters in rural progress. 251 p. Chicago, 1907.
18. Carrier, Lyman. Dr. John Mitchell, naturalist, cartographer, and historian. Washington, 1921. (In Agricultural History Society papers, p. 199–219.) Also in Ann. Rept. of the Amer. Hist. Assoc., 1918.
19. Carrier, Lyman. The beginnings of agriculture in America. 323 p. illus. New York, 1923.

20. Citizens Trade School Convention. Proceedings and addresses. (In dianapolis, June 10–12, 1907.) 53 p. Indianapolis, 1907.
21. Coman, Katherine. The industrial history of the United States. New & rev. ed. 461 p. illus. New York, 1911.
22. Davenport, Eugene. Education for efficiency; a discussion of certain phases of the problem of universal education with special reference to academic ideals and methods. 184 p. Boston, 1909.
23. Davis, N. M. Agricultural education in the public schools. 163 p. Chicago, Ill., 1912.
24. Dexter, E. G. A history of education in the United States. 656 p. New York, 1904.
25. Fellenberg or manual labor movement (The). (In U. S. Bur. Educ. Ann. Rept. (1891–92), v. 1, p. 506–510. Washington, 1894.)
26. Fisher, M. L. Instruction in farm crops. In Proc. Amer. Soc. Agron. v. 3 (1911), p. 40–41. 1912.
27. Gillette, J. M. Constructive rural sociology. (New ed.) 408 p. New York, 1916.
28. Goode, G. B. The origin of the national scientific and educational institutions of the United States. 112 p. New York, 1890. Reprinted from the Papers of the American Historical Society.
29. Greathouse, C. H. Historical sketch of the United States Department of Agriculture, its objects and present organization. 97 p. Washington, 1907. (U. S. Dept. Agr., Div. of Pub. Bul. 3, 2d revision.)
30. Grimes, W. E. Report of the committee on teaching for the year 1920. (In Jour. Farm Econ. v. 3 (1920), p. 100–102.)
31. Handschin, W. F. Report of the committee on teaching for the year 1919. (In Jour. Farm Econ. v. 2 (1919), p. 172–174.)
32. Hanus, P. H. Beginnings in industrial education and other educational discussions. 199 p. Boston, 1908.
33. Highland Society of Scotland. Prize essays and transactions of the Highland Society of Scotland. v. 1–6. Edinburgh, 1799–1824.
34. Hunt, C. L. The life of Ellen Richards. 328 p. illus. Boston, 1912.
35. Industrial Education. American Federation of Labor. 68 p. Washington, 1910.
36. Kandel. I. L. Federal aid for vocational education. 127 p. New York. 1917. (Carnegie Found. Advanc. Teaching Bul. 10.)
37. Keith, J. A. H., and Bagley, W. C. The Nation and the school—a study in the application of the principles of Federal aid to education in the United States. 364 p. New York, 1920
38. Kelley, O. H. Origin and progress of the Order of the Patrons of Husbandry in the United States; a history from 1866 to 1873. 441 p. Philadelphia, 1875.
39. Kern, O. J. Among country schools. 366 p. illus. New York, 1906.
40. Kingsley, C. D. College entrance requirements. 110 p. Washington, 1913. (U. S. Bur. Educ. Bul. 7, 1913.)
41. Knapp, S. A. Experiment Stations. 7 p. [1883]. (Text of Holmes bill and statement indorsing it. Copy in U. S. Dept. Agr.) See also (201).
42. Lacy, Mary G. An early agricultural periodical. Agr. Hist. Soc. papers, v. 2, p. 443. Washington, 1923. Reprinted from annual report of Am. Hist. Asso., 1919. v. 1, p. 443.
43. Lake Placid conference on home economics. Proceedings, 1st–10th, 1899–1908. Lake Placid, N. Y., 1901–1908.
44. Learned, H. B. The president's cabinet, studies in the origin, formation, and structure of an American institution. 471 p. New Haven, 1912.
45. Liautard, A. History and progress of veterinary medicine. (In Amer. Vet. Rev., v. 1 (1877), p. 5–19.)
46. Lipman, C. B. A thorough training for specialists in agronomy. (In Proc. Amer. Soc. Agron., v. 4 (1912), p. 53–58, 1913.)
47. Monroe, Paul, ed. Cyclopedia of education. 5 vol. New York, 1911–1919.
48. Monroe, Paul. Textbook of the history of education. XXIII+772 p. New York, 1911.
49. Myers, C. E. Effectiveness of vocational education in agriculture; a study of the value of vocational instruction in agriculture in secondary schools as indicated by the occupational distribution of former students. 63 p. Washington, 1923. (Fed. Bd. Vocat. Educ. Bul. 82. Agr. Ser. 13.)

50. National Education Association. Report of the committee on industrial education in schools for rural communities. 1905. 97 p.
51. National Education Association. Report of the committee on the place of industries in public education. 1910. 123 p.
52. National society for the promotion of industrial education. Bul. 1–26. New York, 1907–1918. Name changed in 1918 to National Society for Vocational Education.
53. National society for the study of education. Yearbook 1911. Part 2, p. 9–90. Chicago, 1912.
54. Paine, A. E. The Granger movement in Illinois. 53 p. Urbana, Ill., 1904. (Univ. of Ill., The Univ. studies, v. 1, no. 8.) On cover: University of Illinois Bul., v. 2, no. 2.
55. [Papers on development and teaching of agronomy.] (In Proc. Amer. Soc. Agron., v. 1, 1907, 1908, 1909. [Washington, D. C.], 1910.)
56. Parsons, H. G. Children's gardens for special health and education. XII+226 p. illus. New York, 1910.
57. Pearson, R. A. The place of mechanic arts in land-grant institutions. Montpelier, Vt., 1915. (In Proc. Asso. Amer. Agr. Col. and Expt. Stas. 29th (1915), p. 135–140.)
58. Poore, B. P. The Federal and State constitutions, colonial charters, and other organic laws of the United States. 2d ed. 2 v. Washington, 1878.
59. Reber, L. E. University extension in the United States. 63 p. Washington, 1914. (U. S. Bur. Educ. Bul. 19, 1914.)
60. Robison, C. H. Agricultural instruction in the public high schools of the United States. 202 p. 1 map. Thesis Columbia University, 1910.
61. School Garden Association of America. 2d annual report, 1913. 57 p. illus.
62. Shinn, E. H. Present status of elementary agriculture in the rural schools of the United States. Report presented at the meeting of American Asso. for the Advancement of Agr. Teaching, Nov. 12, 1923. (In Proc. Asso. Amer. Agr. Col. and Expt. Stas. 37th (1923), p. 136–147.)
63. Sinclair, Sir John. Origin of the Board of Agriculture, and its progress for three years after its establishment. (In Gt. Brit. Bd. of Agr. Communications to the Board of Agr. on subjects relative to the husbandry and internal improvement of the country. v. 1. 2d ed. p. I–XXXVII. London, 1804.)
64. Snedden, D. S. Problems of educational readjustment. 262 p. Boston, 1913.
65. Swift, F. H. Federal aid to public schools. 47 p. Washington, 1922. (U. S. Bur. Educ. Bul. 47, 1922.) (Contains history of grants of land and money in 1785.
66. Taylor, H. C. The educational significance of the early Federal land ordinances. 138 p. New York, 1922. (Teachers' College, Columbia Univ. Contributions to education, 118. Published also as thesis (Ph. D.) Columbia University, 1920.)
67. True, R. H. The early development of agricultural societies in the United States. Agr. Hist. Soc. papers, v. 3, p. 293–306. Washington, 1925. Reprinted from annual report of Am. Hist. Asso., 1920, p. 293–306.
68. Tucker, G. M. American agricultural periodicals; and historical sketch. [10] p. Albany, 1909.
69. Tull, Jethro. The horse hoing husbandry; or, An essay on the principles of tillage and vegetation. 200 p. London, 1733. 3d ed., very carefully corrected. 432 p. London, 1751.
70. Turnbull, G. H. Samuel Hartlib. A sketch of his life and his relations to J. A. Comenius. 79 p. London (New York, etc.), 1920.
71. United States Agricultural Society Journal. v. 1–5 (1852–1857). Washington, 1852–[1857].
72. Vocational education. United States Chamber of Commerce, Referendum No. 14. 12 p. Spec. bul., June 2, 1916. Washington, 1916.
73. Vocational secondary education. Prepared by the committee on vocational education of the National Education Association. Bur. Educ. Bul. 21, 1916. 163 p.
74. Withers, W. A. The teaching of chemistry in American agricultural colleges. Washington, 1911. (In Proc. Asso. of Off. Agr. Chem. 27th (1916), p. 91–97.) (U. S. Dept. Agr. Bur. Chem. Bul. 137.)

75. Youmans, W. J. Pioneers of science in America. 508 p. ports. New York, 1896.
76. Young, Arthur. Annals of agriculture and other useful arts. v. 1. 467 p. London, 1786.

ALABAMA

77. Alabama Polytechnic Institute. Catalogue of the officers and alumni . . . 1872–1908, with a brief history of the college. 108 p. Opelika, Ala., 1906. (On cover: Bulletin, v. 1, no. 2.)
78. Alabama State Agricultural and Mechanical College. Report of the board of trustees. 1880/81–1887/88. Montgomery, Ala., 1882–1888.
79. Bruce, R. C. Training in agriculture at Tuskegee. (In Ann. Amer. Acad. Polit. and Social Sci. v. 21 (1903), p. 513–514.)
80. Clark, W. G. History of education in Alabama, 1702–1889. 281 p. Washington, 1889. (U. S. Bur. Educ. Circ. of Inform. (1889), no. 3.)
81. Owens, C. J. Secondary agricultural education in Alabama. 30 p. illus. Washington, 1909. (U. S. Dept. Agr., Off. Expt. Stas. Bul. 220.)
82. Washington, B. T. Twenty-five years of Tuskegee. (In World's Work, v. 11. p. 7433–50. illus. April, 1906.)

ARKANSAS

83. Lane, C. H. Arkansas State agricultural schools. 20 p. illus. Washington, 1912. (U. S. Dept. Agr., Off. Expt. Stas. Bul. 250.)
84. Reynolds, J. H., and Thomas, D. Y. History of the University of Arkansas. 555 p. illus. Fayetteville, 1910.

CALIFORNIA

85. California, University of. Report of the College of Agriculture and the Agricultural Experiment Station of the University of California from July 1, 1915, to June 30, 1916. 133 p. illus. Berkeley, 1916.
86. Wickson, E. J. Beginnings of agricultural education and research in California. Berkeley, 1918. (In Calif. Agr. Expt. Sta. Rept., 1917–1918, p. 35–101.)

COLORADO

87. Steinel, A. T., and Working, D. W. History of Agriculture in Colorado, 1858 to 1926. 659 p. illus. Fort Collins, 1926. (Includes history of agricultural education in Colorado.)

CONNECTICUT

88. Buel, Jesse. Address delivered before the agricultural and horticultural societies of New Haven County, Sept. 25, 1839. (In New England farmer and horticultural register, v. 18 (1839), p. 197–198, 205–207.)
89. Connecticut State Agricultural Society. Transactions, 1854. 319 p. Hartford, 1855.
   Connecticut State Agricultural Society. Transactions, 1856. 522 p. Various paging. Hartford, 1857.
90. Cream Hill Agricultural School, West Cornwall, Conn. In A History of Connecticut Agriculture by E. H. Jenkins, p. 361–364. Conn. Agr. Expt. Sta. [1927.]
91. Gold, T. S. In Memoriam. (In Conn. Bd. Agr. Ann. Rpt. 39th, (1905), p. 281–282, 1906.)
92. Gold, T. S. Biographical data. (E. H. Jenkins in Ms.)
93. Holbrook, Josiah. (In American journal of education, v. 8 (1860), p. 229–247.)
94. Holbrook, Josiah. (In Monroe, Paul, Cyclopedia of Education, v. 3, p. 301–302. New York, 1912.)
95. Humphreys, David. A discourse on the agriculture of the State of Connecticut, and the means of making it more beneficial to the State; delivered at New Haven, on Thursday, 12th September, 1816. 44 p. New Haven, 1816.
96. Johnson, S. W. Lectures in agricultural chemistry. In Smithsonian Institution annual report of Board of Regents (1859). p. 119–194, illus. Washington, 1860. (U. S. 36 Cong., 1st sess., H. R. Misc. Doc. No. 90.)

97. Norton, J. P.   Memorials of John Pitkin Norton, late professor of analytical and agricultural chemistry in Yale College, New Haven, Conn.   85 p. port. Albany, 1853.
98. Olcott, H. S.   Outlines of the first course of Yale agricultural lectures. With an introduction by John A. Porter, professor of organic chemistry at Yale College.   186 p.   New York, 1860.
99. Osborne, Mrs. Elizabeth A. (Johnson).   From the letter files of S. W. Johnson, professor of agricultural chemistry in Yale University, 1856–1896, director of the Connecticut Agricultural Experiment Station. 1877–1900.   292 p. illus.   New Haven, 1913.
100. Porter, J. A.   Plan of an agricultural school.   (In Amer. jour. of educ. v. 1 (1856), p. 329–335; same in Connecticut State Agr. Soc. Trans. (1855), p. 157–165.   Hartford, 1856.)
101. Silliman, Benjamin.   (In National cyclopedia of American biography, v. 2, p. 385–386.   New York, 1921.)
102. Silliman, Benjamin, jr.   (In National cyclopedia of American biography, v. 2, p. 386–387.   New York, 1921.)
103. Society for Promoting Agriculture in the State of Connecticut.   Transactions.   22 p.   New Haven, 1802.
104. Trustees of the Storrs Agricultural School at Mansfield, Conn.   Annual reports 1883–1893.   Hartford, Conn., 1884–1894.

DELAWARE

105. Vallandigham, E. W.   Fifty years of Delaware College.   1870–1920.   153 p. Newark, Del.

DISTRICT OF COLUMBIA

106. Barlow, Joel.   Prospectus of a national institution to be established in the United States.   44 p.   Washington, 1806.   Also in the National Intelligencer of Washington, Aug. 1 and Nov. 24, 1806.
107. Columbian Agricultural Society.   Constitution.   (In Agricultural museum, Georgetown, D. C., v. 1. No. 1 (1810), p. 8–11.)
      Columbian Agricultural Society.   [Proceedings] 2d–5th; Nov. 1810–June 1812.   (In Agricultural museum, Georgetown, D. C., v. 1-2, 1811–1812.)

FLORIDA

108. Bush, G. G.   History of education in Florida.   54 p. illus.   Washington, 1889.   (U. S. Bur. Educ. Inform. (1888), No. 7.)

GEORGIA

109. District agricultural schools of Georgia.   48 p.   Athens, Ga., 1907.   (Univ. of Ga. Bul., v. 7, no. 11, July, 1907, Sup.)   Portrait of Gov. J. M. Terrell.
110. Jones, C. E.   Education in Georgia.   154 p.   Washington, 1889.   (U. S. Bur. Educ. Circ. Inform. (1888), No. 4.)
111. Our editor.   [Daniel Lee.]   (In Southern cultivator, v. 5 (1847), p. 120.)
112. University of Georgia.   Centennial catalogue of the trustees, officers, and alumni of the University of Georgia from 1785–1885.   85 p. Athens, Ga., 1885.
113. University of Georgia.   Endowment of the Terrell professorship of agriculture in the University of Georgia.   16 p.   Athens, 1854.

ILLINOIS

114. Carriel, Mary (Turner).   The life of Jonathan Baldwin Turner.   298 p. port.   [Jacksonville, Ill.]   1911.
115. Davenport, Eugene.   History of collegiate education in agriculture.   (In Soc. Prom. Agr. Sci., Proc. 28th (1907), p. 43–53.)
116. Davenport, Eugene.   The next step in agricultural education, or the place of agriculture in our American system of education.   22 p. Urbana, 1908.
117. Illinois Industrial University.   Annual reports of the board of trustees, 1st–13th, 1867–1886.   Springfield, 1868–1887.   1st–7th annual, 8th–13th biennial.   In 1885 the name of the institution was changed to "University of Illinois."

118. Illinois Industrial University. 4th annual report. 1870–1871. p. 215–235. Convention of friends of agricultural education at Chicago, Aug. 24–25, 1871.
119. Illinois Industrial University. Fifth annual report. 1871–1872. Account of first bill that Morrill introduced in Congress. Invitation to hold another meeting at Washington in 1873.
120. Illinois Industrial University. Sixth annual report. 1872–1873. Reference to Washington meeting of 1872 and the Morrill bill.
121. Illinois University, College of Agriculture. Addresses: dedication, agricultural building, University of Illinois, May 21, 1901. 64 p. [Urbana. 1901.]
122. James, E. J. The origin of the land grant act of 1862 (the so-called Morrill Act) and some account of its author, Jonathan B. Turner. 11 p. Urbana, 1910. (Univ. of Illinois, Univ. Studies, v. 4, No. 1.)
123. Kelley, J. H., ed. The alumni record of the University of Illinois including historical sketch and annals of the university, and biographical data regarding members of the faculties and the boards of trustees. 921 p. illus. Urbana-Champaign, 1913.
124. Powell, B. E. The movement for industrial education and the establishment of the university 1840–1870. 631 p. illus. Added t. p. Semicentennial history of the University of Illinois. v. 1. Urbana, 1918.
125. Turner, J. B. Plan for an industrial university. Washington, 1852. (In U. S. Patent Office Report, pt. II. Agriculture (1851), p. 37–44.)
126. Turner, J. B. Plan for the industrial university for the State of Illinois. (In Soc. Prom. Agr. Sci., Proc. 28th (1907), p. 43–53.)
127. Winnebago County [Illinois] schools. Ann. Rept. 1912. 86 p. illus.

INDIANA

128. Hepburn, W. M., and Sears, L. M. Purdue University, fifty years of progress. 203 p. front. Indianapol's, 1925.
129. Indiana Commission on Industrial and Agricultural Education. Report 1912. 133 p. Indianapolis.

IOWA

130. Bishop, E. C., Farrar, R. K., and Hoffman, M. H. Teaching agriculture in rural and graded schools; the correlation scheme and course of study in agriculture. 164 p. illus. Ames, Iowa, 1913. (Iowa State Col. Agr., Agr. Ext. Dept. Schools Circ. 2.)
131. Iowa State Agricultural College and Farm. Biennial reports of the board of trustees, 1866–1889. Des Moines, 1866–1889.
132. Iowa State Agricultural College and Farm. First annual report of the superintendent and secretary . . . to the General Assembly of the State of Iowa, Feb. 1866. 66 p. Des Moines, 1866.
133. Iowa State College of Agriculture and Mechanic Arts. Address delivered at the inauguration of W. I. Chamberlain LL. D., to the presidency of the Iowa State Agricultural College, Nov. 9, 1886. 32 p. Ames, Iowa, 1886.
134. Iowa State College of Agriculture. The annual report of the Iowa Agricultural College. 1871. 125 p. front. Ames, Iowa, 1871.
135. Iowa State College of Agriculture and Mechanic Arts. Catalogue for the year 1886. 84 p. Ames, 1886.
136. Iowa State College of Agriculture and Mechanic Arts. An historical sketch . . . published for the semi-centennial celebration, June 6–9, 1920. 32 p. ports. Ames, Iowa.

KANSAS

137. History and growth of the Kansas State Agricultural College. Kansas Industrial. v. 39, 1913, No. 33, fig. 17.
138. Kansas State Agricultural College. College symposium. 238 p. illus. Topeka, Kansas, 1891.
139. Kansas State Agricultural College, Manhattan, Kans. Handbook. 124 p. Manhattan, Kans., 1874.
140. Kansas State Agricultural College. Record of the alumni. 308 p. illus. Manhattan, 1914. Contains brief history of the college by J. T. Willard, with portraits of the college presidents.

141. Walters, J. D. History of the Kansas State Agricultural College. 226 p. illus. Manhattan, Kansas, 1909.

LOUISIANA

142. Fay, E. W. The history of education in Louisiana. 264 p. Washington, 1898. (U. S Bur. Educ. Circ. Inform. (1898), No. 1.)

MAINE

143. Boardman, S. L. Agricultural bibliography of Maine, biographical sketches of Maine writers on agriculture, with a catalogue of their works; and an index to the volume on the agriculture of Maine, from 1850 to 1892. 117 p. Augusta, 1893.
144. Department of manual labor at Waterville College (A). (In Maine Bd. Agri. Ann. Rept. 12 (1867), p. 189–192. Augusta, 1867.)
145. Fernald, M. C. History of the Maine State College and the University of Maine. 450 p. illus. Orono, Me., 1916.
146. French, E. R. Eulogy on the life and character of Dr. Ezekiel Holmes. (In Maine State Bd. Agr. Ann. Rpt. 116 (1866), p. 44–50. Augusta, 1866.)
147. Maine Board of Agriculture. Ann. Rept. 10th, 1865. 240 p. Augusta, 1865.
     Maine Board of Agriculture. Ann. Rept. 12th, 1867. 248 p. Augusta, 1867.
148. Sheppard, J. H. Reminiscences of the Vaughan family, and more particularly of Benjamin Vaughan, LL. D. Read before the New England Historic-Genealogical Society, August 2, 1865. 40 p. Boston, 1865.
149. True, N. T. Biographical sketch of Ezekiel Holmes. (In Maine State Bd. Agr. Rept. 10 (1865), p. 207–226. Augusta, 1865.) Includes an account of the Gardiner Lyceum.

MARYLAND

150. Agricultural college in Maryland. (In American farmer, v. 8 (1852–1853), p. 193–194, 233; v. 9 (1854), p. 281, 288–289; v. 10 (1854), p. 81–82; v. 11 (1855), p. 19, 162, 165, 243, 372.)
151. [Higgins, James.] Report of James Higgins, M. D., State agricultural chemist to the house of delegates of Maryland, 1st–6th, 1850, 1852, 1853, 1854, 1856, 1858. Annapolis, 1850–1853, and 1856–1858; Baltimore, 1854.
152. Maryland Agricultural College. Charter and acts of assembly, referring to the Maryland Agricultural College with the by-laws. 20 p. Baltimore, 1881.

MASSACHUSETTS

153. Agassiz, E. C., ed. Louis Agassiz, his life and correspondence. 2 v. illus. London, 1885.
154. Agricultural project study. Board of Education of Massachusetts. Bul 4 (1912) 38 p.
155. Agricultural project study bibliography. Board of Education of Massachusetts. Bul. 6 (1912), 48 p.
156. Berkshire Society for the Promotion of Agriculture and the Useful Arts. By-laws and names of officers and committees . . . also a list of honorary and ordinary members. 16 p. Pittsfield, Mass., 1816.
157. Boston Veterinary Institute. Prospectus and regulations for the association, 1855–56. Boston, 1855.
158. Bowker, W. H. The old guard; the famous " Faculty of Four "; the mission and future of the college; its debt to Amherst College, Harvard College, and other institutions. 10 p. Boston, 1908.
159. Caswell, L. B. Brief history of the Massachusetts Agricultural College, semicentennial, 1917. 72 p. illus. Springfield, Mass., 1917.
160. Colman, Henry. Reports on the agriculture of Massachusetts, 1st–4th; 1837–1840. Boston, 1838–1841.
161. Essex (Mass.) Agricultural society. Reports of committees and premiums awarded in 1830; and a list of premiums offered in 1831; with address of James H. Duncan, esq. Pamphlet No. 10, 1830. 88 p. Salem, 1831.

162. Essex (Mass.) Agricultural Society. Transactions. 1818–1831. Various paging. Salem, 1818–1831.
163. Fowler, F. H. Early agricultural education in Massachusetts. (In Mass. State Bd. Agr. Ann. Rept. 54 (1906), p. 331–392. Boston, 1907.)
164. Hoar, G. F. Autobiography of 70 years, v. I, pp. 265 and 266. Reference to his bills for Federal aid to common schools. 1903.
165. Loring, G. B. (In National Cyclopedia of American Biography, v. 4, p. 484. New York, 1897.
166. Mann, Horace. (In Monroe, Paul, Cyclopedia of Education, v 4, p. 118–120. New York, 1913.)
167. Martin, G. H. The evolution of the Massachusetts public school system—an historical sketch. 284 p. New York, 1894.
168. Massachusetts Agricultural College. 48 p. illus. Amherst, Mass., [1897]. An account of the college in 1897.
169. Massachuestts Agricultural College. [Proposed.]   (In New England farmer, v. 4 (1825), p. 54.)
170. Massachusetts Agricultural College. Addresses delivered at the Massachusetts Agricultural College, June 21, 1887, on the twenty-fifth anniversary of the passage of the Morrill Land Grant Act. 61 p. Amherst, Mass., 1887.
171. Massachusetts Agricultural College. Annual reports, 1871–1885. Boston, 1872–1886.
172. Massachusetts Agricultural College. Bibliography of the college, pt. 1. The institution. Semicentennial publication No. 2, 69 p. Amherst, 1917.
173. Massachusetts Agricultural College. Charles Anthony Goessmann. Published jointly by the corporation and the associate alumni of the Massachusetts Agricultural College. 187 p. illus. Cambridge, 1917.
174. Massachusetts Agricultural College. General catalogue, 1882–1886. 128 p. Amherst, 1886.
175. Massachusetts House Doc. 13. Jan., 1851. Report of commissioners concerning an agricultural school. 88 p.
176. Massachusetts House Doc. 126. 1851. An act to establish a State board of agriculture. Reported by the committee on agriculture. 3 p.
177. Massachuset's House Doc. 420. 1871. Report on agricultural college being made an independent institution. 15 p. Reprinted in House Doc. 322, 1879, v. 2.
178. Massachusetts Senate Doc. 108. March, 1863. Report of the joint special committee on so much of the governor's address as relates to the grants of Congress for the establishment of colleges for education in agriculture.
179. Massachusetts Senate Doc. 349. April, 1906. Massachusetts commission on industrial and technical education. Report. 196 p. Boston, 1906.
180. Massachusetts, secretary of the Commonwealth. Statistics of the condition and products of certain branches of industry in Massachusetts, for the year ending April 1, 1845. Prepared from the returns of the assessors, by John G. Palfrey, secretary of the Commonwealth. 391 p. Boston, 1846.
181. Massachusetts, secretary of the Commonwealth. Transactions of the agricultural societies in the State of Massachusetts for 1851. 676 p. Boston, 1852.
182. Massachusetts, secretary of the Commonwealth. Transactions of the agricultural societies in the State of Massachusetts for 1852. Also the proceedings of the State Board of Agriculture. 783 p. Boston, 1853.
183. Massachusetts Society for Promoting Agriculture. Centennial year 1792–1892. 146 p. Salem, 1892.
184. Massachusetts Society for Promoting Agriculture. Laws and regulations . . . with some interesting extracts from foreign and domestic publications. 56 p. Boston, 1793.
185. Massachusetts Society for Promoting Agriculture. Rules and regulations. 78 p. Boston, 1796.
186. Massachusetts Society for Promoting Agriculture. Transactions, n. s., v. 1. 272 p. var. paging. Boston, 1858. Contains abstracts of the proceedings of the society, 1792–1858.

187. Shepard, C. U. An address delivered in Springfield, Oct. 7, and in Northampton, Oct. 14, before the agricultural societies of Hampshire, Franklin, and Hampden Counties, at their anniversary fairs, 1847. 32 p. Northampton, 1847.

188. Stebbins, Calvin. Henry Hill Goodell; the story of his life with letters and a few of his addresses. 340 p. port. Cambridge, 1911.

189. Storer, F. H. Chemistry in its relations to agriculture, 1887. Agriculture in some of its relations with chemistry. 2 v. New York, 1887.

190. Tyler, W. S. History of Amherst College during its first half century, 1821–1871. 671 p. illus. Springfield, Mass., 1873. Contains account of Edward Hitchcock.

191. Wilder, M. P. Historical address before the Massachusetts Agricultural College on the occasion of graduating its first class, July 19, 1871. 37 p. Boston, 1871.

192. Wilder, M. P. (In National Cyclopedia of American Biography, v. 1, p. 358. New York, 1898.)

MICHIGAN

193. Beal, W. J. History of the Michigan Agricultural College and biographical sketches of trustees and professors. 519 p. illus. East Lansing, 1915.

194. Blaisdell, T. C., ed. Semicentennial celebration of Michigan State Agricultural College, May 26, 27, 30, and 31, 1907. 377 p. front. ports. [Chicago, 1908.]

195. Davenport, Eugene. Son of the Timberlands. (In Country Gentleman, Sept., 1925–Feb., 1926.

196. McLaughlin, A. C. History of higher education in Michigan. Washington, 1891. 179 p. illus. (U. S. Bur. Educ. Circ. Inform. (1891), No. 4.)

197. Michigan Agricultural College. Annual catalogue, 1883–1884 and 1887–1888. Lansing, 1884–1888.

198. Michigan State Agricultural Society. Transactions, v. 1–7, 1849–1856. Lansing, 1850–1857.

199. Michigan State Board of Agriculture. Annual reports of the secretary, 1862–1887. Lansing, 1863–1888.

200. Michigan State Board of Agriculture. First biennial report of the secretary. 1880–1882. 667 p. On page 53 there is an account of the meetings of the "teachers of agriculture." Lansing, 1882.

201. Michigan State Board of Agriculture. Twenty-second annual report of secretary. 1882–1883. (Meeting of teachers of agriculture at Columbus, Ohio. July 4 and 5, 1883. Circular on Federal aid for experiment stations by S. A. Knapp. Copy of Holmes bill.) 491 p. Lansing, 1884.

202. Michigan State Board of Agriculture. Twenty-third annual report of secretary. 1883–1884. 462 p. P. 16—Text of bill for experiment stations pending in Congress. Lansing, Mich. 1884.

203. Michigan State Commission on Industrial and Agricultural Education. Report 1910. 95 p.

204. Slosson, E. E. Great American universities. 528 p. illus. New York, 1910. University of Michigan. p. 182–209.

MINNESOTA

205. Johnson, E. B. Forty years of the University of Minnesota. 348 p. illus. Minneapolis, 1910.

206. Owen, S. M. School of agriculture [University of Minnesota.] (In U. S. Bur. Educ. Circ. Inform. (1902) No. 2, p. 133–142.

MISSISSIPPI

207. Agricultural and Mechanical College of Mississippi, Biennial reports of the trustees, president, and other officers, 1881–1887. Jackson, Miss., 1882–1888.

208. Bailey, J. W. List of publications of the Mississippi Agricultural and Mechanical College. 23 p. [Agricultural College, Miss.] 1922. (On cover: The Mississippi A. and M. alumnus, v. 2, no. 10, sec. 2.)

209. Hilgard, E. W. Address on progressive agriculture and industrial education, delivered before the Mississippi Agricultural and Mechanical Fair Association, at Jackson, November 14, 1872. 31 p. Jackson, Miss., 1873.
210. Hilgard, E. W. Report on the organization of the department of agriculture and the mechanic arts of the University of Mississippi. 9 p. 1871.
211. Lee, S. D. The Agricultural and Mechanical College of Mississippi. Its origin, object, management, and results, discussed in a series of papers. 18 p. Jackson, Miss., 1889.
212. Mayes, Edward. History of education in Mississippi. 290 p. illus. Washington, 1899. (U. S. Bur. Educ. Circ. Inform. (1899), No. 2.)
213. Mississippi Agricultural and Mechanical College. First decennial catalogue. 1880–1890. 72 p. front. Jackson, Miss., 1890.
214. Mississippi Agricultural and Mechanical College. Manuscript history. 1924.
215. University of Mississippi. Historical catalogue. 1849–1909. 406 p. Nashville, Tenn., 1910.

MISSOURI

216. Agriculture in Missouri schools. 44 p. illus. Columbia, 1905. (Mo. State Bd. Agr. Bul., v. 4, No. 12.)

NEBRASKA

217. Bruner, Lawrence. Present methods of teaching entomology at the University of Nebraska. (In Jour. Econ. Ent., v. 4 (1911), p. 75–81.)
218. Crawford, R. P. These 50 years, a history of the College of Agriculture of the University of Nebraska. 175 p. Lincoln (Neb.), 1925.

NEW HAMPSHIRE

219. Adams, J. C. Centennial papers. One hundred years' rural progress and reports and addresses relative to the Centennial Exhibition, 1876. 141 p. Concord, 1877.
220. Granite Farmer, a journal of the farm, shop and school, published under the patronage of the New Hampshire State Agricultural Society. Thomas R. Crosby, editor. v. 1–2, 1850–1851. Manchester, N. H.
221. Hillsborough (N. H.) Society for the Promotion of Agriculture and Domestic Manufactures. Constitution and by-laws. 12 p. Amherst, 1818.
222. New Hampshire State Agricultural Society. Transactions, 1850, 1851, and 1852. 400 p. illus. Concord, 1853.
New Hampshire State Agricultural Society. Transactions, 1853. 400 p. Concord, 1854.
223. New Hampshire State Board of Agriculture. The New Hampshire agricultural repository No. 1. 135 p. Concord, 1822.

NEW JERSEY

224. Agricultural Society of New Brunswick. Constitutions . . . considered and adopted at a meeting of the farmers of New Jersey, held at New Brunswick, Feb. 23, 1818. 16 p. New Brunswick, 1818.
225. New Jersey Agricultural Society. Ann. Rept. 1860. 107 p. Trenton, 1861.
226. [New Jersey—Legislature—Agriculture, committee on.] Report of committee on agriculture of the legislative council of New Jersey, February 22, 1839. 8 p. Trenton, 1839.
227. New Jersey State Board of Agriculture. Ann. Rept. 1 (1873) 104 p. Trenton, 1874.
228. [New Jersey] State Agricultural Society. Report, 1855–1856. Newton, N. J., 1857. (In New Jersey Senate journal. Appendix. 13th sess. (1857). p. 201–219.)
229. Rutgers College—The celebration of the one hundred and fiftieth anniversary of its founding as Queens College, 1766–1916. 386 p. illus. New Brunswick, N. J., 1917.

230. Woodward, C. R. The development of agriculture of New Jersey, 1640–1880. (N. J. Agr. Expt. Sta. Bul. 451. 321 p. illus. New Brunswick, N. J., 1927.)

NEW YORK

231. Agricultural extension work; sketch of its origin and progress. p. 325–333. Ithaca, N. Y., 1897. (N. Y. Cornell Agr. Exp. Sta. Bul. 137.)
232. Agricultural schools. (In New York Farmer, and American Gardener's magazine, v. 6 (n.s.v.1), (1833), p. 4–5, 45–46, 73, 84, 100–101, 163, 205, 230, 265–266, 331.)
233. Albany Institute. Transactions v. IX. Historical sketch of the institute, and its predecessors. 1897. 312 p.
234. American Institute. Fifth annual report of the American Institute made to the New York Legislature. April 20, 1847. 558 p. Albany, 1847.
235. American Institute of Instruction. (In Monroe, Paul, Cyclopedia of education, v. 1, p. 110. New York, 1911.)
236. American Lyceum Association. (In Monroe, Paul, Cyclopedia of education, v. 1, p. 111–112. New York, 1911.)
237. Andrews, B. R. Education for the home. Pts. 1–4. Washington, 1914–1915. (U. S. Bur. Educ. Buls. 36, 37, 38, and 39, 1914.)
238. Bailey, L. H. Extension work in horticulture. p. 125–164. Ithaca, N. Y., 1896. (N. Y. Cornell Agr. Expt. Sta. Bul. 110.)
239. Bailey, L. H. Farmers' reading courses. 36 p. Washington, 1899. (U. S. Dept. Agr., Off. Expt. Stas. Bul. 72.)
240. Bailey, L. H. Second report upon extension work in horticulture. p. 471–504. Ithaca, N. Y., 1896. (N. Y. Cornell Agr. Expt. Sta. Bul. 122.)
241. Bailey, L. H. York State Rural Problem, 2 v., Albany, 1913–1915. (Contains brief statement regarding early movements for agricultural education in New York.)
242. Baker, R. P. Chapter in American Education. Rensselaer Polytechnic Institute, 1824–1924. 170 p. New York, 1924.
243. Brewer, W. H. New York State Agricultural College farm. Its characteristics as indicated by its general botany. (In New York State Agr. Soc. Trans. v. 18 (1858), p. 398–406. Albany, 1859.)
244. Buel, Jesse. (In National Cyclopedia of American Biography, v. 11, p. 425–426. New York, 1909.)
245. Buel, Jesse. The farmer's companion: or Essays on principles and practice of American husbandry. With the address prepared to be delivered before the agricultural and horticultural societies of New Haven County, Conn. Sixth edition revised and enlarged, to which is prefixed, The life and character of Judge Buel, by Amos Dean. 336 p. New York, 1847.
246. Columbia University. History of Columbia University, 1754–1904. 493 p. illus. New York, 1904.
247. Comstock, A. B. Handbook of nature-study for teachers and parents, based on the Cornell nature-study leaflets, with much additional material and many new illustrations. 938 p. illus. Ithaca, N. Y., 1913.
248. Comstock, J. H. Present methods of teaching entomology. (In Jour. Econ. Ent., v. 4 (1911), p. 53–63.)
249. Cornell University. College of Agriculture. Cornell reading-course for farmers. No. 1–45, illus. Ithaca, N. Y., 1898–1909.
250. Cornell University. College of Agriculture. Junior naturalist club, lesson 1, 2. Ithaca, N. Y., 1899.
251. Cornell University. College of Agriculture. Teacher's leaflets on nature-study No. 1–11. Ithaca, N. Y., 1899–1901.
252. Cornell University. Record of the class of 1877 from June, 1873, to June, 1923. Ithaca, 1923. (Contains also brief history of Cornell University by Simon Henry Gage.)
253. Cornell University. Register 1869–1870, 1888–1889. Ithaca, 1870–1888.
254. Cornell University. Report of the committee on organization, presented to the trustees of the Cornell University. October 21, 1866. 48 p. Albany, 1867. Report signed by Andrew D. White.
255. Cornell University. Second general announcement. 2d ed., with additions. 27 p. Albany, 1868.

256. Cornell University. Ten-year book III, 1868–1898. 338 p. Ithaca, N. Y., 1898.
257. Craig, John. Sixth report of extension work. (N. Y., Cornell Ag. Expt. Sta. Bul. 206 (1902), p. 125–126.)
258. De Witt, Simeon. Considerations on the necessity of establishing an agricultural college and having more of the children of wealthy citizens educated for the profession of farming. 42 p. Albany, 1819.
259. De Witt, Simeon. (In National Cyclopedia of American Biography. v. 3, 215. New York, 1893.)
260. Francis, J. W. Reminiscences of Samuel Latham Mitchill, M. D., LL. D. Enlarged from Valentine's manual of New York. 31 p. New York, 1859.
261. Halliday, S. D. History of the federal Land-grant Act of July 2, 1862, . . . as relating to Cornell University. 63 p. Ithaca, 1905.
262. Hawkins, L. S. Schools of agriculture, mechanic arts, and home making. 20 p. Albany, 1913. (Univ. of the State of New York Bul. 543.)
263. Hawkins, L. S. Schools of agriculture, mechanic arts, and home making. 27 p. illus. Albany, 1916. (Univ. of the State of New York Bul. 626.)
264. Hewett, W. T. Cornell University, a history. 3 v. illus. New York, 1905.
265. Howard, Harrison. Manuscripts and documents regarding movement for People's College. Cornell University Library, Ref. Book 1.
266. Howard, Harrison. Sketch of the origin of the Mechanics' Mutual Protection Organization, and the establishment of People's College. Prepared January 1, 1886. Manuscript in Cornell University Library.
267. Lamb, M. J. An illustrated chapter of beginnings . . . of the New York Historical Society. (In Magazine of American history, v. 16 (1886), No. 3, p. 209–244.)
268. Mitchill, S. L. (In Appleton's Cyclopaedia of American Biography. v. 4. p. 348–349. New York, 1888.)
269. Mitchill, S. L. (In Kelly, H. A., A cyclopedia of American medical biography, v. 2. p. 179–181. port. Philadelphia, London, 1912.)
270. Mitchill, S. L. Outline of the doctrines in natural history, chemistry, and economics which are now delivering in the College of New York. 31 p. New York, 1792.
271. Mitchill, S..L. Present state of learning in the College of New York. 16 p. New York, 1794.
272. New York Assembly Doc. 151. April 20, 1847. Fifth annual report of the American Institute, 1846. 558 p.
273. New York Assembly Doc. 153. April 24, 1847. Report of the committee on colleges, academies, and common schools on an agricultural and scientific school and experimental farm. 8 p.
274. New York Assembly Doc. 169. May 5, 1847. Report of the committee on agriculture, relative to an experimental farm and agricultural college. 9 p.
275. New York Assembly Doc. 187. September 11, 1847. Report of the committee on colleges, academies, and common schools relative to the establishment of an experimental farm and workshop for mechanical operations and a school for the promotion of agriculture and the mechanic arts. 16 p.
276. New York Assembly Doc. 65. February 2, 1849. Memorial on behalf of the New York State Agricultural Society for the establishment of an agricultural school.
277. New York Assembly Doc. 1. January 2, 1850. Message of Governor Hamilton Fish regarding agricultural college. 29 p.
278. New York Assembly Doc. 30. January 2, 1850. Report of the commissioners appointed to mature and report a plan for an agricultural college and experimental farm. 18 p.
279. New York Assembly Doc. 104. March 1, 1850. Report of the special committee on the agricultural college and experimental farm. 8 p.
280. New York Assembly Doc. 33. January 24, 1851. Report of the committee on agriculture on so much of the governor's message as relates to an agricultural college and mechanical school, and on the memorial of the State agricultural society on the same subject. 29 p.
281. New York Assembly Doc. 116. March 20, 1851. Report of the minority of the committee on agriculture on agricultural college and experimental farm. 3 p.

282. New York Assembly Doc. 100. March 13, 1852. Report of the committee on agriculture on so much of the governor's message as relates to an agricultural institution and an experimental farm. 4. p.

283. New York Assembly Doc. 36. February 18, 1853. Report of the committee on agriculture to establish an agricultural college, etc. 3 p.

284. New York Assembly Doc. 38. February 18, 1853. Report of the minority of the committee on agriculture on the bill to incorporate the People's College. 4 p.

285. New York Assembly Doc. 42. February 18, 1853. Report of the committee on agriculture on the bill to incorporate the People's College. 3 p.

286. New York Assembly Doc. 64. February 16, 1855. Memorial of the trustees and friends of the New York State Agricultural College. 4 p.

287. New York Assembly Doc. 27. January 16, 1860. Annual report of the trustees of the New York State Agricultural College. 10 p.

288. New York Assembly Doc. 20. January 17, 1861. Annual report of the trustees of the State agricultural college [for the year 1860]. 8 p.

289. New York Assembly Doc. 110. March 11, 1863. Report of the trustees of the New York State Agricultural College at Ovid. 5 p.

290. New York Senate Doc. 110. March 26, 1834. Report of the committee on agriculture on so much of the governor's message as relates to the establishment of a board of agriculture, and also several petitions praying for the establishment of an agricultural school. 15 p.

291. New York Senate Doc. 61. March 22, 1855. Report of the committee on finance upon petitions for aid to establish the New York State Agricultural College. 7 p.

292. New York Senate Doc. 26. January 31, 1856. Report of the finance committee on petitions asking aid to establish the New York State Agricultural College. 16 p.

293. New York Senate Doc. 78. March 11, 1863. Report of the trustees of the New York State Agricultural College at Ovid. 5 p.
     New York Senate Doc. 55. March 2, 1864. Report of the trustees of the New York State Agricultural College. 5 p.

294. New York Senate Doc. 39. February 9, 1865. Communication from the comptroller relative to the agricultural college. 4 p.

295. New York Senate Doc. 45. February 15, 1865. Communication from the regents of the university in answer to a resolution of the 4th instant, relative to the People's College at Havana. 12 p.

296. New York Central College Association. First and second annual reports. 1849–1850. Utica, N. Y., 1850.

297. New York State Agricultural College. (In New York State Agri. Soc. Trans., v. 20 (1860). p. 17–19. Albany, 1861.)

298. New York State Agricultural College. Brief history of the college. (In New York State Agri. Soc. Trans. v. 19 (1859), p. 409–424. Albany, 1860.)

299. New York State Agricultural College. Charter, ordinances, regulations, and course of studies, 1859. 16 p. Albany, 1859.

300. New York State Agricultural College. Remarks of Hon. Samuel Cheever, president New York State Agricultural College, at the dedication of the State agricultural hall. (In New York State Agr. Soc. Trans. v. 16 (1856), p. 49–65. Albany, 1856.)

301. New York State Agricultural College. Report of the trustees of the State Agricultural College. (In New York State Agr. Soc. Trans. v. 18 (1858), p. 587–591. Albany, 1859.)

302. New York State Agricultural Convention. Proceedings of the State agricultural convention, held at the capitol in the city of Albany, on the 14th, 15th, and 16th February, 1832. 43 p. Albany, 1832.

303. New York State Agricultural School. (In Cultivator, v. 1 (1834), p. 2; v. 2 (1835), p. 145–146; v. 3 (1836), p. 57–58; v. 4 (1837), p. 33–34; v. 5 (1838), p. 76; v. 6 (1839), p. 50.)

304. New York State Agricultural School. Resolutions offered by Mr. Buel that commissioners be appointed to digest and prepare a plan of an agricultural school, together with an estimate of the monies which will be required to organize and support such schools. (In New York Assembly Journal, 46th session (1823), p. 796. Albany, 1823.)

305. New York State Agricultural Society. Formation of the society. (In New York State Agr. Soc. Trans. v. 1 (1841), p. 5–15. Albany, 1842.)
306. New York State Board of Agriculture. Memoirs. v. 1, 3. Albany, 1821–1826.
307. People's College. 8 p. Lockport, N. Y., 1852.
308. People's College. Circular of the People's College of the State of New York, and act of incorporation, passed April 12, 1853. 12 p. New York, 1858.
309. People's College. Public exercises of the laying of the corner stone of the People's College, at Havana, N. Y., Thursday, September 2, A. D. 1858. 56 p. front. New York, 1858.
310. People's College, Report of commission on location of. January 8, 1857.
311. People's College, report of general agent. August 1–November 24, 1853. (In Cornell Univ. Lib.)
312. People's College. Reports of meetings of trustees. January 8, August 12, and December 13, 1857.
313. Professional education in the United States. Albany, 1900. (Univ. of the State of New York, College Dept., Bul. 11.) Contains chapter on veterinary medicine by H. L. Taylor.
314. Ricketts, P. C. History of Rensselaer Polytechnic Institute, 1824–1914. 269 p. illus. New York, 1914.
315. Roberts, I. P. Autobiography of a farm boy. 331 p. illus. Albany, 1916.
316. Roberts, I. P. An effort to help the farmer. p. 241–268. Ithaca, N. Y., 1899. (N. Y. Cornell Agr. Expt. Sta. Bul. 159.)
317. Roberts, I. P. Fourth report of progress on extension work. p. 633–654. Ithaca, N. Y., 1898. (N. Y. Cornell Agr. Expt. Sta. Bul. 146.)
318. Schools of agriculture, mechanic arts, and home making. 23 p. Albany, N. Y., 1910. (New York State Educ. Dept.—Div. of Trades Schools.)
319. Sherwood, Sidney. History of higher education in New York. 538 p. Washington, 1900. (U. S. Bur. Educ. Circ. 3, 1900.)
320. Society for the Promotion of Useful Arts in the State of New York. Transactions. v. 2–4. Albany, 1807–1819.
321. Society instituted in the State of New York, for the promotion of agriculture, arts, and manufactures. Transactions. v. 1. Pts. 1–4, Albany, 1792–1799. 2d ed. rev. 418 p. Albany, 1801.
322. Some of the memorable events and occurrences in the life of Samuel L. Mitchill, of New York, from 1786 to 1826. 8 p. New York, 1821.
323. Stebbins, R. P. A memorial address on the life and character of Ezra Cornell. Jan. 11, 1875. Ithaca, 1875.
324. Vocational schools. 21 p. Albany, 1913. (Univ. of the State of New York, Bul. 542.)
325. Watson, Elkanah. History . . . of the western canals in the State of New York, from September 1788–1819. Together with the rise of modern agricultural societies, on the Berkshire system, from 1807 to the establishment of the Board of Agriculture in the State of New York, January 10, 1820. 210 p. Albany, 1820.
326. Watson, W. C. Men and times of the Revolution, or memoirs of Elkanah Watson, including journals of travels in Europe and America from 1777 to 1842, with his correspondence with public men and reminiscences and incidents of the Revolution. 460 p. New York, 1856.
327. Webber, H. J. Some facts concerning the New York State College of Agriculture at Cornell University. 20 p. Ithaca, N. Y., March, 1910.
328. White, A. D. Address on agricultural education, delivered before the New York State Agricultural Society at Albany, February 10, 1869. 49 p. Albany, 1869.
329. White, A. D. Speech in New York Senate, March, 1865. (Refers to agricultural college at Ovid and People's College.)
330. Work of Daniel Lee. (In New Genesee Farmer, v. 4 (1843), p. 121, 129, v. 6 (1845), p. 17–18, 51, 81; v. 7 (1846), p. 7, 8, 103, 202, 268.)

NORTH CAROLINA

331. North Carolina. Department of Agriculture. Handbook of North Carolina, embracing historical and physiographical sketches of the State. 291 p. Raleigh, 1879.

OHIO

332. Cincinnatus; devoted to scientific agriculture, horticulture, education, and improvement of rural taste. Published at Farmers' College, College Hill, Ohio. v. 1 (1856) ; v. 3 (1858) ; v. 4 (1859). Cincinnati, 1856–1859.
333. Cope, Alexis. History of the Ohio State University. v. 1, 1870–1910. Edited by T. C. Mendenhall. 612 p. illus. Columbus, 1920.
334. Huston, A. B. Historical sketch of Farmers' College, by A. B. Huston, class of 1847–48. 175 p. illus. (Cincinnati, 190–.)
335. Knight, G. W., and Commons, J. R. History of higher education in Ohio. 258 p. Washington, 1891. (U. S. Bur. Educ. Circ. Inform. (1891), No. 5.)
336. Ohio State Board of Agriculture. Ann. Repts. 1–4 (1846–1850). Columbus, 1847–1850.

PENNSYLVANIA

337. Agricultural College of Pennsylvania. By a committee of the board of trustees, September, 1862. 63 p. Philadelphia, 1863.
338. Agricultural College of Pennsylvania; embracing a succinct history of agricultural education in Europe and America, together with the circumstances of the origin, rise and progress of the Agricultural College of Pennsylvania; also a statement of the present condition, aims, and prospects of this institution, its course of instruction, facilities for study, terms of admission, etc., etc. 63 p. Philadelphia, 1862.
339. Biddle, Craig. Address delivered before the Philadelphia Society for promoting agriculture, on its seventy-fifth anniversary, February 11, 1860. 28 p. Philadelphia, 1860.
340. Browne, P. A. An essay on the veterinary art; setting forth its great usefulness, giving an account of the veterinary colleges in France and England, and exhibiting the facility and utility of instituting similar schools in the United States. 22 p. Philadelphia, 1837.
341. Bryan, James. A plea for the establishment of veterinary colleges in the United States, being a lecture delivered October, 1854, before the State Agricultural Society of Pennsylvania at Powelton, Philadelphia. 16 p. Philadelphia, 1855.
342. Farmers' High School of Pennsylvania. (In Penn. State Agr. Soc. Trans. 1 (1854), p. 477–481; 2 (1854), p. 12–14; 3 (1855), p. 306–307; 4 (1856), p. 22–25, 104–110; 5 (1857–58), p. 28–53, 73–146, 285–287; 6 (1861–63), p. 685–785. Harrisburg, 1854–1863.)
343. Farmers' High School of Pennsylvania. Catalogue of the officers and students . . . for the year 1859. 32 p. Philadelphia, 1859.
344. Farmers' High School of Pennsylvania. Nursery catalogue. 32 p. Philadelphia, 1859.
345. Haskins, C. H., and Hull, W. I. A history of higher education in Pennsylvania. 272 p. Washington, 1902. (U. S. Bur. Educ. Circ. Inform. (1902), No. 4.)
346. Jordan, W. H. Experiments and investigations conducted at the Pennsylvania State College, 1881–82. 29 p. Harrisburg, Pa., 1882.
347. Mairs, T. I. Some Pennsylvania pioneers in agricultural science. 185 p. illus. State College, Pa. 1928.
348. Pennsylvania General Assembly. Report of the committee of the general assembly appointed at the request of the board of trustees to investigate the affairs of the Pennsylvania State College, under a joint resolution approved April 28, 1881; with the laws and decrees of court relating to said college. 381 p. Harrisburg, 1883.
349. Pennsylvania State Agricultural Society. First Annual Report of the Transactions February 18, 1854. Harrisburg, 1854.
350. Pennsylvania State College. Annual reports of the board of trustees. 1869–1899. Harrisburg, 1870–1900.
351. Pennsylvania State College. Annual report, 1875. 103 p. Harrisburg, 1876. Contains acts of Pennsylvania Legislature and court orders relating to the college.
352. Pennsylvania State College. A brief statement of its history and present status. 11 p. 1893.
353. Pennsylvania State College; what it is, and what it is doing as a part of the State system of public education. 19 p. State College, Pa., 1905.

354. Peters, Richard.   (In Appleton's Cyclopaedia of American Biography.
     v. 4. p. 743–744. New York, 1888.)
355. Philadelphia Society for the Promotion of Agriculture. Memoirs. v. 1–4.
     Philadelphia, 1811–1818.
356. Philadelphia Society for the Promotion of Agriculture. Minutes of the
     Philadelphia Society for the Promotion of Agriculture, from its insti-
     tution in February, 1785 to March, 1810. 124 p. Philadelphia, 1854.
357. Pugh, Evan. Biographical sketch. Reprinted from contemporary Amer-
     ican biography, v. 3. New York, 1903.
358. Pugh, Evan.   (In National Cyclopedia of American Biography, v. 11.
     p. 320. New York, 1909.)
359. Pugh, Evan. A report upon a plan for the organization of colleges for
     agriculture and the mechanic arts, with special reference to the or-
     ganization of the Agricultural College of Pennsylvania. 35 p. Har-
     risburg, 1864.
360. Report of the committee on agriculture, to whom was referred the petition
     of citizens of Union County, praying for legislative aid to agriculture
     . . . Read in the Senate of Pennsylvania, March 25, 1837.   (In
     Farmers' cabinet, devoted to agriculture, horticulture, and rural
     economics. v. 1 (1836–1837), p. 310–313.)
361. Smith, William.   (In National Cyclopedia of American Biography. v. 1.
     p. 340. New York, 1898.
362. Smith, William. Discourses on several public occasions during the war
     in America, with an appendix. Contains " account of the college and
     academy of Philadelphia." p. 215–223. London, 1759.
363. Thorpe, F. N., ed. Benjamin Franklin and the University of Pennsylvania.
     450 p. illus. Washington, 1893.   (U. S. Bur. Educ. Circ. Inform. (1892),
     No. 2.)

RHODE ISLAND

364. Wayland, Francis. Thoughts on the present collegiate system in the
     United States. 160 p. Boston, 1842.
365. Wayland, Francis. Presidents of the American Institute of Instruction.
     (In American Journal of Education, v. 15 (1865), p. 211–219.)

SOUTH CAROLINA

366. Farmers' Association of South Carolina. Official report of a committee
     appointed by the Farmers' Association of South Carolina, in conven-
     tion November 4, 1888, to visit the Agricultural and Mechanical College
     of Mississippi, and investigate thoroughly and impartially the workings
     of said institution, and report upon the success or failure of said
     institution according to the conclusion they shall have reached from
     observation. 6 p. 1889.
367. King, Mitchel. The anniversary address of the State Agricultural Society
     of South Carolina, November 26, 1846. 25 p. Columbia, S. C., 1846.
368. Merriwether, Colyer. History of higher education in South Carolina, with
     a sketch of the free school system. 247 p. illus. Washington, 1889.
     (U. S. Bur. Educ. Circ. Inform. (1888), No. 3.)
369. Pendleton (S. C.) Farmers' Society. 208 p. illus. Atlanta, Ga., 1908.
370. Pendleton (S. C.) Farmers' Society. Centennial Souvenir of the Pendleton
     Farmers' Society. 87 p. illus. Anderson, S. C., 1916.
371. South Carolina Society for Promoting and Improving Agriculture and
     Other Rural Concerns. Address and rules. 8 p. Charleston, 1799.
372. Walker, C. I. History of the South Carolina Agricultural Society. 168 p.
     [Charleston, 1919.]
373. Winyaw Indigo Society. Rules of the Winyaw Indigo Society, with a
     short history of the society and lists of living and deceased members.
     32 p. Charleston, S. C., 1874.

TENNESSEE

374. University of Tennessee, Knoxville, Tenn.   (In Monroe, Paul. Cyclopedia
     of education, v. 5, p. 563–564. New York, 1919.)

VERMONT

375. Ellis, W. A., comp. Norwich University, 1819–1911; her history, her
     graduates, her roll of honor. 3 v. illus. Montpelier, Vt., 1911.

376. Morrill, J. S. Letter of December 8, 1885, regarding first land-grant bill. Manuscript in Cornell University Library.
377. Morrill, J. S. State aid to the United States land-grant colleges; an address in behalf of the University of Vermont and State agricultural college, delivered in the hall of the House of Representatives, at Montpelier, October 10, 1888. 24 p. Burlington, 1888.
378. Norwich University, Northfield, Vermont. (In Monroe, Paul, Cyclopedia of Education, v. 4, p. 504. New York, 1913.)
379. Parker, W. B. The life and public service of Justin Smith Morrill. 378 p. illus. Boston, 1924.

VIRGINIA

380. Adams, H. B. Thomas Jefferson and the University of Virginia. 308 p. Washington, 1888. (U. S. Bur. Educ. Circ. Inform. (1888), No. 1.)
381. Brooke, W. E., ed. The agricultural papers of George Washington. 145 p. Boston, 1919.
382. Gilman, D. C. James Monroe. 312 p. Boston, 1909. (American statesmen series.)
383. Hampton Normal and Agricultural Institute. 118 p. Washington, 1923. (U. S. Bur. Educ. Bul. 27 (1923). Prepared under direction of W. C. John.)
384. Haworth, P. L. George Washington: farmer; being an account of his home life and activities. 336 p. Indianapolis, 1915.
385. Hunt, Gaillard. The life of James Madison. 402 p. port. New York, 1902.
386. Madison, James. Letter of October 21, 1822, communicated to the presidents of the different agricultural societies in the State of Virginia, regarding agricultural professorship at University of Virginia. (In Niles register, v. 23 (1822), p. 202–203.)
387. Rives, W. C. History of the life and times of James Madison. 3 v. Boston, 1859–1868.
388. Ruffin, Edmund. Premium essay on agricultural education submitted to the executive committee of the Southern central agricultural association. 24 p. (2d ed.) Richmond, Va., 1853.
389. Society of Virginia for Promoting Agriculture. Memoirs. 132 p. Richmond, 1818.
390. Swem, E. G. An analysis of Ruffin's Farmers' Register, with a bibliography of Edmund Ruffin. 144 p. Richmond, 1919. (Virginia State Library, Bul. v. 11 (1918), No. 3, 4.)
391. Taylor, John. (In the National Cyclopedia of American Biography. v. 9, p. 509. New York, 1907.)
392. Taylor, John. Arator; being a series of agricultural essays, practical and political; in 61 numbers. 296 p. Georgetown, D. C., 1813.
393. ———— ———— 2d ed., rev. and enl., 279 p. Georgetown, D. C., 1814.
394. ———— ———— 3d ed., rev. and enl., 220 p. Baltimore, 1817.
395. ———— ———— 6th ed., rev. and enl., 239 p. Petersburg, 1818.
396. True, R. H. Early days of the Albemarle Society. Washington, 1921. (In Argicultural History Society papers. p. 243–259. Also in Ann. Rept. of the Amer. Hist. Asso., 1918.)
397. True, R. H. Minute book of the Albemarle (Virginia) Agricultural Society. Washington, 1921. (In Agricultural History Society papers. p. 261–349. Also in Ann. Rept. of the Amer. Hist. Assoc., 1918.)
398. True, R. H. Thomas Jefferson in relation to botany. (Scientific monthly, v. 3 (1916), No. 4. p. 345–360.)
399. Virginia State Agricultural Society. Journal of agriculture; v. 1. 430 p. Richmond, 1879. Contains brief history of the agricultural societies of Virginia.
400. Virginia State Agricultural Society. Journal of Agriculture (Transactions) v. 1. 430 p. Richmond, 1879. (Contains brief history of State agricultural societies, including Society of Virginia for Promoting Agriculture, Memoirs. 1818.)
Virginia State Agricultural Society. Journal of transactions (1853), v. 1. 201 p. Richmond. 1853.
401. Washington, George. Letters from His Excellency George Washington, to Arthur Young, Esq., F. R. S., and Sir John Sinclair, bart., M. P., containing an account of his husbandry. 128 p. Alexandria, 1803.
402. Washington, H. A., ed. The writings of Thomas Jefferson; being his autobiography, correspondence, reports, messages, addresses, and other writings, official and private. 9 v. Washington, 1853–54.

WASHINGTON

403. Nelson, C. A., and Windes, E. E. A type rural high school, Mount Vernon union high school, Skagit County, Washington. 36 p. illus. Washington, 1924. (U. S. Bur. Educ. Bul. 4, 1924.)

WISCONSIN

404. Allen, W. F., and Spencer, D. E. Higher education in Wisconsin. 68 p. illus. Washington, 1889. (U. S. Bur. Educ. Circ. Inform. (1889), No. 1.)
405. Establishment of agricultural department at the University of Wisconsin. (In Wisconsin State Agri. Soc. Trans. v. 1 (1851), p. 18–19, 295. Madison, 1852.)
406. Lathrop, J. H. Agricultural education. (In Wisconsin State Agr. Soc. Trans. v. 2 (1852), p. 441–445. Madison, 1853.)

CONGRESSIONAL

407. Committee on agriculture and forestry. Report on Senate bill 3, February 26, 1912. Sen. Doc. 405, 62d Cong., 2d sess. 75 p.
408. Committee on Industrial Education of the American Federation of Labor. Report, August 17, 1912. Compiled and edited by C. H. Winslow. Sen. Doc. 936, 62d Cong., 2d sess. 114 p.
409. Country Life Commission. Report, November 9, 1909. Sen. Doc. 705, 60th Cong., 1st sess. 65 p.
410. National Agricultural Convention. Proceedings of the National Agricultural Convention, held at Washington, D. C., February 15, 16, and 17, 1872. 84 p. Washington, 1872. (U. S. 42d Cong., 2d. sess., Sen. Misc. Doc. No. 164.)
411. Page, C. S. Vocational education, speech . . . delivered in the Senate of the United States June 5, 1912. 134 p. Washington, 1912. (U. S. 62d Cong., 2d sess.. Sen. Doc. 845.)
412. Vocational Education. Report of the commission on national aid to vocational education, together with the hearings held on the subject. 2 v. Washington, 1914. (U. S. 63d Cong., 2d sess. H. R. Doc. 1004.)

UNITED STATES PATENT OFFICE

413. Historical sketch of the United States Agricultural Society. Washington, 1860. (In U. S. Pat. Off. Rept., Agr. (1859), p. 22–30.)
414. National Agricultural Society. Washington, 1842. (In U. S. Pat. Off. Repts. (1841), p. 3; (1842), p. 2.)

DEPARTMENT OF AGRICULTURE

415. Abbey, M. J. Normal-school instruction in agriculture. 31 p. Washington, 1909. (U. S. Dept. Agr., Off. Expt. Stas. Circ. 90.)
416. Butterfield, K. L. Agricultural economics as a subject of study in the agricultural college. (U. S. Dept. Agr., Off. Expt. Stas. Rept. 1903, p. 713–718.)
417. Conover, Milton.[3] The Office of Experiment Stations; its history, activities, and organizations. 178 p. Baltimore, Md., 1924. (Institute for Government Research. Service monographs of the United States Government, No. 32.)
418. Convention of agriculturists held in the Department of Agriculture January 10–18, 1882. Proceedings. 204 p. Washington, 1882. (U. S. Dept. Agr., Rept. No. 22.)
419. Convention of agriculturists held in the Department of Agriculture January 22–29, 1883. Proceedings. 345 p. Washington, 1883. (U. S. Dept. Agr., Misc. Rept. 2.)
420. Convention of delegates from agricultural colleges and experiment stations held at the Department of Agriculture July 8 and 9, 1885. Proceedings. 196 p. Washington, 1885. (U. S. Dept. Agr., Misc. Spec. Rept. 9.)

---

[3] Not a Federal publication.

421. Crosby, D. J. Boys' agricultural clubs. Washington, 1905. (In U. S. Dept. Agr. Yearbook, 1904, p. 489–496, illus.)
422. Crosby, D. J. Report on school gardens. (U. S. Dept. Agr., Off. Expt. Stas. Rept. 1903, p. 573–584.
423. Crosby, D. J. Instruction in agriculture in land-grant colleges and schools for negro persons. (U. S. Dept. Agr., Off. Expt. Stas. Ann. Rept. 1903, p. 719–749.)
424. Crosby, D. J. Special and short courses in agricultural colleges. 59 p. Washington, 1903. (U. S. Dept. Agr., Off. Expt. Stas. Bul. 139.)
425. Crosby, D. J. Training courses for teachers of agriculture. Washington, 1908. (In U. S. Dept. Agr. Yearbook, 1907, p. 207–220.)
426. Crosby, D. J. The use of illustrative material in teaching agriculture in rural schools. Washington, 1906. (In U. S. Dept. Agr. Yearbook, 1905, p. 257–274, illus.)
427. Editorial on rural economics in agricultural colleges. (In U. S. Dept. Agr., Expt. Sta. Rec. v. 15 (1904), p. 739–741.)
428. Exhibits at the Louisiana Purchase Exposition. U. S. Dept. Agr., Off. Expt. Stas. Ann. Rept. 1904, p. 687–691. Washington, 1905.
429. Four-years' course in agriculture. 36 p., Washington, 1906. (U. S. Dept. Agr., Off. Expt. Stas. Circ. 69.) (Summary of reports 1–5 and 8 of the Committee on Methods of Teaching Agriculture of the Association of American Agricultural Colleges and Experiment Stations.)
430. French, H. F. Agricultural colleges. Washington, 1866. (In U. S. Com. Agr. Rept. 1865, p. 137–186.)
431. Galloway, B. T. School gardens; a report upon some cooperative work with the normal schools of Washington, with notes on school-garden methods followed in other American cities. Washington, 1905. 47 p. illus. (U. S. Dept. Agr., Off. Expt. Stas. Bul. 160.)
432. Hays, W. M. Education for country life. 49 p. illus. Washington, 1909. (U. S. Dept. Agr., Off. Expt. Stas. Circ. 84.)
433. Houck, U. G.[4] The Bureau of Animal Industry of the United States Department of Agriculture; its establishment, achievements, and current activities. 390 p. illus. Washington, D. C., 1924.
434. Howe, F. W. How to test seed corn in school. 7 p. illus. Washington, 1910. (U. S. Dept. Agr., Off. Expt. Stas. Circ. 96.)
435. Merritt, Eugene. Use of land in teaching agriculture in secondary schools. 12 p. Washington, 1915. (U. S. Dept. Agr. Bul. 213.)
436. Organization, work, and publications of the agricultural education service. 15 p. Washington, 1910. (U. S. Dept. Agr., Off. Expt. Stas. Circ. 93.)
437. Our industrial colleges. (In U. S. Com. of Agr. Ann. Repts. 1867–1868.) 1867 p. 317–333. 1868 p. 541–554. Washington, 1868–1869.
438. Poore, B. P. History of the agriculture of the United States. (In U. S. Com. Agr. Ann. Rept. 1866.)
439. Progress in agricultural education and farmers' institutes. (In U. S. Dept. Agr., Off. Expt. Stas. Ann. Repts. 1902–1912.) Washington, 1903–1913.
440. Progress of industrial education. (In U. S. Com. Agr. Ann. Repts. 1869–1876.) Washington, 1870–1877.
441. Relation of the natural sciences to agriculture in a 4-year college course. 15 p. Washington, 1903. (U. S. Dept. Agr., Off. Expt. Stas. Circ. 55.) The eighth report of the committee on methods of teaching agriculture of the Asso. Amer. Agr. Col. and Expt. Stas.
442. Report and recommendations regarding veterinary colleges in the United States. 13 p. Washington, 1908. (U. S. Dept. Agr., Bur. Anim. Indus. Circ. 133.)
443. Smith, H. R. A secondary course in animal production. 56 p. Washington, 1911. (U. S. Dept. Agr., Off. Expt. Stas. Circ. 100.)
444. Spethmann, M. T. Institutions in the United States giving instruction in agriculture. 15 p. Washington, 1910. (U. S. Dept. Agr., Off. Expt. Stas. Circ. 97.)
445. Spethmann, M. T. Statistics of land-grant colleges and agricultural experiment stations. Washington, 1905, 1906. (U. S. Dept. Agr., Off. Expt. Stas. Circ. 61, 64.)

[4] Not a Federal publication.

446. Statistics of agricultural colleges and experiment stations, 1894. 18 p. Washington, 1895. (U. S. Dept. Agr., Off. Expt. Stas. Circ. 27.)
447. True, A. C. Agricultural education in the United States. Washington, 1900. (In U. S. Dept. Agr. Yearbook, 1899, p. 157–190.)
448. True, A. C. Education and research in agriculture in the United States. Washington, 1895. (In U. S. Dept. Agr. Yearbook, 1894, p. 81–116.)
449. True, A. C. Introduction of elementary agriculture into schools. Washington, 1907. (In U. S. Dept. Agr. Yearbook, 1906, p. 151–164.)
450. True, A. C. Popular education for the farmer in the United States. Washington, 1898. (In U. S. Dept. Agr. Yearbook, 1897, p. 279–290, illus.)
451. True, A. C. Some problems of rural common school. Washington, 1902. (In U. S. Dept. Agr. Yearbook, 1901, p. 133–154, illus.)
452. True, A. C. Some types of American agricultural colleges. Washington, 1899. (U. S. Dept. Agr. Yearbook, 1898, p. 63–80, illus.)
453. True, A. C., and Crosby, D. J. The American system of agricultural education. 27 p., illus. Washington, 1909. (U. S. Dept. Agr., Off. Expt. Stas. Circ. 83. Same. Revised 1911 and 1912.)
454. True, A. C., and Crosby, D. J. Instruction in agronomy at some agricultural colleges. 85 p., illus. Washington, 1903. (U. S. Dept. Agr., Off. Expt. Stas. Bul. 127.)
455. United States Department of Agriculture, Division of Entomology. Insect life. v. 3, 7. 1890–91, 1894–95. Washington, 1890–1895.
456. Work of the agricultural colleges in training teachers of agriculture for secondary schools. 29 p. Washington, 1913. (U. S. Dept. Agr., Off. Expt. Stas. Circ. 118.)

UNITED STATES BUREAU OF EDUCATION

457. Agricultural teaching in secondary schools. Papers read at the second annual meeting of the American Association for the Advancement of Agricultural Teaching. 53 p. Washington, 1912. (U. S. Bur. Educ. Bul. 6, 1912.)
458. Agricultural instruction in secondary schools. Papers read at the third annual meeting of the American Association for the Advancement of Agricultural Teaching. Atlanta, Ga., November 12, 1912. 51 p. Washington, 1913. (U. S. Bur. Educ. Bul. 14, 1913.)
459. Agricultural teaching. Papers presented at the fourth annual meeting of the American Association for the Advancement of Agricultural Teaching, 1913. 87 p. Washington, 1914. (U. S. Bur. Educ. Bul. 27, 1914.)
460. Bailey, L. H. On the training of persons to teach agriculture in the public schools. 53 p. Washington, 1908. (U. S. Bur. Educ. Bul. 1, 1908.)
461. Bibliography of education in agriculture and home economics. 62 p. Washington, 1912. (U. S. Bur. Educ. Bul. 10, 1912.)
462. Biennial survey of education. 1916–18. 4 v. Washington, 1919. (U. S. Bur. Educ. Bul. 87–91, 1918.)
    Biennial survey of education. 1918–20; Statistics. 597 p. illus. Washington, 1923. (U. S. Bur. Educ. Bul. 44, 1923.)
    Biennial survey of education, 1920–22, v. 1, 773 p., illus. Washington, 1924. (U. S. Bur. Education Bul. 13, 1924.)
463. Capen, S. P., and John, W. C. A survey of higher education, 1916–18. Washington, 1919. (U. S. Bur. Educ. Bul. 22, 1919.)
464. Ferriss, E. N. The rural high school—its organization and curriculum. 74 p. Washington, 1925. (Bur. Educ. Bul. 10, 1925.)
465. Jarvis, C. D. Agricultural education. 26 p. Washington, 1921. (U. S. Bur. Educ. Bul. 40, 1921.)
466. Jarvis, C. D. American agricultural colleges. Washington, 1918. (U. S. Bur. Educ. Bul. 29, 1918.)
467 Jarvis, C. D. Vocational teachers for secondary schools, what the land-grant colleges are doing to prepare them. 85 p. Washington, 1917. (U. S. Bur. Educ. Bul. 38, 1917.)
468. Jewell, J. R. Agricultural education including nature study and school gardens. 146 p. Washington, 1907. (U. S. Bur. Educ. Bul. 2, 1907.) Same. (2d ed. rev. 1908.) 148 p.

469. John, W. C. Land-grant college education 1910–1920; part 1. History and educational objectives. 51 p. illus. Washington, 1925. (U. S. Bur. Educ. Bul. 30, 1924.)
John, W. C. Land-grant college education. Part 2. The liberal arts and sciences, including miscellaneous subjects and activities. 108 p. Washington, 1925. (U. S. Bur. Educ. Bul. 37, 1924.)
John, W. C. Land-grant college education. Part 3. Agriculture. 108 p. Washington, 1925. (U. S. Bur. Educ. Bul. 4, 1925.)
470. Monahan, A. C. Opportunities for graduate study in agriculture in the United States. 16 p. Washington, 1911. (U. S. Bur. Educ. Bul. 2, 1911.)
471. Monahan, A. C., and Dye, C. H. Institutions in the United States giving instruction in agriculture 1915–16. 115 p. Washington, 1917. (U. S. Bur. Educ. Bul. 34, 1917.)
472. Monahan, A. C., and Wright, R. H. Training courses for rural teachers. 61 p. Washington, 1913. (U. S. Bur. Educ. Bul. 2, 1913.)
473. Mutchler, Fred, and Craig, W. J. A course of study for the preparation of rural-school teachers; nature study, elementary agriculture, sanitary science, and applied chemistry. 23 p. Washington, 1912. (U. S. Bur. Educ. Bul. 1, 1912.)
474. Reinoehl, C. M. Analytical survey of state courses of study of rural elementary schools. 116 p. Washington, 1923. (U. S. Bur. Educ. Bul. 42, 1922.)
475. Robison, C. H., and Jenks, F. B. Agricultural instruction in high schools. 80 p. Washington, 1913. (U. S. Bur. Educ. Bul. 6, 1913.)
476. Stimson, R. W. The Massachusetts home project plan of vocational agricultural education. 104 p. illus. Washington, 1914. (U. S. Bur. Educ. Bul. 8, 1914.)
477. Stimson, R. W. Use of land by high schools teaching agriculture. Washington, 1914. (In U. S. Bur. Educ. Bul. 27, 1914, p. 50–62.)
478. True, A. C., et al. Report of progress of the subcommittee on college instruction in agriculture. 11 p. Washington, 1920. (U. S. Bur. Educ. Higher Educ. Circ. 21, 1920.)

FEDERAL BOARD FOR VOCATIONAL EDUCATION

479. Agricultural education; some problems in State supervision; State supervision, State supervision and teacher training, professional improvement of teachers in service. 32 p. Washington, 1918. (Fed. Bd. Voc. Educ. Bul. 26. Agr. Ser. 4.)
480. Agricultural teacher training. Principles of organization for the training of teachers of agriculture. 45 p. Washington, 1923. (Fed. Bd. Voc. Educ. Bul. 90. Agr. Ser. 18.)
481. Federal Board for Vocational Education. Annual reports, 1–8, 1917–1924. Washington, 1917–1924.
482. Federal Board for Vocational Education. Yearbook, 1923. General description of outstanding development and summary of progress by States. 443 p. Washington, 1924.
483. Hawkins, L. S. Agricultural education, organization and administration. 43 p. Washington, 1918. (Fed. Bd. Voc. Educ. Bul. 13. Agr. Ser. 1.)
484. Heald, F. E. The home project as a phase of vocational agricultural education. 43 p. Washington, 1918. (Fed. Bd. Voc. Educ. Bul. 21. Agr. Ser. 3.)
485. Hummel, W. G. The training of teachers of vocational agriculture. 47 p. Washington, 1919. (Fed. Bd. Voc. Educ. Bul. 27. Agr. Ser. 5.)
486. Lathrop, F. W. Principles underlying distribution of aid to vocational education in agriculture. Bases of apportioning aid to local communities and limiting provisions under which aid is granted. 83 p. Washington, 1923. (Fed. Bd. Voc. Educ. Bul. 84. Agr. Ser. 15.)
487. Linke, J. A. Agricultural evening schools. Methods of organizing and conducting evening schools and suggestions for content of courses. 41 p. Washington, 1923. (Fed. Bd. Voc. Educ. Bul. 89. Agr. Ser. 17.)
488. Maltby, R. D. Supervised practice in agriculture. Aims and values of such practice and responsibilities of pupils, teachers, State administrators, and local boards of education. 55 p. Washington, 1923. (Fed. Bd. Voc. Educ. Bul. 83. Agr. Ser. 14.)

489. Merrill, F. A.   Job lesson units for selected truck and fruit crops adapted to southern conditions.   Suggestions to teachers for organizing instruction on the basis of job analysis of crop production.   61 p.   Washington, 1924.   (Fed. Bd. Voc. Educ. Bul. 91.   Agr. Ser. 19.)

490. Myers, C. E.   Effectiveness of vocational education in agriculture.   A study of the value of vocational instruction in agriculture in secondary schools as indicated by the occupational distribution of former students.   63 p.   Washington, 1923.   (Fed. Bd. Voc. Educ. Bul. 88. Agr. Ser. 13.)

491. Schopmeyer, C. H.   Analysis of the management of a farm business. Managerial-training content of the type jobs of a farm as a business unit.   28 p.   Washington, 1923.   (Fed. Bd. Voc. Educ. Bul. 88. Agr. Ser. 16.)

492. Schopmeyer, C. H.   Analyzing a potato enterprise.   Suggestions for teachers.   39 p.   Washington, 1922.   (Fed. Bd. Voc. Educ. Bul. 74. Agr. Ser. 10.)

493. Schopmeyer, C. H.   Analyzing a poultry enterprise.   Suggestions for teachers.   39 p.   Washington, 1922.   (Fed. Bd. Voc. Educ. Bul. 75. Agr. Ser. 11.)   (Revision of Bul. 63.   Agr. Ser. 8.)

494. Schopmeyer, C. H.   A unit course in swine husbandry.   46 p.   Washington, 1921.   (Fed. Bd. Voc. Educ. Bul. 68.   Agr. Ser. 9.)

495. Shinn, E. H.   Lessons in animal production for southern schools.   136 p. Washington, 1920.   (Fed. Bd. Voc. Educ. Bul. 56.   Agr. Ser. 7.)

496. Shinn, E. H.   Lessons in plant production for southern schools.   183 p. Washington, 1920.   (Fed. Bd. Voc. Educ. Bul. 53.   Agr. Ser. 6.)

497. Statement of policies.   70 p.   Washington, 1917.   (Fed. Bd. Voc. Educ. Bul. 1.)   Rev. ed. April, 1922.

498. Stewart, W. F.   Rooms and equipment for the teaching of vocational agriculture in secondary schools, 30 p. illus.   Washington, 1923.   (Fed. Bd. Voc. Educ. Bul. 81.   Agr. Ser. 12.)

ASSOCIATION OF AMERICAN AGRICULTURAL COLLEGES AND EXPERIMENT STATIONS

499. Proceedings 2d–38th, 1889–1924.   Burlington, Vt. 1889–1925.

Note.—A preliminary convention was held in 1885, the proceedings of which were published as Miscellaneous Special Rept. 9 of the United States Department of Agriculture.   Proceedings of the first convention, 1887, were never published.   Manuscript summary by C. E. Thorne, on file in Office of Experiment Stations, Department of Agriculture.   Proceedings of the 2d–23rd, 1889–1909, published at Washington, D. C., as Miscellaneous Bulletin 1–3, Bulletins 7, 16, 20, 24, 30, 41, 49, 65, 76, 99, 115, 123, 142, 153, 164, 184, 196, 212, and 228 of the Office of Experiment Stations, United States Department of Agriculture.   24th–38th issued independently by the association.   Title varies: 2–23d, Proceedings of the . . . annual convention of the Association of American Agricul.ural Colleges and Experiment Stations.   From 1920, Association of Land-Grant Colleges.

500. Partial index of subjects in the proceedings of the Land-Grant College Association, 1885–1924.   Proc. 1924, p. 110–140.

SELECTED LIST OF SUBJECTS

501. Association of American Agricultural Colleges and Experiment Stations, 1887.   Report of the committee on s.ation work at the convention at Washington, October, 1887.   32 p.   Published as a separate by the Commissioner of Agriculture, Washington, 1888.

502. Atherton, G. W.   The legislative career of Justin S. Morrill.   Proc. 1900, p. 60–72.

503. Bevier, Isabel.   Home economics in the college course.   Proc. 1906, p. 91–95.

504. Buckham, M. H. [Address and resolutions on the death of Senator Morrill.]   Proc. 1899, p. 30–36.

505. Burnett, E. A.   The function of the land-grant college in promoting agricultural education in secondary schools.   Proc. 1909, p. 87–93.

506. Burnett, E. A.   Shall practical experience be required before granting the bachelor's degree in agriculture?   Proc. 1912, p. 172–176.

507. Butterfield, K. L. The social phase of agricultural education. Proc. 1904, p. 56–61.
508. Card, F. W. The educational status of horticulture. Proc. 1900, p. 134–137.
509. Craig, J. University extension in agriculture at Cornell University. Proc. 1900, p. 137–138.
510. Crosby, D. J. The correlation of secondary and short courses with the 4-year course. Proc. 1910, p. 137–140.
511. Davenport, Eugene. The American agricultural college. Proc. 1912, p. 156–166.
512. Davenport, Eugene, Stone, W. E., Hunt, T. F., Hays, W. M., and Claxton, P. P. Further legislation in the interest of agriculture. Proc. 1911, p. 76–94.
513. Eaton, T. H. Improvement of college teaching. Proc. 1921, p. 117–127.
514. Fairchild, G. T. Evolution of agricultural education. Proc. 1897, p. 32–38.
515. Fairchild, G. T., and White. H. C. What should be taught in our colleges of agriculture? Proc. 1896, p. 69–80.
516. Galloway, B. T. Farm demonstration and farm management work of the Bureau of Plant Industry of the United States Department of Agriculture. Proc. 1911, p. 97–98.
517. Galloway, B. T., and Davenport, Eugene. Relation of the United States Department of Agriculture to the agricultural colleges and experiment stations. Proc. 1913, p. 117–133.
518. Henry, W. A. The agricultural college and the State: a plea for a new division of college and station workers. Proc. 1906, p. 95–97.
519. Henry, W. A. Memorial to Henry Cullen Adams. Proc. 1906, p. 36–39.
520. Hibbard, D. H., and Taylor, H. C. Economics in the agricultural course. Proc. 1923, p. 189–200.
521. Hunt, T. F., Hays, W. M., Cooke, W. W., and True, A. C. Methods of instruction in teaching agriculture. Proc. 1895, p. 35–42.
522. Improvement of college teaching in vocational subjects. Proc. 1920, p. 67–79 and Proc. 1921, p. 94–100.
523. Jenks, F. B. Agricultural courses in the land-grant colleges. Proc. 1912, p. 108–111.
524. Jesse, R. H., Hilgard, E. W., and Hays, W. M. Preparatory work in colleges of agriculture. Proc. 1897, p. 59–61.
525. Jordan, W. H. Exhibit at the St. Louis Exposition. Proc. 1903, p. 44–45. (See also Proc. 1904, p. 25–27.)
526. Lazenby, W. R. How shall we teach horticulture? Proc. 1895, p. 60–64.
527. Mann, A. R. The determination of the major aims of the college of agriculture. Proc. 1922, p. 101.
528. Miller, M. F. The proper correlation of scientific and practice work in agricultural college curricula. Proc. 1912, p. 112–118.
529. Mumford, F. B. Cooperation in extension service between the United States Department of Agriculture and the agricultural colleges. Proc. 1912, p. 135–138.
530. Pammel, L. H. Botany in the agricultural colleges. Proc. 1903, p. 162–170.
531. Pearson, R. A., Hunt, T. F., and True, A. C. The preparation required for the college teacher in agriculture. Proc. 1915, p. 156–165.
532. Proposed field of work of departments of agriculture. Report of the executive committee. Proc. 1917, p. 68–69.
533. Prosser, C. A. The Smith-Hughes Act as related to land-grant colleges. Proc. 1917, p. 79–90.
534. Rane, F. W. Courses in agriculture, horticulture and allied subjects. Proc. 1905, p. 77–89.
535. Relations of high-school agriculture to agriculture as taught in the land-grant colleges. Proc. 1916, p. 64–88.
536. Roberts, I. P. How may university extension work be best conducted by the colleges of agriculture? Proc. 1897, p. 55–57.
537. Smith-Lever Act, administration of. Proc. 1914, p. 111–119.
538. Smith-Lever Act, legislative history. Proc. 1915, p. 32–44.
539. Spillman, W. J. The farm problem extension work of the United States Department of Agriculture. Proc. 1911, p. 95–97.
540. Stimson, R. W. Student labor. Proc. 1906, p. 84–88.

541. Stone, G. E.   Vegetable physiology in agricultural colleges.   Proc. 1896, p. 99–103.
542. Taylor, W. A.   The relation of the work of the Bureau of Plant Industry to agricultural extension.   Proc. 1912, p. 140–149.
543. Thompson, W. O.   Elementary instruction in land-grant colleges.   Proc. 1904, p. 79–82.
544. Thompson, W. O.   The influence of the Morrill Act upon American higher education.   Proc. 1912, p. 87–94.
545. Thompson, W. O.   Some problems in the colleges of agriculture and mechanic arts.   Proc. 1904, p. 33–42.
546. True, A. C.   Brief history of the Morrill Land Grant College Act of 1890.   Proc. 1925, p. 90–98.
547. True, A. C.   Notes on early scientific and agricultural instruction.   Bibliographer's report.   Proc. 1907, p. 18–23.
548. True, A. C.   Relation of Smith-Lever Act to organization and work of agricultural colleges.   Proc. 1914, p. 86–96.
549. True, A. C.   Secondary education in agriculture in the United States.   Proc. 1909, p. 17–19.
550. True, A. C.   Training of extension teachers.   Proc. 1910, p. 202–204.
551. Vivian, Alfred.   How shall we determine the curriculum best suited to meet the needs of agricultural students?   Proc. 1923, p. 165–174.
552. Vivian, Alfred.   The major aims of the agricultural college.   Proc. 1923, p. 171.
553. Vivian, Alfred, and Wheeler, H. J.   The preparation of men for teaching and for station work.   Proc. 1911, p. 98–107.
554. Waters, H. J.   Graduate instruction in agriculture.   Proc. 1909, p. 80–84.
555. Wilcox, E. M.   Plant physiology and pathology in college curricula.   Proc. 1902, p. 108–112.
556. Woods, A. F.   Introductory courses in botany.   Proc. 1903, p. 172–179.
557. Woodward, C. R.   Some basic principles underlying the curriculum of the College of Agriculture.   Proc. 1921, p. 127–135.

INDEX